Atomic number → 6

C ← **Symbol**

Carbon ← **Name**

Atomic mass → 12.0

						VIIIA

			IIIA	IVA	VA	VIA	VIIA	2 **He** Helium 4.0
			5 **B** Boron 10.8	6 **C** Carbon 12.0	7 **N** Nitrogen 14.0	8 **O** Oxygen 16.0	9 **F** Fluorine 19.0	10 **Ne** Neon 20.2
	IB	IIB	13 **Al** Aluminum 27.0	14 **Si** Silicon 28.1	15 **P** Phosphorus 31.0	16 **S** Sulfur 32.1	17 **Cl** Chlorine 35.5	18 **Ar** Argon 39.9
28 **Ni** Nickel 58.7	29 **Cu** Copper 63.5	30 **Zn** Zinc 65.4	31 **Ga** Gallium 69.7	32 **Ge** Germanium 72.6	33 **As** Arsenic 74.9	34 **Se** Selenium 79.0	35 **Br** Bromine 79.9	36 **Kr** Krypton 83.8
46 **Pd** Palladium 106.4	47 **Ag** Silver 107.9	48 **Cd** Cadmium 112.4	49 **In** Indium 114.8	50 **Sn** Tin 118.7	51 **Sb** Antimony 121.9	52 **Te** Tellurium 127.6	53 **I** Iodine 126.9	54 **Xe** Xenon 131.3
78 **Pt** Platinum 195.1	79 **Au** Gold 197.0	80 **Hg** Mercury 200.6	81 **Tl** Thallium 204.4	82 **Pb** Lead 207.2	83 **Bi** Bismuth 208.9	84 **Po** Polonium [210]	85 **At** Astatine [210]	86 **Rn** Radon [222]

64 **Gd** Gadolinium 157.3	65 **Tb** Terbium 158.9	66 **Dy** Dysprosium 162.5	67 **Ho** Holmium 164.9	68 **Er** Erbium 167.3	69 **Tm** Thulium 168.9	70 **Yb** Ytterbium 173.0	71 **Lu** Lutetium 175.0
96 **Cm** Curium [247]	97 **Bk** Berkelium [249]	98 **Cf** Californium [251]	99 **Es** Einsteinium [254]	100 **Fm** Fermium [253]	101 **Md** Mendelevium [256]	102 **No** Nobelium [253]	103 **Lr** Lawrencium [257]

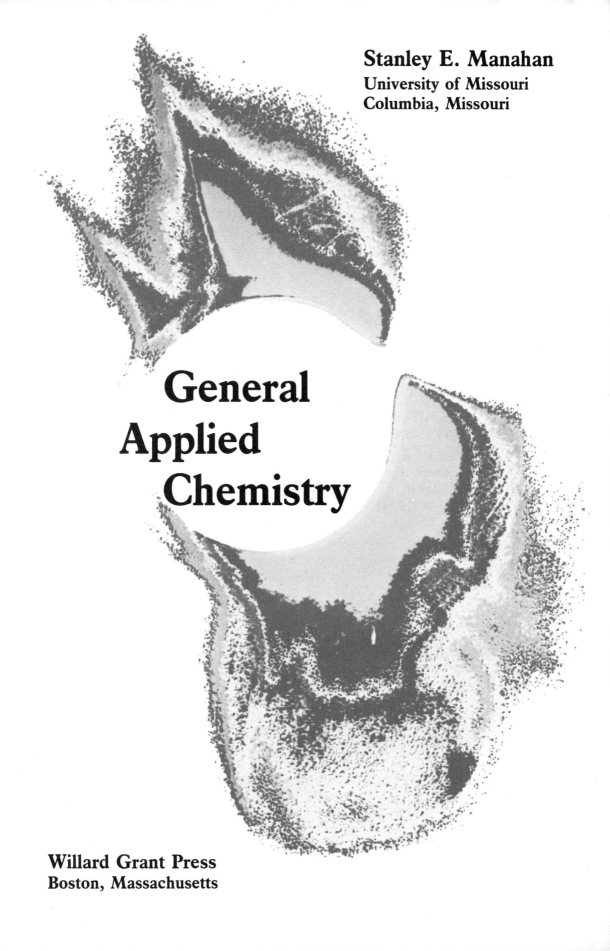

Stanley E. Manahan
University of Missouri
Columbia, Missouri

General
Applied
Chemistry

Willard Grant Press
Boston, Massachusetts

Printed in the United States of America.

Library of Congress Cataloging in Publication Data

Manahan, Stanley E
General applied chemistry.

Includes index.
1. Chemistry. I. Title.
QD31.2.M36 540 77-15135
ISBN 0-87150-723-4

Designed by Eileen Katin and the staff of Willard Grant Press. Composed in the typeface Plantin on the Monophoto 600 by Santype International, Ltd., Salisbury, England. Illustrations by N. Parker Prescott and Bill Ogden. Printed and bound by Halliday Lithograph Corporation. Cover printing by New England Book Components. Cover photo, courtesy of NASA, shows the sun's hot outer atmosphere, or corona, color-coded to distinguish levels of brightness.

Preface

Chemistry is often regarded as strictly a laboratory and industrial science, separated from the surroundings and daily life of the average citizen. But everyone constantly uses and depends on chemistry. A major goal of this text is to show how chemistry not only can be interesting, but how it can be important to every person: nurse, farmer, homemaker, police officer, business manager, politician. Today's citizen must make decisions for which a knowledge of chemistry is essential. How harmful are food additives? Which is the best fertilizer to use? Is nuclear fission a better source of energy than gas or coal? This book was written to help students answer such questions for themselves.

General Applied Chemistry is intended for the nonscience major and has no prerequisites. It can be used in a terminal liberal arts course or in an introductory course. Both the order of presentation and the topics covered have been designed to allow maximum flexibility. Chapter 1, "Atoms: The Building Blocks of Matter," defines chemistry, explains atoms and their component parts, and shows a simple molecule and chemical bond. Chapter 2, "Elements: The Alphabet of Chemistry," covers the first 20 elements, including their atomic structure and uses. This provides the student with a basic chemical "alphabet," which can be used in the chapters that follow. Chapter 3 discusses chemical compounds made from the elements, and Chapter 4 covers chemical reactions by which these compounds are formed, emphasizing the significance of chemical equations. Chapter 5, "The Arithmetic of Chemical Reactions," presents stoichiometry very simply. It eases the student into chemical calculations in a step-by-step fashion which seeks to avoid "scaring off" the reader.

After Chapter 5 the chapters are designed so they do not have to be taken in a rigid order. The core of an introductory chemistry course most likely would consist of Chapters 1 through 9, or through Chapter 10, if coverage of organic chemistry is desired. Biologically oriented courses should also cover Chapter 11, "The Chemistry of Life."

This book can be used to satisfy the requirements of almost any specialized group of students. For example, allied health science students could cover Chapters 1–11 and Chapter 16, "Chemistry and Medicine." Law enforcement students might cover Chapters 1–10, along with Chapter 12, "Instruments Used in Chemical Analysis," and Chapter 17, "Chemistry and Crime." The instructor can readily adapt other sequences for students in industrial, agricultural, and food management curricula. A general liberal arts course might provide the option of letting students select among later chapters as their interests suggest.

Many feel that the best way to appreciate chemistry is to know its uses. Virtually every chemical fact and phenomenon in this book is illustrated with an applied example. This approach has the fringe benefit of providing factual knowledge about the applications of chemistry, but, more important, it gives meaning to chemistry. The person taking the course with a particular vocational objective sees many examples of how chemistry applies to that vocation. Those taking it as a general requirement see the vast number of ways in which chemistry affects every aspect of life.

The author wishes to thank all those who provided advice and assistance on the development of this text, especially John A. Jones, Miami-Dade Community College; Dean Nelson, University of Wisconsin, Eau Claire; Peter Baine, California State University, Long Beach; Stanley Willard, Shoreline Community College; Eugene Roberts, City College of San Francisco; Irving Russell, Boston College; Clair Wood, University of Maine, Orono; and Dr. Michael J. Camp, Institute of Chemical Analysis, Applications and Forensic Science at Northeastern University, Boston.

Stanley E. Manahan

Contents

3

Putting the Atoms Together to Make Compounds

4

Chemical Reactions and Equations

8

Water and Water Pollution

9

Gases and the Atmosphere

10

Organic Chemistry

11

The Chemistry of Life

14
Agricultural and Soil Chemistry

15
Chemistry of Food and Household Products

16
Chemistry and Medicine

17

Chemistry and Crime

18

Chemistry and Energy

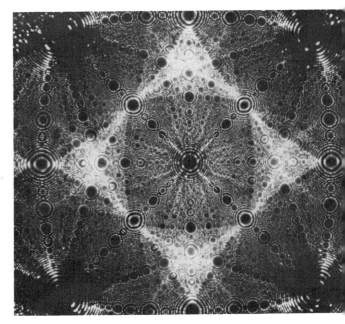

This photo, taken with a field-ion microscope, shows the pattern of individual atoms in a platinum crystal magnified about 800,000 times. Each atom shows up as a dark circle where the "light" in the microscope "bends" around the atom. The field-ion microscope actually works with radiation other than light. (Courtesy of Professor Erwin Muller, Pennsylvania State University)

1

Atoms: The Building Blocks of Matter

1.1

Chemistry: The Science of Matter

If you were to make a list of all of the kinds of matter around us, you would soon have a very long list. It would include such things as the ground underneath us, building materials, gasoline, and food. The list would include even our own bodies. All of these things are made of matter. And chemistry considers them all. Chemistry is the study of matter.

Most matter, such as that constituting a brick wall, is very easy to observe. A brick wall can be seen. It certainly can be felt, especially if one runs into it. Other kinds of matter are not so apparent. We are usually not aware of the matter making up the air we breathe. However, on a very hot day we do know that the air around us is uncomfortably warm. Similarly, on a cold winter day we notice a draft of cold air. A blast of air from a high pressure air hose can feel almost as hard as a baseball bat. Some other kinds of matter that we cannot easily observe can be very damaging. We cannot feel, taste, or smell carbon monoxide in the air which we breathe. But if there is too much present, the carbon monoxide can kill us.

The mention of hot and cold air brings up the topic of **energy**. Hot air has more heat energy than cold air. The notion of energy is very important in chemistry. Energy is involved in holding matter together, breaking it apart, or changing it. Most chemical processes involve changes in the form of energy. Small quantities of matter can be changed to very large quantities of energy. This happens in atomic bombs and nuclear power reactors. Certainly, the study of chemistry must consider energy along with matter.

To understand chemistry, it helps to consider just what matter is. Water is a common example of matter. What is water? In a glass, water is a colorless liquid. It is possible to study some of what are called the **physical properties** of water. Heated to its boiling point it turns to steam, which can be used to heat buildings or drive turbines and generate electrical power. Cooled in a refrigerator, water can form ice cubes. To understand chemistry of water, though, it is necessary to know something about it at a very small level.

It may come as a surprise to learn that a drop of water is mostly empty space. This space contains very small particles held together by extremely strong forces. The properties and interactions of these particles determine all the properties of water. They determine the temperature at which water boils, how well it dissolves sugar, or how wet it is.

If a drop of water were cut into smaller and smaller pieces, eventually a very small particle would be obtained known as a water molecule, shown in Figure 1.1. This is the smallest particle that can still be called water. It is read as an "H-two-Oh" molecule, written H_2O.

FIGURE 1.1
A water molecule, H_2O.

H_2O is the **chemical formula** of water. Even this tiny molecule can be further broken down into smaller particles. These smaller particles are no longer water, however. Suppose that the water molecule were heated to an extremely high temperature. This could be done with an electrical spark. The molecule would break up into three separate particles called **atoms**. The water molecule produces 2 hydrogen atoms and 1 oxygen atom as can be seen in Figure 1.2. This breaking up can be written in an even simpler way,

$$H_2O \longrightarrow 2\,H + O$$

which is an example of a **chemical reaction**. Chemical reactions are an essential part of chemistry and are discussed in detail later in the book.

So far we have described how a drop of water may be cut into

FIGURE 1.2

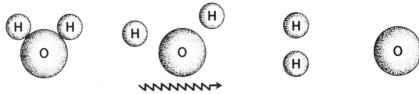

A water molecule   can be broken up to form   2 hydrogen atoms   and 1 oxygen atom.

smaller and smaller pieces until only a water molecule remains. The molecule can be broken up into 2 hydrogen atoms and an oxygen atom. In this form it is no longer water. However, even the atoms can be broken up. This is done in an "atom smasher," which breaks the atoms into even smaller particles called **electrons**, **protons**, and **neutrons**. Observe in Figure 1.3 that when the oxygen atom is "smashed," it produces 8 electrons, 8 protons, and 8 neutrons.

That is the extent to which we need to go in breaking down matter in order to understand chemistry. And so, it is where we will begin. We will start with three very small, simple particles: the electron, the proton, and the neutron. We will show how they can be put together to form different kinds of atoms. A total of 106 chemically different kinds of atoms are known, counting a few "man-made" atoms. However, we will be concerned mostly with just a few of the simplest and more important of these. After assembling some atoms from electrons, protons, and neutrons, we will show how the atoms hook together with each other. This can be done in many different combinations and many different ways. The joining together of atoms forms the great variety of chemicals and materials that surround us, that we eat, wear, and use in our homes and jobs.

A lot of the basics of chemistry have been mentioned in these first few paragraphs. We have seen that matter is made up of extremely small particles called molecules. These consist of atoms joined together. Later we will study the **chemical bonds** that join these atoms together. A chemical formula, H_2O, has been shown. We have even seen a chemical reaction, the breaking up of H_2O to form H and O. We have seen that the atoms are made up of even smaller particles called electrons, protons, and neutrons. All the chemistry that most people need to know can be understood with simple ideas such as those just discussed. Even the arithmetic needed to understand chemistry does not need to be very difficult. An approach based on the understanding of very simple ideas is the one used throughout this book.

FIGURE 1.3

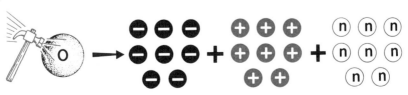

An oxygen atom contains   8 electrons,   8 protons,   and 8 neutrons.

1.2

The Proton

A proton is an extremely small particle with an electrical charge. Each proton has one **positive** electrical charge, +1. A proton weighs so little that its weight is expressed with a special term called the **atomic mass unit.** This is abbreviated as **amu.** The term **mass** is used rather than weight because the weight of an object varies depending on its location, but mass does not. That does not make much difference in most cases. However, an astronaut weighs considerably less on the surface of the moon than on the earth. His mass is the same in both places, though. A proton weighs 1 amu. To give you an idea of how small that really is, a 120-lb person weighs 32,770,000,000,000,000,000,000,000,000 amu.

Protons are seldom found by themselves. They are produced for short periods of time in some "atom smashers." In outer space they occur as cosmic rays. At the first opportunity, however, a proton with its positive charge seeks out a particle with a negative charge. This particle is called an electron and is discussed next.

1.3

The Electron

The **electron** is another small particle having an electrical charge. It has one negative charge, −1. The electron weighs even less than the proton. It takes 1835 electrons to weigh as much as a proton. Free electrons can

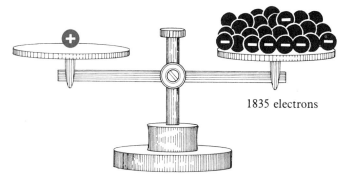

1835 electrons

be produced for very short periods of time. It is a beam of rapidly moving electrons, which draws the picture on the picture tube screen of a television set, much in the way that a picture can be drawn on a wall with paint from a can of spray paint. When the electron beam hits the screen, it causes it to glow, giving the picture. In addition, the movement of electrons carries electrical charge through power lines and electrical circuits. It also carries lightning between the clouds and ground.

The most important property of electrons in chemistry is their ability to serve as "glue" holding different atoms together. This is done through chemical bonds.

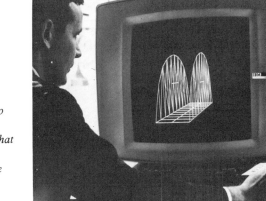

A focused beam of electrons produces the patterns displayed on the screen attached to the computer terminal. The term "cathode-ray tube" is used for a surface that emits light under electron bombardment. A more familiar form of the cathode-ray tube is the television picture tube. (Courtesy of International Business Machines Corp.)

1.4

Putting the Proton and Electron Together: The Simplest Atom

Bring together 1 proton and 1 electron. Opposite electrical charges attract each other. For that reason, the positive electrical charge of the proton attracts the negative electrical charge of the electron. Although they are attracted to each other, the proton and the electron do not touch or fuse together. Instead, the electron goes around the proton very rapidly. Because it is by far the lighter of the two particles, the electron has to do all the moving. It buzzes around the proton like a nervous fly around a drop of syrup—attracted to it, but never quite lighting upon it.

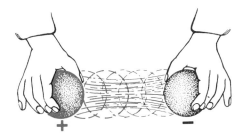

This combination of a proton and an electron orbiting around it produces the simplest possible *atom*. It is an atom of hydrogen. Hydrogen is the first of 106 known **elements**. The **chemical symbol** for hydrogen is H. This letter, and the hydrogen atom for which it stands, is the first letter of the alphabet in which the language of all chemistry is written.

A simple picture of a hydrogen atom shows the proton in the center and the electron going in a circle around it as can be seen in Figure 1.4. This is the best way that we can show the atom simply. Two things about this picture should be pointed out, though. The first is that the electron

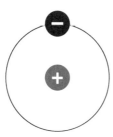

FIGURE 1.4
The hydrogen atom.

and the proton are very small compared to the distance between them. An atom is in fact mostly empty space. The second point is that the electron does not just go in one circle around the proton. Instead, it literally sort of "buzzes around" inside an imaginary ball surrounding the proton. Sometimes the electron is fairly close to the proton. At other times it is pretty far away. For most purposes, though, the simple picture of the electron orbiting around the proton is good enough for understanding chemistry.

Small and simple as it is, the hydrogen atom has the features and characteristics common to all atoms. These are very important. We regard the proton of this simple hydrogen atom as a **nucleus**, which, as we have shown, is in the center of the atom. The hydrogen atom weighs 1 amu (atomic mass unit). Essentially all of the weight is due to the proton. The very simple hydrogen atom can join together with other atoms. This forms molecules, such as the water molecule described previously. The bonding of just a few kinds of atoms with each other is what forms all of the different chemical substances which surround us. Hydrogen atoms are contained in many of these substances including water, gasoline, sugar, and the proteins in our own bodies.

Hydrogen fluid is used as fuel for spacecraft to yield thrust as it combines with oxygen to produce very hot exhaust gas (water). (Courtesy of NASA)

1.5

Padding the Atom: The Neutron

The hydrogen atom just described has a larger brother called **deuterium**. Chemically it behaves just like hydrogen, but it weighs twice as much. Like hydrogen, deuterium combines with oxygen to form a kind of substance called **heavy water**, which is present in natural water. The deuterium atom weighs 2 amu and gets its extra weight from a particle called a **neutron**. The neutron is very small, like the proton. It, too, weighs only 1 amu, but the neutron has no electrical charge.

If a neutron is added to a hydrogen atom, it joins with the proton to form a heavier nucleus in the atom as is illustrated in Figure 1.5.

FIGURE 1.5

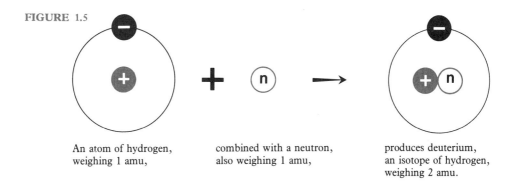

An atom of hydrogen, weighing 1 amu,

combined with a neutron, also weighing 1 amu,

produces deuterium, an isotope of hydrogen, weighing 2 amu.

Since the neutron has no electrical charge, it does not change much of anything except the weight of the atom. That is why hydrogen can exist as two different kinds of atoms. An atom of ordinary hydrogen with just a proton in its nucleus weighs 1 amu. A deuterium atom with a proton and a neutron in its nucleus weighs 2 amu. These two forms of hydrogen are sometimes called hydrogen-1 and hydrogen-2. A special name is given to atoms of the same element which have different weights. They are called **isotopes**. Only one out of every 7000 hydrogen atoms is a deuterium atom.

An even more rare isotope of hydrogen is **tritium** (Figure 1.6). Tritium atoms weigh 3 amu. The tritium nucleus contains 1 proton and 2 neutrons. Tritium is very rare in nature, but it can be prepared in nuclear reactors. The nucleus of the tritium atom is not stable. After a time it gives off excess energy in the form of a negatively charged particle

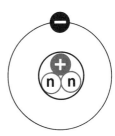

FIGURE 1.6

Tritium is a radioactive isotope of hydrogen. The tritium nucleus contains 2 neutrons and 1 proton. Therefore, the tritium atom weighs 3 amu.

In the nuclear reactor, uranium nuclei split apart releasing energy and other neutrons, which cause more uranium nuclei to undergo fission. This chain reaction is used as an energy source. The TVA's Browns Ferry Nuclear Power Plant is the world's largest nuclear power plant with a generating capacity of nearly 3.5 million kilowatts in 1065 megawatt units. (Courtesy of Tennessee Valley Authority)

called a **beta particle**. The beta particle is actually a rapidly moving electron. The atom that remains is no longer an atom of hydrogen. It is instead an atom of another element called helium. An isotope like tritium having a nucleus that is not stable is said to be **radioactive**.

Since hydrogen atoms are the isotope weighing 1 amu, we can consider the average weight of all hydrogen atoms as being very close to 1. The average weight of all of the atoms of an element is called its **atomic weight**. The atomic weight of hydrogen is 1.

To summarize, hydrogen is the lightest and simplest of the elements. Each hydrogen atom has 1 electron. Each hydrogen nucleus has 1 proton which has a charge of $+1$. There are 3 isotopes of hydrogen. The lightest and by far the most common of these has 1 proton in its nucleus and weighs 1 amu. The next heavier isotope, deuterium, has a nucleus made up of 1 neutron and 1 proton. It weighs 2 amu. An atom of tritium weighs 3 amu and has 1 proton and 2 neutrons in its nucleus. Like all hydrogen atoms, the tritium atom has 1 electron. Although the tritium atom behaves chemically like all other hydrogen, its nucleus is unstable. Eventually the tritium nucleus gives off a beta particle and leaves an isotope of the element helium behind. The atomic weight of hydrogen is 1.

Hydrogen atoms come in three different weights but act the same chemically.

1.6

Helium: An Unsociable Atom in a Closed Shell

All of chemistry depends upon the fact that atoms react with each other. But there are several elements whose atoms do not care at all to form bonds with other atoms. All of these elements are gases. Because they do not like to have much to do with other elements, they are called **noble gases**. The lightest of these, helium, does not engage in any chemistry at all.

The nucleus of the helium atom contains 2 protons and 2 neutrons, and it is surrounded by 2 electrons as shown in Figure 1.7. Because it has 2 protons and 2 electrons, the atomic number of helium is 2. With 2 protons and 2 neutrons in the nucleus, the helium atom weighs 4 amu. Thus the atomic weight of helium is 4. The chemical symbol of helium is He. The 2 electrons give the helium atom a characteristic called a *closed shell*. These terms describe the very unsociable nature of helium. The helium atom is content with exactly the number of electrons it has and wants no electrons from any other atom. It does not try to give any electrons away to other atoms either. The desire to lose or gain electrons is what makes atoms interact in chemical reactions. Because it is content with its number of electrons, helium does not get involved in chemical reactions.

Helium makes up only 5 of each million parts of air. Natural gases from some sources contain from 1 to 10% He. Helium is recovered from these gases and then stored and sold. Helium has no color, odor, or taste. It is not toxic. It can be inhaled in a mixture with oxygen by people who have some kinds of respiratory ailments. A similar mixture is used in the breathing equipment of deep-sea divers. The helium prevents divers from getting painful "bends." Since helium is a very light gas, balloons filled with it rise in the air. Helium has been used to fill air ships, such

FIGURE 1.7
A helium atom contains 2 protons and 2 neutrons in its nucleus. It has 2 electrons and weighs 4 amu.

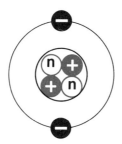

Helium-filled balloons carrying radar transmitters report weather conditions as high up as 100,000 ft. (Courtesy of National Oceanic and Atmospheric Administration)

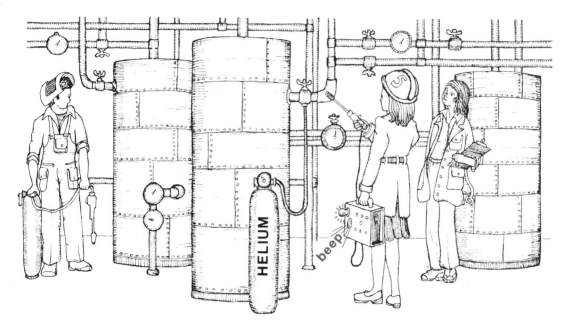

Helium can be used for the detection of leaks in pipes and other apparatus.

as the well-known Goodyear Blimp. Weather balloons are filled with helium.

The atoms of helium are so small and move so rapidly that they go through very small openings. Because of this property helium is used to detect leaks. The apparatus to be tested for a leak is filled with helium gas. The helium gas leaks out through any very small cracks. The gas is detected with a special device called a mass spectrometer. When the probe of the mass spectrometer is brought near a crack from which helium is leaking, the helium is detected. The mass spectrometer is designed to sound a loud "beep" when helium is detected.

In recent years helium has been widely used in the science of **cryogenics** to obtain very low temperatures. Liquid helium is extremely cold. It is widely used in food processing, industrial processes, and basic scientific studies. Liquid helium boils at only $4.2°K$ (degrees above absolute zero in the Kelvin scale), or $-451°F$ (Fahrenheit). Absolute zero is the lowest possible temperature (see Figure 1.14).

1.7

Putting Atoms Together: The Chemical Bond

We have just seen that the helium atom is very stable because its electron shell containing 2 electrons is filled. Let us look again at the hydrogen atom. It has only 1 electron. The electron shell of hydrogen would be much more stable if it had 2 electrons like helium. However, the hydrogen atom cannot just pick up another electron. That would result in the atom's acquiring one more negative charge than positive charge. Even if the hydrogen atom were surrounded by other hydrogen atoms, none of these other atoms would part with their electrons. The solution to this problem is one which is basic to all of chemistry. Two hydrogen atoms *share* their electrons. In this way each hydrogen atom can lay claim to 2 electrons. This magic number provides hydrogen with the same filled shell of 2 electrons, which makes helium so stable.

Free hydrogen atoms are so rare that they are found only high in the atmosphere where there are very few other atoms to join. When 2 hydrogen atoms come together, they produce a **hydrogen molecule**, H_2, which is shown in Figure 1.8. This process can be written simply as a chemical reaction.

$$H + H \longrightarrow H_2$$

The 2 hydrogen atoms making up the H_2 molecule are held together very strongly by a **chemical bond**. In the case of the hydrogen molecule the chemical bond consists of 2 electrons shared by the 2 atoms. The sharing of 2 electrons is the most common type of chemical bond. There are other types which will be described later.

FIGURE 1.8

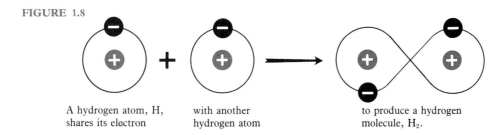

A hydrogen atom, H, shares its electron

with another hydrogen atom

to produce a hydrogen molecule, H_2.

It is a little cumbersome to show chemical bonds by drawings of electrons spinning around atoms in figure eight patterns. For that reason, we will use a sort of shorthand way of showing electrons and the bonds which they form. This notation shows each electron as a dot. It is called an **electron-dot symbol.** A hydrogen atom is shown as H with 1 dot,

$$H\cdot$$

where the dot stands for its electron. Electron-dot symbols can be used to show the reaction of 2 hydrogen atoms,

chemical bond consisting of 2 electrons

$$H\cdot + H\cdot \longrightarrow H:H$$

to produce a hydrogen molecule. The 2 dots between the H's in the molecule indicate that there are 2 electrons shared by 2 hydrogen atoms to make up a chemical bond between the 2 atoms. These 2 electrons together are called a **bonding electron pair**.

The pure element, hydrogen, occurs as molecules of H_2, rather than as H atoms. Pure hydrogen is a colorless, odorless, tasteless gas. It is the *lightest* substance of all. For this reason, balloons filled with hydrogen float even better than balloons filled with helium. During the

1930's Germany used commercial dirigibles filled with hydrogen gas to carry passengers across the Atlantic. Unlike helium, however, hydrogen burns and explodes violently. The tragic von Hindenberg explosion and fire in 1937 brought an end to the dirigible era of transportation. It serves as a reminder of the hazards of hydrogen gas.

Hydrogen gas is widely used in industry, generally to react with other chemicals. Some of these uses are explained in detail later in the book. It is used in manufacturing petroleum, in preparing semi-solid margarines from vegetable oils, and as fuel for rockets in its liquid state—liquid hydrogen boils at a very cold $-253°C$ temperature. A fuel consisting of liquid hydrogen and liquid oxygen was burned in the second and third stages of the Saturn V launch vehicles employed in the Apollo missions to the moon. Hydrogen and oxygen burn together with an extremely hot flame, which is used in some specialized welding processes.

Important: The chemical bond—such as that holding two hydrogen atoms together—is about the most significant thing in all of chemistry. Chemical bonds are like nails in a house. Nails are used by the carpenter to fasten together all of the two-by-fours, plasterboard, sheeting, siding, flooring, and shingles which make up the house. If you consider chemical bonds to be like nails, you will easily see how the chemist can fasten together different kinds of atoms in all the different ways required to make up thousands of individual chemicals.

1.8

Radioactivity and Nuclear Science

We have already noted that the nucleus of tritium is unstable and eventually gives off a beta particle. Many isotopes of other elements are also unstable. They are said to be radioactive. The study of radioactivity and other changes involving the atomic nucleus is called **nuclear science**.

Nuclear science involves the study of a number of things that have become important as a means of destroying or prolonging life. Investigations of changes occurring in the uranium nucleus led to the development of atomic bombs and hydrogen bombs. Nuclear reactors fueled with uranium now produce electricity. Chemical compounds containing tritium are combined with compounds which give off light in the presence of radioactive materials and are used to paint the faces of watches and clocks. Chemicals "labelled" with radioactive atoms are used to locate tumors in the body. The penetrating radiation given off by a form of the element cobalt is used to treat cancer. Radioactive isotopes can be dangerous pollutants in water, air, and food. (While radioactivity and other nuclear phenomena are introduced here, particular parts of nuclear science are discussed in later chapters. Pollution from radioactive materials is discussed in Chapter 8. The uses of radioactivity in chemical analysis are covered in Chapter 11. Chapter 16 mentions the applications of radioactivity in medicine. Chapter 18 includes a discussion of the extraction of useful energy from nuclear reactions.)

1.9

Types of Radioactivity

Elements heavier than hydrogen and helium have nuclei which are made up of increasing numbers of protons and neutrons. In general, as 1 proton is added to make the next higher element, 1 neutron is also added. With heavier elements an average of a little more than 1 neutron is present in the nucleus for each proton. Because they have the same charge, protons tend to push each other apart. The neutrons act to prevent the protons from "seeing" each other and enable them to stay together in the nucleus. Neutrons are a sort of "glue" necessary for keeping the nucleus together (Figure 1.9).

FIGURE 1.9

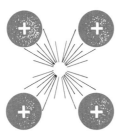

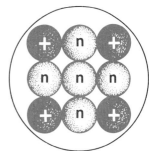

Protons have the same charge and repel each other.

In a nucleus, neutrons prevent protons from "seeing" each other and enable the nucleus to stay in one piece.

Recall that isotopes of the same element have different numbers of neutrons in the nucleus. In cases where the isotope has either an unusually high or unusually low number of neutrons, the nucleus is not stable. It has an excess of energy. A nucleus can lose energy by giving off particles or rays. The three most common of these are the **beta particle**, the **alpha particle**, and **gamma rays**. The beta particle is a fast-moving electron. Recall that the electron has a -1 charge. It only weighs 0.00055 amu, which is less than one thousandth the weight of the proton. The alpha particle is much heavier. It is in fact the nucleus of a helium atom. It consists of 2 neutrons and 2 protons. Therefore, the alpha particle weighs 4 amu and has a charge of $+2$. Gamma rays are **electromagnetic radiation**. Other examples of electromagnetic radiation are visible light and X rays. Gamma rays have more energy and are more penetrating than even X rays. (See Figure 1.10.)

FIGURE 1.10

Beta particles are high energy electrons given off by a nucleus.

The alpha particle is a helium atom nucleus. It has a charge of $+2$ and weighs 4 amu.

Gamma rays are similar to X rays but have more energy and are more penetrating.

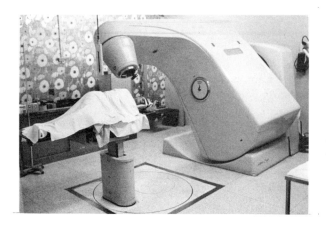

Ionizing radiation, such as X rays and gamma rays, penetrate and destroy malignant growth in cancer therapy. The linear accelerator producing ionizing radiation allows more precise definition of the dosage area so that cancer tissue receives the maximum dosage with minimal effect on healthy tissue. (Courtesy of American Cancer Society; Bernard Lawrence, photographer)

The loss of a beta particle or an alpha particle from a nucleus changes the charge of the nucleus. Consider in Figure 1.11 the tritium nucleus, which has a $+1$ charge. The loss of a beta particle having a -1 charge means that the nucleus now has an additional positive charge. This leaves it with a $+2$ charge. Such a nucleus requires 2 electrons in its electron shell. An atom with a nucleus having a $+2$ charge and with 2 electrons in its shell is a helium atom. The loss of the beta particle does not change the weight of the atom very much, so it still weighs 3 amu. Such a helium atom is a stable isotope weighing 3 amu. It is a rare form of helium in nature because most helium atoms weigh 4 amu.

FIGURE 1.11

hydrogen   helium

The nucleus of the radioactive tritium atom loses a beta particle with a -1 charge. This gives the nucleus an additional $+1$ charge for a total of $+2$.

A nucleus with a charge of $+2$ is that of a helium atom. It has 2 electrons in its outer shell. This isotope of helium weighs 3 amu.

Alpha particles are given off by very heavy atoms, such as radium. The loss of an alpha particle makes the nucleus lighter by 4 amu. The loss of the 2 positive charges with the alpha particle means that the remaining nucleus has a charge of 2 less than the original nucleus. This gives an element with an atomic number of 2 less than the original element.

Beta particles, alpha particles, and gamma rays can all be damaging to the body. They tear apart the molecules that compose living systems, and in cases where the molecules affected are those that act to control cell functions, the control mechanism which regulates cell reproduction is disturbed. The cells may start reproducing uncontrollably, causing cancer or leukemia. In other cases where the genetic material controlling human reproduction is disturbed, mutations can occur. Most of these mutations produce undesirable changes in the offspring. Exposure to a very large amount of radioactivity can cause sterility.

The effects of alpha particles, beta particles, and gamma rays depend upon their penetrating power. Alpha particles cannot penetrate even a sheet of paper, so they cause little damage outside the body. However, once they enter the body, alpha emitters are extremely destructive to molecules around them. During the 1930's a very tragic case of exposure to alpha emitters occurred among young women painting watch dials with paint containing radium. Radium is an alpha emitter, and it causes the dial to glow in the dark. Generally a worker would "point" her small brush by touching the tip of the brush to her tongue. The radium taken into the body caused a large number of these women to die from cancer.

Beta particles can travel for about 1 meter (approximately 1 yd) through air, or 1 centimeter (approximately $\frac{1}{2}$ in.) through body tissue. Gamma rays penetrate roughly 10 times as far. The distance penetrated by both beta particles and gamma rays depends upon their energy. Both beta particles and gamma rays cause the breakdown of molecules in the body. Gamma rays are particularly hazardous outside the body because of their penetrating ability.

The ability of gamma radiation to break down body tissue is used to advantage to treat cancer. A gamma ray source made of a radioactive isotope of cobalt metal is used to produce gamma rays. A beam of gamma rays is directed at the cancerous tissue. The patient is rotated so that the beam would fall on the cancer. The beam destroys normal tissue, too, as it passes through different parts of the body in getting to the malignant spot. Fast-growing cancer tissue is more easily destroyed by gamma radiation than is normal tissue. It is interesting to note that radiation from radioactive materials can both cause cancer in normal tissue and be used to destroy cancerous tissue.

1.10

Radioactive Decay

The process by which an isotope gives off radioactivity is called **radioactive decay**. Its rate depends upon the number of radioactive atoms present. Starting with a sample of a radioactive isotope (usually made in a nuclear reactor) the rate at which radioactivity is given off decreases with time as more and more atoms decay and reach a stable form. This is known as **half-life**. Each radioactive isotope has a half-life. After each half-life has gone by, only half as many atoms of the radioactive isotope are present as there were at the beginning of the half-life. This means that after a period of time equal to the half-life has gone by, the rate at which radiation is given off is equal to half of what it was at the beginning of that time period. This can best be shown by the following

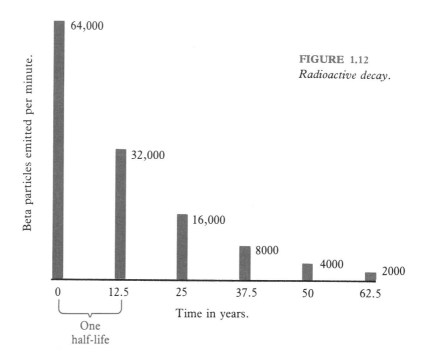

FIGURE 1.12
Radioactive decay.

example. The sample of radioactive tritium initially gives off 64,000 beta particles per minute. Figure 1.12 shows the activity after several half-lives.

There is no way of changing the rate at which a radioactive isotope decays. The half-lives of some of the very dangerous radioactive isotopes that are presently being produced in nuclear reactors are several thousand years or even longer. These waste products can only be stored in a deep underground place where they will never contact human beings, or above ground in tanks that must be guarded for thousands of years to come. This is a major problem that has discouraged a rapid development of nuclear energy.

1.11

Nuclear Fission

In addition to radioactive decay, another important phenomenon involving the nucleus is **nuclear fission.** Nuclear fission occurs in atomic bombs and in nuclear power reactors. The word fission means to "break apart," and consequently, nuclear fission is the process of breaking the nucleus apart. Fission occurs among some very heavy elements. Isotopes of uranium, plutonium, and some other elements split apart when a neutron enters the nucleus as shown in Figure 1.13. The fission of the nucleus releases large quantities of energy and more neutrons. Two smaller nuclei are produced belonging to isotopes of elements much lighter than the element undergoing fission. These product isotopes are normally very radioactive. They are the radioactive fission products produced in atomic

FIGURE 1.13

 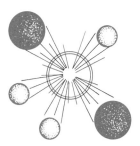

The fission process starts when a neutron enters the nucleus of a uranium atom

making the nucleus so unstable

that it splits apart, releasing more neutrons, energy, and radioactive isotopes of lighter atoms.

bombs or nuclear power reactors. The neutrons released in fission can be absorbed by other nuclei to generate additional fissions. In this way a **chain reaction** can be maintained. If, on the average, all but one of the neutrons produced in each fission is absorbed by material that does not undergo fission, the fission reaction proceeds at a steady rate. This is what occurs in a nuclear power reactor. However, if most of the neutrons produced by a fission in turn create other fissions, the result is a rapid multiplying effect bringing about more and more fissions. In an atom bomb, such an extremely rapid reaction releases a tremendous amount of energy in the form of an explosion.

An underground nuclear explosion performed by the Los Alamos Scientific Laboratory at a Nevada test site. (Courtesy of the Energy Research and Development Administration)

This photograph shows the kind of crater produced by a nuclear excavation experiment, which was performed by the Lawrence Radiation Laboratory in Nevada. This crater is about 125 ft deep and 400 ft in diameter. (Courtesy of the Energy Research and Development Administration)

1.12

Measurements in Chemistry

Exact measurement is extremely important in chemistry. Consider that the exact reproduction of a paint color, for example, demands that the proportions of pigments added be measured very accurately. Likewise, the ingredients going into a particular kind of medication must be measured very carefully. Most of the chemical knowledge that we have is based upon extremely careful measurements.

Perhaps the most fundamental measurement of all is the quantity of matter. This is called **mass**. Mass has several ways of making itself felt. A 5 mi/hr "tap" on your rear bumper from a Cadillac is felt more strongly than a collision at the same speed with a Volkswagon, because the larger car has a much greater **mass**. On this planet, mass is felt by the pull of gravity from the center of the Earth. This is called **weight**. Weight varies, but mass does not. An astronaut wearing his space suit may weigh 190 lb on the Earth's surface, nothing in a space ship between the Earth and the moon, and about 27 lb on the moon's surface. The mass is the same in each place, however.

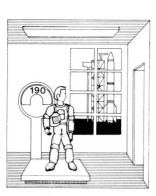  

Scientific measurements are made in terms of the units in the **metric system**. The basic unit of mass is the **gram**. A gram does not represent very much physical matter. It takes 453.6 g to equal a pound. Other units of mass, which are more convenient for very large or very small masses, are expressed by multiplying or dividing the gram by 10, 100, 1000, and so forth. This system is explained in Table 1.1. This table shows an important point regarding metric measurements. There is a basic measurement, in this case the gram. Other units are expressed by placing a prefix in front of the name of the basic measurement. For example, "kilo" in front of "gram" means 1000 g. These prefixes are the same regardless of the kind of measurement (mass, length, volume) being made. The prefixes are summarized in Table 1.2.

TABLE 1.1

Unit of Mass	Abbreviation	Number of Grams	Number of Pounds
Metric ton	T	1,000,000	2,204.5
Kilogram*	kg	1,000	2.2045
Gram**	g	1	0.002045
Decigram	dg	0.1	0.0002045
Centigram	cg	0.01	0.00002045
Milligram	mg	0.001	0.000002045
Microgram	μg	0.000001	0.000000002045

* Kilograms are commonly used instead of pounds.
** Grams are used to express weights in the laboratory.

TABLE 1.2

Prefix	Multiply the Basic Unit by
Mega	1,000,000
Kilo	1,000
Hecto	100
Deka	10
Deci	0.1
Centi	0.01
Milli	0.001
Micro	0.000001
Nano	0.000000001

The basic unit of length in the metric system is the **meter**. A meter is 39.37 in. long. This is just slightly longer than a yard (36 in.). Table 1.3 summarizes metric measurements of length.

TABLE 1.3

Unit of Length	Abbreviation	Number of Meters
Kilometer	km	1000 (used in place of U.S. miles)*
Meter	m	1 (substitute for U.S. yards)**
Centimeter	cm	0.01 (common substitute for inches)†
Millimeter	mm	0.001
Micrometer (micron)	μm	0.000001 (size of many bacteria)
Nanometer	nm	0.000000001 (light wavelength unit)

* To convert miles to kilometers, multiply the number of miles by 1.609347.
** To convert yards to meters, multiply the number of yards by 0.91440183.
† To convert inches to centimeters, multiply the number of inches by 2.540005.

Chemists must often measure volumes. Many chemical reactions are carried out between substances dissolved in water. Rather than weighing the chemicals, various volumes of solutions may be measured conveniently. Chemical analysis is frequently done by measuring the volumes of solutions that react with each other. The metric unit for volume is the liter. A liter is equal to 1000 cubic centimeters and a milliliter is 1 cm³. A liter has the same volume as 1.057 qt. The commonly used metric units of volume are given in Table 1.4.

TABLE 1.4

Unit of Volume	Abbreviation	Number of Liters
Kiloliter (cubic meter)	m³	1000*
Liter	l	1 (used in place of gallons)
Deciliter	dl	0.1
Centiliter	cl	0.01
Milliliter (cubic centimeter or cm³)	ml	0.001 (roughly teaspoon size)**
Microliter	μl	0.000001†

* Used to express volumes of air in air pollution studies.
** Very common chemical measurement, particularly for chemical analysis.
† Measurement of small volumes of biological samples and very small scale chemical analysis.

The metric unit of temperature measurement is the **degree Celsius**. It is abbreviated as °C. In the U.S. nonscientific temperature measurements are still commonly made in Fahrenheit degrees, °F. It takes 1.8°F to equal 1°C. Observe in Figure 1.14 that water freezes at 0°C and 32°F. It boils at 100°C and 212°F. It is sometimes convenient to express temperatures in a system having "zero" at the lowest temperature that can possibly be reached. This is the **absolute**, or

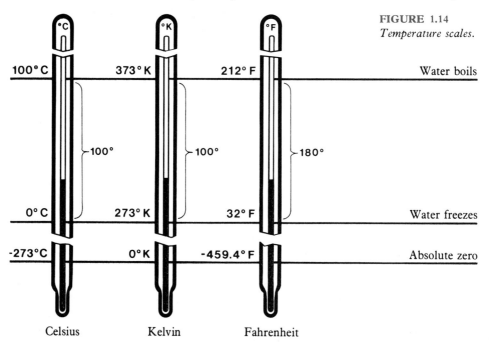

FIGURE 1.14
Temperature scales.

Kelvin scale. A degree on the Kelvin scale is the same size as on the centrigrade scale, but the Kelvin number is always 273° higher than the Celsius number. Water freezes at 273°K and boils at 373°K.★

The amount of heat energy is measured by the **calorie**. One calorie is the quantity of heat required to raise the temperature of 1 g of water by 1°C. Unfortunately, the quantity of energy contained in food is also expressed as Calories spelled with a capital C. These are actually **kilocalories**, each of which is equal to one thousand regular calories. Heat energy is also expressed as **Btu** units. The Btu stands for British thermal unit. The Btu is the amount of heat energy required to raise the temperature of 1 lb of water by 1°F. It is equal to 252 cal. The output of heating and air conditioning systems is often expressed in Btu's per hour.

One important property of matter that should be mentioned is **density**. Density is the weight of matter in a particular volume. The density of gases varies a lot with temperature and pressure. The densities of solids and liquids change a little bit with changes in temperature. The density of liquid water is approximately 1 gram per cubic centimeter (g/cm³) of water; that is, a cube of water, of 1 cm edges, weighs 1 g. Observe how this density compares with a solid such as lead, shown in Figure 1.15. The density of lead is 11.4 g/cm³. Sometimes density is expressed as **specific gravity**. Specific gravity is the ratio of the density of a particular substance to that of water. It has no units such as grams per cubic centimeter. Since lead is 11.4 times as dense as water, its specific gravity is 11.4.

Lead   Water

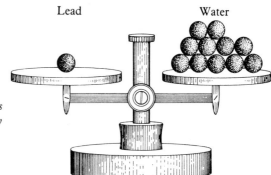

FIGURE 1.15
Slightly more than 11 volumes
of H₂O weigh as much as only
1 volume of lead.

Chapter Summary

This chapter has covered some essential facts about chemistry. Let us review what has been learned so far.

Chemistry is the science of *matter*. To understand chemistry it is necessary to know some things about matter. If matter such as water is taken apart to yield smaller and smaller pieces, a *molecule* is finally obtained. A molecule is extremely tiny and invisible to the naked eye. But

★ For purposes of comparison, a degree symbol is used here when referring to degrees Kelvin. However, standard notation for degrees Kelvin does not use this symbol.

it can be broken down into even smaller particles called *atoms*. Even atoms can be broken down into *protons, neutrons,* and *electrons*. A proton has a +1 electrical charge and weighs 1 amu (atomic mass unit). An electron has a −1 electrical charge and weighs almost nothing. A neutron has no electrical charge and weighs 1 amu.

The protons, neutrons, and electrons of an atom are assembled in two places: At the center there is a mass called a *nucleus,* and orbiting around it are one or a number of electrons. The simplest atom has a nucleus consisting of only 1 proton. This is the *hydrogen atom*. Other atoms have both protons and neutrons in the nucleus. The weight of the atom in atomic mass units is the same as the total number of protons and neutrons in the nucleus. Each atom has the same number of electrons as it has protons. These electrons are in motion around the nucleus.

Electrons, instead of light, are used in a scanning electron microscope to greatly magnify materials that cannot be observed with ordinary microscopes. The operator in this picture is examining an experimental synthetic fiber. (Courtesy of AMR Corp.)

A substance made from atoms having the same number of protons is an *element*. The number of protons in each atom of that element is the *atomic number* of the element. There are 106 known elements. Not all atoms of an element are the same. They may have different numbers of neutrons in the nucleus. These different atoms are called *isotopes*. They have different weights. The most common hydrogen isotope with just a proton in its nucleus weighs 1 amu. Another hydrogen isotope, *deuterium,* has 1 proton and 1 neutron in the nucleus and weighs 2 amu. A third hydrogen isotope is the very rare radioactive *tritium,* which has 1 proton and 2 neutrons in the nucleus and weighs 3 amu. The average weight of all the isotopes making up an element is the *atomic weight* of the element. Since the most abundant hydrogen isotope weighs 1 amu, most of the atoms in hydrogen weigh 1 amu. Thus the atomic weight of hydrogen is 1.0.

The element with the atomic number 2 is *helium*. Helium atoms have 2 protons and 2 electrons, which gives helium an atomic number of 2. The helium atom nucleus contains 2 protons and 2 neutrons so that the atom weighs 4 amu. Therefore, the atomic weight of helium is 4. The 2 electrons in the helium atom give it a characteristic described as a *closed shell.* This means that the helium atom is perfectly content with the number of electrons it has. The atom does not accept or give away electrons. It does not undergo chemical reactions.

The hydrogen atom is most stable when it obtains 2 electrons like helium. But, since it is not possible for each hydrogen atom to have 2 electrons, which would give the atom a negative charge, 2 hydrogen atoms will *share* their electrons. This sharing keeps the 2 hydrogen atoms together in the form of a hydrogen molecule, H_2. The 2 shared electrons make up a *chemical bond.* The process of 2 hydrogen atoms coming together to form a hydrogen molecule can be written as a *chemical reaction* $H + H \longrightarrow H_2$. The *chemical formula* of the hydrogen molecule, H_2, shows that the molecule is made up of 2 hydrogen atoms joined together by a chemical bond.

Electrons can be shown simply as dots. The hydrogen atom with its 1 electron is

$$H \cdot$$

The hydrogen molecule with its 2 shared electrons is

$$H:H$$

We will make a lot of use of *electron-dot formulas* in this book.

The nuclei of some atoms are capable of undergoing important changes. When these nuclei are unstable, they are said to be *radioactive.* Radioactive nuclei give off *alpha particles, beta particles,* or *gamma rays.* The decay of a particular radioactive isotope occurs with a definite *half-life.* The half-life is the period of time in which half of the atoms originally present in that isotope decay. After the end of each half-life, the rate at which radioactivity is given off is half of what it was at the beginning of the half-life.

Nuclear fission occurs when the nuclei of some very heavy atoms, such as uranium or plutonium, absorb neutrons. The nucleus splits into 2 smaller nuclei. In so doing it releases energy and more neutrons. This occurs in a nuclear reactor, and the energy is used to generate electricity. If the fission is not controlled, an extremely rapid release of energy occurs. This happens during an atomic bomb explosion where the use of neutrons from fission to bring about more fission results in a *chain reaction.*

Exact measurements are essential to chemistry. Most chemical measurements are expressed in the *metric system.* This system has a basic unit for each kind of measurement, such as the gram for weight. Smaller or larger units are given as multiples of 10 times the basic unit. These are indicated by prefixes. The prefix, *kilo-,* indicates that the basic unit is to be multiplied by 1000. Therefore, a *kilogram* is 1000 g. Similarly, the prefix, *centi-,* means that the basic unit is to be multiplied by 0.01. Therefore, a *centimeter* is one hundredth of a meter. The basic units of measurement in the metric system are the *gram* for weight, the *meter* for length, the *liter* for volume, the *degree Celsius* for temperature, and the *calorie* for heat energy.

Chapter Review Questions

The following questions are designed as a self-teaching tool to help you review Chapter 1. The answers to each question follow.

After you read Chapter 1, work through this review carefully, question-by-question. Look up the correct answer *after* you have answered each question. If you do not understand the answer, go back and read the material in the text that deals with the question. To make best use of this review, set aside a block of time so that you can work through the entire review at one time.

1. Chemistry is the study of _____.

2. If you took a substance such as water and divided it into smaller and smaller particles, the smallest particle which is still that substance is a _____.

3. A water molecule is made up of 2 _____ atoms and 1 _____ atom.

4. The breaking up of a water molecule, $H_2O \rightarrow 2\,H + O$, is an example of a _____.

5. The three kinds of particles which make up atoms are _____, _____, and _____.

6. The proton weighs _____ amu and has a charge of _____.

7. The neutron weighs _____ amu and has an electrical charge of _____.

8. The electron weighs _____ amu and has an electrical charge of _____.

9. In an atom, protons and neutrons are located in the _____ at the _____ of the atom and electrons are found _____ _____.

10. The simplest atom of all is an atom of _____ made up of 1 _____ in the nucleus with 1 _____ buzzing around it.

11. An atom of hydrogen weighing 2 amu is called _____ and contains 1 _____ and 1 _____ in the nucleus.

12. Atoms of the same element which have different weights are called _____.

13. Tritium is an isotope of _____ which weighs _____ amu, has _____ proton(s) and _____ neutron(s) in its nucleus and is _____. (This question has to do with how stable the tritium nucleus is.)

14. Helium is called a _____ because it does not react chemically with other elements.

15. The helium atom has _____ electrons which make up a _____ so that the helium atom neither wants to lose nor accept electrons.

16. One of the main ways in which atoms join together is by sharing _____ to form molecules held together by _____.

17. The dot in H· stands for _____.

18. The 2 dots in H:H stand for _____ making up a _____.

19. An isotope having an unstable nucleus which gives off energy in the form of particles or rays is said to be _____.

20. The three types of particles and rays given off by a radioactive isotope are _____, _____ and _____.

21. The decay behavior of a radioactive isotope in respect to time is characterized by its _____.

22. Nuclear fission occurs when a neutron enters the nucleus of some heavy atoms, which causes the nucleus to _____, releasing _____ and _____.

23. Scientific measurements are made in the _____ system.

24. In this system the unit of mass is the _____, the basic unit of length is the _____, that of volume is the _____. Temperature is measured in _____ and heat energy in _____.

25. The basic measurement units in the metric system are expressed as multiples of 10. These multiples are indicated by prefixes. The prefix, kilo-, means to multiply by _____, centi- by _____, and milli- by _____.

26. The weight of a substance per unit volume is its _____.

Answers to Chapter Review Questions

1. matter
2. molecule
3. hydrogen, oxygen
4. chemical reaction
5. protons, neutrons, electrons
6. 1, +1
7. 1, zero
8. almost zero, −1
9. nucleus, center, in motion around the nucleus
10. hydrogen, proton, electron
11. deuterium, proton, neutron
12. isotopes
13. hydrogen, 3, 1, 2, radioactive
14. noble gas
15. 2, closed shell
16. electrons, chemical bonds
17. an electron
18. an electron pair, chemical bond
19. radioactive
20. alpha particles, beta particles, gamma rays
21. half-life
22. split, more neutrons, energy
23. metric
24. gram, meter, liter, degrees Celsius, calories
25. 1000, 0.01, 0.001
26. density

Exercises for Chapter 1

1. It was stated in this chapter that an oxygen atom could be "smashed" to produce 8 electrons, 8 protons, and 8 neutrons. What is the weight of this atom in atomic mass units?

2. It takes _____ electrons to weigh as much as a proton.

3. "Free" electrons do a lot of things. Describe how they are involved in (a) a television set, (b) transmitting electrical power through power lines, (c) in lightning.

4. The atomic weight of hydrogen is just very slightly over 1. This atomic weight is the average weight of all hydrogen atoms in nature. Each deuterium atom weighs 2 amu. What does the atomic weight of the hydrogen element tell us about the fraction of deuterium in this element?

5. What are three uses for helium gas?

6. What is meant by *cryogenics*?

7. What is the chemical formula of the hydrogen molecule? The water molecule?

8. How could you tell by an easily observed chemical reaction whether a small balloon contained hydrogen gas or helium gas?

9. What is the chemical symbol for helium?

10. Name three uses of hydrogen, one each from industry, food preparation, and space.

11. For what purpose is helium used along with a mass spectrometer?

12. What is *heavy water*?

13. Are the nucleus of an atom and the electrons going around it large compared to the distances between the nucleus and the electrons?

14. Would it be possible to have a nucleus made up of 2 protons and no neutrons?

15. What happens when an extra neutron enters the nucleus of a uranium atom?

16. One very rare isotope of helium has a nucleus containing 2 protons and 1 neutron. How many electrons must it have? What does an atom of this isotope weigh?

17. What is wrong with saying that the chemical formula of hydrogen gas is H?

18. What kind of particle does a tritium nucleus give off?

19. What is the significance of the temperature $-273°C$?

20. Give a specific way in which things that happen to the nuclei of atoms apply to (a) warfare, (b) generation of energy, (c) medicine.

21. Complete the following table dealing with things given off by radioactive nuclei.

Type of Radioactivity	Charge	Mass in amu	Ability to Penetrate Matter
Alpha	_____	4	_____
Beta	_____	_____	Moderate
Gamma	0	_____	_____

22. Why is an alpha-emitting radioactive isotope particularly dangerous when taken into the body?

23. Carbon is an element that will be discussed in the next chapter. A radioactive form of carbon, carbon-14, is produced when cosmic rays interact with nitrogen in the upper atmosphere. This carbon is incorporated into plants by photosynthesis of carbon dioxide from the atmosphere. The carbon-14 eventually decays so that none is found in coal, limestone, or other sources of "very old" carbon. The half-life of carbon-14 is 5600 years. Suppose that a sample of carbon from an ancient campfire uncovered during an archaeological investigation has exactly one-fourth of the carbon-14 activity as that of a sample containing the same amount of total carbon from freshly burned wood. How many years old is the charcoal from the campfire?

24. The half-life of tritium is 12.5 years. Suppose a sample of water contains 100,000 tritium atoms chemically bound in the water. How many tritium atoms will remain after 50 years?

25. When a nuclear reactor is operating at a steady power output, exactly one neutron from each fission is used to produce exactly one other fission. Each

fission event actually produces an average of 2.5 neutrons. A nuclear reactor is controlled by control rods, which are lowered into the core of material undergoing fission to slow the rate of fission and are lifted to increase the rate of fission. From this information, how do you think the control rods interact with neutrons?

26. A pound is how many kilograms? What is your weight in kilograms?

27. What is the number of centimeters per inch? What is your height in centimeters?

28. What is the length of a football field in meters?

29. What is the 55 mile per hour speed limit expressed in kilometers per hour?

30. Normal body temperature is 98.6°F. What is it in degrees Celsius?

31. A cube sample of a mineral with edges measuring 5 cm weighs 250 g. What is its density in grams per cubic centimeter?

32. What is the specific gravity of the mineral mentioned in the above question?

33. A candle was placed under a can containing 50 g of water. The temperature of the water increased by 2°C. How much heat energy was transferred from the candle flame to the water?

34. What units of measurement in the metric system are commonly substituted for (a) pounds, (b) inches, (c) quarts?

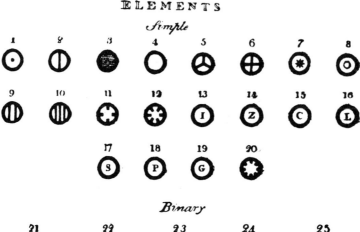

ELEMENTS

Simple

Binary

Dalton's table of elements anticipated the system of organizing elements into a table according to weights. His system of signs has since been replaced by the modern letter system devised by Berzelius.

2

Elements: The Alphabet of Chemistry

2.1

What are the Elements?

Chapter 1 described the first two elements. These are hydrogen and helium. It was explained that each of these elements is made up of specific kinds of atoms. The atoms of each element are alike in that they each have the same number of protons and electrons: Hydrogen has 1 proton and 1 electron; and helium has 2 protons and 2 electrons. But, atoms of the same element can be different with regard to the number of neutrons in the nucleus. Such atoms are called isotopes. Hydrogen has three possible isotopes whose atoms weigh 1, 2, and 3 amu (atomic mass units). Helium can exist as isotopes weighing 3 and 4 amu.

Helium atoms have two electrons. This makes the helium atom very stable. It has a "full shell" of electrons. It has no tendency to give away, accept, or share electrons. This means that helium does not react chemically. Hydrogen atoms tend to desire 2 electrons. When this happens, they also have a full shell. In pure hydrogen an atom obtains such stability by sharing electrons with another hydrogen atom so that each atom has access to 2 electrons. For that reason, pure hydrogen exists as molecules of hydrogen, H_2. Hydrogen can also share electrons with atoms of other elements. The sharing of electrons by two atoms forms one type of chemical bond. Chemical bonding is the key to all of chemistry.

At the present time, there are a total of 106 elements known. To understand chemistry, it is necessary to learn something about some of these elements. Fortunately, it is not necessary to be familiar with all of the elements. In fact, fourteen of these are man-made and are not encountered daily in ordinary chemical systems. Many of the others are rarely present in day-to-day activities. We will use a very simple approach, which will allow us to discuss a lot of chemistry. This involves concentrating mostly on the first 20 elements. They are among the most abundant. Their chemistry is extremely important and reasonably simple. Three of the first 20 elements are noble gases, which are not involved in many chemical reactions. Three more, lithium, beryllium, and boron, are not used in many products; so we will not need to spend a great deal of time on their chemistry. That leaves 14 elements, which are involved in so much chemistry that whole books are written about the chemistry of each. It will be easy to remember the names and chemical symbols of these elements. We can also remember how their atoms are put together in simple chemical formulas. By seeing some of their chemical reactions, we can begin to predict what they will do chemically. This will provide a firm foundation for branching out to study some of the other elements later in the book.

2.2

The Periodic Table:
An Orderly Arrangement for the Elements

So far, two elements, hydrogen and helium, have been described. Before getting on with the others, it would be helpful to consider an arrangement that is used by scientists to keep the elements in order. This is the *periodic table*. The periodic table is a chart listing the elements across several rows. It is arranged so that elements in the same column on the chart have similar properties and proceed from the lightest elements at the top of the column to the heaviest at the bottom. The table is called "periodic" because it has been found that the properties of elements tend to be repeated at regular intervals that go from the lightest to heaviest elements. We will explain later how this happens to be the result of the arrangements of the electrons in the atoms.

The periodic table is a little bit like a month on the calendar. For some people, at least, Sunday is always a day of rest where one can behave like a "noble gas" not doing much of anything. Monday can always be a day of furious activity when the work week starts with a burst of energy. Friday is often a day of much reduced activity compared to Monday.

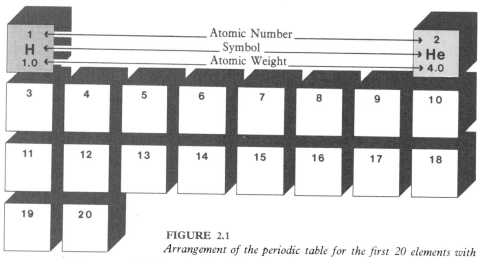

FIGURE 2.1
Arrangement of the periodic table for the first 20 elements with **hydrogen** *and* **helium** *in place. Note that the chemical symbol for helium is He. For those elements represented by a chemical symbol consisting of two letters, the first letter is always a capital letter and the second letter is always a lower case letter. It would not be correct to write this symbol as either* HE *or* He.

We will first prepare a simple periodic table of the first 20 elements. Each slot on the table will have a number. This is the *atomic number* of the element. It is the number of protons and the number of electrons that each atom of the element has. Each element will be represented by one or two letters. For example, hydrogen is shown as H and helium as He. This is the *symbol* of the element. The third thing shown for each element on the periodic table is the *atomic weight*. This is the average weight of all of the atoms of each element. It takes into consideration the different weights and different abundances of the isotopes of the element. Because it is the average of several different weights, it will not always be a whole number. The periodic table is shown in Figure 2.1 with hydrogen and helium already in place. During the rest of this chapter the remaining blanks will be filled in.

2.3

Lithium

The number 3 element is lithium. The chemical symbol for it is Li. Lithium is the first of the chemical elements classified as a metal. It is the lightest of the metals. Its **specific gravity** is only 0.534. This means that an amount of lithium weighing 0.534 kg (kilogram) has the same volume as an amount of water weighing exactly 1 kg (see Figure 2.2). By way of comparison the same volume of lead metal weighs 11.34 kg, over 20 times as much as the lithium! Lithium metal has a silvery white color. The metal is very active chemically and combines with many gases. Lithium is sometimes added to other metals to eliminate gas bubbles that form in the melted metal.

FIGURE 2.2

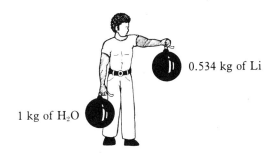

0.534 kg of Li

1 kg of H_2O

There are several common applications of lithium compounds. Lithium hydroxide is used in lubricating greases and alkaline storage batteries. Chemical combinations of lithium and hydrogen give off hydrogen when heated and are used as sources of hydrogen. Lithium carbonate has been found to be very effective in the control of manic-depressive mental disorders.

The atomic number of lithium is 3. Recall that this would mean each lithium atom has 3 protons and 3 electrons. Two kinds of lithium atoms occur naturally. One is an isotope containing 3 protons and 3 neutrons. It weighs 6 amu. The other isotope has 3 protons and 4 neutrons, so it weighs 7 amu. Of a thousand lithium atoms, 74 are the lighter isotope, and 926 the heavier isotope (Figure 2.3). The average weight of all lithium atoms is 6.9 amu. Therefore, we find the atomic weight of lithium to be 6.9.

FIGURE 2.3

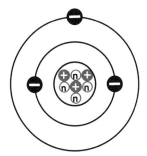

An atom of lithium weighing 6 amu. Of every 1000 lithium atoms, 74 are this isotope.

An atom of lithium weighing 7 amu. Of every 1000 lithium atoms, 926 are this isotope.

2.4

Another Look at the Atom

It will be helpful at this point to examine the lithium atom in some detail. We learned in Section 1.4 that each atom has a nucleus. The nucleus contains protons and neutrons. The weight of the atom in atomic mass units is equal to the total number of protons plus neutrons in the nucleus. The more abundant lithium atom weighing 7 amu has 3 protons and 4 neutrons. Since we know that each atom has the same number of electrons as it has protons, we can correctly conclude that each lithium atom has 3 electrons. You will notice something different in the arrangement of electrons in the lithium atom shown in Figure 2.4. Two electrons are shown closer to the nucleus than the remaining one. The 2 electrons closest to the atom are **inner electrons**. Recall that helium has 2 electrons. These make up a filled shell for the helium atom so that it does not form any chemical bonds. The same is true with lithium's 2 inner electrons. They make up a filled shell and are not involved in chemical bonding. The 1 electron in lithium's outer shell is very active in forming chemical bonds, however. This second shell needs a total of 8 electrons to be stable. It is very unstable with just 1 electron in it. As we will see later, lithium reacts chemically by losing that electron to the other atoms.

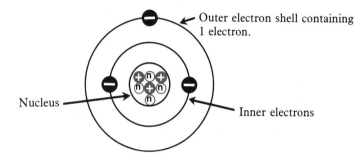

Outer electron shell containing 1 electron.

Nucleus

Inner electrons

FIGURE 2.4
Lithium atom showing the nucleus, the inner electrons, and the outer shell.

The nucleus and inner electrons make up the **kernel** of the atom. This is the part of the atom that is not involved in any chemical reactions. Recall from Chapter 1 that it is helpful to show atoms with *electron-dot symbols*. The hydrogen atom was shown with 1 dot, $H\cdot$, to indicate that it has 1 electron. The hydrogen molecule is shown with 2 dots, $H:H$, to indicate the 2 electrons involved in the chemical bond holding the 2 hydrogen atoms together. For simplicity the electrons in the kernel of an atom are not shown. It is not necessary to show them because they do not become involved in chemical bonding. Therefore, the electron-dot symbol of lithium is

$$Li\cdot$$

which shows lithium's 1 **outer electron**.

2.5

Beryllium

The element with atomic number 4 is beryllium. Its chemical symbol is Be. Beryllium metal is used in mixtures with other metals to give them some desired properties. Such mixtures of metals are called *alloys*. The most important of these are alloys involving copper and beryllium. These alloys are almost as hard as heat-treated steels. Unlike steel, though, they conduct electricity and heat well, resist corrosion, and do

The element beryllium is extracted from the beryl crystal. (Courtesy of American Museum of Natural History)

not spark readily. Beryllium metal has a high melting temperature, 1285°C. Because of this and the fact that it absorbs and conducts heat well, it is used in airplane brake parts. The metal is also widely used in the construction of nuclear reactors.

Beryllium and its chemical compounds are hazardous to health. Exposure to these causes *berylliosis,* a condition marked by deterioration of the lungs. This disease can develop as long as 20 years after exposure to beryllium. Exposure through the air is especially dangerous. For that reason the allowable level of beryllium in the air that workers breathe has been set at a lower value than any other metal, including even mercury.

All beryllium atoms have 4 protons, 5 neutrons, and 4 electrons. Therefore, each atom weighs 9 amu. The atomic weight of beryllium is 9. A picture of this distribution of particles in the beryllium atom is given in Figure 2.5. Two of the electrons are contained in the inner shell. The other 2 electrons are in the outer shell and can become involved in chemical bonds. The electron-dot symbol of beryllium is

$$\cdot Be \cdot$$

Beryllium and lithium are both metals. Metals have a shiny appearance. They conduct electricity and heat well. Metals are generally *malleable,* which means they can be hammered into sheets. They are also ductile, which means they can be drawn into wires.

Kernel of Be atom

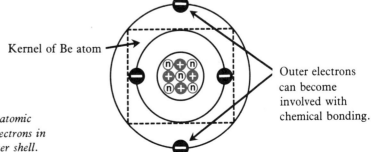

Outer electrons can become involved with chemical bonding.

FIGURE 2.5

An atom of beryllium with an atomic weight of 9. The atom has 2 electrons in the inner shell and 2 in the outer shell.

2.6

Boron

Boron is the element with atomic number 5. Its symbol is B. Boron is a hard, brittle substance. It has a very high melting point of 2300°C. Boron produces some desirable qualities when added to copper or aluminum. A very small amount added to steel greatly improves the hardening qualities of the steel. Some chemical compounds of boron are extremely hard. A chemical combination of boron and nitrogen formed under special high pressure processes produces a material as hard as diamond. The boron isotope weighing 10 amu absorbs neutrons very well. It is used in the control rods that control nuclear reactors. "Borax," a chemical compound of boron, is used in some cleaning formulations. Boron is not very harmful to man, but it can be toxic to plants.

All boron atoms have 5 protons and 5 electrons. Three of the electrons are outer shell electrons, so the electron-dot symbol for boron is

$$\cdot \overset{\cdot}{B} \cdot$$

There are two naturally occurring isotopes of boron as shown in Figure 2.6. Of 1000 boron atoms, 188 have 5 neutrons and weigh 10 amu. The other 812 have 6 neutrons and weigh 11 amu. Because there are more boron atoms weighing 11 amu than there are atoms weighing 10 amu, the atomic weight of boron is closer to 11 than to 10. The atomic weight of boron is 10.8.

FIGURE 2.6

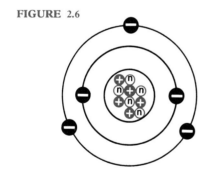

A boron atom with 5 protons and 5 neutrons in the nucleus. This isotope weighs 10 amu.

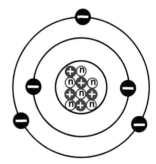

A boron atom with 5 protons and 6 neutrons in the nucleus. This isotope weighs 11 amu.

2.7

Lithium, Beryllium, and Boron in the Periodic Table

Thus far we have discussed five elements. You will remember that each of these elements has a symbol consisting of one or two letters. These symbols are summarized in Table 2.1. Note that when the symbol contains two letters, the first is always a *capital*, the second *lower case*.

TABLE 2.1

Element	Symbol
Hydrogen	H
Helium	He
Lithium	Li
Beryllium	Be
Boron	B

It is now time to "seat" lithium, beryllium, and boron in the periodic table. These elements are placed in the table as shown in Figure 2.7. Remember that the place for each element is shown by an atomic

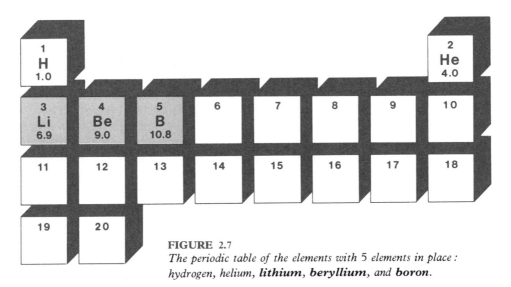

FIGURE 2.7
*The periodic table of the elements with 5 elements in place: hydrogen, helium, **lithium**, **beryllium**, and **boron**.*

number. The atomic number is equal to the number of protons in the nucleus of the atom. It is also equal to the number of electrons in each atom of the element. The symbol for each element is placed in the square containing that element's atomic number. Below the symbol is the atomic weight. It is the average weight of the atoms of that element. Because atoms of the same element may have different numbers of neutrons (different isotopes), the atomic weight is not always a whole number.

2.8

Carbon: The Element that Makes Us Possible

The element with atomic number 6 is carbon, C. As the pure element, carbon occurs in many forms. It can be seen as the heavy black smoke pouring from the exhaust of a diesel truck shouldering its way up a steep

The diamond is composed entirely of carbon. It is the hardest substance known to man. Its pure, flawless form has great value as a gem stone; the less perfect varieties are used industrially. (Courtesy of the Smithsonian Institution)

hill. In another form it is the clear, sparkling diamond on an engagement ring. Slippery, gray graphite used to lubricate a speedometer cable is made of a form of pure carbon. Pressed together with a binder material acting as "glue," graphite is used as the "lead" in a "lead pencil." These different forms of carbon occur because carbon atoms join together with each other in several different ways.

Carbon atoms have 6 protons in the nucleus and 6 electrons. Practically all carbon atoms have 6 neutrons (Figure 2.8). Therefore, the atomic weight of carbon is 12, and the electron-dot symbol is

There are also isotopes of carbon that have 7 or 8 neutrons in their nuclei. The isotope with 8 neutrons weighs 14 amu and is called carbon-14. The nucleus of this isotope is not stable. Eventually it loses excess energy by ejecting a beta particle (the high energy electron discussed in Chapter 1 responsible for one form of radioactivity). Atoms with unstable nuclei, such as carbon-14 and tritium, are called *radioactive isotopes*. The beta particle, which comes from a carbon-14 nucleus, moves very fast and has lots of energy. It can be "seen" by a device for detecting radioactive materials. A beta particle entering the detector results in a pulse, much like the electrical spark we feel when we touch a metal object after walking briskly across a cold carpet.

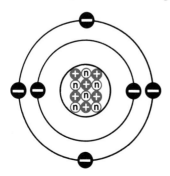

FIGURE 2.8
An atom of carbon with 6 protons and 6 neutrons in the nucleus. Most carbon atoms are in the form of this isotope, weighing 12 amu.

As material containing carbon gets older, it loses more and more of the radioactive isotope. From the amount of radioactivity present, the age of the material containing carbon can be determined. This carbon-14 dating procedure is very important to archaeologists. It is used to determine the ages of charcoal from ancient Indian campfires and other old objects made from wood. Carbon is especially important because of its combinations with other atoms. A carbon atom will join with other atoms, including other carbon atoms, in a tremendous number of ways. This is getting a little ahead of our story, but let us consider materials made of just carbon and hydrogen bonded in different ways and proportions: There is methane (natural gas), an excellent fuel, which burns cleanly to heat homes or is used as a raw material for fertilizers. The liquids in gasoline are made from combinations of carbon and hydrogen. So is solid polyethylene used to make garbage bags, plastic bottles, and book covers. All of these materials exist because carbon is so versatile in the ways in which it forms chemical bonds. This has given rise to the discipline called *organic chemistry*, which is the study of chemical compounds made primarily of carbon. The organic chemist has produced an enormous number of products, including drugs, solvents, plastics, and building materials. Some of this tremendous productivity is coming back to trouble us in the form of pesticides that kill birds and other wild animals, food additives that may be harmful to our health, and drugs whose misuse has destroyed many fine young minds.

The most important function of carbon, however, is its role in life substances. The materials in all living substances contain carbon as a key element. Consider the molecules that make up a human body. These molecules carry oxygen to our tissues. They send directions from the brain to the finger tips of a pianist. They tell the sperm and egg, which merge to form a new human being, whether to create a boy baby or a girl baby, how to make the eyes, how large the nose must be, or whether the hair is to be straight or curled. Imagine how complicated those blueprints have to be. Such complex blueprints are possible only because carbon can bond to itself and other elements in so many different ways. The study of the chemistry of these complicated biological materials is called **biochemistry**.

The 6-inch diameter logs shown consist of coal dust and tar mixed and compressed. These logs will be fed into a pilot-scale coal gasification system developed by GE, which is currently converting more than 3/4 of a ton of low-grade coal per hour into 100,000 ft³ of fuel gas suitable for running electric power plants. (Courtesy of General Electric Research and Development Center)

2.9

Air is Mostly Nitrogen

Atoms of element number 7 have 7 protons, 7 neutrons, and 7 electrons. The atomic weight of this element is 14. It is called nitrogen and its symbol is N. A drawing of a nitrogen atom in Figure 2.9 shows that it has 5 electrons in its outer shell. This outer shell can contain a maximum of 8 electrons, so it is beginning to get filled up. The electron-dot symbol of nitrogen is

$$:\overset{\cdot}{\underset{\cdot}{N}}\cdot$$

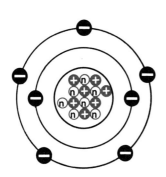

FIGURE 2.9

A nitrogen atom with a nucleus containing 7 protons and 7 neutrons. The atom has 7 electrons.

Nitrogen gas makes up 4 out of every 5 parts of air. By volume, air is 80% nitrogen. Like hydrogen atoms, the atoms of nitrogen gas are always found in pairs. Nitrogen atoms always combine to form nitrogen molecules, designated N_2.

$$N + N \longrightarrow N_2$$

Nitrogen gas can be converted to a liquid at very low temperatures. Liquid nitrogen boils at $-190°C$, so liquid nitrogen is extremely cold. Liquid nitrogen is used for quick freezing meats and other frozen foods. It is also used in freeze-drying processes for preparing instant coffee and other foods.

Pure nitrogen is prepared by changing air to a liquid at very low temperatures and separating out the other gases in air by the differences in their boiling temperatures in the liquid form. Nitrogen gas does not react chemically very easily, so it is used where an *inert atmosphere* is desired. This property is useful in some industrial processes. Foods, such as fruit, stay fresh longer in the atmosphere of nitrogen gas than they do in air.

The combinations of nitrogen with other elements are extremely important and are discussed in many places in this book. Nitrogen is an essential element for life. It is found in all **proteins** in living organisms. The exchange of nitrogen between the atmosphere and living and nonliving matter on the earth results in a very important natural process called the **nitrogen cycle** illustrated in Figure 2.10. It is difficult to get N_2 to combine with other elements. The combination of nitrogen and hydrogen is accomplished in factories by using very high pressures, temperatures, and a lot of energy. The product is ammonia gas. An

FIGURE 2.10 *The nitrogen cycle.*

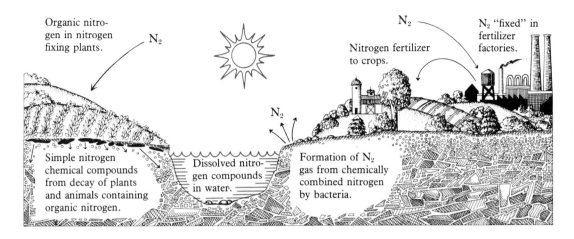

ammonia molecule is made up of 1 atom of nitrogen and 3 atoms of hydrogen. The formula for this molecule is, therefore, NH_3. A few living organisms fix nitrogen from the atmosphere; that is, they convert it to chemical compounds which can be used by the organism. An interesting example is *Rhizobium* bacteria, which live in little clumps (nodules) on the roots of certain plants. These plants are legumes, such as clover and peas. The bacteria provide the chemically combined nitrogen needed to make up the protein in the plant. The plant in return provides a home and food for the bacteria. It is a good arrangement for both.

2.10

Oxygen: Required by Both Humans and Gasoline Engines to Burn Their Fuel

About one-fifth of the air we breathe is oxygen gas. Recall that almost four-fifths of the atmosphere is nitrogen gas. These two gases together make up practically all of the air we breathe. Considering chemically combined oxygen in water and minerals, oxygen makes up about half of the total weight of the outer part of the earth. About two-thirds of our bodies are oxygen by weight. Most of this oxygen is chemically combined as water.

Pure oxygen ranks third in production among all industrial chemicals. Its greatest use is in the manufacture of iron and steel. Oxygen is employed along with acetylene in welding and cutting torches. Liquid oxygen is used in rocket engines. As a substitute for air in sewage treatment plants, oxygen speeds up the breakdown of sewage. In medicine oxygen is used to treat heart disease, pneumonia, emphysema, and other diseases where the patient may have difficulty obtaining enough of this essential gas from the air. It is also helpful in treating carbon monoxide poisoning.

Oxygen is supplied to the steel-making process from the beginning with the extraction of iron ore through to the conditioning of finished steel parts, where it is used to burn off surface defects from red-hot slabs of steel. The dramatic spectacle shown is molten steel being charged into a basic oxygen furnace to be converted to high-quality steel. (Courtesy of Bethlehem Steel Corp.)

Practically all oxygen atoms weigh 16 amu (Figure 2.11). These atoms contain 8 protons, 8 neutrons and 8 electrons. The atomic number of oxygen is 8 and its atomic weight is 16. The electron-dot symbol of oxygen is

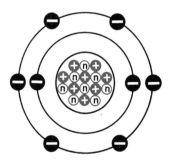

FIGURE 2.11
An oxygen atom weighing 16 amu.

Like hydrogen and nitrogen, the oxygen atoms in oxygen gas occur as pairs in the oxygen molecule, O_2:

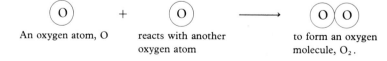

An oxygen atom, O   reacts with another oxygen atom   to form an oxygen molecule, O_2.

Another form consists of molecules containing 3 atoms of oxygen. This is ozone gas, O_3. Ozone is produced when an electrical spark passes through oxygen. It has a strong, sort of "clean" odor. It is toxic when present in concentrations of as little as one molecule of O_3 per million molecules of air! Ozone reacts with rubber causing it to become brittle and crack. It occurs in smog and does a lot of damage to rubber and other materials. Some plants such as pine trees are harmed by ozone.

Ozone is not all bad, however. It can be used as a disinfectant in place of chlorine. Ozone many miles up in the atmosphere serves as a "filter," which is very valuable to life on the earth. This ozone is produced by high energy chemical processes high in the atmosphere. The ozone layer absorbs much strong, damaging ultraviolet light from the sun. If this light reached the earth's surface, it would burn exposed skin very rapidly. This would cause skin cancer and eye damage.

The most important property of oxygen is that it combines with many other substances to produce heat. These substances include gasoline, coal, and even the food in our bodies. For example, when charcoal in a charcoal grill burns, oxygen from the air combines with the hot carbon in the charcoal to produce carbon dioxide gas and heat (Figure 2.12). Similarly, the oxygen that a human breathes combines with food to produce the energy used to walk, lift, or think.

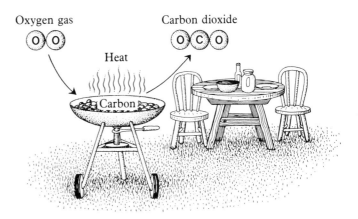

FIGURE 2.12
Oxygen from the air combines with hot carbon in charcoal and gives off heat and CO_2.

2.11

Fluorine: A Vicious Element

The element with atomic number 9 is fluorine, F. Each fluorine atom has 9 protons, 10 neutrons, and 9 electrons. The atomic weight of fluorine is 19. Fluorine is a greenish-yellow gas. It occurs as molecules which each contain 2 fluorine atoms. The chemical formula of fluorine is F_2. The structure of the fluorine atom shows that it contains 7 electrons in the outer shell (Figure 2.31). The electron-dot symbol of fluorine is

$$:\overset{..}{\underset{..}{F}}\cdot$$

This shell is filled when it has 8 electrons. The fluorine atom only needs 1 more electron.

Fluorine is the most chemically active of all elements. It is so active that it might be called a "vicious" element. It will even attack

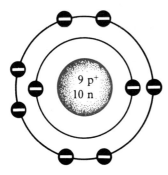

FIGURE 2.13

A fluorine atom with 7 electrons in the outer shell. Only 1 more electron is needed for a filled shell.

glass. Before extremely strict controls were put into effect, persons working around industrial processes where fluorine was used had to replace their eyeglasses after some time because the fluorine "fogged" the glass. Fluorine gas is very toxic to humans.

One of the main reasons for the extremely high activity of the fluorine atom is the fact that it lacks only 1 electron to have the 8 electrons needed for a filled second electron shell. Chemically the fluorine atom reacts by taking electrons from other atoms. It does this very aggressively.

In pure fluorine, each atom gets 8 electrons in the outer shell by sharing with another fluorine atom. The electron-dot formula of the resulting molecule of F_2 is

The circle drawn around each of the 2 atoms in the molecule shows that by sharing each can have 8 electrons in the outer shell. The pair of shared electrons between the two atoms makes up the chemical bond holding the molecule together.

Fluorine is used widely to make a large variety of other chemicals. Some of these are discussed later in the book. It is used to make Freons, which are the cooling fluids in refrigerators and propellants in aerosol cans. Fluorine is an ingredient of Teflon coatings on "no stick" cooking utensils. Chemically combined fluorine in the form of "fluoride" is added to drinking water and toothpastes to prevent tooth decay. Fluorine has many other uses.

2.12

Neon: Another Unsociable Element at the End of the Row

We have just seen that element number 9, fluorine, is the most chemically active element of all. The next element, neon with atomic number 10, does not react chemically at all. It is an "unsociable element," like the helium discussed in Chapter 1. Helium's two electrons give it a filled shell. In going to elements with atomic numbers higher than 2, the third, fourth, etc., electrons were shown to be farther from the nucleus in a second "shell." Just as hydrogen and helium are stable with 2 electrons in their first shell, atoms with an atomic number around 10 are most satisfied to have 8 electrons in their second shell. Atoms of neon, Ne, have exactly 8 electrons in the second shell, so they are satisfied without sharing electrons with other atoms. Therefore, Ne is a "noble gas," not caring to have anything to do with other atoms. The electron-dot symbol of neon is

$$: \overset{\cdot\cdot}{\underset{\cdot\cdot}{Ne}} :$$

The most common isotope of neon has 10 protons and 10 neutrons in the nucleus. All neon atoms, of course, have 10 electrons. Although most neon atoms weigh 20 amu as shown in Figure 2.14, about 1 out of 10 weighs 22 amu, and a very few weigh 21 amu. As a result the atomic weight of neon is 20.2.

Filled second electron shell containing 8 electrons.

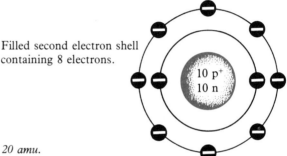

FIGURE 2.14
An atom of neon weighing 20 amu.

Neon is found in the air. About 2 parts of every thousand parts of air are neon. Neon is one of the products when liquid air is distilled to produce pure nitrogen and oxygen. Neon gas is used in lasers, switching devices, pilot lamps, and fluorescent light starters. It is best known as the filler gas in glass tubes from which neon signs are made. When electricity is passed through the neon, the gas absorbs some of the electrical energy, then releases it again as a glow of light. Neon signs are made in many shapes and sizes.

We have come to the end of a row in the periodic table. It is Sunday in our eight-day week on the calendar of the elements. Just as traditionally Sunday is a "day of rest," neon is "an element of rest" that does not react chemically with other elements. The periodic table with the first 10 elements in place is shown in Figure 2.15.

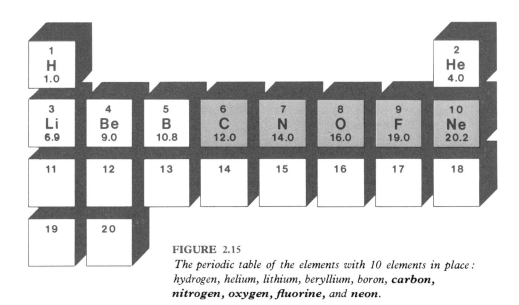

FIGURE 2.15
*The periodic table of the elements with 10 elements in place:
hydrogen, helium, lithium, beryllium, boron,* **carbon,**
nitrogen, oxygen, fluorine, and neon.

2.13

Sodium: One of the Elements in Table Salt

Element number 11, sodium, is the sixth most abundant element. Sodium is directly below lithium in the periodic table. Like lithium, it is a metal. Sodium is a very soft metal. It can be cut even with a dull knife. Combined with other elements, sodium is a very "calm" element. It is one of the two elements in common table salt. Sodium in the combined form is essential for life and is found in blood and other body fluids. But in the pure form sodium is extremely active and dangerous. It must be stored under kerosene or some other water-free solvent to keep it from burning. Don't undertake it yourself, but you may want to ask your instructor to drop a very small piece of sodium (about the size of a match head) into a container of water. The sodium attacks the water. It melts into a little ball and buzzes all around the surface of the water. The reaction gives off hydrogen gas with a hissing sound. A caustic, choking white smoke drifts away from the container. Finally, the sodium may become so hot it catches fire and burns with a bright yellow flame on the surface of the water.

The chemical symbol of sodium is Na. This comes from *natrium,* the Latin name for sodium. All naturally occurring sodium atoms have 11 protons and 12 neutrons. So, the atomic weight of sodium is 23. The arrangement of the 11 electrons in the sodium atoms is interesting. Recall from the discussion of neon that 10 electrons fit into 2 filled electron shells, the first shell with 2 electrons, the second with 8, which gives a very stable arrangement of electrons. The eleventh electron in sodium goes into a third shell that is on the outside of the two filled, "satisfied" ones as shown in Figure 2.16. This is what makes the

Sodium chloride is usually extracted from deep deposits within the earth by a method in which the brine is evaporated in heated coils as it is pumped out of the salt mine. The brine is then collected in salt beds and left for final evaporation. (Courtesy of the Salt Institute)

element such a "dissatisfied" species. Sodium atoms, like lithium atoms, have a very strong tendency to give this electron away when they react with other atoms. This electron is shown as 1 dot in the electron-dot symbol for sodium:

$$Na \cdot$$

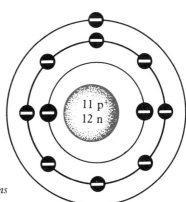

FIGURE 2.16
An atom of sodium with 11 protons and 12 neutrons in the nucleus.

Sodium metal is made by breaking down sodium chloride (table salt) electrically. The metal is used in sodium vapor lamps, which give off a sort of weird yellow color and use electricity efficiently. The eye is very sensitive to the color from these lamps, so that they are especially useful for lighting highways.

2.14

Magnesium: A Light, Strong Metal

Element number 12 is magnesium, Mg. It is the eighth most abundant element on the Earth's surface. Magnesium is a light metal and is relatively strong. Mixed with other metals as alloys, it is used for aircraft parts, castings for portable tools, hand trucks, and parts for printing machines. Magnesium is used as a "sacrificial anode" to protect water heater tanks, pipelines, and ship bottoms from corrosion. Basically, as illustrated in Figure 2.17, strips of magnesium safeguard iron, steel, or other metals from corrosive materials in the water.

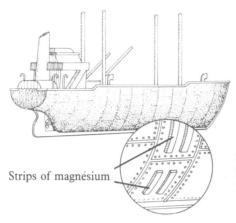

Strips of magnesium

FIGURE 2.17
Strips of magnesium prevent the steel on ship bottoms from rusting caused by corrosive sea water.

Chemically, magnesium is a relatively active element, although not nearly so active as its neighbor sodium. Finely divided magnesium will burn with an extremely intense white flame. A magnesium fire is extremely difficult to put out. Magnesium keeps on burning in the carbon dioxide gas from a CO_2 fire extinguisher! "Incendiary bombs" designed to burn their way right through a building from the roof to the basement contain magnesium metal. Explosively burning magnesium causes the "flash" in flash bulbs.

Magnesium is one of the elements used in a photo-flash to produce a single momentary combustion of high light intensity. (Courtesy of Eastman Kodak Co.)

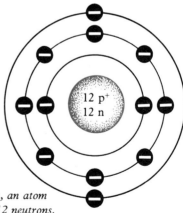

FIGURE 2.18
The most common isotope of magnesium, an atom weighing 24 amu with 12 protons and 12 neutrons.

All magnesium atoms have 12 protons and 12 electrons. Out of 1000 magnesium atoms, 786 have 12 neutrons, 101 have 13 neutrons, and 113 have 14 neutrons. This gives magnesium an atomic weight of 24.3. Magnesium atoms have 2 electrons in the outer shell (see Figure 2.18). The electron-dot symbol for magnesium is

$\cdot Mg \cdot$

2.15

Aluminum

Like magnesium, aluminum, Al, is a light, strong metal. Approximately five million tons of aluminum are produced each year in the U.S. About one-fourth of this production is used in building and construction, 20% for transportation equipment (e.g., automobiles, airplanes), and 15% for electrical goods, including long distance electrical transmission lines. The rest is used for machinery, equipment, consumer goods, containers (beverage cans), and other applications. On a weight basis aluminum conducts electricity better than copper, although the aluminum wires have to be larger because aluminum is such a light metal. In recent years aluminum wiring substituted for copper in house wiring has caused a number of fires due to shorts caused by corrosion. The need to save weight in automobiles, buses, and trains in order to conserve energy are resulting in increased aluminum use in transportation equipment. Another advantage that aluminum has over other metals is that the surface corrodes very slightly to form a thin film which protects it from further corrosion.

Aluminum is a good conductor of electricity and also an excellent reflector of light and radiation. Aluminized clothing, which is also lightweight, is used in many industries to protect workers against heat and flame. (Courtesy of the Aluminum Company of America)

Aluminum is the third most abundant element in the earth's crust, which is 8% aluminum by weight. In nature it is always found in a chemically combined form. It occurs in many minerals. With presently used technology, however, aluminum is extracted only from bauxite ore. There is not much high quality bauxite ore in the U.S. Most of the high quality U.S. bauxite is located in Arkansas. About 60% of the bauxite used in the U.S. is imported from Jamacia. Price increases in recent years have resulted in the investigation of other aluminum minerals in the U.S. as potential sources of this metal.

Aluminum atoms have 13 protons, 14 neutrons, and 13 electrons. Therefore, the atomic number of aluminum is 13; and the atomic weight is 27. There are 10 electrons in the first 2 shells of the aluminum atom. This leaves 3 electrons for the outer shell as shown in Figure 2.19.

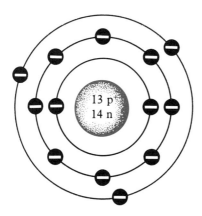

FIGURE 2.19

An aluminum atom which contains 13 protons, and 14 neutrons and weighs 27 amu.

Aluminum is the last metal in its row. The next element, silicon, is a nonmetal. The electron-dot symbol for aluminum is

$$\cdot \overset{\cdot}{Al} \cdot$$

2.16

Silicon: The Second Most Abundant Element

Element number 14 is silicon, Si. It is the second most abundant element in the Earth's crust, which consists of about one-quarter silicon. It is always found in a combined form with other elements, particularly oxygen and aluminum. Sand is a chemical combination of silicon and oxygen. Clay and many other minerals contain combined silicon. This element is an essential ingredient of a large number of products including ceramics, glass, cement, and asbestos. "Carborundum," a combination of silicon and carbon, is an extremely hard material used in grinding wheels and abrasives. Chemical combinations of silicon and organic materials known as **silicones** are relatively new materials with many useful properties. Tough, water-resistant, silicone caulking compounds are excellent for caulking around bathtubs. Silicone breast implants are sometimes used to give nature a lift. Special silicone greases are used as heat-resistant greases.

Elemental silicon "doped" with traces of boron or phosphorus makes an excellent semiconductor. Such silicon is widely used in power rectifiers to change alternating current to direct current. It is also employed in transistors, diodes, and other electronic parts. Solar cells for the conversion of sunlight to electricity contain silicon. Development of this promising energy source as a major supplier of electricity would require a truly massive silicon industry.

Silicon is the first nonmetal in its row of the periodic table. Each atom has 14 protons and 14 electrons. Most atoms have 14 neutrons and weigh 28 amu. A few silicon atoms weighing 29 amu have 15 neutrons, and a few have 16 neutrons and weigh 30 amu. The resulting atomic weight of silicon is 28.1.

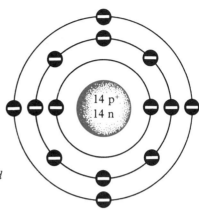

FIGURE 2.20
A silicon atom which contains 14 protons and 14 neutrons and weighs 28 amu. This is the most common isotope of silicon.

The electronic structure of the arrangement of electrons around the silicon nucleus is shown in Figure 2.20. Look back at the electronic structure of carbon, C in Figure 2.8. In what respect are the structures of these two atoms alike? Where is silicon in relation to carbon in the periodic table? The electron-dot symbol of silicon is

$$\cdot \overset{\cdot}{\underset{\cdot}{Si}} \cdot$$

It is time to look again at the periodic table. Four more elements have been added: These are the metals sodium (Na), magnesium (Mg), and aluminum (Al), and the nonmetal, silicon (Si) just described. This takes us through atomic number 14. The periodic table with the first 14 elements in place is shown in Figure 2.21.

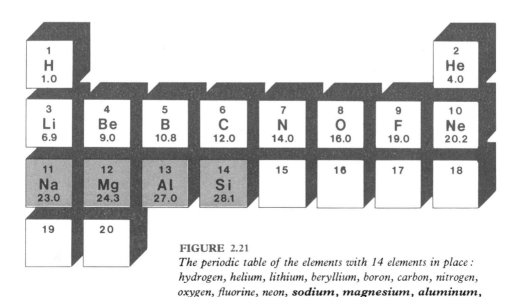

FIGURE 2.21
*The periodic table of the elements with 14 elements in place: hydrogen, helium, lithium, beryllium, boron, carbon, nitrogen, oxygen, fluorine, neon, **sodium, magnesium, aluminum, and silicon.***

2.17

Phosphorus: An Element with Several Faces

We saw in Section 2.8 that pure carbon occurs in several different forms ranging from sparkling diamonds to black smoke. Phosphorus, P, is another element which has different elemental forms. There are white phosphorus and red phosphorus. White phosphorus has to be stored under water because it catches fire when exposed to air. It is also very poisonous. An ounce (28 g) of white phosphorus is enough to kill several hundred people. Red phosphorus is not nearly as dangerous as white phosphorus. It does not catch fire spontaneously when exposed to air. It can be ignited with a flame, and it gives off dangerous choking fumes when it burns. Red phosphorus, too, should be handled with care.

White phosphorus mixed with flour is an ingredient of some types of rat poison. Red phosphorus is an ingredient of some fireworks, munitions, and tracer bullets. It is one of the materials used to make smoke screens.

The atomic number of phosphorus is 15; each phosphorus atom has 15 protons and 15 electrons. Naturally occurring phosphorus atoms weigh 31 amu and contain 16 neutrons (Figure 2.22). Therefore, the atomic weight of phosphorus is 31.0. The electron-dot symbol of phosphorus is

$$: \overset{\cdot}{\underset{\cdot}{P}} \cdot$$

Compare the structure of the phosphorus atom to that of nitrogen. Where are these two elements in relation to each other in the periodic table?

We will be most concerned with what phosphorus does in combination with other elements. Chemically bound phosphorus is essential to the human body. It is a major part of the hard mineral matter in bones and teeth. It is an ingredient of the protoplasm in living cells. It is important in nervous tissue. It is a key ingredient of the genetic materials, which are the blueprints for cell and tissue growth and development. It is involved in the complicated processes by which living things extract energy from food.

Fireworks in Boston, July 4, 1977. Red phosphorus is often used in the manufacture of fireworks. (Michael E. Katin, photographer)

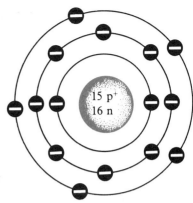

FIGURE 2.22
*Structure of a phosphorus atom. It has 15
electrons with 6 in the outer shell. The nucleus
contains 15 protons and 16 neutrons.*

Combined phosphorus is an ingredient of detergent formulations
and fertilizers. "Phosphate" is considered to be a polluting substance in
water, which is sometimes unfairly labelled "deadly phosphate." In fact,
it is such an essential nutrient that it causes plant life to grow too well
in the water. The rapidly growing plants eventually die and cause the body
of water to become choked up with dead plant material. This material
decays and uses up the oxygen needed by fish in the water. Water in which
this has happened is said to be *eutrophied.*

Certain combinations of phosphorus with other elements can be
deadly, however. The incredibly toxic nerve gases contain phosphorus.
Their offspring, the organophosphate pesticides, which have replaced
DDT, must be handled with extreme care.

2.18

Sulfur

Element number 16 is sulfur, S. It is a brittle, bright yellow nonmetal,
which has been known to humans since ancient times. It occurs in
nature in both the pure form and combined with other elements. An
interesting process is used to bring pure sulfur out of deposits in the
ground. Extremely hot water under very high pressure is forced into
wells drilled into the sulfur deposit. The water melts the sulfur, which
is then forced to the surface. This method of "mining" is called the
Frasch process. It is shown in Figure 2.23.

An idea can be gained of the enormous quantities of sulfur used
in industry from the mountains of bright yellow sulfur piled beside sulfur
mines awaiting shipment. Or one can look down from a mountain
roadway beside the Canadian Pacific Railway in Eastern British Columbia
and see whole unit trains consisting of gondola cars loaded with sulfur
roaring through the forests to Pacific ports. The sulfur has been removed
from "sour" natural gas produced in Alberta. It occurs in the gas in a
chemical combination with hydrogen called hydrogen sulfide. This is a
poisonous gas with the odor of rotten eggs. A pollutant is removed and
a valuable product, sulfur, is recovered. This illustrates a point. Most

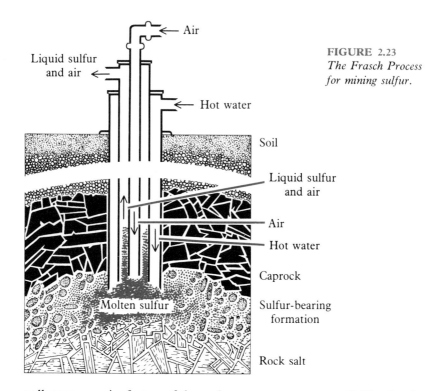

FIGURE 2.23
The Frasch Process for mining sulfur.

pollutants are in fact useful products gone to waste. Sulfur is also a pollutant in most coal, particularly, the abundant bituminous coal in the eastern U.S.

Sulfur enters into many chemical combinations discussed later in the book. It is one of the elements essential for life and occurs in some components of proteins. It is part of the chemical formulas of some drugs, notably the sulfa drugs. One sulfur compound, sulfuric acid, is the most widely produced industrial chemical. Sulfur atoms have 16 electrons and 16 protons. Most have 16 neutrons and weigh 32 amu as shown in Figure 2.24. A few have 17 or 18 neutrons, and a very few sulfur atoms have 20. There are enough of these heavier sulfur isotopes to make its atomic weight 32.1. The electron-dot symbol of sulfur is

$$: \overset{\cdot}{\underset{\cdot\cdot}{S}} \cdot$$

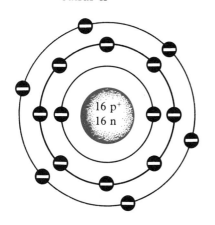

FIGURE 2.24
A sulfur atom with 16 electrons, 16 protons, and 16 neutrons. This atom has the same number of electrons in its outer shell as oxygen. Where are these elements in relation to each other in the periodic table?

2.19

Chlorine: A Deadly Green Gas that has Saved Many Lives

On a battlefield in France in 1915 soldiers stumbled from their trenches coughing and choking in agony, the linings of their lungs destroyed from inhaling chlorine gas. This was the first gas used as a poison for chemical warfare. Since that time "better" poisonous gases have been developed. Incidents of chlorine poisoning still occur. Occasionally barges loaded with chlorine get loose on a waterway, or a derailed tank car leaking liquid chlorine may cause evacuation of a whole town. However, this element has a good side. It is widely used to disinfect water supplies. Since chlorination of water has been practiced on a large scale, many lives have been saved through the elimination of diseases such as typhoid or cholera carried by contaminated water. In addition, chlorine is a widely used industrial chemical employed in the manufacture of solvents, plastics, pesticides, and many other chemical products. It ranks seventh among chemicals in annual production in the U.S. About 20 billion pounds of chlorine are manufactured in the U.S. every year.

The chemical symbol for chlorine is Cl. Its atomic number is 17, so each atom contains 17 protons and 17 electrons. Of a thousand chlorine atoms, 754 have 18 neutrons (Figure 2.25). Each of these atoms weighs 35 amu. The other 246 atoms each have 20 neutrons. This isotope weighs 37 amu. The average weights of these gives 35.5 for the atomic weight of chlorine. The electron-dot symbol of chlorine is

$$:\overset{\bullet\bullet}{\underset{\bullet\bullet}{Cl}}\cdot$$

Chlorine atoms are paired as chlorine molecules, Cl_2.

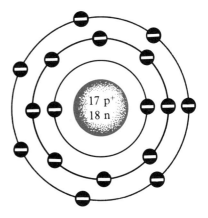

FIGURE 2.25
A chlorine atom with 17 electrons, 17 protons, and 18 neutrons. 75.4% of all chlorine atoms are this isotope.

Chlorine resembles fluorine in having 7 electrons in its outer shell. This is 1 electron short of the magic number of 8 electrons needed for a filled shell. As a result, chlorine has a very strong tendency to either take electrons from other atoms or share electrons with them.

In pure chlorine, each atom gets 8 electrons in the outer shell by sharing with another chlorine atom. The electron-dot formula of the resulting molecule of Cl_2 is

2.20

Argon

Element number 18 is argon, Ar. It is a noble gas like the helium and neon elements that we have studied. Like all noble gases it has no color, odor, or taste. It does not react chemically. In fact, the name, argon, means "the lazy one." This property makes it very useful for some applications. The most important of these applications is to provide a shield of inert gas around a welding arc to keep chemically active metals from burning during welding. Millions of cubic feet of argon gas are used in this application each year. Argon is also used as a filling gas for incandescent lamp bulbs as is illustrated in Figure 2.26. These bulbs produce light when electricity passes through a fine wire (filament) made of tungsten metal. The current makes the filament so hot that it glows white. At this temperature atoms of tungsten can escape, causing the filament to become thinner and break down. When the bulb is filled with argon gas, the escaping tungsten atoms "bounce back" to the filament, which prevents them from escaping. A noble gas has to be used to prevent the tungsten from reacting chemically with the filler gas.

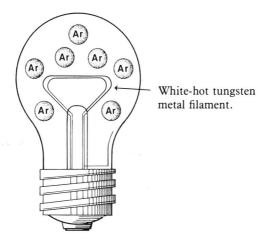

White-hot tungsten metal filament.

FIGURE 2.26

Argon, used as a filling gas for incandescent lamp bulbs.

Argon gas is also used in fluorescent lamps and in certain types of gas-filled electronic tubes. About 4 billion cubic feet (slightly more than 100 billion liters) of argon are produced in the U.S. every year. Argon is a byproduct of the separation of oxygen and nitrogen from liquid air. Air is about 1% argon by volume.

All argon atoms have 18 protons and 18 electrons. Practically all argon atoms have 22 neutrons and weigh 40 amu. A much less common isotope of argon weighs 36 amu, and another rare isotope weighs 38 amu. Therefore, the average weight of all argon atoms is slightly less than 40 amu. The atomic weight of this element is 39.9. The electron-dot symbol of argon is

$$\overset{\cdot\cdot}{\underset{\cdot\cdot}{:\text{Ar}:}}$$

The electron structure of the argon atom shows 8 electrons in the outer shell (see Figure 2.27). Just like the other noble gases, the argon atom has a filled outer shell, so it has no tendency to either acquire or lose electrons.

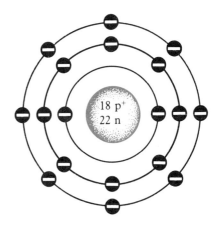

FIGURE 2.27
An isotope of argon weighing 40 amu.

We have arrived at the end of another row of the periodic table. Since we last looked at the table, 4 more elements have been added. These are phosphorus, sulfur, chlorine, and argon. This makes a total of 18 elements that have been discussed. The periodic table with these 18 in place is shown in Figure 2.28.

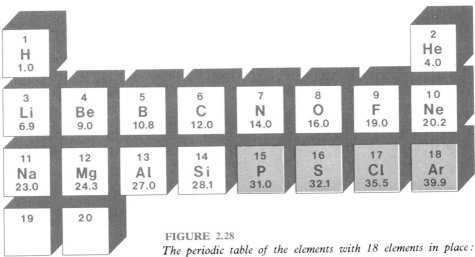

FIGURE 2.28
The periodic table of the elements with 18 elements in place:
hydrogen, helium, lithium, beryllium, boron, carbon, nitrogen, oxygen, fluorine, neon,
*sodium, magnesium, aluminum, silicon, **phosphorus, sulfur, chlorine, argon.***

2.21

Potassium: Another Lively Metal

The last element discussed was argon. It is a noble gas found in the atmosphere all around us. It is completely harmless and does not react with anything. But look what happens with the next element, which is like argon except for the addition of one more proton and one more electron. This element, potassium, is a soft metal that reacts violently with many other elements such as oxygen. It reacts almost explosively with water in the same way as sodium, which is the element just above it in the periodic table.

The symbol for potassium is K. This comes for the Latin name for potassium, *kalium*. All potassium atoms have 19 electrons and 19 protons. The most common isotope of potassium has 20 neutrons and weighs 39 amu. A few potassium atoms have 22 neutrons and weigh 41 amu. The average atomic weight of potassium is 39.1. This is kind of a curiosity. Recall that the previous element, argon, has an atomic weight of 39.9, which is *higher* than potassium. In general, argon has more neutrons. This makes its atomic weight higher than potassium but does not affect its chemistry. When chemists first started to arrange the elements in order on a periodic table, they arranged them by atomic weight. This put potassium ahead of argon, so that the chemical properties of these two did not fit at all. It caused much confusion until the idea of atomic number was developed. The electron-dot symbol of potassium is

K·

As indicated by the electron-dot symbol, potassium has one more electron than the stable argon "kernel." This electron goes into a fourth shell. In trying to get back to the very stable argon structure, potassium has a great tendency to lose this electron. This is what makes potassium such a chemically active element. The complete electronic structure of potassium is shown in Figure 2.29.

Being such a reactive element, potassium is not found free in nature. Potassium occurs in some minerals, and potassium compounds are found

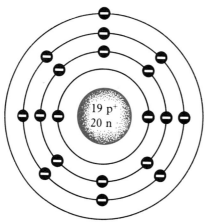

FIGURE 2.29
A potassium atom with 19 protons and 20 neutrons in its nucleus. The atom has 19 electrons. One of these is in the outer shell.

in underground deposits around the world. One of the best of these is in Saskatchewan, Canada, a major producer of potassium. Dissolved potassium compounds are found in some salt lakes, such as Searles Lake near Trona, California.

Various potassium compounds are widely used in industry. The most important use of potassium compounds is for plant fertilizer. Potassium salts, along with chemically combined nitrogen and phosphorus, are the three main ingredients of fertilizers. Potassium is also essential for the body and is involved with the complex processes by which nerves transmit their signals.

It is interesting that a radioactive isotope of potassium, potassium-40, occurs naturally. Potassium-40 makes up 0.01% of naturally occurring potassium. The radioactivity of this isotope can be measured to determine the amount of potassium in the body. The quantity of potassium can in turn be related to the relative amounts of fat and muscle in the body. Because of the radioactive potassium-40 in our bodies, those who sleep with someone else receive slightly more radiation (due to the radioactivity of the potassium-40 in the other person's body) than do those who sleep alone. Figure 2.30 describes how potassium-40 in the body can be measured. The amount of radioactivity is so slight, however, that it should not be high on the list of one's concerns.

FIGURE 2.30

A very sensitive radiation counter can be employed to measure radioactive potassium-40 in the body and determine the relative amounts of body fat and muscle.

Massive lead shield containing counters.

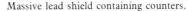

2.22

Calcium

There is one place left on the abbreviated chart of the elements. This place is reserved for calcium, Ca. All calcium atoms have 20 protons and 20 electrons. Most calcium atoms have 20 neutrons and weigh 40 amu. But there are 5 other isotopes of calcium that have more neutrons and are heavier. Averaging these in, the atomic weight of calcium is 40.1. As shown in Figure 2.31 there are 2 electrons in the outer shell. The electron-dot symbol of calcium is

$$\cdot Ca \cdot$$

Pure calcium metal is a white, silvery substance. It is rather similar to magnesium, which is right above calcium in the periodic table. Calcium metal is used in making alloys with many other metals. Metals for bearings are made of lead-calcium or lead-barium-calcium mixtures. Calcium is frequently alloyed with aluminum. Lead used for

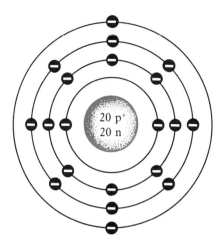

FIGURE 2.31

A calcium atom with 20 protons, 20 neutrons, and 20 electrons.

battery plates or cable sheathing is hardened by the addition of calcium. Calcium is added to some metals to react with oxygen or sulfur.

Chemically, calcium is very active. It is never found in nature in the pure form. Limestone, one of the most common of minerals, contains combined calcium. Limestone is heated to produce lime, a chemical combination of calcium and oxygen. The second most abundant chemical produced in the U.S. is lime. About 20 million tons are produced each year. Chemically combined calcium is part of many important chemicals.

These man-made limestone caverns in Kansas City have been converted to office and storage space after mining operations had already hollowed them out. (Courtesy of the Underground Development Corp.)

2.23

The Abbreviated Periodic Table is Full!

We have now gotten through the first 20 elements. The last two, potassium and calcium, can now be added to the periodic table as can be seen in Figure 2.32. It may have seemed like a long, slow process going through element by element, discussing the electronic structure and the isotopes of each. But it is worth the effort. By understanding the

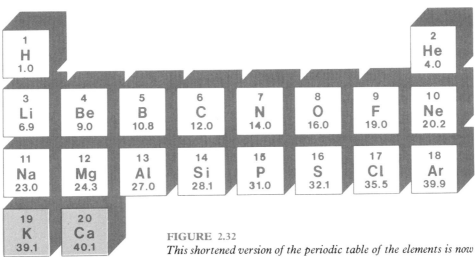

FIGURE 2.32

*This shortened version of the periodic table of the elements is now full with the first 20 elements in place: hydrogen, helium, lithium, beryllium, boron, carbon, nitrogen, oxygen, fluorine, neon, sodium, magnesium, aluminum, silicon, phosphorus, sulfur, chlorine, argon, **potassium, and calcium**.*

elements in this chapter, you have acquired the tools needed to discuss chemistry. You have learned the alphabet necessary to "write chemistry." It is not very long. Of these 20 elements, 3 are noble gases, so that leaves only 17 taking part in chemical reactions. As the chemistry of these is discussed, you will gradually become familiar with their names, symbols, and atomic numbers. Try to remember in particular the number of outer electrons that each has. This is an important key to understanding their chemistry. The electron-dot symbol is an especially useful device for showing the outer electrons.

The periodic table was constructed by going across it in order of increasing atomic number. Hydrogen is a special case, which behaves much differently from any other element on the table. Element number 2, helium, is a noble gas. Consider the properties of the elements in going across the first long row, however. Starting with element number 3, lithium is a soft, chemically active metal. The next element, beryllium, is a harder, much less active metal. Boron, carbon, nitrogen, and oxygen are nonmetals. Fluorine is an extremely active nonmetal. The last element on the row is a noble gas, neon. It has a filled outer shell of electrons. Starting on the next row, the pattern is largely repeated. Element number 11, sodium, is a soft, active metal much like lithium. Magnesium is much harder and much more stable. Aluminum is still a metal, but pretty stable in the elemental form. Silicon, phosphorus, sulfur, and chlorine are nonmetals. Chlorine resembles fluorine in being very active. The last position (element number 18) is occupied by another noble gas, argon. Element number 19, potassium, is very much like lithium and sodium in its properties. Like these 2 elements it has 1 electron in its outer shell. Finally, element number 20 has 2 electrons in its outer shell. It is quite a bit like magnesium and beryllium in many ways.

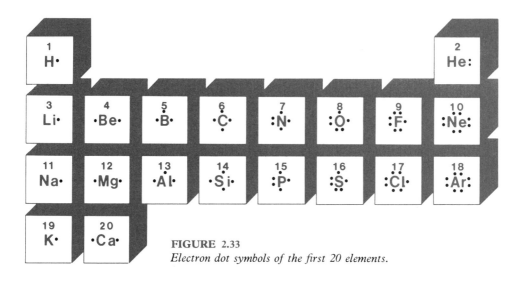

FIGURE 2.33
Electron dot symbols of the first 20 elements.

From the above discussion of the periodic table, it is seen that elements in columns (up and down) have some similar chemical reactions and properties. These groups of chemically related elements are called **families**. Each of the elements in a particular column in the periodic table has the same number of electrons in the outer shell (with the exception of helium, which has a filled shell of only 2 electrons). Observe these characteristics in Figure 2.33. This periodic arrangement of the elements is very convenient in considering the chemistry of the elements.

Elements beyond atomic number 20 are not shown in the shortened version of the periodic table discussed above. As we explained early in this chapter, it is easier to learn some basic chemistry with just a few of the more common elements. Also, above atomic number 20 the arrangements of electrons in the atoms become much more complicated. However, it will be necessary to refer to some of the heavier elements later in the book. For that reason all of the known elements are listed by atomic number, name, symbol, and atomic weight in Table 2.2. A complete periodic table appears on the inside front cover.

2.24

A More Detailed Look at Electrons in Atoms

This chapter views the arrangement of electrons in atoms in terms of shells or energy levels. This simple picture makes it easy to visualize the arrangements of electrons that surround the atom's nucleus. It is readily seen that atoms with the same number of outer shell electrons have similar properties and are arranged in vertical columns in the periodic table. In the next chapter we will see how the need for 2 electrons in the outer shells of hydrogen, lithium, beryllium, and boron and for 8 electrons in the outer shells of most of the other lighter elements largely determines the chemical behavior of atoms and the nature of the compounds that they form.

TABLE 2.2

Complete list of elements.

Atomic Number	Name	Symbol	Atomic Weight*	Atomic Number	Name	Symbol	Atomic Weight*
1	Hydrogen	H	1.0	54	Xenon	Xe	131.3
2	Helium	He	4.0	55	Cesium	Cs	132.9
3	Lithium	Li	6.9	56	Barium	Ba	137.3
4	Beryllium	Be	9.0	57	Lanthanum	La	138.9
5	Boron	B	10.8	58	Cerium	Ce	140.1
6	Carbon	C	12.0	59	Praseodymium	Pr	140.9
7	Nitrogen	N	14.0	60	Neodymium	Nd	144.2
8	Oxygen	O	16.0	61	Promethium	Pm	(145)
9	Fluorine	F	19.0	62	Samarium	Sm	150.4
10	Neon	Ne	20.2	63	Europium	Eu	152.0
11	Sodium	Na	23.0	64	Gadolinium	Gd	157.2
12	Magnesium	Mg	24.3	65	Terbium	Tb	158.9
13	Aluminum	Al	27.0	66	Dysprosium	Dy	162.5
14	Silicon	Si	28.1	67	Holmium	Ho	164.9
15	Phosphorus	P	31.0	68	Erbium	Er	167.3
16	Sulfur	S	32.1	69	Thulium	Tm	168.9
17	Chlorine	Cl	35.5	70	Ytterbium	Yb	173.0
18	Argon	Ar	39.9	71	Lutetium	Lu	175.0
19	Potassium	K	39.1	72	Hafnium	Hf	178.5
20	Calcium	Ca	40.1	73	Tantalum	Ta	180.9
21	Scandium	Sc	45.0	74	Tungsten	W	183.8
22	Titanium	Ti	47.9	75	Rhenium	Re	186.2
23	Vanadium	V	50.9	76	Osmium	Os	190.2
24	Chromium	Cr	52.0	77	Iridium	Ir	192.2
25	Manganese	Mn	54.9	78	Platinum	Pt	195.1
26	Iron	Fe	55.8	79	Gold	Au	197.0
27	Cobalt	Co	58.9	80	Mercury	Hg	200.6
28	Nickel	Ni	58.7	81	Thallium	Tl	204.4
29	Copper	Cu	63.5	82	Lead	Pb	207.2
30	Zinc	Zn	65.4	83	Bismuth	Bi	209.0
31	Gallium	Ga	69.7	84	Polonium	Po	(210)
32	Germanium	Ge	72.6	85	Astatine	At	(210)
33	Arsenic	As	74.9	86	Radon	Rn	(222)
34	Selenium	Se	79.0	87	Francium	Fr	(223)
35	Bromine	Br	79.9	88	Radium	Ra	226.0
36	Krypton	Kr	83.8	89	Actinium	Ac	(227)
37	Rubidium	Rb	85.5	90	Thorium	Th	232.0
38	Strontium	Sr	87.6	91	Protactinium	Pa	231.0
39	Yttrium	Y	88.9	92	Uranium	U	238.0
40	Zirconium	Zr	91.2	93	Neptunium	Np	237.0
41	Niobium	Nb	92.9	94	Plutonium	Pu	(242)
42	Molybdenum	Mo	95.9	95	Americium	Am	(243)
43	Technetium	Tc	98.9	96	Curium	Cm	(245)
44	Ruthenium	Ru	101.1	97	Berkelium	Bk	(249)
45	Rhodium	Rh	102.9	98	Californium	Cf	(249)
46	Palladium	Pd	106.4	99	Einsteinium	Es	(253)
47	Silver	Ag	107.9	100	Fermium	Fm	(254)
48	Cadmium	Cd	112.4	101	Mendelevium	Md	(256)
49	Indium	In	114.8	102	Nobelium	No	(254)
50	Tin	Sn	118.7	103	Lawrencium	Lr	(257)
51	Antimony	Sb	121.7	104	Rutherfordium	Rf	(257)
52	Tellurium	Te	127.6	105	Hahnium	Ha	(260)
53	Iodine	I	126.9	106	Not named yet		

* Atomic weights in parentheses are for synthetically produced elements.

Theory and experiment give a much more detailed picture of electrons in atoms than the one we found so convenient to use in this chapter. This is the **quantum mechanical theory** of the atom. Students going on in the sciences may need to know something about the quantum mechanical atom. Therefore, the theory is discussed briefly here.

The quantum mechanical atom visualizes electrons arranged in **principal energy levels**. These differ from each other by the amount of energy released when an electron from completely outside the atom enters a particular level. For an atom with three such levels, the most energy would be released for an electron entering level 1 nearest the nucleus, and the least for an electron entering level 3 farthest from the nucleus. On the other hand, it takes the most energy to take an electron out of level 1, and the least to take an electron out of level 3. (Look at the comparison in Figure 2.34.) These levels, or shells, are the same as the ones which we have discussed throughout this chapter. They are designated by the **principal quantum numbers,** 1, 2, 3, etc.

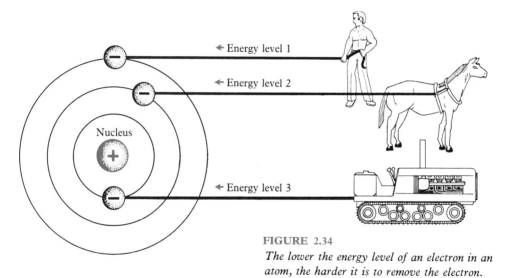

FIGURE 2.34

The lower the energy level of an electron in an atom, the harder it is to remove the electron.

Energy levels are divided into **sublevels**. These were not considered in our simple picture of the electronic structure of atoms. There are differences in energies of electrons in different sublevels within the same principal energy level. The sublevels are indicated by the letters, *s*, *p*, *d*, and *f*. Principal energy level 1 has only the *s* sublevel. Principal energy level 2 has *s* and *p* sublevels. Principal energy level 3 has *s*, *p*, and *d* sublevels. Principal energy level 4 has all four sublevels. For a given principal energy level, there can be 2 *s* electrons, 6 *p* electrons, 10 *d* electrons, and 14 *f* electrons.

It was already noted in Section 1.4 that a particular electron does not just go around an atom nucleus in a circle. Instead, an electron buzzes around a certain volume outside the nucleus. If the electron is an *s* electron, the space is like that inside a ball. At times the electron is near the outside surface of the "ball"; at other times it is near the

FIGURE 2.35

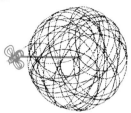

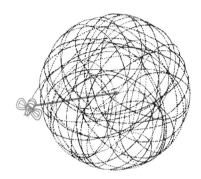

A bumblebee tethered to a skyhook by a strand of rubber would fly around in a sphere-shaped volume. If he had lost a lot of energy getting into principal energy level 1, the sphere would be smaller because the bee would not have much energy left to stretch the rubber.

If the bee were placed in principal energy level 3, for example, he would not have lost so much energy and would have enough strength left to stretch the strand of rubber farther, thus making a bigger sphere.

center (or nucleus). This may confuse the idea of energy level a bit, but let us look at an analogy, which is illustrated in Figure 2.35. Suppose it were possible to fasten one end of a broken rubber band to a "skyhook" suspended in space and the other end to a bumble bee. The average bumble bee would buzz around a sphere-shaped volume with the skyhook at the center. At times he would be near the center, and at other times, "at the end of his rope" near the surface of the imaginary sphere.

A space, such as a sphere, occupied by an electron is called an *orbital*. It is possible to have 2 electrons in each orbital, so both *s* electrons in a particular principal energy level can occupy the same sphere. Only *s* electrons occupy sphere-shaped orbitals. The *p* electrons have orbitals with shapes shown in Figure 2.36. A maximum of 6 *p* electrons is possible. These electrons occur in pairs occupying the same orbital, so three different orbitals are needed for *p* electrons.

It is convenient to know the number and types of electrons in an atom. This can be expressed by a shorthand expression called **spectral notation**. For example, consider the oxygen atom with 8 electrons. The

FIGURE 2.36
The orbitals in p sublevels have the shapes shown and may be oriented in three different ways in space.

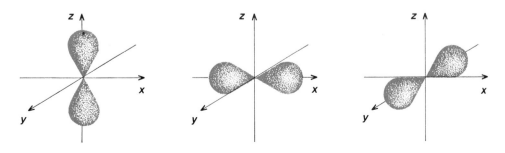

spectral notation for the oxygen atom is:

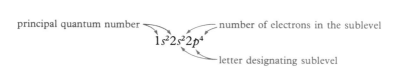

principal quantum number $1s^2 2s^2 2p^4$ number of electrons in the sublevel, letter designating sublevel

This notation tells us that there are 2 electrons in the *s* sublevel of the shell with principal quantum number 1. It also shows 2 *s* electrons and 4 *p* electrons in the shell with principal quantum number 2. By adding up the total number of electrons in the superscripts, we can see that the oxygen atom has a total of 8 electrons. Some other examples of spectral notation are helium, $1s^2$; carbon, $1s^2 2s^2 2p^2$; fluorine, $1s^2 2s^2 2p^5$; sodium, $1s^2 2s^2 2p^6 3s^1$; and argon, $1s^2 2s^2 2p^6 3s^2 3p^6$.

Many more pages could be devoted to the quantum mechanical picture of the atom. For the purposes of this book, however, it is enough to know a few of the basic terms and concepts. Those students going on to more advanced science courses will learn more about this topic.

Chapter Summary

The objective of Chapter 2 was to describe the elements through atomic number 20 and to arrange these elements in the manner of the *periodic table*. In addition to its *atomic number*, each element has a *name*, a *symbol*, and an *atomic weight*.

The atomic number of an element is equal to the number of protons in the nucleus and the number of electrons each atom of the element has. Atoms of the same element may have different numbers of neutrons. Such atoms are called *isotopes*. The atomic weight of an element is equal to the average weight of all its atoms. Because of differences in weights of isotopes, the atomic weights of elements are often not whole numbers.

The chemistry of the elements is determined by the arrangements of electrons in the atoms. These electrons go into different *shells*. The outermost of these is called the *outer shell*. The first of these shells is filled when it has 2 electrons. The second and third are filled with 8 electrons each. A filled outer shell makes the atom very stable. An element with just the right number of electrons to have a filled outer shell is a *noble gas*. It does not react much, if at all, chemically. Other atoms try to get filled outer shells by losing, sharing, or gaining electrons. It is this tendency that makes atoms react chemically.

In considering the chemistry of the elements, it is normally necessary to consider only the electrons in the outer shell. It is convenient to show these by way of an *electron-dot symbol*. The electron-dot symbol for carbon with 4 outer shell electrons is

·Ċ·

Electron dots can be used to show electrons in molecules. The hydrogen molecule can be shown as,

$$H:H$$

where the 2 dots indicate its 2 electrons. Located between the 2 H's, they indicate a chemical bond.

Elements in vertical columns in the periodic table tend to be alike. All 106 known elements are listed in Table 2.2. Some of the heavier ones will be discussed later in the book.

Chapter Review Questions

The following questions are designed as a self-teaching tool to help you review Chapter 2. The answers to each question follow. See Chapter Review Questions for Chapter 1 for further instructions.

1. The periodic table is so called because _____

_____

2. The three things normally shown for each element in the periodic table are its _____, _____ and _____.

3. The atomic weight of an element is _____

_____

4. Fill in the blanks below for each of the elements discussed.

Atomic Number	Name	Symbol	Atomic Weight
1	_____	_____	_____
2	_____	_____	_____
3	_____	_____	_____
4	_____	_____	_____
5	_____	_____	_____
6	_____	_____	_____
7	_____	_____	_____
8	_____	_____	_____
9	_____	_____	_____
10	_____	_____	_____
11	_____	_____	_____
12	_____	_____	_____
13	_____	_____	_____
14	_____	_____	_____
15	_____	_____	_____
16	_____	_____	_____
17	_____	_____	_____
18	_____	_____	_____
19	_____	_____	_____
20	_____	_____	_____

5. What do the dots indicate in an electron-dot symbol? _____

_____.

6. If X represents just an atom in general, which elements discussed previously have an electron-dot symbol of $X \cdot$? _____

_____

$\overset{\cdot}{\underset{}{\cdot}}\text{X} \cdot$ _____

$\overset{\cdot}{\underset{\cdot}{:}}\text{X} \cdot$ _____

$\cdot \text{X} \cdot$ _____

$: \overset{\cdot}{\text{X}} \cdot$ _____

$\cdot \overset{\cdot}{\underset{\cdot}{\text{X}}} \cdot$ _____

$: \overset{\cdot}{\underset{\cdot}{\text{X}}} :$ _____

$: \overset{\cdot}{\underset{\cdot}{\text{X}}}$ _____

7. The elements discussed in this chapter that are metals are _____, _____, _____, _____, _____, _____, and _____.

8. Of the metals discussed, the three that are chemically most active are _____, _____, and _____.

9. The most active nonmetals discussed are _____ and _____.

10. The electrons that are not in the outer shell of the atom are called _____. These plus the _____ make up the kernel of the atom.

11. The elements studied that are gases made up of molecules each containing 2 atoms are _____, _____, _____, _____, and _____.

12. Those elements that are gases made up of unbound single atoms are _____, _____, and _____. They are called _____ gases.

13. When a chemical symbol consists of two letters, the first letter is always a _____ letter and the second is always a _____ letter.

14. The chemical symbol for an element usually fits in well with its name. Examples are H for hydrogen or Si for silicon. An exception which we have studied is the symbol, _____, which comes from the Latin name, _____, or the symbol, _____, which comes from the Latin, _____.

15. In general, the chemical properties of an element are most likely to resemble those of the element either _____ or _____ it in the periodic table.

16. An atom with 6 protons and 8 neutrons is an isotope of _____, which is _____.

17. The element that can exist as molecules containing three atoms of the same element is _____, and this special form is called _____.

18. The elements produced commercially by distilling liquid air are _____, _____, _____, and _____.

19. One of the most important chemical properties of oxygen is _____ _____, a process which releases _____.

20. Two elements that produce light when used in special electrical lamps are _____ and _____. A third used for a different purpose in incandescent light bulbs is _____.

21. Three nonmetal elements that are very toxic to humans are _____, _____, and white _____.

22. The atomic number of sulfur is 16. A very few sulfur atoms weigh 36 amu. This isotope contains _____ neutrons.

23. The two naturally occurring isotopes of chlorine weigh _____ amu and _____ amu, and the average atomic weight of Cl is _____.

24. Two elements discussed that have naturally occurring radioactive isotopes in nature are _____ and _____.

25. If an attempt were made to construct a periodic table based on atomic weight, two elements would be switched around. These are _____ and _____.

26. The three elements most commonly involved in plant fertilizers are _____, _____, and _____.

Answers to Chapter Review Questions

1. the properties of the elements tend to be repeated at intervals with increasing atomic number
2. atomic number, symbol, atomic weight
3. the average weight in atomic mass units of all of the atoms of that element
4.

Name	Symbol	Atomic Weight
Hydrogen	H	1.0
Helium	He	4.0
Lithium	Li	6.9
Beryllium	Be	9.0
Boron	B	10.8
Carbon	C	12.0
Nitrogen	N	14.0
Oxygen	O	16.0
Fluorine	F	19.0
Neon	Ne	20.2
Sodium	Na	23.0
Magnesium	Mg	24.3
Aluminum	Al	27.0
Silicon	Si	28.1
Phosphorus	P	31.0
Sulfur	S	32.1
Chlorine	Cl	35.5
Argon	Ar	39.9
Potassium	K	39.1
Calcium	Ca	40.1

5. the number of electrons in the outer shell
6. X· hydrogen, lithium, sodium, potassium

   ·Ẋ· carbon, silicon

   :Ẋ· fluorine, chlorine

   ·X· beryllium, magnesium, calcium

   :Ẋ· nitrogen, phosphorus

   ·Ẋ· boron, aluminum

   :Ẍ: neon, argon

   :Ẍ· oxygen, sulfur

7. lithium, beryllium, sodium, magnesium, aluminum

8. lithium, sodium, potassium

9. fluorine, chlorine, potassium, and calcium.

10. inner electrons, nucleus

11. hydrogen, nitrogen, oxygen, fluorine, chlorine

12. helium, neon, argon, noble

13. capital, lower case ("small")

14. K, kalium, Na, natrium

15. directly above, directly below

16. carbon, radioactive

17. oxygen, ozone

18. nitrogen, oxygen, neon, argon

19. its combination with other substances, energy (heat)

20. neon, sodium, argon

21. fluorine, chlorine, phosphorus

22. 20

23. 35, 37, 35.5

24. carbon, potassium

25. argon, potassium

26. nitrogen, phosphorus, potassium

Exercises for Chapter 2

1. Most hydrogen atoms are the "normal" isotope with 1 proton in the nucleus weighing 1 amu. If, instead, exactly 50% of all hydrogen atoms were this isotope and the other 50% were the deuterium isotope weighing 2 amu, what would be the atomic weight of hydrogen?

2. What is a major use of lithium carbonate as a drug?

3. How many electrons are in the kernel of all of the atoms in the row of the periodic table starting with sodium and ending with argon?

4. Name and describe two forms (not isotopes) of carbon.

5. What does 14 stand for in the name, carbon-14?

6. What is the name of the branch of chemistry dealing with the specialized chemistry of carbon?

7. Which gas occurs in the greatest percentage in air?

8. Name two things that "fix" nitrogen from the atmosphere, binding it chemically as a compound.

9. Which element ranks third or fourth in production of industrial chemicals?

10. What good thing is done by the layer of ozone in the Earth's upper atmosphere?

11. What is the electron-dot formula of the fluorine molecule, F_2?

12. From a knowledge of the Frasch process, what would you estimate, roughly, to be the melting point of sulphur?

13. What function might be served by magnesium strips fastened to a steel fuel tank buried underground?

14. What is bauxite?

15. Of which two elements is carborundum made?

16. What are the two forms of the element phosphorus?

17. What are two sources of phosphorus as a water pollutant?

18. What is the function of argon in an incandescent lamp bulb?

19. Which radioactive isotope is "counted" to measure body fat?

Sand dunes in Death Valley,
California. Sand is a combination of
silicon and oxygen called silicon
dioxide. (Courtesy of the National
Park Service, U.S. Dept. of the
Interior)

3

Putting the Atoms Together to Make Compounds

3.1

Atoms Join Together: That is What Chemistry is All About

In Chapter 1 we considered how many atoms become more stable by combining with other atoms. Even the simplest atom, hydrogen, is very unstable by itself. Two hydrogen atoms join together to form a hydrogen *molecule*.

$$\text{H} + \text{H} \longrightarrow \text{H}\,\text{H}$$

Two hydrogen atoms react to form a hydrogen molecule.

The atoms in the molecule are held together by a *chemical bond* made of 2 electrons shared between the atoms. The *chemical formula* of hydrogen is H_2. This shows that elemental hydrogen consists of 2 hydrogen atoms tied together by a chemical bond forming a hydrogen molecule. The *chemical reaction* for the formation of molecules of hydrogen from hydrogen atoms is written as

$$H + H \longrightarrow H_2 \quad \text{or} \quad 2\,H \longrightarrow H_2$$

Why do 2 hydrogen atoms react to form a hydrogen molecule consisting of two atoms? What is the chemical bond holding the molecule together? Recall that in Chapter 1 a hydrogen atom is described as consisting of 1 proton and 1 electron. The structure is repeated in Figure 3.1. The hydrogen atom is most stable when it has 2 electrons. The

FIGURE 3.1
A hydrogen atom.

2 electrons give the atom a *filled first shell* of electrons. A hydrogen atom gets a filled shell by sharing electrons with another hydrogen atom as is illustrated in Figure 3.2. It is this sharing that makes up the chemical

FIGURE 3.2

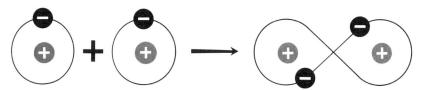

Two hydrogen atoms, each with 1 electron,

share their electrons to make up a hydrogen molecule held together with a chemical bond made up of the 2 shared electrons.

bond holding the 2 atoms together in the molecule. Such a chemical bond is called a **covalent bond**. Another type of bond will be discussed later in this chapter.

If the hydrogen atoms in the H_2 molecule are taken apart, the electrons no longer may be shared. Energy must be applied to take the atoms apart because separating atoms requires breaking the chemical bond. The energy that holds the atoms together is called *bonding energy*.

If atoms combined only with other atoms of their own element, there would be no chemistry. But atoms of an element combine with atoms of other elements to form many different kinds of molecules. When atoms of one element combine with atoms of another element, the product is a *chemical compound*. The focus of this chapter is how atoms of different elements join together to form chemical compounds.

Lightning often develops at the base of a cloud where there is dense negative charge. A series of cloud-to-cloud discharges follow involving an initiating stroke, called a "leader," and a return stroke, pictures (1) and (2). In (2) as a leader nears the ground, a spark from the ground moves up to meet it. Subsequent leader-return stroke formations, pictures (3)–(6), heat gases in the air producing thunder. (From M. King Hubbert, "The Energy Resources of the Earth," Scientific American, Sept. 1971)

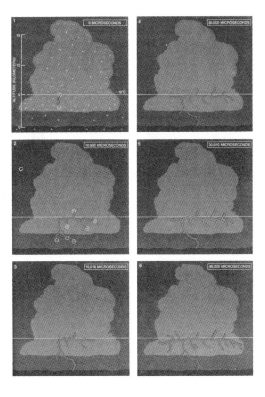

3.2

Chemical Bonds and the Periodic Table

To discuss chemical compounds, it is helpful to refer to the periodic table. The section of the periodic table developed in Chapter 2 is shown in Figure 3.3. Recall that it is a listing of the elements by atomic number. For simplicity, the atomic weights of the elements are not shown in Figure 3.3. However, the electron-dot symbols are shown. These dots are very important for a picture of chemical bonding. When atoms form chemical compounds, they lose, gain, or share electrons in order to attain an arrangement of electrons like that of a noble gas (helium, neon, argon). For the elements at the left side of the table, this means achieving a structure which would resemble the *next lower* noble gas. In the process, they lose electrons. For example, lithium combines chemically to get an electron configuration like helium. For the elements at the right side, the desired structure is similar to that of the *next higher* noble gas. This may involve either taking electrons away from other atoms or sharing electrons. So we see an element such as chorine combining chemically to get an electronic structure like argon. The electron-dot symbols make it much easier to get a picture of what happens to the electrons in chemical bonding.

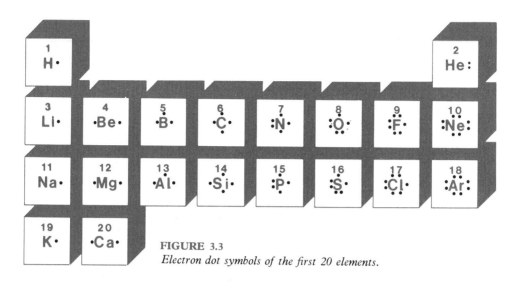

FIGURE 3.3
Electron dot symbols of the first 20 elements.

Not all electrons are available for chemical bonding. These unavailable electrons are the ones in the filled shells of the atom. Recall from Chapter 2 that the nucleus of the atoms plus these filled shells of electrons make up the *kernel* of the atom. The electrons outside the kernel are the ones that can be involved in bonding and are shown as dots. They have a special name. They are called **valence electrons.**

3.3

Some Chemical Compounds of Hydrogen

The idea of chemical bonding and the formation of chemical compounds can be shown clearly by looking at some chemical compounds of hydrogen. We will consider the formation of four very important chemical compounds resulting when hydrogen atoms combine with atoms of carbon, nitrogen, oxygen, and chlorine.

The atoms are shown with their valence electrons. When hydrogen reacts with other elements, it shares electrons. Then the electron structure of hydrogen becomes like that of helium, which we know is a noble gas and has *two* electrons in its outer shell. On the other hand, the atoms of the other elements shown have altogether *eight* electrons in their outer shell when they are chemically combined.

Let us consider first the very simple case of a hydrogen atom combining with a chlorine atom.

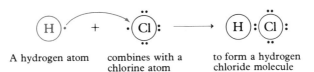

A hydrogen atom   combines with a   to form a hydrogen
chlorine atom   chloride molecule

When hydrogen combines with chlorine a molecule is formed consisting of an atom of hydrogen bonded to an atom of chlorine. These 2 shared electrons make up the chemical bond holding the atoms together. In this arrangement the hydrogen atom has 2 electrons both of which are shared with chlorine. The chlorine atom has 8 electrons in its outer shell. Two of these are shared with hydrogen. This is more easily seen by drawing a dashed circle around each atom to include the electrons in its outer shell.

shared electrons

The chemical compound formed when hydrogen and chlorine combine is called *hydrogen chloride*. The name indicates the 2 elements from which it is made. The *chemical formula* is HCl. This formula shows that the hydrogen chloride molecule consists of 1 hydrogen atom and 1 chlorine atom. Hydrogen chloride is a colorless gas with a choking odor. It dissolves in water to produce *hydrochloric acid*. This acid is sometimes sold under the name *muriatic acid*. Hydrochloric acid has many uses, such as in metal cleaning or for dissolving rock in petroleum-bearing rock formations to increase the flow of crude oil (see Figure 3.4). About 2.5 million tons of hydrochloric acid are produced in the U.S. each year. Interestingly, this acid is found in the stomach, in gastric fluid, and is essential for the digestion of food.

We have just seen that the chlorine atom needs *one* more electron to get an outer shell of *eight* electrons. Now, let us examine the oxygen atom. It has 6 electrons in its outer shell and needs *two* more for a filled shell. How may it get these electrons by bonding to hydrogen atoms?

FIGURE 3.4

Hydrochloric acid forced into petroleum-bearing rock formations in an oil well dissolves some of the rock and increases the flow of crude oil into the well. This can often make the difference between an economical and uneconomical well.

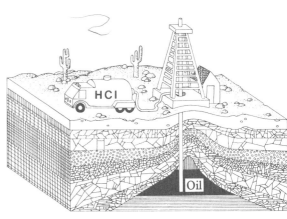

We see that this is accomplished by bonding with *two* hydrogen atoms, each contributing 1 electron to the sharing arrangement.

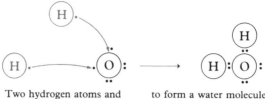

Two hydrogen atoms and 1 oxygen atom combine   to form a water molecule containing 2 hydrogen atoms bonded to the oxygen atom.

The chemical formula of water is H_2O. This formula shows that the water molecule consists of 2 hydrogen atoms bonded to 1 oxygen atom. Examination of the molecule shows that there are 8 valence electrons surrounding the oxygen atom, which give it a "satisfied," filled outer shell. Four of these electrons are shared with the 2 hydrogen atoms. Each hydrogen atom has the 2 electrons. These are shared with the oxygen atom. There are 2 chemical bonds in the water molecule. Each of these bonds attaches a hydrogen atom to the oxygen atom.

Water is a clear liquid at room temperature. It freezes at 0°C and boils at 100°C. About 70 % of the Earth's surface is covered with water. The human body is also composed of about 70 % water. Water's most important function is as a **solvent**. A large variety of things dissolve in water to form **solutions**. (see Figure 3.5).

Let us turn to the bonding of hydrogen atoms with the nitrogen atom. The electron-dot symbol shows that nitrogen has 5 valence electrons. It needs 3 more to have a filled shell of 8. This is accomplished by joining with 3 hydrogen atoms.

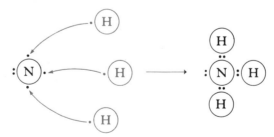

A nitrogen atom bonds chemically   to form a molecule of ammonia.
to 3 hydrogen atoms

The product is *ammonia*. The chemical formula, NH_3, shows that the ammonia molecule contains 1 nitrogen atom and 3 hydrogen atoms. In this compound the nitrogen atom has 8 electrons. Three pairs of electrons (a total of six) are shared with the 3 hydrogen atoms. Each of the hydrogen atoms shares 2 electrons with nitrogen.

Ammonia is a colorless gas with a sharp, pungent odor. It is made by reacting hydrogen and nitrogen together at a high temperature and very high pressure. About 16 million tons of ammonia are manufactured in the U.S. each year. Thus in quantity it ranks third or fourth (depending

FIGURE 3.5
*Water is an
excellent solvent.*

on the year) in chemical production. Ammonia is used as fertilizer (see Figure 3.6), to make plastics, and in many industrial applications. It is very soluble is water.

FIGURE 3.6

*Anhydrous (water-free) ammonia
is applied to soil as fertilizer.
It is injected into the ground
and stays there because it dissolves in water in the soil.*

How can the carbon atom attain a stable 8-electron outer shell by combining with hydrogen? Four hydrogen atoms combine with one carbon atom to produce a molecule with the chemical formula, CH_4. This compound is called **methane**.

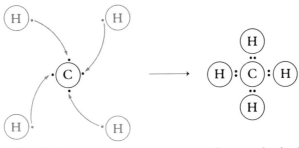

Four hydrogen atoms
bond to 1 carbon atom

to form a molecule of
methane, CH_4.

In the methane molecule the carbon atom has 8 electrons in its outer shell, all of which are shared with hydrogen atoms. Each hydrogen atom

The atmosphere of Jupiter, first observed by Galileo in 1610, when viewed through an optical telescope appears to be crossed by a series of parallel bands. The near white areas have been found to be composed mainly of ice crystals of solidified ammonia. These are the highest and coldest zones; at lower altitudes, ammonia melts and forms compounds with other elements in Jupiter's environment. (Courtesy of NASA)

has 2 electrons, which it shares with carbon. There are 4 chemical bonds in the methane molecule. Each of these bonds attaches a hydrogen atom to a carbon atom.

Methane is the simplest of a large number of chemical compounds called **hydrocarbons**. Quite obviously the name is derived from the chemical combination of *hydrogen* and *carbon*. Methane is the hydrocarbon in **natural gas**. Methane makes an ideal fuel because it is easily transported by pipeline, and it is safe, convenient, and burns very cleanly. About 30% of U.S. energy is supplied by natural gas, resulting in about 24 *trillion* cubic feet of natural gas consumed in the U.S. each year. In addition to its use as a fuel, methane is consumed in large quantities as a raw material in the manufacture of many other chemicals. The hydrogen required to make ammonia is prepared by "splitting" methane molecules. Methane is also the source of carbon black, which is added in large quantities to tire rubber. Because of its popularity, natural gas is in short supply. Reserves are dangerously low in the U.S. Eventually methane will have to be manufactured from coal, and alternate energy sources will need to be considered in place of natural gas.

We have just discussed some simple chemical compounds in which the simplest atom, hydrogen, is bonded to other atoms. The four

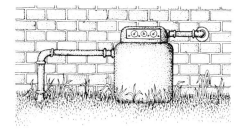

Reserves of natural gas (methane) are very low. In most parts of the U.S., it is no longer possible to obtain a gas hookup for new construction.

compounds discussed were hydrogen chloride, water, ammonia, and methane. All of these are very important chemical compounds. It is relatively easy to predict the resulting chemical formulas from the fact that each atom bonded to hydrogen gets 8 electrons due to the bonding.

3.4

Oxides: Chemical Compounds Containing Oxygen

Chemical bonding can be much more complicated than that shown in the simple examples in Section 3.3. In fact, analyses of some kinds of bonding are subject to sophisticated mathematical calculations on the computer involving lengthy programs, which can take hours of computer time to run. However, for the purpose of this course the important thing to realize is that atoms do combine in various formations to create chemical compounds held together by chemical bonds of various kinds.

The next element whose compounds we will examine is oxygen. It is an abundant element that is a component of an extremely large number of chemical compounds. Because air consists of 21 % oxygen, there is always a lot of this element around for something to react with. The chemical combination of oxygen with one other element is normally called an **oxide**. Water, H_2O, is an oxide of hydrogen. In this section we examine some of the common oxides and discuss their significance.

Recall that the electron-dot symbol for oxygen is

There are 6 outer shell electrons. Two more are needed for a filled shell. Consider first the chemical combination of carbon and oxygen. One carbon atom and 1 oxygen atom can combine to form a molecule of **carbon monoxide**, CO.

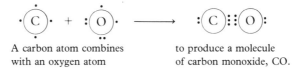

| A carbon atom combines with an oxygen atom | to produce a molecule of carbon monoxide, CO. |

Each of these atoms needs 8 outer shell electrons. This is achieved by sharing *six* electrons in a chemical bond. We have seen previously that a chemical bond can consist of a pair of electrons. A bond made up of 3 pairs of electrons (to give a total of 6 electrons) is called a **triple bond**.

Carbon monoxide is a colorless, odorless, toxic gas. It is produced when fuels containing carbon burn without sufficient oxygen. Carbon monoxide is generated by automobile engines. As a result, the CO in the atmosphere reaches temporarily high levels in localized high traffic areas. The fraction of automobiles with some CO control is now relatively high. When a person inhales air containing low concentrations of carbon

Smog produced from automobile combustion and industrial furnaces menaces the city and reduces visibility. (Courtesy of Massachusetts Audubon Society and Aerial Photos of New England, Inc.)

monoxide, headache, dizziness, and a lack of awareness result. Higher concentrations cause unconsciousness and even death. The carbon monoxide compound is toxic because it attaches to the hemoglobin in blood. The attacked blood cells can no longer carry oxygen to the brain and other parts of the body.

A carbon atom can also bond with *two* oxygen atoms. The molecule formed is called carbon dioxide.

Two atoms of oxygen combine with 1 atom of carbon   to produce a molecule of carbon dioxide, CO_2.

Its chemical formula is CO_2, which is pronounced "see-oh-two." In the name, carbon dioxide, *carbon* refers to one of the elements present, *di-* means 2, and *oxide* stands for oxygen when it is combined with another element. Therefore, the name indicates a carbon atom combined with 2 oxygen atoms.

Millions of tons of carbon dioxide are produced each year when fuels are burned. It is also one of the products created in the "burning" of food by living things, including man. Carbon dioxide makes up only about 1 part of every 10,000 parts of air. This relatively small fraction of carbon dioxide is the only source of carbon for plants. Plants convert the carbon in CO_2 to carbon-containing materials, which make up the plant structure. (They acquire energy for this process from sunlight.)

Carbon dioxide dissolves in water. It is the gas which gives a soda drink its "fizz". It can be cooled to make solid "dry ice". Under high pressures carbon dioxide is a liquid at room temperature. This liquid is contained in carbon dioxide fire extinguishers. When squirted on a flame, the carbon dioxide keeps air away and puts out the fire. Carbon dioxide is produced when sugar is fermented by yeasts. This causes bread to rise. It is also responsible for the bubbles in the head of foam on a glass of beer. Carbon dioxide from fermentation can build up very high pressures. More than one "do-it-yourself" beer brewer has found this out by way of popped stoppers and burst bottles from attempts to make "home brew".

Next, we consider silicon, the element just below carbon in the periodic table. Recall that silicon has the same number of valence electrons as carbon.

How does silicon combine with oxygen? Two oxygen atoms combine with 1 silicon atom. The product is silicon dioxide, SiO_2.

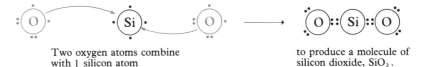

Two oxygen atoms combine with 1 silicon atom

to produce a molecule of silicon dioxide, SiO_2.

Silicon dioxide is what we see as ordinary sand!

Combinations of sulfur with oxygen are important. A sulfur atom combines with 2 oxygen atoms to produce sulfur dioxide, SO_2.

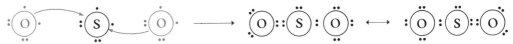

A sulfur atom and 2 oxygen atoms combine

to form a molecule of sulfur dioxide, SO_2.

The electron-dot structure of sulfur dioxide shows a double bond (4 electrons) between the sulfur atom and one of the oxygen atoms. There is a single bond with the other oxygen atom. This does not mean that the 2 oxygen atoms are different. One can visualize the sulfur dioxide molecule shifting rapidly between the two structures shown in the diagram. In effect, we have in this molecule a situation where very simple pictures of bonding begin to break down. However, at this point, the only important thing to remember is that 2 oxygen atoms do in fact bond to 1 sulfur atom to form a molecule of sulfur dioxide.

Sulfur dioxide is a colorless gas with a choking odor. If it weren't for sulfur dioxide, there would not be much of an energy problem in the U.S. Most of our cheaper, more readily available fuel reserves consist of high-sulfur coal. When this coal is burned, sulfur dioxide is produced. In the air this sulfur dioxide damages materials and is harmful to breathe. It is converted to corrosive sulfuric acid by chemical reactions in the air. In some parts of the world at times it literally rains very dilute sulfuric acid.

There is another oxide of sulfur. This is sulfur trioxide, SO_3. The sulfur trioxide molecule consists of 1 atom of sulfur and 3 atoms of oxygen. Sulfur trioxide is a liquid at room temperature. It freezes at 17°C and boils at 43°C. It dissolves in water to form sulfuric acid. In fact, it will even take water vapor from the air for this purpose.

Nitrogen forms several oxides. Nitric oxide, NO, is produced at the high temperatures and pressures that occur in the cylinders of automobile engines. Like carbon monoxide, it is a major air pollutant because of the number of cars on the road. In the air nitric oxide is converted to nitrogen dioxide, NO_2. This molecule has 2 atoms of oxygen per atom of nitrogen. It is a poisonous red gas. It absorbs sunlight in the atmosphere. In so doing, it traps energy from the sun and starts a series of complicated chemical processes involving organic materials such as unburned gasoline vapor. Smog is the final product of these reactions. Smog is a witches brew of irritating chemicals, which cause eyes to burn and noses to smart. Eliminating nitrogen oxides from automobile exhausts is one of the most challenging tasks in air pollution control.

3.5

Table Salt: Another Way of Putting Atoms Together

Consider once more the electron-dot symbols for the sodium atom and the chlorine atom:

sodium atom   chlorine atom

Can these 2 atoms combine? Each of these atoms needs 8 electrons in its outer shell. It is particularly hard to imagine any sharing arrangement that would put 7 more electrons in the sodium atom's outer shell. The sodium atom has only 1 electron in its outer shell. The chlorine atom has 7 electrons in its outer shell and needs 1 more electron. Let us look at the electronic structure of the sodium atom in more detail. Observe in Figure 3.7 that if it weren't for the 1 outermost electron, the sodium would have an outer shell with 8 electrons. For this reason, sodium readily gives away its 1 "extra" electron. When sodium and chlorine combine, the electron from the sodium atom is given to the chlorine atom. Let us count the electrons left after sodium loses an electron to chlorine. We find there are 10 electrons as are shown in Figure 3.8. Each of these electrons has a negative ($-$) charge. But, sodium still has 11 protons, each with a positive ($+$) charge. This gives the sodium atom

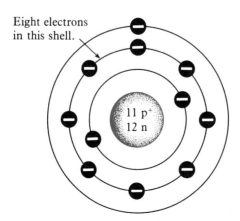

Eight electrons
in this shell.

11 p$^+$
12 n

FIGURE 3.7
A sodium atom.

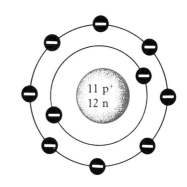

FIGURE 3.8
A sodium "atom," which has lost 1 electron.
It is now an ion with a +1 charge.

An electron is
transferred from
a sodium atom

to a chlorine
atom

to form sodium chloride
consisting of a positively
charged sodium ion and a
negatively charged chloride
ion.

an excess of one positive charge. This kind of electrically charged atom is called an **ion**. Because of its + charge, it is a positive ion. Positive ions are called **cations**. The sodium cation is given the symbol, Na^+. The Na shows that it is sodium and the $^+$ indicates that it is an ion with a +1 charge. The chlorine atom has gained an electron in the exchange. It now has one more electron than proton and has a −1 charge. This kind of negatively charged ion is called an **anion**. This can be shown by writing the symbol of chloride ion as Cl^-.

The chemical formed by combining sodium and chlorine is sodium chloride with a chemical symbol, NaCl. The ions that make up sodium chloride are not held together by *covalent bonds* made up of *shared* electrons. Instead, they are held together by electrical attraction between the positive sodium ions and the negative chloride ions. This kind of bond is called an **ionic bond**, or an **electrovalent bond**.

Sodium chloride is common table salt. Like most ionic compounds, it is a solid. Dissolved sodium chloride is found in body fluids such as blood or urine. Sea water contains a lot of dissolved sodium chloride in vast underground deposits. Sodium chloride is also a widely used industrial chemical.

There are many other ionic compounds. They exist mostly in combinations with one of the elements at the far left of the periodic table (except hydrogen) and with one at the right (except for the noble gases). The elements with 1 electron in their outer shell (lithium, sodium, potassium) tend to lose that electron. Beryllium, magnesium, and calcium, with 2 electrons in their outer shell, tend to lose 2 electrons. Even aluminum may lose all three of its outer shell electrons. These are all metals. The ability to lose electrons in forming electrovalent chemical bonds is one of the main chemical characteristics of metals. Except for the noble gases, the elements at the right of the periodic table readily accept electrons in forming ionic compounds. Fluorine and chlorine each accept 1 electron to gain an outer shell with 8 electrons. Oxygen and sulfur each accept 2 electrons. In forming chemical compounds nonmetals such as oxygen and sulfur usually gain or share electrons.

From the numbers of electrons gained or lost when ionic compounds are formed, it is easy to determine the chemical formulas of these compounds. We can observe this by considering several more examples. The first of these is the combination of calcium and chlorine. Consider the electron-dot structures of the calcium atom and the chlorine atom.

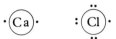

Each calcium atom has 2 electrons to lose. Each chlorine atom needs to gain 1 electron to have a filled outer shell of 8 electrons. The calcium atom donates its 2 electrons to 2 chlorine atoms.

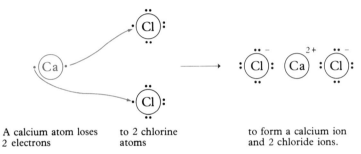

| A calcium atom loses 2 electrons | to 2 chlorine atoms | to form a calcium ion and 2 chloride ions. |

The calcium atom becomes a calcium ion, Ca^{2+}, with a charge of $+2$. Each of the chlorine atoms becomes a chloride ion, Cl^-, with a charge of -1. The chemical formula of the product is $CaCl_2$. It is called calcium chloride.

Pure calcium chloride is a white solid. It has a tremendous appetite for water and will rapidly draw enough moisture from the air to dissolve itself. About 1.25 million tons of this chemical are produced every year as a by-product in the manufacture of other chemicals. Its uses are limited, so disposal is a problem. Fairly large quantities are spread in the winter to melt ice on streets and sidewalks.

As another example, consider the reaction of calcium and oxygen.

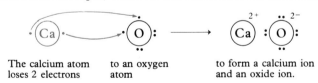

| The calcium atom loses 2 electrons | to an oxygen atom | to form a calcium ion and an oxide ion. |

The product is calcium oxide, CaO. It is made of calcium ions, Ca^{2+}, and oxide ions, O^{2-}, held together by ionic bonds. The common name for calcium oxide is *quicklime*. It is a very important industrial and commercial product. It is used to treat water and to manufacture many products including plaster, glass, and bleaching powder.

Two more examples of ionic compounds will be considered. The first of these is formed by the combination of sodium atoms and sulfur atoms.

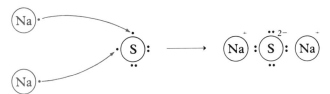

Two sodium atoms each   to a sulfur atom   to form sodium ions, Na^+,
lose an electron   and a sulfide ion, S^{2-}.

Because each sodium atom has 1 electron to lose and each sulfur atom
needs to gain 2 to fill the outer shell, 2 sodiums are required for each
sulfur. The chemical formula of the compound is Na_2S. The compound
is called sodium sulfide.

Finally, consider the chemical combination of aluminum and
oxygen.

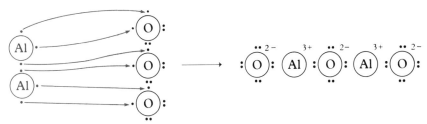

Two aluminum atoms lose   to 3 oxygen atoms   to form 2 aluminum ions,
a total of 6 electrons Al^{3+}, and 3 oxide ions, O^{2-}.

The product of this reaction is aluminum oxide, Al_2O_3. This compound
occurs naturally as a mineral called *corundum*. Several kinds of precious
stones, such as ruby, are made of corundum containing traces of other
minerals. Corundum melts at 2020°C. It is very hard. Only a few other
materials, such as diamond and carborundum, are harder.

3.6

Oxidation and Reduction

In the previous examples it was shown that ionic compounds are created
when one kind of atom loses electrons to another kind. This happens in
all cases of ionic compounds. Even covalent bonds often involve unequal
sharing of electrons between the two atoms involved. The loss or gain of
electrons in chemical bond formation is described by the important concept of **oxidation** and **reduction**.

It was seen that when oxygen combines with calcium or aluminum,
the oxygen *gains* electrons. In general, when oxygen combines with other
elements, the oxygen atoms gain electrons. That gives rise to the term,
oxidation. When an element reacts with oxygen, losing electrons in the
process, the element is said to be **oxidized**. Oxygen is called the
oxidizing agent. In general, when an element *loses* electrons in a

Many automobile manufacturers use a process called "electrodeposition" to stop the oxidation-reduction reaction, which causes auto bodies to rust. (Courtesy of Monsanto Co.)

chemical reaction, that element is *oxidized*. The element *gaining* the electrons is the *oxidizing agent*.

Reduction is the opposite of oxidation. When an element *gains* electrons in a chemical reaction, it is said to be **reduced**. Sulfur gains electrons when it reacts with sodium, so the sulfur is reduced. The element giving the electrons away is called the **reducing agent**. In reacting with sulfur to form Na_2S, sodium is the reducing agent. Hydrogen, H_2, is one of the most common reducing agents.

Many chemical reactions are classified as oxidation–reduction reactions. Such reactions are responsible for the production of iron metal from iron ore, the generation of electrical energy from stored chemical energy in an automobile battery, and the energy-yielding metabolic reactions that occur in our own bodies. Oxidation and reduction are best understood by looking at simple combinations of elements, such as those discussed in this chapter. Several of these are summarized in Table 3.1.

TABLE 3.1

Elements Combining	Product	Element Gaining Electrons (oxidizing agent, which is reduced)	Element Losing Electrons (reducing agent, which is oxidized)
Ca and O	CaO	O, to form O^{2-}	Ca, to form Ca^{2+}
Al and O	Al_2O_3	O, to form O^{2-}	Al, to form Al^{3+}
Na and Cl	NaCl	Cl, to form Cl^-	Na, to form Na^+
Na and S	Na_2S	S, to form S^{2-}	Na, to form Na^+

3.7

The Chemical Formula

A number of examples of chemical formulas have been given in this chapter. Chemical formulas are extremely important because they give a lot of information about the makeup of a chemical compound. Later, when chemical equations and calculations from chemical equations are discussed, an understanding of chemical formulas will be essential. The chemical formula states the kinds of atoms present. It also gives the relative numbers of atoms. For example, NaCl stands for the compound, sodium chloride, containing 1 atom of chlorine per atom of sodium. (Of course in the compound these occur as charged ions.) The formula of calcium chloride, $CaCl_2$, shows 2 atoms of chlorine per calcium atom.

The information contained in a chemical formula can be summarized for a typical chemical compound. Such a summary is shown below for aluminum oxide, Al_2O_3.

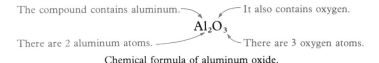

The compound contains aluminum. — It also contains oxygen.

Al_2O_3

There are 2 aluminum atoms. — There are 3 oxygen atoms.

Chemical formula of aluminum oxide.

3.8

Chemical Compounds

This chapter has been about **chemical compounds**. Chemical compounds are formed when two or more elements combine. So far we have limited the discussion to combinations of two elements. In later chapters combinations involving more than two elements are described.

The reason why elements combine to form chemical compounds is best understood by considering the atoms of the elements. It is the tendency of these atoms to attain a filled outer shell of electrons that causes chemical compounds to form. By rearranging electrons the atoms form chemical bonds with each other. These chemical bonds hold the chemical compounds together. Two different types of chemical bonds have been discussed. One of these is the covalent bond in which electrons are shared between 2 atoms. Two electrons make up a single covalent bond. It is also possible to have double bonds with 4 electrons and triple bonds with 6 electrons. It is seen that covalent chemical bonds are made up of electron pairs. Chemical compounds bonded together by covalent bonds consist of molecules. Molecules are distinct pieces of matter. Such chemical compounds are called *covalent compounds*.

The other type of chemical compound discussed may be called *ionic compounds*. Here the kind of chemical bonding is different. The electrons are not shared. Instead, they are transferred from one atom to another. Positively charged cations and negatively charged anions are formed in the process. The ions in these compounds are held together by the attraction of opposite electrical charges. Normally ionic compounds exist as crystals of solid material. It is because the ions in these compounds are stacked together in a rigid way with cations next to anions. In sodium chloride, the ions are located in an arrangement resembling a cube. A section of this arrangement is shown in Figure 3.9. In the cube-shaped sodium chloride crystal, this arrangement continues throughout each crystal. Each sodium ion is next to 6 chloride ions and each chloride ion is next to 6 sodium ions. For that reason no chloride ion belongs to a specific sodium ion, and no sodium ion belongs to a specific chloride ion. It is not really correct, therefore, to refer to a sodium chloride molecule. In discussing NaCl in chemical equations later, we will occasionally call it a "sodium chloride."

We have explained how atoms combine in logical ways to form chemical compounds whose chemical formulas can be predicted rather

TABLE 3.2

Some Important Chemical Compounds.

Elements Combining	Compound Formula	Compound Name	Properties and Importance
H and C	CH_4	Methane	Flammable gas (natural gas)
H and N	NH_3	Ammonia	Pungent smelling gas used for fertilizer and in industry
H and O	H_2O	Water	Colorless liquid (at room temperature)
H and F	HF	Hydrogen fluoride	Colorless, irritating, toxic gas which attacks even glass
H and S	H_2S	Hydrogen sulfide	Toxic gas with "rotten egg" odor
H and Cl	HCl	Hydrogen chloride	Colorless, irritating gas that dissolves in water to produce hydrochloric acid and is made in huge quantities for industry
C and O	CO	Carbon monoxide	Colorless flammable toxic gas
	CO_2	Carbon dioxide	Colorless gas produced when fuels containing carbon are burned in a plentiful supply of oxygen
C and Cl	CCl_4	Carbon tetrachloride	Colorless liquid used as solvent
N and O	NO	Nitric oxide	Colorless gas produced by autos
	NO_2	Nitrogen dioxide	Toxic red-brown gas
N and Cl	NCl_3	Nitrogen trichloride	Yellow oil sometimes produced when water containing dissolved ammonia is disinfected by chlorination
Al and O	Al_2O_3	Corundum	High-melting, very hard substance
Al and Cl	$AlCl_3$	Aluminum chloride	White solid, one form of which is present in antiperspirants
Si and O	SiO_2	Silicon dioxide, or silica	Sand. In a very pure form it transmits light extremely well and is used in specialized optical instruments.
Si and Cl	$SiCl_4$	Silicon tetrachloride	Liquid, which is quite active chemically, used to make silicones
Na and F	NaF	Sodium fluoride	White solid used for water fluoridation
Na and Cl	NaCl	Sodium chloride	White crystalline solid, table salt (large, well formed crystals are clear)
Ca and O	CaO	Calcium oxide	Quicklime
Ca and Cl	$CaCl_2$	Calcium chloride	Solid with tremendous "appetite" for water, chemical byproduct, used to melt ice

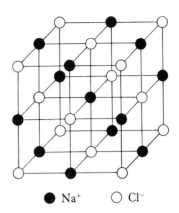

FIGURE 3.9
*Arrangement of sodium ions and chloride
ions in a sodium chloride crystal.*

● Na⁺　　○ Cl⁻

accurately. Some very logical examples of chemical bonding were shown.
We began to run into a little trouble, though, with sulfur dioxide.
Here we had to use a picture of an SO_2 molecule held together by
a single bond and a double bond which traded places rapidly. In the
cases of NO and NO_2, there is an uneven number of electrons leaving
an extra "unpaired" electron. We did not attempt to show the electrons
in those compounds. We would predict that lithium, sodium, and
potassium would form the ionic compounds, Li_2O, Na_2O, and K_2O with
oxygen. These compounds do, indeed, exist. However, when sodium or
potassium react directly with O_2, sodium forms a "peroxide," Na_2O_2,
and potassium forms a "superoxide," KO_2. For the most part the
compounds that we will discuss will be fairly "normal" compounds.
Simple pictures of compound formation given in this chapter are essential
to understanding chemistry. We must point out, though, that many things
cannot be explained with a simple picture, and that chemicals will be
encountered which do not appear to obey the rules.

Some important chemical compounds are summarized in Table 3.2.
Others, which can be made from the elements discussed so far, are not
listed. Some of these are left for the exercises at the end of the
chapter.

Chapter Summary

The key to chemistry is the combination of atoms of different *elements*
to form *compounds*. By joining together, atoms get more stable arrangements of their electrons. Atoms in compounds are held together by
chemical bonds. Breaking these bonds requires energy. An idea of how
different kinds of atoms are likely to join together may be gained by
examining the electron-dot symbols of the atoms. These dots indicate
the electrons which can be involved in bonding. The atoms will attempt
to gain structures in which 8 (or for some elements, 2) electrons are
present in the *outer shell*.

The *covalent bond* is one major type of chemical bond. It consists
of pairs of electrons shared between 2 atoms. Sharing of 2 electrons in

1 bond gives a *single bond*. Four electrons shared between 2 atoms make up a *double bond*, and 6 electrons are a *triple bond*. Simple covalent compounds consist of distinct *molecules*.

Hydrogen atoms form a number of important covalent compounds. By sharing an electron with another atom, the hydrogen atom attains the 2 electrons needed in its electron shell. Carbon needs 4 more electrons in its outer shell, so it combines with 4 hydrogen atoms to give CH_4. Nitrogen needs 3 more electrons, so it forms NH_3. Oxygen needs 2 more, making H_2O. The Cl atom needs 1 more electron and forms HCl.

A combination of two elements can result in more than one compound. When carbon combines with a limited amount of oxygen, the product is CO, carbon monoxide. When more oxygen is available, the product is CO_2, carbon dioxide. Different ways of bonding are involved. Carbon monoxide has a triple bond between the 2 atoms. Carbon dioxide, CO_2, has a double bond between the carbon and each of the oxygens.

Not all chemical compounds are bonded together by shared electrons. *Ionic compounds* are formed by the transfer of electrons from one atom to another. Such an atom does not have the same number of protons as it has electrons after the transfer. This gives the atom an electrical charge. A charged atom is called an *ion*. Positively charged ions are *cations*. Negatively charged ions are called *anions*. The sodium cation is written Na^+. The chloride anion is written Cl^-. Ionic compounds are held together by attraction between the oppositely charged ions. A particular cation does not "belong to" a particular anion. Therefore, separate molecules of ionic compounds do not exist. Normally ionic compounds are formed by combinations of elements at the left of the periodic table (metals, which tend to lose electrons) with elements at the right of the periodic table (nonmetals, which tend to gain electrons).

An element that loses electrons as the result of a chemical combination is said to be *oxidized*. It is the *reducing agent* in the chemical combination. An element that gains electrons as the result of a chemical combination is said to be *reduced*. It is called an *oxidizing agent*. Oxygen gains electrons when it combines chemically with other electrons, so it is an oxidizing agent. Oxidation–reduction reactions are extremely important in chemistry.

Compounds are shown by their chemical formulas. A *chemical formula* consists of the symbols for the elements involved and numbers, which give the numbers of atoms of each element in the compound. For example, the chemical formula for methane,

$$CH_4$$

tells us that methane contains carbon (C) and hydrogen (H). The subscript 4 after the H shows that there are 4 hydrogen atoms for each carbon atom. The absence of any subscript after C indicates *one* carbon atom.

Considering even just a few elements, a tremendous number of different chemical compounds are possible. Compounds made from rather

Carbon dioxide gives soft drinks their "fizz." This Coca-Cola tray is known to collectors as "Juanita," circa 1905. (From the collection of Gary Jacobson; Michael E. Katin, photographer)

similar atoms may have greatly different qualities. For example, oxygen is just above sulfur in the periodic table. The outer electron structures of the atoms of these two elements are the same. The combination of hydrogen with oxygen is water, H_2O. The combination of hydrogen with sulfur is hydrogen sulfide, H_2S. Water is a liquid at room temperature. It is odorless and essential for life. Hydrogen sulfide is a toxic gas. It has an objectionable, rotten egg odor. A similar example can be given for the oxides of carbon and silicon. Carbon is just above silicon in the periodic table. Carbon dioxide, CO_2, is a colorless gas produced when fuels burn and in animal respiration. Silicon dioxide in its purest form is a clear, hard, high melting glass. Impure forms of silicon dioxide are the main ingredients of sand.

It is interesting to note that some of the simple chemical compounds discussed in this chapter are among the most common and abundant. Included is methane, CH_4, produced as natural gas in quantities of trillions of cubic feet each year. Ammonia, NH_3, is an important industrial and agricultural chemical. Another example is water, H_2O, which occurs in vast quantities on the Earth's surface.

Chapter Review Questions

The following questions are designed as a self-teaching tool to help you review Chapter 3. The answers to each question follow. See Chapter Review Questions for Chapter 1 for further instructions.

1. The expression, $2 H \rightarrow H_2$ is an example of a _____ in which 2 hydrogen atoms join together to form a _____, which is held together by a _____.

2. In regard to the arrangement of their electrons, atoms react chemically in order to attain _____.

3. A chemical bond in which electrons are shared is called _____, and one in which electrons are transferred from one atom to another is _____.

4. A chemical combination of two or more different kinds of atoms is a
   _____.

5. Outer shell electrons available for chemical bonding are called _____
   electrons.

6. The term, NH_3, indicates a chemical combination of the element,
   _____ with _____. It is an example of a _____
   showing the kinds and relative numbers of atoms in a chemical compound.

7. Fill in the blanks below referring to the chemical compounds formed by
   bonding of hydrogen, H, with the element listed.

Element Combining with H	Compound Formula	Compound Name
Carbon	_____	_____
Nitrogen	_____	_____
Oxygen	_____	_____
Chlorine	_____	_____

8. Methane is the main component of _____, widely used as a
   _____.

9. Ammonia is used in agriculture as a _____.

10. When dissolved in water, HCl gas produces _____.

11. One of the most important functions of water is its ability to act as a good
    _____ to form _____.

12. Methane is an example of a large general class of chemical compounds
    called _____ formed by various combinations of the elements
    _____ and _____.

13. The names and formulas of the two oxides of carbon are _____,
    formula, _____ and _____, formula, _____.

14. The chemical bond in carbon monoxide is a _____ bond consisting
    of _____ electrons.

15. The carbon dioxide molecule has 2 _____ bonds, each involving
    _____ shared electrons.

16. Carbon monoxide is toxic because _____
    _____.

17. The chemical compound formed from the combination of silicon and oxygen
    is called _____, its formula is _____, and it is found in
    ordinary _____.

18. The two oxides of sulfur are _____, formula _____ and
    _____, formula _____.

19. Sulfur trioxide dissolved in water produces _____.

20. The formula of the nitrogen oxide produced by automobiles is _____
    and that of the nitrogen dioxide involved in smog formation is _____.

21. Positively charged ions are called _____, and negatively charged
    ions are _____.

22. Sodium chloride crystals consist of alternate _____ ions and
    _____ ions packed together in an orderly arrangement.

23. An atom that loses electrons when it enters into a chemical combination is
    said to be _____, and it is called a _____ agent.

24. An atom that gains electrons when it enters into a chemical combination is said to be _____, and it is called an _____ agent.

25. Phosphorus and oxygen combine to form phosphorus pentoxide, whose chemical formula is P_2O_5. In this formula the P indicates the element _____, the O stands for _____, and the 2 means that there are 2 _____ atoms for every _____ oxygen atoms.

26. There is really no such thing as a sodium chloride molecule because _____
_____.

Answers to Chapter Review Questions

1. chemical reaction, hydrogen molecule, chemical bond
2. a filled outer shell
3. a covalent bond, an electrovalent or ionic bond
4. chemical compound
5. valence
6. nitrogen, hydrogen, chemical formula

7.

Compound Formula	Compound Name
CH_4	Methane
NH_3	Ammonia
H_2O	Water
HCl	Hydrogen chloride

8. natural gas, fuel
9. fertilizer
10. hydrochloric acid
11. solvent, solutions
12. hydrocarbons, carbon, hydrogen
13. carbon monoxide, CO, carbon dioxide, CO_2
14. triple, 6
15. double, 4
16. it attaches to blood hemoglobin preventing it from carrying oxygen
17. silicon dioxide, SiO_2, sand
18. sulfur dioxide, SO_2, sulfur trioxide, SO_3
19. sulfuric acid
20. NO, NO_2
21. cations, anions
22. Na^+, Cl^-
23. oxidized, reducing
24. reduced, oxidizing
25. phosphorus, oxygen, phosphorus, 5
26. a specific sodium ion does not go with a specific chloride ion

Exercises for Chapter 3

1. Elemental nitrogen exists as N_2 molecules. What is the electron-dot structure of N_2? Which chemical compound studied in this chapter has the same electron-dot structure?

2. What is the electron-dot structure of carbon tetrachloride?

3. A hydrogen atom can lose an electron to form a hydrogen ion, H^+. This ion can attach to a molecule of ammonia, NH_3, to form an ammonium ion, NH_4^+. What is the electron-dot structure of the ammonium ion?

4. Predict the chemical formulas of combinations of the following elements.
   a. Beryllium and fluorine   b. Magnesium and chlorine
   c. Magnesium and nitrogen (magnesium nitride)
   d. Aluminum and sulfur

5. Which elements studied have 5 valence electrons?

6. If the proper number of hydrogen atoms weighing 1 amu (atomic mass unit) each combine with 1 carbon atom weighing 12 amu, what does the molecule that is produced weigh?

7. Which acid mentioned in this chapter occurs in the stomach?

8. The human body is about _____ percent water, and water covers about _____ of the Earth's surface.

9. Ammonia, NH_3, is toxic. Yet, it can be applied to soil as a fertilizer without too much danger to the person operating the machinery required. What property of anhydrous (water free) ammonia enables it to be used in this way?

10. Suppose that soil tests show that soil should have 140 lb of chemically combined N applied per acre. Knowing the atomic weights of N and H, how many pounds per acre of NH_3 is this?

11. Although areas of fields in the U.S. are still commonly measured in acres, and fertilizer applied in pounds per acre, these quantities eventually will be measured in metric units. The metric substitute for the acre is the hectare. One hectare is an area of 10,000 square meters and is equal to 2.471 acres. The number of pounds in a kilogram was given in Chapter 1. If the fertilizer application discussed in Exercise 10 was expressed in units of kilograms per hectare, what would this rate be?

12. A poisonous gas called phosphine is formed from the chemical combination of hydrogen and phosphorus. Predict the chemical formula of this compound and explain.

13. When natural gas burns, it reacts with oxygen in the air to produce two new chemical compounds and heat. From the compounds discussed in this chapter, what two might likely be produced?

14. Name three different elements which each form two different oxides.

15. Carbon monoxide, CO, combines with oxygen, and can even be burned as a fuel. What is the chemical product when CO and oxygen combine?

16. Give the names and chemical formulas of two air pollutants discussed in this chapter.

17. What is the role of NO_2 in the smog-forming process?

18. What chemical compound is used for water fluoridation?

19. What is the chemical formula of corundum? What is one of its most important properties?

20. Consider the boiling temperatures of the following compounds:

Compound	Boiling Temperature
CO	$-190°C$
NH_3	$-78°C$
H_2S	$-62°C$
LiCl	$1353°C$
CaO	$2850°C$
NaF	$1700°C$

Three of the compounds have very low boiling temperatures and three have very high boiling temperatures. How might this be related to different types of bonds and the nature of ions and molecules?

As a lightning stroke is discharged to the ground, processes between clouds cause additional areas to be discharged. Electrons accelerated by an electric field of rain droplets created by the lightning collide with molecules in the air, free more electrons, and leave a path of partially ionized air. (Courtesy of the National Oceanic and Atmospheric Administration)

4

Chemical Reactions and Equations

4.1

Chemicals Reacting with Each Other

In Chapter 3 we discussed how atoms join together to form *chemical compounds*. Each of the chemical compounds discussed so far contain only two kinds of elements. These compounds are described by a *chemical formula*. The chemical formula tells us the kinds of atoms in the chemical compound. It tells us the relative numbers of each kind of atom. For example, consider the chemical formula for phosphorus pentoxide.

$$P_2O_5$$

This formula states that the compound contains phosphorus (P) and oxygen (O). It also tells us that there are 5 oxygen atoms for every 2 phosphorus atoms.

There are many ways of making chemical compounds. In fact, they are usually not made by simple combinations of individual atoms. Instead, chemical compounds are produced by interactions of a more complicated chemical nature, which often occur in a series of steps. The interaction process is called a *chemical reaction*. The overall chemical relationships involved can be described conveniently by a *chemical equation*. The idea of the chemical equation is a very important one for understanding chemistry. One might consider the chemical symbols of the elements as letters in the chemistry alphabet. Chemical formulas are like words. Just as it is possible to spell millions of words with the 26 letters in the alphabet, it is possible to write millions of chemical formulas with symbols from the periodic table. Words are put together to make sentences. Similarly, chemical formulas are arranged to make chemical equations. Just as a sentence tells us something, a chemical equation is a statement in "chemical language." For a sentence to make sense it must be constructed in particular ways which are understood by everyone speaking the language. This is even more true of chemical equations. A sentence can be a little sloppy and nongrammatical but still get a message across. A chemical equation must be absolutely correct to avoid being totally misleading.

4.2

The Chemical Equation

In Chapter 3, 2 hydrogen atoms were shown combining with 1 oxygen atom to form a molecule of water. This may be written as

$$H + H + O \longrightarrow H_2O$$

However, individual hydrogen atoms and individual oxygen atoms are very rare. In Chapters 1 and 2 it was shown that hydrogen occurs as hydrogen molecules each containing 2 hydrogen atoms and written as H_2. Also, oxygen gas consists of molecules containing 2 oxygen atoms written O_2. What really happens when hydrogen and oxygen combine chemically? Suppose that hydrogen gas and oxygen gas are mixed together in a balloon and that a match is set to it to get the reaction started. First of all there will be a thunderous explosion, because the reaction goes very rapidly and very violently. The chemical process that occurs is a combination of hydrogen from H_2 with oxygen from O_2 to produce water, H_2O. This process is described by the chemical equation

$$\underbrace{2\,H_2 + O_2}_{\text{reactants}} \longrightarrow \underbrace{2\,H_2O}_{\text{product}}$$

This chemical equation tells us many things. The information given by it is summarized as follows:

1. There are two *reactants*. These are hydrogen and oxygen.

2. There is one *product*. It is water, H_2O.

3. The hydrogen reactant is in the form of a hydrogen molecule, H_2.

4. The oxygen reactant is in the form of an oxygen molecule, O_2.

5. Two hydrogen molecules react. This is indicated by the 2 in front of H_2.

6. One oxygen molecule reacts.

7. Two water molecules are produced as indicated by the 2 in front of H_2O.

8. There are 4 H atoms altogether on the left side of the equation (reactants). These are contained in the 2 H_2 molecules each containing 2 H atoms.

9. There are 4 H atoms altogether on the right side of the equation (products). These are contained in the 2 H_2O molecules which each contain 2 H atoms.

10. There are 2 O atoms on the left contained in the O_2 molecule made up of 2 O atoms.

11. There are 2 O atoms on the right. They are contained in the 2 H_2O molecules, each of which contains 1 O atom.

Chemical equations are like mathematical equations in that the left side of the equation must equal the right side of the equation. The proportions are expressed in atoms: **In a chemical equation the same number of each specific kind of atom must appear on both sides of the equation.** The chemical equation describing the reaction of hydrogen with oxygen has 4 H atoms on the left and 4 on the right. It has 2 O atoms on the left and 2 on the right.

Chemical equations may be much more complicated than the one shown for the reaction of hydrogen and oxygen. In the equation producing H_2O the two elements are reacting. However, two compounds may react with each other to form two different compounds. Elements may react with compounds. Several compounds may react to form several different compounds. This chapter discusses some of these kinds of chemical equations. The importance of chemical equations and the information that can be obtained from them are explained. **Balancing** chemical equations will receive special emphasis. This is the process of arranging the equation so that the same number of each specific kind of atom appears on both sides of the equation. Simple ways of balancing equations are explained in this chapter.

4.3

The Reaction of Oxygen and Acetylene:
The Acetylene Torch

Figure 4.1 shows a construction worker cutting through a steel beam with an acetylene torch used in combination with oxygen. A very hot flame is obtained from the chemical reaction of pure oxygen and pure acetylene. When acetylene burns, particularly in pure oxygen, it gives one of the

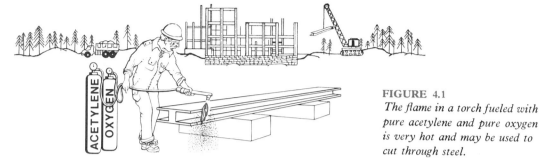

FIGURE 4.1
The flame in a torch fueled with pure acetylene and pure oxygen is very hot and may be used to cut through steel.

hottest flames that can be obtained by a common chemical reaction. This is obvious from the fast rate at which a bright blue acetylene flame cuts through steel, spewing out yellow sparks of melted steel.

Acetylene gas is a hydrocarbon. Its chemical formula is C_2H_2. The 2 carbon atoms are joined together by a triple bond made of 6 shared electrons. (See carbon monoxide in Section 3.4 for another example of a triple bond.) The electron-dot structure of acetylene is

$$H : C :: C : H$$

The chemical reaction between acetylene and oxygen is

$$C_2H_2 + O_2 = \underset{products}{\underline{CO_2 + H_2O}} + \text{much heat}$$
$$\underset{reactants}{\underline{}}$$

This equation is not balanced. It has 2 carbons on the left and only 1 on the right. It has 2 oxygens on the left and 3 on the right. The next step is to balance this chemical equation.

The best way to balance a chemical equation is to balance one atom at a time until the same number of each kind of atom shows up on both sides of the equation. In this case start with carbon. The 2 carbons on the left can be balanced by putting a 2 in front of the CO_2 on the right. This gives the equation in the form

$$C_2H_2 + O_2 = 2\,CO_2 + H_2O + \text{much heat}$$

Balancing the equation can be visualized as placing molecules on the pans of a double-pan balance shown in Figure 4.2. Now there are 5 oxygens on the right, but only 2 on the left. Multiplying the O_2 by 5 yields the equation,

$$C_2H_2 + 5\,O_2 \longrightarrow 2\,CO_2 + H_2O + \text{much heat}$$

This gives a total of 10 oxygen atoms on the left, where only 5 were needed. This can be taken care of by multiplying everything else in the equation by 2. Doing that gives 2 C_2H_2 molecules. Multiplying through by 2 on the right side of the equation gives 4 CO_2's and 2 H_2O's (see Figure 4.3). The final equation is

$$2\,C_2H_2 + 5\,O_2 = 4\,CO_2 + 2\,H_2O + \text{much heat}$$

It is easy to see that balancing an equation may take several steps. Since it is always possible for something to go wrong in each step, it is a good idea to check each equation to see if it is really balanced. That is done by adding up all of the atoms of each element on both sides of the equal sign.

Left side of the equation

2 C_2H_2 molecules each containing 2 C atoms yields **4 C atoms**

2 C_2H_2 molecules each containing 2 H atoms yields **4 H atoms**

5 O_2 molecules each containing 2 O atoms yields **10 O atoms**

Right side of the equation

4 CO_2 molecules each containing 1 C atom yields **4 C atoms**

2 H_2O molecules each containing 2 H atoms yields **4 H atoms**

There are 8 O atoms in 4 CO_2 molecules, which each contain 2 O atoms, and there are 2 O atoms in 2 H_2O molecules, giving a total of **10 O atoms**

The equation checks out with the same number of each kind of atom on both sides of the equation. Therefore, it is balanced.

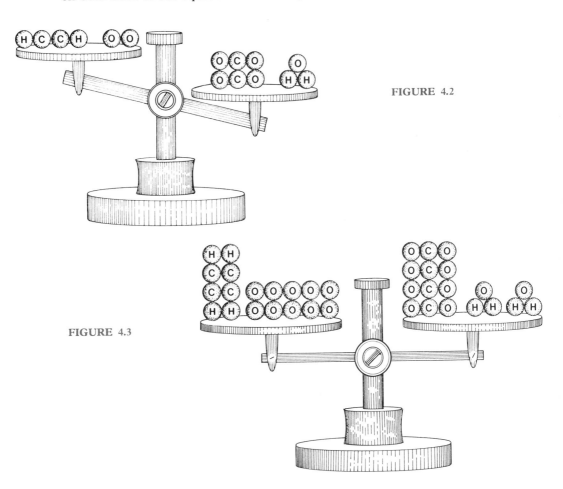

FIGURE 4.2

FIGURE 4.3

4.4

Quick Energy: Fuel for the Body

Food, of course, provides the energy needed to keep us going. Most of the food that we eat consists of a large number of proteins, fats, sugars, and starches having relatively complicated formulas. Most of this organic material is broken down in the digestive system to glucose, a simple sugar. However, a natural sugar such as honey is largely glucose. Glucose can be used by the body directly without going through the digestive system. For example, persons who cannot ingest food orally following surgery are given glucose intravenously. The chemical formula of glucose

A person who cannot take food by mouth can get energy from glucose dissolved in water and allowed to run slowly into a vein. (Courtesy of Abbott Laboratories)

is $C_6H_{12}O_6$. This chemical formula shows that each glucose molecule contains 6 carbon atoms, 12 hydrogen atoms and 6 oxygen atoms. Through a somewhat complicated *biochemical process* glucose is converted to carbon dioxide and water in the body according to the following overall equation:

$$C_6H_{12}O_6 + O_2 \longrightarrow CO_2 + H_2O + energy$$

The oxygen required enters the bloodstream through the lungs and the carbon dioxide waste product leaves by the same route. Notice that the above equation is not balanced. The 6 carbons on the left can be balanced by placing 6 CO_2's on the right.

$$C_6H_{12}O_6 + O_2 \longrightarrow 6\,CO_2 + H_2O + energy$$

The 12 hydrogens on the left can be balanced by putting 6 H_2O's, each containing 2 H atoms, on the right.

$$C_6H_{12}O_6 + O_2 \longrightarrow 6\,CO_2 + 6\,H_2O + energy$$

Next we consider oxygen. The 6 CO_2 molecules on the right contain a total of 12 O atoms. When these are added to the 6 O atoms in the water, the result is a total of 18 O atoms on the right side of the equation. Taking 6 O_2 molecules on the left,

$$C_6H_{12}O_6 + 6\,O_2 \longrightarrow 6\,CO_2 + 6\,H_2O + \text{energy}$$

balances oxygen and gives a balanced equation.

With a little practice it is often possible to balance an equation just by looking at it rather than going through it element-by-element. For example, one could look at the reaction between glucose and oxygen and see rather easily that the "$H_{12}O_6$" part of the glucose molecule will yield 6 H_2O's, and that the remaining 6 C's will require 6 O_2 to yield 6 CO_2. While it is useful to acquire the skill to balance chemical equations rapidly by just looking at them and to calculate proportions mentally, it is easy to make mistakes. Any arithmetic should always be checked. In balancing chemical equations, check the answer to make sure that *the same total number of each kind of atom appears on both sides of the equation.*

4.5

What Does a Chemical Equation Tell Us?

Thus far in this chapter we have examined and balanced several chemical equations. But, before we proceed further, let us stop and review the significance of chemical equations and the kinds of information they can give.

Chemical equations are made up of two parts. At the left of the equation are *reactants,* the chemicals that react with each other. The chemical reaction shown by an arrow yields *products,* which appear to the right of the arrow. Both reactants and products are represented by *chemical formulas. Chemical formulas may not be changed in order to balance the equation.* A balanced chemical equation gives the correct number of molecules of reactants and the correct number of molecules of products. It always has the same total number of each individual kind of element on the reactant side as it has on the product side.

This information can be reviewed by looking at another example of a chemical equation. Consider the burning of propane gas in a lantern, camp stove, or a grain dryer used on the farm to remove moisture from

Grain drying is used on farms to dry freshly harvested corn and cereals before storing. The technician in the photograph is adjusting the controls on the batch dryer. (Courtesy of USDA)

corn and other grains. Propane's structure is

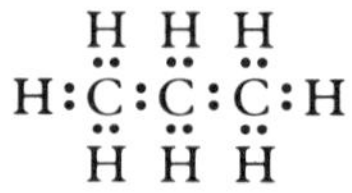

$$\begin{array}{ccc} H & H & H \\ H:C:C:C:H \\ H & H & H \end{array}$$

where each dot represents a bonding electron. This configuration may be written as the formula C_3H_8. The reaction of propane with oxygen in air,

$$C_3H_8 + O_2 \longrightarrow CO_2 + H_2O + heat$$

produces carbon dioxide and water as chemical products. The equation is balanced quickly by observing that the 3 C's in propane will produce 3 CO_2's and that the 8 H's will produce 4 H_2O's.

$$C_3H_8 + O_2 \longrightarrow 3\,CO_2 + 4\,H_2O$$

In the products, 6 O's in 3 CO_2's and 4 O's in 4 H_2O molecules give a total of 10 O's. This requires 5 O_2's among the reactants;

$$C_3H_8 + 5\,O_2 \longrightarrow 3\,CO_2 + 4\,H_2O + heat$$

to give a balanced equation. Now we can examine the information contained in the balanced chemical equation to see what it tells us. It is summarized in Figure 4.4.

| Propane with a chemical formula of C_3H_8 reacts | with oxygen molecules, O_2 to give | carbon dioxide having the formula, CO_2, | and water, H_2O. | Heat is also produced, which is why this reaction is so useful. |

$$C_3H_8 \quad + \quad 5\,O_2 \longrightarrow 3\,CO_2 \quad + \quad 4\,H_2O \quad + \quad heat$$

|⌞————reactants————⌟| |⌞——————— products ———————⌟|

| One propane molecule reacts with 5 oxygen molecules. These are the *reactants*. | When 1 propane molecule reacts with oxygen, 5 carbon dioxide molecules and 4 water molecules are the *products*. | It is not necessary to show the heat in the chemical equation, and heat is not considered in balancing the equation. However, this information may be added to the equation. |

FIGURE 4.4 *The chemical equation is **balanced** with 3 C's, 8 H's, and 10 O's on each side. The **chemical formulas** of reactants and products were not changed in balancing the equation. Propane has to be written as C_3H_8, oxygen as O_2, carbon dioxide as CO_2, and water as H_2O.*

4.6

Reaction of Calcium Oxide and Water

Recall from Chapter 3 that calcium oxide, CaO, is a widely used chemical known as "quicklime." It reacts with water

$$CaO + H_2O \longrightarrow Ca(OH)_2$$

to form "slaked lime," $Ca(OH)_2$. Slaked lime is a very important chemical used in water purification, to take excess acid out of soil, and for many other industrial uses. The chemical name for slaked lime is calcium hydroxide. Notice that the formula for calcium hydroxide contains O and H in parentheses. Parentheses are used in chemical formulas to indicate atoms that go through chemical reactions in groups. The group in parentheses here is the hydroxide anion, OH^-. The 2 in the subscript after the (OH) shows 2 hydroxide anions. These 2 hydroxides contain altogether 2 oxygens and 2 hydrogens. The formula, $Ca(OH)_2$, represents 1 calcium atom, 2 oxygen atoms, and 2 hydrogen atoms.

The hydroxide ion has a certain significance. Hydroxide ion is produced when a **base** is dissolved in water. Bases react chemically with **acids**. Acids and bases are chemical opposites. Whereas bases are characterized by the OH^- ion, acids have the H^+ ion. These two chemicals combine to give H_2O in an **acid–base reaction**. This general type of chemical reaction is one of the most common in all of chemistry. Therefore, acids and bases are very important in chemistry. Much more will be said about them later in this book.

Calcium hydroxide reacts with carbon dioxide.

$$Ca(OH)_2 + CO_2 \longrightarrow CaCO_3 + H_2O$$

"Whitewash," made of $Ca(OH)_2$ in a fairly thick mixture with water was once commonly used as a cheap "paint" for fences. Reaction of the $Ca(OH)_2$ with CO_2 in the air formed a coating of $CaCO_3$, which stayed on the fence for at least a while.

This is a useful reaction which occurs when lime in mortar is exposed to air. Soft, water-soluble calcium hydroxide reacts with carbon dioxide in the air to produce hard, water-insoluble $CaCO_3$. This compound is called calcium carbonate. It consists of ions. The cation is the Ca^{2+} ion. The anion is the carbonate ion. Its formula is CO_3^{2-}. This shows that it is made up of 1 carbon atom and 3 oxygen atoms. The formula also shows that the carbonate ion has a charge of -2.

What happens if calcium carbonate is heated? At about 825°C it breaks up. Calcium oxide and carbon dioxide are formed.

$$CaCO_3 + heat \longrightarrow CaO + CO_2\uparrow$$

What does the arrow pointing up after the CO_2 mean? It indicates that the carbon dioxide is a gas and is driven off. This chemical reaction demonstrates how quicklime is prepared for industrial use.

Notice that in our discussion of reactions, we started out with CaO and ended up with CaO. This portrays a cycle consisting of three reactions. Such reactions are in fact used in water treatment. Consider Figure 4.5 which shows part of a water treatment operation. Calcium oxide is added to incoming water, and it is immediately changed to $Ca(OH)_2$. The calcium hydroxide settles some undesirable impurities out of the water. Next, CO_2 is bubbled into the water, and calcium carbonate drops out of the water solution as a solid. After drying, the $CaCO_3$ is heated to make more CaO to start the cycle again.

$$CaO + H_2O \longrightarrow Ca(OH)_2$$

Calcium oxide reacts with water to produce water-soluble calcium hydroxide.

$$Ca(OH)_2 + CO_2 \longrightarrow CaCO_3\downarrow + H_2O$$

Calcium carbonate falls out of solution.

$$CaCO_3 + heat \longrightarrow CaO + CO_2\uparrow$$

Carbon dioxide gas is driven off.

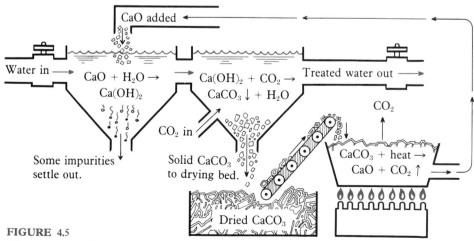

FIGURE 4.5
Lime treatment of water.
Spent lime can be recalcined and recycled.

Observe in the reaction between $Ca(OH)_2$ and CO_2 that there is an arrow pointing down, $\downarrow$, after the $CaCO_3$. This indicates that the calcium carbonate does not stay in solution in water, but "falls out" as a solid. A solid that comes out of solution as the result of a chemical reaction is called a **precipitate**.

4.7

Reaction of Sulfur Trioxide and Water

Recall that one of the common oxides of sulfur is sulfur trioxide, SO_3. Sulfur trioxide gas reacts with water to produce sulfuric acid, H_2SO_4.

$$H_2O + SO_3 \longrightarrow H_2SO_4$$

Sulfuric acid is the chemical most widely used in industry. Almost 70 billion pounds of sulfuric acid are manufactured in the U.S. each year, that is, about 300 pounds for each one of us.

Pure sulfuric acid is a heavy, clear liquid. It is very corrosive, such that when it comes in contact with organic material like clothing or skin, it leaves a charred black mass. The presence of sulfuric acid is one of the best reasons for wearing laboratory aprons and safety glasses in the chemistry laboratory. Sulfuric acid can spatter and destroy skin, eyes, and clothing. Sulfuric acid is the liquid in an automobile storage battery. Because of the presence of sulfuric acid in the filling solution, car batteries should be handled carefully. In addition to its use in storage batteries, some of the major uses of sulfuric acid involve the manufacture of fertilizers, steel, gasoline, and nylon.

When dissolved in water, sulfuric acid forms two kinds of ions. The cation is H^+, the hydrogen ion. The anion is the sulfate ion, SO_4^{2-}. Recall that it is the H^+ ion in water that makes a substance an acid. Sulfuric acid is an excellent source of H^+ ions.

4.8

Reactions of Acids and Bases

We have just discussed an acid and a base. The acid is sulfuric acid, H_2SO_4. The base is calcium hydroxide, $Ca(OH)_2$. It was stated that acids and bases react with each other. Consider what happens when calcium hydroxide and sulfuric acid react.

$$Ca(OH)_2 + H_2SO_4 \longrightarrow 2\,H_2O + CaSO_4$$

| calcium hydroxide | sulfuric acid | | calcium sulfate |

A colored box has been positioned on the hydrogen in the sulfuric acid and the hydroxide in the calcium hydroxide. This indicates that these hydrogen and hydroxide ions combine during an acid-base reaction. The product of such a reaction is water, H_2O. When an acid and a base react in water, H^+ ion from the acid always combines with OH^- ion from the base to produce H_2O.

$$H^+ + OH^- \longrightarrow H_2O$$

Water which contains excess acid is said to be *acidic*. Water containing excess base is *basic*. Water that has neither excess acid nor base is said to be *neutral*. Therefore, the reaction between acids and bases is a *neutralization reaction*.

Consider another neutralization reaction. Recall that when hydrogen chloride gas, HCl, is dissolved in water it produces hydrochloric acid. Now consider what happens when sodium oxide, Na_2O, reacts with water.

$$Na_2O + H_2O \longrightarrow 2\,NaOH$$

The product is sodium hydroxide, NaOH. Note that in the equation above a 2 is placed in front of the NaOH. Why? Is the equation balanced?

Now consider the reaction between sodium hydroxide and hydrochloric acid.

$$NaOH + HCl \longrightarrow H_2O + NaCl$$

In addition to water, common table salt, NaCl, is produced. In this reaction the H^+ cation from HCl combines with the OH^- anion from NaOH to produce water. This leaves the Na^+ cation and the Cl^- anion. These are the two ions in sodium chloride.

4.9

Another Look at Chemical Formulas

This chapter has introduced some more complicated chemical formulas. Compounds with three elements have been introduced. We have seen that groups of atoms occur in compounds and go through chemical reactions together. A typical group consists of 1 sulfur atom and 4 oxygen atoms in the sulfate anion, SO_4^{2-}. With that in mind, let us consider a somewhat more complicated chemical formula, that of aluminum sulfate.

Aluminum sulfate is a common industrial chemical widely used in pulp and paper manufacture and in water purification. Its chemical formula is $Al_2(SO_4)_3$. It can be made in the laboratory by reacting aluminum hydroxide and sulfuric acid.

$$Al(OH)_3 + H_2SO_4 \longrightarrow H_2O + Al_2(SO_4)_3$$

| aluminum | sulfuric | aluminum |
| hydroxide | acid | sulfate |

This equation is not balanced. First balance Al by placing a 2 in front of the $Al(OH)_3$ at the left. Each $Al(OH)_3$ has 3 OH^- ions. In addition, 2 aluminum hydroxides are needed to react with the sulfuric acid, resulting in a total of 6 OH^- ions that must be neutralized by 6 H^+ from H_2SO_4. A 3 in front of the H_2SO_4 provides the 6 H^+ ions needed. Since 6 H^+ combining with 6 OH^- produces 6 H_2O, a 6 may be placed in front of the H_2O. The balanced equation is

$$2\,Al(OH)_3 + 3\,H_2SO_4 \longrightarrow 6\,H_2O + Al_2(SO_4)_3$$

Having shown how it is prepared, we may now consider in detail the aluminum sulfate formula. (See Figure 4.6.)

Aluminum sulfate contains:

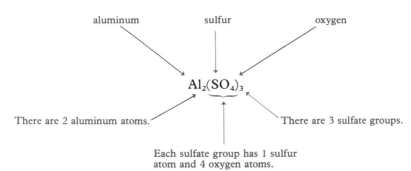

FIGURE 4.6   *In the 3 sulfate groups there is a total of 3 sulfur atoms and 12 oxygen atoms. The whole aluminum sulfate formula indicates the presence of 2 aluminum atoms, 3 sulfur atoms, and 12 oxygen atoms.*

4.10

Types of Chemical Reactions

There are several different types of chemical reactions. Some of these involve putting elements together to make compounds, or taking compounds apart to make elements. Compounds can react with other compounds to make different compounds. Reactions between compounds and elements may occur. In many reactions electrons are transferred between atoms. These are oxidation-reduction reactions. It is not necessary to memorize all of the different kinds of chemical reactions which can occur. However, examination of several different kinds can be helpful in understanding chemistry.

The breakdown of a compound to its elements is a **decomposition** reaction. A typical example is the chemical reaction that occurs when

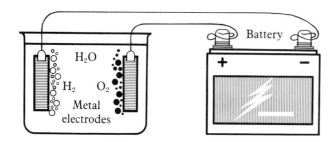

FIGURE 4.7

Electricity from a battery can be passed through water and cause the water to break up into hydrogen gas and oxygen gas.

electricity from a battery is passed through water shown in Figure 4.7. The H_2O breaks up

$$H_2O \longrightarrow H_2\uparrow + O_2\uparrow$$

to produce hydrogen gas and oxygen gas. The fact that gases are involved is designated by the arrows pointing upward and placed after the gaseous chemical formulas in the equation. When balanced, the equation is

$$2\,H_2O \longrightarrow 2H_2\uparrow + O_2\uparrow$$

Actually, in order to produce this reaction, it is necessary to fudge a bit by putting some ionic compound into the water. Sodium sulfate, Na_2SO_4, works well for this purpose. In water it breaks up into Na^+ and SO_4^{2-} ions. These ions have an electrical charge, which enables water to carry electricity. Because electricity passes through the water to cause H_2O molecules to break down into the components H_2 and O_2, the reaction is called an **electrolysis** reaction. It is only one example of many reactions in which a chemical compound such as water is *decomposed* to give the elements that make it up.

In Chapter 3 we saw many examples of **combination** reactions where elements combine with each other to produce compounds. People who have been very close to a spot struck by lightning (and who have lived to remember it) frequently have noticed a sharp stinging odor. This is caused in part by a combination reaction in which the tremendous energy of the lightning forces nitrogen and oxygen in the air to combine with one another.

$$N_2 + 2\,O_2 \longrightarrow 2\,NO_2$$

The nitrogen dioxide product has a sharp odor. Fortunately, since air is composed of 21% oxygen and the rest mostly nitrogen, this reaction does not continue on its own after the lightning flash has disappeared. This is one of the few ways nature draws nitrogen into a chemical compound. Nitrogen in compounds, called *fixed nitrogen,* is required for plant growth. Lightning in the atmosphere produces significant amounts of this fertilizer nitrogen.

Some chemical reactions are **replacement reactions**. A piece of sodium metal placed in water replaces part of the hydrogen

$$2\,Na + 2\,H_2O \longrightarrow 2\,NaOH + H_2\uparrow$$

to produce sodium hydroxide and hydrogen gas, H_2. This is a favorite laboratory demonstration because the reaction is so vigorous. Remember the spectacular fire-in-water effect described in Section 2.13 with regard to this experiment.

Most of the reactions presented thus far have involved at least one element as a reactant or a product. However, compounds can react to produce other compounds. For example, compare, on the human scale, the combination of intensive study for a test, too little sleep, too much beer, and, or too much pizza (totaling all of these factors is not unknown among students). This commonly causes a condition that advertisers refer to as "gastric hyperacidity" or "heartburn." It results in part from an accumulation of excess hydrochloric acid, HCl, in the stomach. This

Many antacid preparations contain magnesium hydroxide, which neutralizes excess stomach acid.

acid is a normal component of digestive juices, but in excess it can cause discomfort. Antacids, which can be purchased in drugstores or in some restaurants, perhaps lacking confidence in their food, react with stomach acids to form harmless products. Many of these antacids contain magnesium hydroxide, $Mg(OH)_2$, which when taken for the gastric, HCl condition, forms magnesium chloride and water.

$$Mg(OH)_2 + 2\,HCl \longrightarrow MgCl_2 + 2\,H_2O$$

A chemical reaction occurs in the stomach in which two compounds react to form two new compounds. It is also a reaction in which an *acid* reacts with a *base* to produce water and a *salt*. Such a reaction is called a **neutralization** reaction.

Chemical reactions, like people, have driving forces that keep them going. The forces motivating the chemistry student may be the desire to receive a good grade so that the transcript will look good to a prospective employer, or the desire not to flunk with the dreadful consequences of scholastic probation and repeating the course. The chemistry professor may be prompted to teach effectively due to a joy of seeing students learn, or the desire to get good teacher ratings which aid promotion and salary increases. An acid-base reaction such as the last one discussed is driven forward by the formation of very stable water. Consider an example outside the human body such as the reaction of hydrochloric acid with limestone ($CaCO_3$),

$$2\,HCl + CaCO_3 \longrightarrow CaCl_2 + H_2O + CO_2\uparrow$$

is driven in part by the formation of carbon dioxide gas, which fizzes off from the rock surface.

Another kind of driving force is the formation of a *precipitate*. A precipitate is the name given to a chemical compound that comes out of a liquid solution as a solid material and settles to the bottom of the container. You have surely noticed the cloudy white precipitate that forms when ordinary soap is used in hard water (scum known as the "bathtub ring"). This is an insoluble—and useless—form of soap created by the reaction of magnesium and calcium in water with hand soap. An example of a useful precipitate-forming reaction is that which occurs when aluminum sulfate reacts with a base in water. The reaction of aluminum sulfate with sodium hydroxide is

$$Al_2(SO_4)_3 + 6\,NaOH \longrightarrow 2\,Al(OH)_3\downarrow + 3\,Na_2SO_4$$

The aluminum hydroxide product is a jelly-like material resembling the white of an egg. When it is produced by a chemical reaction in water, the $Al(OH)_3$ settles out, carrying impurities with it. It is especially useful for dragging very small particles of dirt and other matter to the bottom of a container of water. Thus it *clarifies* the water, literally clearing it up as shown in Figure 4.8. This makes aluminum hydroxide a very useful chemical for water treatment.

The preceding discussion of aluminum sulfate reactions has involved solutions. Solutions are very important in chemistry. They will be discussed in detail in Chapter 6. However, several important terms involving solutions should be emphasized here. **Soluble** chemical compounds **dissolve** in water to form **solutions**. Compounds that do not dissolve appreciably in water are said to be **insoluble**. When a chemical reaction in solution produces an insoluble compound, the compound comes out of solution as a **precipitate**. The process is called **precipitation**, and the reaction is a **precipitation reaction**.

The loss and gain of electrons through oxidation and reduction can be a powerful force driving chemical reactions. For example, finely divided aluminum can be burned in pure oxygen to produce aluminum oxide, Al_2O_3. This reaction goes very strongly because oxygen has such a strong tendency to pick up electrons and aluminum so readily gives them away. The unbalanced chemical reaction between aluminum and oxygen is

$$Al + O_2 \longrightarrow Al_2O_3$$

It is not at all difficult to balance this equation by inspection. However, more complicated oxidation-reduction equations are often difficult to balance. Balancing is made much easier by the fact that the total number of electrons *lost* by all of the atoms of the element that is

FIGURE 4.8

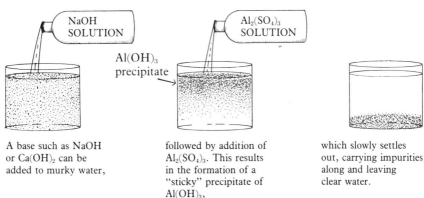

A base such as NaOH or Ca(OH)₂ can be added to murky water,

followed by addition of Al₂(SO₄)₃. This results in the formation of a "sticky" precipitate of Al(OH)₃,

which slowly settles out, carrying impurities along and leaving clear water.

oxidized equals the total number of electrons *gained* by all of the atoms of the element that is *reduced*. In the case of the reaction between aluminum and oxygen, aluminum loses electrons and is oxidized. Oxygen gains electrons and is reduced. This is easily seen by inspecting the electron-dot symbols for these elements shown in Figure 4.9.

When Al reacts with O_2, each O atom gains 2 electrons. This means that the 2 O atoms in O_2 gain a total of 4 electrons. Each aluminum atom loses 3 electrons. Balancing the equation requires that the smallest whole number of O_2 molecules be selected in which the number of electrons lost by the Al atoms equals the number of electrons gained by the O_2 molecules. This can be accomplished by taking 4 Al and 3 O_2. The 4 Al atoms lose a total of 12 electrons. The 3 O_2 molecules gain a total of 12 electrons. Balancing these reactants at the left of the equation gives

$$4 \, Al + 3 \, O_2 \longrightarrow Al_2O_3$$

The equation is completely balanced by placing a 2 in front of Al_2O_3 yielding

$$4 \, Al + 3 \, O_2 \longrightarrow 2 \, Al_2O_3$$

This balanced equation has 4 Al at the left and 4 at the right. There are 6 O at the left and 6 at the right.

$$\cdot \dot{Al} \cdot \longrightarrow Al^{3+}$$

Each aluminum atom loses 3 valence electrons

to produce an aluminum ion with a charge of +3.

$$: \dot{O} \cdot \longrightarrow : \ddot{O} :^{2-}$$

Each oxygen atom gains 2 electrons

to produce an oxide ion with a charge of −2.

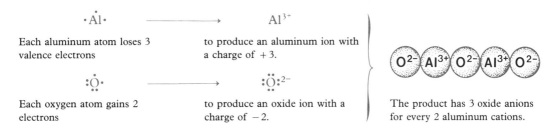

The product has 3 oxide anions for every 2 aluminum cations.

FIGURE 4.9 *Electron-dot diagrams illustrates how aluminum loses electrons and is oxidized and how oxygen gains electrons and is reduced.*

Chapter Summary

This chapter discusses chemicals reacting with each other. The simplest picture of a chemical reaction is that of two atoms of different elements coming together to form a chemical compound. Generally, however, chemical reactions involve species that are much more complicated than atoms. Even many of the elements do not exist simply as atoms. For example, the important gases, nitrogen, oxygen, fluorine, chlorine, and hydrogen consist of molecules containing two atoms.

Chemicals taking part in chemical reactions may consist of molecules of compounds, molecules of elements, ions in solid crystals, ions dissolved in solution, and other species. These are shown in the chemical equations that describe chemical processes.

It is interesting to compare chemistry to a language. Such a comparison is summarized in Table 4.1 for the reaction of methane with oxygen. A chemical equation contains a great deal of information.

TABLE 4.1

Language	Chemistry
Letters of the alphabet: A, B, C, ...	Symbols of the elements: H, C, O, ...
Words: methane, oxygen, carbon dioxide, water	Chemical formulas: CH_4, O_2, CO_2, H_2O
Sentences: Methane reacts with oxygen to produce carbon dioxide, water, and heat.	$CH_4 + 2\,O_2 \longrightarrow$ $CO_2 + 2\,H_2O + heat$

For example, consider the equation for the reaction between calcium hydroxide and hydrochloric acid yielding calcium chloride and water.

$$Ca(OH)_2 + 2\,HCl \longrightarrow CaCl_2 + 2\,H_2O$$

Reactants are at the left side of the equation. In this case the reactants are $Ca(OH)_2$ and HCl. *Products* are at the right side of the equation. Here the products are calcium chloride and water. One $Ca(OH)_2$ reacts with 2 HCl's. The 2 HCl's are shown by a 2 in front of the HCl. From this reaction 1 $CaCl_2$ and 2 H_2O's are produced. There are 4 H's at the left. Two of these are in the $Ca(OH)_2$, and 2 are in the 2 HCl's. There are also 4 H's at the right, all of them in the 2 H_2O molecules. There are 2 O's at the left, both contained in the $Ca(OH)_2$. There are 2 O's at the right contained in the 2 H_2O molecules. There is 1 Ca at the left (in the $Ca(OH)_2$) and 1 Ca at the right (in the $CaCl_2$). There are 2 Cl's in the 2 HCl's at the left. There are 2 Cl's in the $CaCl_2$ at the right.

After the correct reactants and products are known for a chemical equation, it is necessary to balance it. *The same number of each kind of atom must appear on both sides of the equation.* The equation discussed above is balanced. To show the process of balancing an equation,

Stalagtites and stalagmites are formed by the action of water, dissolved carbon dioxide, and calcium carbonate over many years. (Courtesy of Ward's Natural Science Establishment, Inc.)

consider the reaction of ammonia with oxygen to yield nitric oxide and water.

$$NH_3 + O_2 \longrightarrow NO + H_2O$$

The reaction is balanced, one element at a time. Hydrogen may be balanced by taking 2 NH_3's and 3 H_2O's, giving 6 H's at both sides.

$$2\,NH_3 + O_2 \longrightarrow NO + 3\,H_2O$$

Next, nitrogen is balanced with 2 NO's.

$$2\,NH_3 + O_2 \longrightarrow 2\,NO + 3\,H_2O$$

There are now 5 O's on the right. These can be balanced by taking $\frac{5}{2}\,O_2$.

$$2\,NH_3 + \frac{5}{2}\,O_2 \longrightarrow 2\,NO + 3\,H_2O$$

To avoid having fractions, each thing on each side is multiplied by 2 yielding

$$4\,NH_3 + 5\,O_2 \longrightarrow 4\,NO + 6\,H_2O$$

Check by adding the total number of each type of atom on both sides of the equation. In this case each side has 4 N's, 12 H's, and 10 O's.

Some groups of atoms tend to occur together in chemical compounds and to stay together in chemical reactions. One such group is the sulfate ion, SO_4^{2-}. Parentheses are often put around such groups in a chemical formula. For example, the 3 sulfate ions are shown as $Al_2(SO_4)_3$ in aluminum sulfate.

Some of the most important chemical reactions are those involving acids and bases. Most commonly, acids are compounds that contain the hydrogen ion, H^+. Bases are those which contain the hydroxide ion, OH^-. These 2 ions react to produce water, H_2O.

It is sometimes convenient to place chemical reactions in several different classes. A decomposition reaction is one in which a chemical compound is broken up. An example is the production of hydrogen and oxygen when an electrical current is passed through water:

$$2 H_2O \longrightarrow 2 H_2\uparrow + O_2\uparrow$$

A combination reaction occurs when two elements combine to give a compound. The reverse of the above reaction to yield water from hydrogen and oxygen is a combination reaction. A replacement reaction occurs when one element replaces another from a compound:

$$2 K + 2 H_2O \longrightarrow 2 KOH + H_2\uparrow$$

A reaction between an acid and a base is a neutralization reaction. A precipitation reaction is one in which a solid "falls out" when chemicals dissolved in water react.

Many important chemical reactions are oxidation-reduction reactions. In these reactions the total number of electrons lost by all of the atoms of the element that is oxidized is equal to the total number of electrons gained by all of the atoms of the element that is reduced. This fact can be useful in balancing oxidation-reduction equations.

Chapter Review Questions

The following questions are designed as a self-teaching tool to help you review Chapter 4. The answers to each question follow. See Chapter Review Questions for Chapter 1 for further instructions.

1. In comparing chemistry to a language, the letters of the chemistry alphabet are _____, the words are _____, and the sentences are _____.

2. The following,

$$Mg + 2 HCl \longrightarrow MgCl_2 + H_2\uparrow$$

is an example of a _____.

3. In the chemical equation above, Mg and HCl are _____ and $MgCl_2$ and H_2 are _____.

4. In a chemical equation the same number of each specific kind of _____ must appear on _____ of the equation.

5. A chemical equation that meets the requirements set out in Question 4 is said to be _____.

6. The chemical formula for the hydrocarbon, ethane, is C_2H_6. Balance the following equation for the burning of ethane in oxygen by placing the correct number in each of the blanks:

    _____C_2H_6 + _____O_2 $\longrightarrow$ _____CO_2 + _____H_2O

7. Consider the balanced equation in Question 6. On each side of the equation there are _____ C atoms, _____ H atoms, and _____ O atoms.

8. The electron-dot formula for acetylene is _____.

9. Glucose is a simple sugar that can be injected directly into the veins of patients who cannot take food orally. Its chemical formula is _____, and the balanced equation for its reaction with oxygen is _____ _____.

10. What must never be changed in order to balance a chemical equation? _____.

11. The reaction of CaO with water yields _____, a compound which is an example of a _____ because it contains the _____ anion.

12. A precipitate in chemistry is a _____

_____.

13. In a chemical equation, the arrow, →, is used to separate the _____ from the _____.

14. The arrow, ↑, indicates formation of a _____ and ↓ shows formation of a _____.

15. Sulfur trioxide with a chemical formula _____ reacts with water to form a compound called _____ having a chemical formula _____.

16. The ion produced by acids dissolved in water is called _____, and its symbol is _____.

17. A solution containing a lot of H^+ ion is said to be _____ and one containing a lot of OH^- ion is _____.

18. Acids containing H^+ and bases containing OH^- combine to produce _____.

19. The reaction between an acid and a base is called a _____ reaction.

20. In the formula, $Al_2(SO_4)_3$, the Al stands for the element, _____, S stands for _____, and O is _____.

21. The "SO_4" group has a charge of _____ and is called the _____ ion.

22. In the formula for aluminum sulfate in Question 20, the 3 shows that there are _____ for every _____ Al's.

23. The breaking up of water to produce hydrogen gas and oxygen gas is an example of a _____ reaction.

24. The reaction of N_2 and O_2 to yield NO_2 is a _____ reaction.

25. The reaction of sodium metal and water is a _____ type reaction.

26. The chemical formula of the precipitate formed when a solution of $Al_2(SO_4)_3$ is added to a solution of sodium hydroxide is _____.

Answers to Chapter Review Questions

1. the symbols of the elements, the chemical formulas, the chemical equations

2. chemical equation

3. reactants, products

4. atom, both sides

5. balanced

6. 2, 7, 4, 6

7. 4, 12, 14

8. $H\!:\!C\!:\!:\!C\!:\!H$

9. $C_6H_{12}O_6$, $C_6H_{12}O_6 + 6\,O_2 \longrightarrow 6\,CO_2 + 6\,H_2O$

10. chemical formulas

11. $Ca(OH)_2$, base, OH^-

12. solid material that forms when a chemical reaction takes place with chemicals dissolved in solution

13. reactants, products

14. gas, precipitate (solid from solution)

15. SO_3, sulfuric acid, H_2SO_4

16. hydrogen ion, H^+

17. acidic, basic

18. water, H_2O
19. neutralization
20. aluminum, sulfur, oxygen
21. -2, sulfate
22. 3 sulfates, 2
23. decomposition
24. combination
25. replacement
26. $Al(OH)_3$

Exercises for Chapter 4

1. Benzene is an organic compound with the chemical formula C_6H_6. When it burns with oxygen in the air, what are the products of the chemical reaction?

2. What is the balanced chemical reaction between benzene and oxygen?

3. Consider the unbalanced reaction between phosphoric acid and calcium metal:

$$H_3PO_4 + Ca \longrightarrow Ca_3(PO_4)_2 + H_2$$

    If one tried to balance it as follows,

$$H_2PO_4 + Ca \longrightarrow CaPO_4 + H_2$$

    what would be wrong with the "balanced" equation?

4. Magnesium, a very light metal used in making airplanes, lightweight extension ladders, etc., burns very intensely with a blinding white light. A carbon dioxide (CO_2) fire extinguisher does not work well on a magnesium fire because the magnesium will take oxygen away from carbon dioxide and keep on burning, giving off a cloud of black carbon particles. Magnesium is directly above calcium in the periodic table (see Figure 2.32), and the formula of calcium oxide is CaO. What would you guess to be the balanced chemical equation for the reaction of magnesium and carbon dioxide?

5. In preparing nitric acid, a common industrial chemical and fertilizer component made from ammonia, the NH_3 is forced to react with oxygen to form N_2O_5. This nitrogen pentoxide dissolves in water to produce nitric acid, HNO_3. What is the balanced chemical reaction between ammonia and oxygen? What is the balanced chemical equation for the reaction of nitrogen pentoxide, N_2O_5, and water to produce nitric acid?

6. A student attempted to make a solution of calcium fluoride, CaF_2, by dissolving some of that salt in water. Although the particles of CaF_2 were stirred vigorously with water, none appeared to dissolve. Knowing that acids react with bases to form salts, the student mixed a solution of hydrofluoric acid, HF, (a very dangerous acid to handle) and calcium hydroxide, $Ca(OH)_2$. Describe what happened and give the balanced chemical equation.

7. Sodium bicarbonate, $NaHCO_3$, is commonly used as an antacid to relieve "excess stomach acid" and "heartburn." With what acid does it react? What are the products? What is the balanced chemical equation?

8. Many fire extinguishers contain carbon dioxide under pressure. Sodium bicarbonate, $NaHCO_3$, sprinkled on a fire sometimes puts it out. Sodium bicarbonate undergoes a decomposition reaction when heated. Neither Na_2O nor NaOH is a product of the decomposition reaction. With a chemical reaction and an explanation, show how $NaHCO_3$ may act to put out a fire.

9. The chemical structure of propane, C_3H_8, was given as

$$H:\overset{\overset{\textstyle H}{\cdot\cdot}}{\underset{\underset{\textstyle H}{\cdot\cdot}}{C}}:\overset{\overset{\textstyle H}{\cdot\cdot}}{\underset{\underset{\textstyle H}{\cdot\cdot}}{C}}:\overset{\overset{\textstyle H}{\cdot\cdot}}{\underset{\underset{\textstyle H}{\cdot\cdot}}{C}}:H$$

The closely related compound, butane, has the chemical formula, C_4H_{10}, and can have 4 carbon atoms bonded to each other in a row. Like propane it is used as a fuel, particularly for farm dwellings, and as "bottled gas." Show the structure of butane, with pairs of electron dots making up chemical bonds.

10. What is the balanced chemical equation for the burning of butane?

11. In the chemical formulas of ionic compounds, the electrical charges of the ions must balance. The formula of sodium chloride is NaCl because the $+1$ charge of the Na^+ ion exactly balances the -1 charge of the Cl^- anion. Calcium chloride is $CaCl_2$ because it takes 2 Cl^- ions, each with a -1 charge to balance the $+2$ charge of the Ca^{2+} cation. Figure out the chemical formulas of the compounds formed when each of the cations at the left of the following table combines with each of the anions at the right.

Cation	Anion
K^+	Cl^-
Mg^{2+}	SO_4^{2-}
Al^{3+}	PO_4^{3-}

12. Read again the section about the oxidation of glucose in the body. Consider how the products leave the body. Consider also the chemical reactions of calcium hydroxide which were discussed. If you exhale through a straw into a test tube containing $Ca(OH)_2$, a white, powdery solid forms in the tube. What is its formula? What is the chemical reaction? Where did each of the reactants come from?

13. Too much magnesium is undesirable in municipal water systems or in water used for some industrial applications. It is removed from water by adding a base, which causes a white magnesium compound to come out of solution as a precipitate. Write a chemical equation for the reaction that occurs if a NaOH solution is added to water containing dissolved magnesium chloride, $MgCl_2$. Do you think $Mg(OH)_2$ dissolves very well in water?

14. Heat energy at extremely high temperatures can cause water to decompose into H_2 and O_2. What type of energy can accomplish the same thing at room temperature?

15. If the formula of sodium nitrate is $NaNO_3$, what is the formula of the nitrate ion?

16. What phenomenon can result in the formation of NO_2 in the atmosphere?

17. When SO_2 gas is bubbled into water, an acid is formed. It is called sulfurous acid. What is its chemical formula?

18. What is the purpose of an "antacid preparation" purchased in a drugstore?

19. What is the chemical formula of limestone?

20. Aluminum metal reacts with sulfuric acid to give aluminum sulfate. The aluminum is oxidized in the reaction.
    a. What is reduced, and what is the product of the reduction?
    b. What is the chemical formula of aluminum sulfate?
    c. What is the balanced chemical reaction?

In the burning of organic material, such as a forest fire, a product of the reaction is carbon dioxide. (Courtesy of the Forest Service, USDA; B. W. Muir, photographer)

5

The Arithmetic of Chemical Reactions

5.1

What Does an Atom Weigh?

In Chapter 1 an atom was described as an extremely small and light particle of matter. The weights of these very small atoms, however, determine the huge quantities of chemicals used in chemical industries. For example, the relative weights of nitrogen and hydrogen atoms determine how many thousands of tons of nitrogen must be reacted with a large quantity of hydrogen for the monthly output of an ammonia manufacturing plant. No matter how large they are, it is possible to calculate the quantities of material that are involved in a chemical process with a knowledge of the correct chemical reaction and the weights of the atoms involved.

One particular isotope of carbon has been chosen as a standard for atomic weight. The weights of all other atoms are based upon this isotope. The isotope is carbon-12, which has 6 protons and 6 neutrons in its nucleus. It has been agreed that an atom of this isotope weighs exactly 12 amu (atomic mass units). Almost all carbon is made up of this isotope. A total of 50,000,000,000,000,000,000,000,000 (5.0×10^{25}) carbon atoms are required to make up 1 kg (kilogram) of pure carbon. If this carbon is in the form of charcoal briquettes, it is about enough to stoke up a small charcoal grill. A kilogram of carbon weighs 600,000,000,000,000,000,000,000,000 (6.0×10^{26}) amu! It is easy to see that the atomic mass unit is too small to use conveniently for expressing weights of bulk quantities of material. However, it is the most convenient unit for expressing the weights of individual atoms and molecules. We will start discussing the arithmetic of chemical reactions using atomic mass units as weight units. Then we will show how these weights are scaled up to give weights used in the laboratory, or in a chemical factory. We will express these weights in several different units. For laboratory chemical reactions, we will use grams as the most convenient measure. For large scale industrial chemicals, tons will be used. Although the metric system is replacing the English system which most of us still use in the U.S., we still need to know how to use pounds in some chemical calculations. For very small quantities milligrams will be used.

5.2

Why is Chemical Arithmetic Important?

The automobile engineer must calculate how much air should be mixed with a specific amount of gasoline to make an engine run properly. If there is too little air, not all of the gasoline will burn; and polluting black smoke will pour from the exhaust. Mileage will be reduced, which is to be avoided with today's gasoline prices. If there is too much air, the engine will misfire and will not run properly.

The steelmaker must know how much coke to mix with iron ore to produce iron with the right properties. The engineer in an ammonia plant must know how much hydrogen and nitrogen to mix in the chemical reactor which produces ammonia by the reaction,

$$N_2 + 3 H_2 \longrightarrow 2 NH_3$$

All of these calculations involve chemical arithmetic. Chemical arithmetic is the calculation of the quantities of chemicals that react with each other and the quantities of chemicals that are produced. The chemist calls this **stoichiometry**. In order to do stoichiometric calculations, you need to know the correct, balanced chemical equation. You also need to know the atomic weights of the elements involved in the chemical reaction. From there on it is simple arithmetic. In this chapter we show how such calculations are made.

5.3

Some Simple Chemical Arithmetic

Example 1. As the first example let us take the reaction of carbon with oxygen. This is the same reaction that produces the heat in a charcoal grill. The chemical reaction produces carbon dioxide:

$$C + O_2 \longrightarrow CO_2$$

The atomic weight of carbon is 12. The atomic weight of oxygen is 16. Each oxygen atom weighs 16 amu. Each oxygen molecule with its 2 oxygen atoms weighs 32 amu. The carbon dioxide molecule that is produced weighs the same as a carbon atom plus 2 oxygen atoms:

$$
\begin{aligned}
\text{carbon atom} &= 12 \quad \text{amu} \\
\text{oxygen atom} &= 16 \quad \text{amu} \\
\text{oxygen atom} &= \underline{16} \quad \text{amu} \\
CO_2 \text{ molecule} &= 44 \quad \text{amu}
\end{aligned}
$$

The carbon dioxide molecule weighs 44 amu (see Figure 5.1). This important number gives the *molecular weight* of carbon dioxide. To find the molecular weight of a compound, add together the weights of all of the atoms making up the compound. In the case of the CO_2 molecule, the molecular weight is found by adding the atomic weight of carbon and two times the atomic weight of oxygen. The arithmetic of the reaction between carbon and oxygen is simplified by writing down the atomic and molecular weights of the atoms and molecules involved:

$$C + O_2 \longrightarrow CO_2$$
$$12 \qquad 32 \qquad\qquad 44$$

FIGURE 5.1

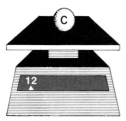

One carbon atom, weighing 12 amu,

combines with 2 oxygen atoms, each weighing 16 amu,

to form a carbon dioxide molecule, weighing 44 amu.

Notice the reaction states that an atom of carbon weighing 12 amu reacts with a molecule of oxygen weighing 32 amu to produce a molecule of carbon dioxide weighing 44 amu. From these calculations, we can find the weight of carbon dioxide produced when the number of atoms of both elements are increased to obtain a greater quantity of CO_2.

Enormous quantities of steel are produced every year. In industrial production, chemical arithmetic is usually done in terms of extraordinarily large numbers. Shown here are finished steel sheets being rolled out of a vacumn-degassing machine. (Courtesy of Bethlehem Steel Corp.)

As an example, we will find the weight of carbon dioxide produced from 2 atoms of carbon reacting with oxygen as follows:

The 2 atoms weigh a total of 24 amu.

These 2 atoms of carbon react with twice as much oxygen as 1 atom of carbon does, or 64 amu of oxygen.

Twice as much CO_2, a total of 88 amu, is produced.

$$2\,C + 2\,O_2 \longrightarrow 2\,CO_2$$
$$\quad 24 \qquad 64 \qquad\qquad\qquad 88$$

It is easy to scale up from amu to grams. As we have just seen, 12 amu of carbon react with 32 amu of oxygen to produce 44 amu of CO_2. Essentially in scaling up to grams, the proportions remain the same. Consider how much O_2 would react with 12 g (grams) of carbon:

Quantities in amu	Reaction	Quantities in grams
12 amu	C	12 g
	+	
32 amu	O_2	32 g
	↓	
44 amu	CO_2	44 g

Should we have *twice* as much carbon, say 24 g, the proportions are multiplied by a factor of 2.

12 g	C	24 g (12 g × 2)
	+	
32 g	O_2	64 g (32 g × 2)
	↓	
44 g	CO_2	88 g (44 g × 2)

Exactly twice as much carbon reacts to produce exactly twice as much carbon dioxide. What if there were only *one-half* of 12 g of carbon reacting? How much oxygen would react with 6 g of carbon? How much carbon dioxide would be produced?

12 g	C	$6 \text{ g} \left(12 \text{ g} \times \dfrac{1}{2}\right)$
	+	
32 g	O_2	$16 \text{ g} \left(32 \text{ g} \times \dfrac{1}{2}\right)$
	↓	
44 g	CO_2	$22 \text{ g} \left(44 \text{ g} \times \dfrac{1}{2}\right)$

Exactly one-half as much oxygen reacts to produce exactly one-half as much carbon dioxide.

Since we are dealing with proportion, we know from the atomic weight of carbon and the molecular weight of carbon dioxide that twice as much carbon will produce twice as much carbon dioxide, and one-half as much carbon will produce one-half as much carbon dioxide. When some odd weight of carbon is involved, the calculation is still rather simple. To show this we calculate the number of grams of oxygen that will react with 7 g of carbon. We will also very easily find how many grams of CO_2 are produced.

Consider again the one-to-one relationship of grams to atomic mass units in balancing the reaction of carbon with oxygen to produce carbon dioxide. Recall

$$C + O_2 \longrightarrow CO_2$$
$$12 \text{ g} \quad 32 \text{ g} \qquad 44 \text{ g}$$

Since we are investigating the number of grams of oxygen that will react with 7 g of carbon, we take the proportion of this number to the original 12 g of carbon and by simple multiplication obtain the values for O_2 and CO_2:

$$C + O_2 \longrightarrow CO_2$$
$$7.0 \text{ g} \quad 18.7 \text{ g} \qquad 25.7 \text{ g}$$
$$\left(32 \text{ g} \times \frac{7}{12}\right) \qquad \left(44 \text{ g} \times \frac{7}{12}\right)$$

To get the weight of oxygen, we must first know that 12 g of carbon react with 32 g of oxygen. Therefore, 7 g of carbon react with 7/12 of 32 g of oxygen. We need to calculate 7/12 times 32. Multiplying 7 by 32 gives 224. Dividing 224 by 12 gives 18.7 g of oxygen. Likewise, the weight of carbon dioxide can be obtained on the basis that 12 g of carbon produce 44 g of carbon dioxide. Therefore, 7 g of carbon must produce 7/12 of 44 g of carbon dioxide. Multiplying 7 by 44 we get 308. The number 308 divided by 12 yields 25.7 g of carbon dioxide.

Example 2. Hydrogen gas, H_2, and sulfur react to form poisonous hydrogen sulfide gas, H_2S, which has a characteristic rotten egg odor.

$$H_2 + S \longrightarrow H_2S$$

What weight of hydrogen is required to react with 224 g of sulfur? How many grams of hydrogen sulfide are produced?

The atomic weight of hydrogen is 1, and the atomic weight of sulfur is 32. This is information needed to calculate the molecular weights of H_2 and H_2S:

H_2 has a molecular weight of $1 + 1 = 2$

H_2S has a molecular weight of $1 + 1 + 32 = 34$

Calculate the weight of H_2 that will react with 224 grams of sulfur:

$$\begin{array}{ccc} ? & 224 \text{ g} & \\ H_2 + & S & \longrightarrow \quad H_2S \\ 2 \text{ g} & 32 \text{ g} & \end{array}$$

$$\frac{2 \text{ g of } H_2 \times 224 \text{ g of S}}{32 \text{ g of S}} = 14 \text{ g of } H_2$$

Calculate the weight of H_2S produced:

$$\begin{array}{ccc} 224 \text{ g} & & ? \\ H_2 + & S & \longrightarrow \quad H_2S \\ & 32 \text{ g} & 34 \text{ g} \end{array}$$

$$\frac{34 \text{ g of } H_2S \times 224 \text{ g of S}}{32 \text{ g of S}} = 238 \text{ g of } H_2S$$

The 238 g of H_2S product weighs the same as the 224 g of S plus the 14 g of H_2 which reacted.

Example 3. Anyone who has spent much time around college chemistry departments has had the experience of walking by a laboratory fogged up with a white "smog." Chances are the visibility is obscured by very small particles of solid ammonium chloride, NH_4Cl. This compound forms in the atmosphere when somebody pours a concentrated solution of ammonia, NH_3, into an open beaker on the laboratory bench, ignoring the little footnote, "Perform this operation in the fume hood," given in the laboratory directions. At the other end of the bench somebody else pours a solution of concentrated hydrochloric acid, HCl, into a beaker. Both NH_3 and HCl are gases. When dissolved in water, some of their molecules escape into the atmosphere as molecules of NH_3 and HCl (Figures 5.2 and 5.3). These gases cannot be seen, but their sharp, pungent odors can certainly be smelled. When the molecules of NH_3 and HCl meet in the middle of the room, they react to form solid ammonium chloride, NH_4Cl:

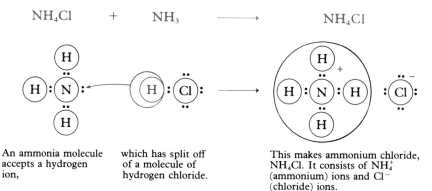

An ammonia molecule accepts a hydrogen ion,	which has split off of a molecule of hydrogen chloride.		This makes ammonium chloride, NH_4Cl. It consists of NH_4^+ (ammonium) ions and Cl^- (chloride) ions.

It does not take much ammonium chloride to get things pretty much fogged up. Just a few milligrams will do it. A milligram (mg) is only one thousandth of a gram, and a gram isn't very much. We may calculate how much HCl we would need to react with NH_3 to form 10 mg of ammonium chloride. Recall that the atomic weight of H is 1, the atomic weight of N is 14, and the atomic weight of chlorine is 35.5. Adding these values we get the following molecular weights:

molecular weight of HCl = 1 + 35.5 = 36.5

molecular weight of NH_3 = 14 + 1 + 1 + 1 = 17

molecular weight of NH_4Cl = 14 + 1 + 1 + 1 + 1 + 35.5 = 53.5

Now it is possible to calculate the weight of NH_3 required to form

FIGURE 5.2

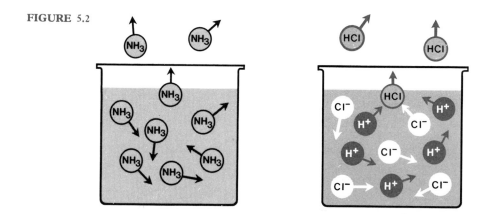

FIGURE 5.3

Ammonium chloride is a white
solid, which forms as a fog in
the air between open containers
of solutions of ammonia
and hydrochloric acid.

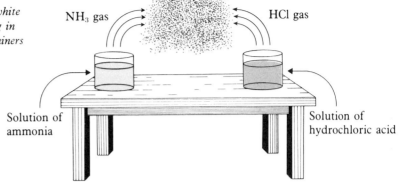

NH₃ gas   HCl gas

Solution of
ammonia

Solution of
hydrochloric acid

10 mg of NH_4Cl:

$$\begin{array}{ccccc} & ? & & 10\text{ mg} \\ HCl & + & NH_3 & \longrightarrow & NH_4Cl \\ & 17\text{ mg} & & 53.5\text{ mg} \end{array}$$

$$\frac{17\text{ mg of }NH_3 \times 10\text{ mg of }NH_4Cl}{53.5\text{ mg of }NH_4Cl} = 3.18\text{ mg of }NH_3$$

The weight of HCl reacting is also easily calculated:

$$\begin{array}{ccccc} ? & & & 10\text{ mg} \\ HCl & + & NH_3 & \longrightarrow & NH_4Cl \\ 36.5\text{ mg} & & & 53.5\text{ mg} \end{array}$$

$$\frac{36.5\text{ mg of }HCl \times 10\text{ mg of }NH_4Cl}{53.5\text{ mg of }NH_4Cl} = 6.82\text{ mg of }HCl$$

As expected, the total weight of reactants is the same as the weight of product:

$$\begin{array}{rl} 6.82 & \text{mg of }HCl \\ \underline{3.18} & \text{mg of }NH_3 \\ 10.00 & \text{mg of reactants} = \text{same weight as }NH_4Cl\text{ product.} \end{array}$$

5.4

Chemical Arithmetic at the Water Treatment Plant

Chemical arithmetic may be used to calculate how much of a raw material must be taken to produce a needed amount of product. For example, suppose a water treatment facility needs 900 lb of quicklime each week to treat the water. The chemical formula of quicklime is CaO. It is obtained by heating limestone ($CaCO_3$). The process is called *calcination*.

$$CaCO_3 \longrightarrow CaO + CO_2\uparrow$$

How many pounds of limestone must be calcined each week to produce the 900 lb of CaO needed to treat the water?

To work this problem it is first necessary to make sure that the chemical equation is balanced. We see that it is. Next, we must calculate the molecular weights of $CaCO_3$, CaO, and CO_2 (Figure 5.4).

$CaCO_3$

Weight of 1 Ca atom is   40
Weight of 1 C atom is   12
Weight of 3 O atoms,
 each weighing 16 is   48
        100 is the molecular weight of $CaCO_3$

CaO

Weight of 1 Ca atom is 40
Weight of 1 O atom is 16
      56 is the molecular weight of CaO

CO_2

Weight of 1 C atom is 12
Weight of 2 O atoms,
 each weighing 16 is 32
      44 is the molecular weight of CO_2

Now these numbers may be included with the chemical reaction:

$$CaCO_3 \longrightarrow CaO + CO_2$$
$$100 \qquad\qquad 56 \quad\ 44$$

If we are talking in terms of pounds, the reaction tells us that 100 lb of $CaCO_3$ when heated yields 56 lb of CaO and 44 lb of CO_2:

$$CaCO_3 \longrightarrow CaO + CO_2$$
$$100\ lb \qquad\qquad 56\ lb \quad 44\ lb$$

FIGURE 5.4

Calcium carbonate,
weighing 100 amu,

is broken down by heat
to produce calcium oxide
(quicklime), weighing 56 amu

and carbon dioxide,
weighing 44 amu.

We have just seen that 100 lb of $CaCO_3$ are required to produce 56 lb of CaO. But the water treatment plant needs 900 lb of CaO each week. How much $CaCO_3$ will the plant require?

$$\overset{?}{CaCO_3} \longrightarrow \overset{900\ lb}{CaO} + CO_2$$
$$\underset{100\ lb}{} \qquad \underset{56\ lb}{} \quad \underset{44\ lb}{}$$

The answer is found by the following calculation:

$$\frac{100\ lb\ of\ CaCO_3 \times 900\ lb\ of\ CaO}{56\ lb\ of\ CaO}$$

yields

$$\frac{90,000}{56}\ lb$$

which is 1607 lb of $CaCO_3$.

Carbon dioxide is produced in the reaction that we have been discussing. It can also be used in treating the water, and the treatment plant operator will need to know how much carbon dioxide is produced along with the 900 lb of CaO. It is already known that 44 lb of CO_2 are produced when 56 lb of CaO are made. When 900 lb of CaO are made, we can calculate that,

$$\frac{44\ lb\ of\ CO_2 \times 900\ lb\ of\ CaO}{56\ lb\ of\ CaO}$$

yields

$$\frac{39,600}{56}\ lb$$

which is 707 lb of CO_2.

Looking at the above reaction, one would expect that the total weight of CaO and CO_2 produced should equal the weight of $CaCO_3$. A quick calculation shows that this is indeed the case:

$$\overset{1607\ lb}{\overbrace{\underset{900\ lb \quad 707\ lb}{}}}$$
$$\underset{CaCO_3}{1607\ lb} \longrightarrow CaO + CO_2$$

We see in this chemical reaction an important point regarding chemical arithmetic. It is that *in any chemical reaction, the total weight of products is the same as the total weight of material reacting.* In this case, a total of 1607 lb of CaO and CO_2 are produced from 1607 lb of $CaCO_3$.

5.5

What is a Mole?

One of the most useful concepts in chemical arithmetic is the **mole**. To understand what a mole is, consider some of the weights which have been discussed in this chapter. We have used *molecular weight* in several calculations. For example, the molecular weight of CO_2 in the preceding example was shown to be 44. It is obtained by adding the atomic weight of carbon (12) to twice the atomic weight of oxygen $(16 + 16 = 32)$. We also referred to molecular weights of CaO and $CaCO_3$. Here we run into a technicality which should be mentioned. These compounds are *ionic compounds*. For example, $CaCO_3$ does not consist of separate, distinct molecules of calcium carbonate. Instead, it is made up of equal numbers of Ca^{2+} and CO_3^{2-} ions packed together in a crystal. It is not really correct to refer to a molecule of $CaCO_3$. But it is useful to visualize the smallest amount of material that can still be called calcium carbonate. This consists of one Ca^{2+} ion and one CO_3^{2-} ion. We call that a **formula unit** of calcium carbonate and think of it as "one $CaCO_3$." One formula unit of $CaCO_3$ weighs 100 amu as shown by the following calculation:

$$
\begin{array}{rcrl}
1 \text{ Ca atom weighing 40 amu} & = & 40 & \text{amu} \\
1 \text{ C atom weighing 12 amu} & = & 12 & \text{amu} \\
3 \text{ O atoms each weighing 16 amu} & = & 48 & \text{amu} \\
\hline
1 \text{ formula unit of } CaCO_3 \text{ weighs} & & 100 & \text{amu}
\end{array}
$$

Since there are no molecules of calcium carbonate as such, instead of saying that the molecular weight is 100, it is better to say that the **formula weight** is 100.

In making chemical calculations, it is convenient to think in terms of quantities that contain the same number of formula units of material. These formula units may be atoms of C, molecules of O_2, or pairs of Ca^{2+} and CO_3^{2-} ions making up a unit of $CaCO_3$. A mole is a standard quantity considered for formula weight so that the number of units of each substance being counted is the same regardless of the kind of substance. *A mole of anything contains 6.02×10^{23} formula units.* In Section 5.1 we mentioned that carbon-12, which weighs 12 amu, is the standard used for atomic weight. One mole of carbon-12 weighs 12 g. The number of carbon-12 atoms in 12 g of carbon is 6.02×10^{23}, which may also be expressed as 602,000,000,000,000,000,000,000. This is truly a huge number. Were atoms the size of Ping-Pong balls, these little balls would cover the surface of the Earth to a depth exceeding 60 miles! This huge number has a special name. It is called **Avogadro's number**.

Impressive as an Earth covered with a 60-mile layer of Ping-Pong balls might be, the definition of a mole in terms of Avogadro's number is not really used much in making calculations. Another definition of the mole is extremely useful, however. This definition is: *A mole is the number of grams of a chemical that is equal numerically to the formula weight.* This is best illustrated by examples.

Carbon (C) has an atomic weight of 12. 1 mole weighs 12 g.

Oxygen (O_2) has a molecular weight of 32. 1 mole weighs 32 g.

Carbon dioxide (CO_2) has a molecular weight of 44. 1 mole weighs 44 g.

Calcium carbonate ($CaCO_3$) has a formula weight of 100. 1 mole weighs 100 g.

Neon (Ne) has an atomic weight of 20.2. 1 mole weighs 20.2 g.

We next show how moles are used to simplify chemical arithmetic.

5.6

Chemical Arithmetic with the Mole-Ratio Method

The **mole-ratio method** is a very convenient way to calculate weights of materials involved in chemical reactions. To understand how this method works, consider first the very simple chemical reaction between sulfur trioxide and water to produce sulfuric acid.

$$H_2O + SO_3 \longrightarrow H_2SO_4$$

In terms of *molecules* this reaction states: *One molecule of water reacts with one molecule of sulfur trioxide to produce one molecule of sulfuric acid,* H_2SO_4. In terms of *moles* it states: *One mole of water reacts with one mole of sulfur trioxide to produce one mole of sulfuric acid.*

Now suppose that we want to know how many *grams* of sulfur trioxide are required to produce 490 g of H_2SO_4. What is the weight of water required? First the molecular weights must be calculated. This is done knowing that the atomic weight of hydrogen is 1, that of oxygen is 16, and that of sulfur is 32:

H_2O has molecular weight of $1 + 1 + 16 = 18$. One mole weighs 18 g.

SO_3 has molecular weight of $32 + 16 + 16 + 16 = 80$. One mole weighs 80 g.

H_2SO_4 has molecular weight of

$$1 + 1 + 32 + 16 + 16 + 16 + 16 = 98.$$

1 mole weighs 98 g.

The weight of SO_3 required to produce 490 g of H_2SO_4 is now calculated by the following steps:

Step 1. What is the mole ratio of SO_3 to H_2SO_4?

$$\text{mole ratio} = \frac{\text{moles of } SO_3}{\text{moles of } H_2SO_4} = \frac{1 \text{ mole of } SO_3}{1 \text{ mole of } H_2SO_4}$$

This simply states that 1 mole of sulfur trioxide is required for each mole of sulfuric acid produced.

Step 2. Calculate the number of moles of sulfuric acid, knowing that 1 mole of sulfuric acid weighs 98 g.

$$\text{moles of } H_2SO_4 = \frac{490 \text{ g of } H_2SO_4}{98 \text{ g of } H_2SO_4 \text{ per mole of } H_2SO_4}$$

moles of H_2SO_4 = 5 moles of H_2SO_4

Step 3. Calculate the number of moles of sulfur trioxide by multiplying the moles of sulfuric acid times the mole ratio.

moles of SO_3 = (moles of H_2SO_4) × (mole ratio)

$$\text{moles of } SO_3 = (5 \text{ moles of } H_2SO_4) \times \frac{1 \text{ mole of } SO_3}{1 \text{ mole of } H_2SO_4} = 5 \text{ moles of } SO_3$$

Step 4. Calculate the weight of sulfur trioxide by multiplying the weight of a mole of SO_3 times the number of moles of SO_3. Recall that a mole of SO_3 weighs 80 g.

weight of SO_3 = (80 g per mole) × (5 moles) = 400 g of SO_3

The weight of water consumed can also be calculated by the mole-ratio method as shown in the following steps.

Step 1. Calculate the mole ratio of H_2O to H_2SO_4.

$$\text{mole ratio} = \frac{1 \text{ mole of } H_2O}{1 \text{ mole of } H_2SO_4}$$

Step 2. Calculate the number of moles of H_2O by multiplying the moles of H_2SO_4 times the mole ratio.

$$\text{moles of } H_2O = (5 \text{ moles of } H_2SO_4) \times \frac{1 \text{ mole of } H_2O}{1 \text{ mole of } H_2SO_4} = 5 \text{ moles of } H_2O$$

Step 3. Calculate the weight of H_2O by multiplying the weight of a mole of H_2O times the number of moles of H_2O. A mole of water weighs 18 g.

weight of H_2O = (18 g per mole) × (5 moles) = 90 g of H_2O

As a final check on the calculation, we see that the sulfuric acid *product* weighs 490 g. A total of 400 g of SO_3 and 90 g of H_2O in the *reactants* add up to 490 g. So, the total weight of reactants equals the total weight of products.

5.7

Some More Complicated Chemical Arithmetic

The advantages of the mole-ratio method are more obvious when somewhat more complicated chemical reactions are involved. This can be shown by the reaction for the synthesis of ammonia, NH_3. This important compound was discussed in Chapter 3. Atmospheric nitrogen, N_2, is "fixed" when it reacts with hydrogen to form NH_3. Huge chemical factories produce around 16 million tons of ammonia each year in the U.S. Most of this is used for fertilizer. Smaller amounts are used to manufacture explosives, fabrics, plastics, and other materials. An interesting problem in chemical arithmetic is to calculate the weight of nitrogen required to produce this enormous quantity of ammonia. We may also calculate the weight of hydrogen required.

To make this calculation, we first need the chemical equation for the production of ammonia. We know that N_2 and H_2 react to form NH_3.

$$N_2 + H_2 \longrightarrow NH_3$$

This equation is not yet balanced. There are 2 nitrogen atoms at the left, and only 1 at the right. To balance nitrogen, put a 2 in front of the NH_3.

$$N_2 + H_2 \longrightarrow 2\,NH_3$$

This gives 2 hydrogen atoms at the left and 6 at the right. Hydrogen is balanced by placing a 3 in front of the H_2.

$$N_2 + 3\,H_2 \longrightarrow 2\,NH_3$$

Now the equation is balanced. But the 3 in front of the H_2 and the 2 in front of the NH_3 are going to make the calculation a little more complicated. We can easily understand how to do it though by considering what happens when 1 molecule of N_2 reacts with 3 molecules of H_2 to produce 2 molecules of NH_3. The molecular weights involved are

Molecular weight of $H_2 = 1 + 1 = 2$

Molecular weight of $N_2 = 14 + 14 = 28$

Molecular weight of $NH_3 = 14 + 1 + 1 + 1 = 17$

From these molecular weights, we can show how much nitrogen and hydrogen react, and how much ammonia is produced. The results appear in Figure 5.5.

We have defined moles in terms of grams. The mole that we have defined is actually a "gram-mole." We can work just as readily with "kilogram-moles," or some other convenient units. In the case of industry producing ammonia an answer is desired in units of tons. We may therefore define a "ton-mole" as the number of *tons* of the chemical that is equal numerically to the formula weight. We consider

FIGURE 5.5

One molecule of N_2, weighing 28 amu, reacts with

3 molecules of H_2, each weighing 2 amu (a total of 6 amu for all 3 H_2's),

to produce 2 molecules of NH_3, each weighing 17 amu (a total of 34 amu).

the molecular weights of the molecules involved in the synthesis of ammonia:

> There are 2 tons of hydrogen per ton-mole of H_2.

> There are 28 tons of nitrogen per ton-mole of N_2.

> There are 17 tons of ammonia per ton-mole of NH_3.

With this information it is possible to calculate the weight of nitrogen required for the annual U.S. production of 16 million tons of ammonia per year. This is accomplished by the following steps:

Step 1.   Calculate the mole ratio of nitrogen to ammonia.

$$\text{mole ratio} = \frac{\text{ton-moles of } N_2}{\text{ton-moles of } NH_3} = \frac{1 \text{ ton-mole of } N_2}{2 \text{ ton-moles of } NH_3}$$

This simply says that 1 ton-mole of N_2 is required for each 2 ton-moles of ammonia produced.

Step 2.   Calculate the number of ton-moles of ammonia, knowing that 1 ton-mole of NH_3 weighs 17 tons.

$$\text{ton-moles of } NH_3 = \frac{16,000,000 \text{ tons of } NH_3}{17 \text{ tons of } NH_3 \text{ per ton-mole}}$$

$$\text{ton-moles of } NH_3 = 941,200$$

Step 3.   Calculate the number of ton-moles of nitrogen by multiplying the ton-moles of NH_3 times the mole ratio.

$$\text{ton-moles of } N_2 = (\text{ton-moles of } NH_3) \times (\text{mole ratio})$$

$$\text{ton-moles of } N_2 = (941,200 \text{ ton-moles of } NH_3) \times \frac{1 \text{ ton-mole of } N_2}{2 \text{ ton-moles of } NH_3}$$

$$\text{ton-moles of } N_2 = 470,600 \text{ ton-moles of } N_2$$

Step 4.   Calculate the weight of nitrogen by multiplying the weight of a ton-mole of nitrogen times the number of ton-moles of N_2. A ton-mole of N_2 weighs 28 tons.

weight of N_2 = (28 tons per ton-mole) × (470,600 ton-moles)

weight of N_2 = 13,180,000 tons of N_2

The weight of H_2 consumed can also be calculated by the mole-ratio method as shown in the following steps.

Step 1. Calculate the mole ratio of H_2 to NH_3.

$$\text{mole ratio} = \frac{3 \text{ ton-moles of } H_2}{2 \text{ ton-moles of } NH_3}$$

Step 2. Recall from the previous calculation that ton-moles of NH_3 = 941,200.

Step 3. Calculate the number of ton-moles of hydrogen by multiplying the moles of ammonia by the mole ratio.

$$\text{ton-moles of } H_2 = (941,200 \text{ ton-moles of } NH_3) \times \frac{3 \text{ ton-moles of } H_2}{2 \text{ ton-moles of } NH_3}$$

ton-moles of H_2 = 1,410,000

Step 4. Calculate the weight of hydrogen by multiplying the weight of a ton-mole of H_2 times the number of ton-moles of H_2. A ton-mole of H_2 weighs 2 tons.

weight of H_2 = (2 tons per ton-mole) × (1,410,000 ton-moles)

weight of H_2 = 2,820,000 tons of H_2

The preceding calculations have involved some large numbers. It is hard to keep track of all the zeroes in calculations with such large numbers. The numbers can be simplified by expressing them in powers of ten. For example, the 16,000,000 tons of NH_3 can be written as 1.6×10^7. The raised number after the 10 shows how many places the decimal has to be moved to the right. That is shown by the following:

$$1 . \underbrace{6\,0\,0\,0\,0\,0\,0}_{1\;\;2\;\;3\;\;4\;\;5\;\;6\;\;7} = 16,000,000$$

1.6×10^7 means that you start with 1.6 and move the decimal point 7 places to the right to get 16,000,000.

Some of the other quantities involved in the previous calculations are

941,200 ton-moles of NH_3 = 9.412×10^5 ton-moles of NH_3

13,180,000 tons of N_2 = 1.318×10^7 tons of N_2

2,820,000 tons of H_2 = 2.82×10^6 tons of H_2

5.8

The Factor-Label Method in Chemical Arithmetic

In all of the problems worked thus far in this chapter, we have been working with *numbers* and with *units,* such as grams and moles. It is important to emphasize that units are handled like numbers when doing chemical arithmetic. To take a very simple example, suppose that we have 2 moles of H_2SO_4. How many grams of H_2SO_4 is this? To do such a calculation, we need to know that 1 mole of H_2SO_4 weighs 98 g. This is expressed mathematically as

$$\frac{98 \text{ g of } H_2SO_4}{1 \text{ mole of } H_2SO_4}$$

In words this says: "There are 98 g of H_2SO_4 per mole of H_2SO_4." The calculation of the number of grams of H_2SO_4 in 2 moles of H_2SO_4 is

$$(2 \text{ moles of } H_2SO_4) \times \frac{98 \text{ g of } H_2SO_4}{1 \text{ mole } H_2SO_4} = 196 \text{ g of } H_2SO_4$$

In this calculation, "moles of H_2SO_4" cancel out. The remaining units are "grams of H_2SO_4." This checks out as our solution because it gives the weight of H_2SO_4 in grams, which is what we wanted.

This approach to problem solving is called the **factor-label** method, or **dimensional analysis**. These are formidable names for a really very simple and important idea. The idea is that units, as well as numbers, must be carried through calculations. If at the end of the calculation, you have the wrong units left over, you know that the calculation was not done correctly.

We will do several calculations, which emphasize the factor-label method. As an example, consider the preparation of phosphorus pentoxide, P_2O_5. It is used to manufacture phosphoric acid, H_3PO_4. Phosphoric acid is then used to make fertilizer, pesticides, and many other products.

The phosphorus used to make phosphorus pentoxide is obtained from *fluorapatite*. The chemical formula of fluorapatite is $Ca_5F(PO_4)_3$. Florida is the main source of this important mineral in the U.S. Phosphorus is obtained from fluorapatite by heating the mineral with sand (SiO_2) and coke (pure carbon) as shown in Figure 5.6. This is done in an electrical arc furnace. Temperatures in this furnace are higher than 1500°C. Carbon monoxide and yellow phosphorus come off as vapors. The waste minerals are drained off as a hot, melted slag. The phosphorus is condensed from the vapor and is used to make P_2O_5 and other chemicals.

Phosphorus burns in air by combining with oxygen to give dense white fumes of phosphorus pentoxide, P_2O_5. The balanced equation is

$$4 P + 5 O_2 \longrightarrow 2 P_2O_5$$

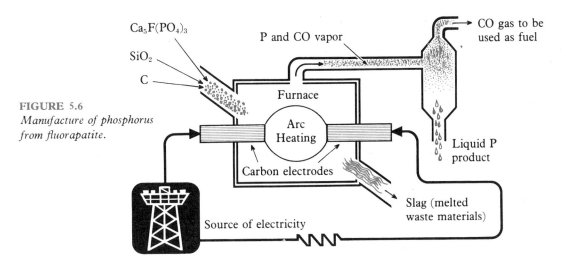

FIGURE 5.6
*Manufacture of phosphorus
from fluorapatite.*

Suppose that a chemist wishes to make 1 g of P_2O_5 by burning phosphorus. How much phosphorus is required? How much oxygen is consumed? To do these calculations the following information is needed:

The atomic weight of P is 31. Therefore, a mole of P weighs 31 g.

The atomic weight of O is 16.

The molecular weight of O_2 is 32. Therefore, a mole of O_2 weighs 32 g.

The molecular weight of P_2O_5 is that of 2 P atoms plus 5 O atoms $(31 + 31 + 16 + 16 + 16 + 16 + 16) = 142$. Therefore, a mole of P_2O_5 weighs 142 g.

Using the factor-label method, the weight of phosphorus required to prepare 1 g of P_2O_5 is calculated as shown in Figure 5.7. Reading across this calculation from left to right shows how units cancel out. First we may cancel out grams of P_2O_5, top and bottom. Next, moles of P_2O_5 cancel, and finally, moles of P. This leaves only grams of P. Since that is what is desired, we know that the calculation is set up properly.

$$(1 \text{ g of } P_2O_5) \times \frac{1 \text{ mole } P_2O_5}{142 \text{ g } P_2O_5} \times \frac{4 \text{ moles P}}{2 \text{ moles } P_2O_5} \times \frac{31 \text{ g P}}{1 \text{ mole P}} = 0.437 \text{ g P}$$

| desired weight | weight of 1 mole in grams | mole ratio | g per mole | weight of P required to make 1 g P_2O_5 |

Carried this far, the calculation gives moles of P_2O_5

Up to here gives moles of P

Up to here gives grams of P

FIGURE 5.7   *The factor-label method is used to show how the weight of P_2O_5 can be converted from units of moles to grams.*

Slag is tapped from a blast furnace several times during a cast and passes in an opposite direction to huge pots loaded on railroad cars for delivery to the slag dump. (Courtesy of Bethlehem Steel Corp.)

The calculation of the weight of oxygen required to make 1 g of P_2O_5 is set up in a similar manner:

$$(1 \text{ g } P_2O_5) \times \frac{1 \text{ mole } P_2O_5}{142 \text{ g } P_2O_5} \times \frac{5 \text{ moles } O_2}{2 \text{ moles } P_2O_5} \times \frac{32 \text{ g } O_2}{1 \text{ mole } O_2} = 0.563 \text{ g } O_2$$

Again, you see how all the top and bottom units cancel out except for the desired units in grams of O_2. This shows that the calculation was set up properly. The results may be checked by comparing the weights of the reactants with the weight of product.

Reactants	Product
0.437 g of P	
0.563 g of O_2	1.000 g of P_2O_5
1.000 g of reactants = 1.000 g of product	

5.9

What is Left Over?

Frequently when chemicals are mixed together, there is an excess of one or the other when they react. With chemical arithmetic it is easy to calculate which of the reactants is in excess, and how much of it will be left over from the chemical reaction.

Suppose that 1.000 g of phosphorus is ignited in a closed bottle of air containing exactly 0.300 g of O_2 as shown in Figure 5.8. We have just seen that a little more oxygen than phosphorus is required when these two elements react. So, there is an excess of phosphorus. All of the oxygen will be used up. How much phosphorus will be burned? How much of it will remain?

The calculation of the weight of phosphorus reacting is calculated from the expression

FIGURE 5.8

Excess phosphorus burning in a container of air uses up all of the oxygen in the container. The chemical reaction is $4P + 5O_2 \rightarrow 2P_2O_5$.

$$(0.300 \text{ g-}O_2) \times \frac{1 \text{ mole } O_2}{32 \text{ g } O_2} \times \frac{4 \text{ moles } P}{5 \text{ moles } O_2} \times \frac{31 \text{ g P}}{1 \text{ mole } P} = 0.233 \text{ g P}$$

This tells us that all of the oxygen in a bottle containing 0.300 g of O_2 will react with 0.233 g of phosphorus. If 1.000 g of burning phosphorus had been placed in the bottle, the quantity of phosphorus left over would be

weight excess P $= 1.000$ g $- 0.233$ g $= 0.767$ g excess P

5.10

Calculations with the Electronic Calculator

The pocket electronic calculator is one of the few things that has decreased in price from the early to mid-1970's. These devices range from very simple models priced less than this book, to sophisticated miniature computers costing several hundreds of dollars. Some people believe that this development will lead to a generation of mathematical illiterates totally helpless in such simple exercises as balancing a checkbook without their "electronic brains" at hand. Their doubts may be justified. Others, who have always had trouble remembering multiplication tables, hail the calculator as a marvelous instrument, which enables their brainpower to be used for tasks more important than routine "number crunching" addition, subtraction, multiplication, and division. The fact remains that practically every student taking a course involving mathematical calculations owns, or borrows, an electronic calculator. It is here to stay. Learning how to use it will enable you to do many more calculations than was previously possible. Keep in mind that the calculator also enables you to make mistakes faster. Overall, however, it decreases the number of mistakes. Assuming fully charged batteries and good connections, the calculator will perform accurately. It will give you the correct answer to 0.300 divided by 32, for example. The same cannot be said with such certainty about a person doing the same calculation by hand.

There are some differences in the operation of individual types of calculators (see Figure 5.9). One has to consult the directions, of course. Typically, you enter a number, then press a button telling the calculator to do a particular operation with a number that is entered next. Pressing $\boxed{+}$ tells the calculator to add, $\boxed{-}$ to subtract, $\boxed{\times}$ to multiply, $\boxed{\div}$ to divide, and $\boxed{=}$ to display the final answer. With this kind of operation, to divide the sum of 2 plus 6 by 4, you would press the buttons on the calculator in the following sequence:

$$2 \boxed{+} 6 \boxed{\div} 4 \boxed{=}$$

The number flashed back by the calculator would be 2, the answer to this problem.

FIGURE 5.9

This scientific pocket calculator assists scientists in arithmetic operations. Special purpose calculators such as this one have functions built into their circuits so they can provide swift and accurate results to complicated problems. (Courtesy of Hewlett-Packard)

A major advantage with the electronic calculator is that, with practice, you can carry out a whole sequence of mathematical operations without having to stop to record any of the numbers except the desired answer. To show how this is done refer back to the calculation of the weight of phosphorus reacting with 0.300 g of oxygen covered in Section 5.9. The sequence is the following:

$$4 \boxed{\div} 5 \boxed{\times} \underbrace{0.300} \boxed{\div} 32 \boxed{\times} \underline{\;\;31\;\;} \boxed{=} \;\; 0.233$$

| mole ratio | moles of O_2 | atomic weight of P | grams of P reacting |

Chapter Summary

We have considered how to calculate the weights of substances produced or consumed in chemical reactions. This is the *arithmetic of chemical reactions*. The official name of such calculations is *stoichiometry*.

Chemical arithmetic is important for many reasons. It tells the engineers responsible for producing industrial chemicals how much of each ingredient to mix to get the desired product. The production of major chemicals such as sulfuric acid, ammonia, sodium hydroxide, and lime is measured in millions of tons each year. Mistakes involving calculations of such large amounts could cost a lot of money. At the other end of the scale, some chemicals are so rare and valuable that the yield of a product from a complicated preparation process may be only a few milligrams. Although just barely enough for one to see, such a quantity may be worth hundreds of dollars. Here, too, accurate calculations are obviously essential.

As we shall see later, the analytical chemist uses chemical arithmetic along with laboratory measurements to determine many things. These include how much iron is in a barge load of iron ore, how much metal is accumulating in the crankcase of a diesel engine (indicating wear on the piston rings), how much sulfur dioxide is in polluted air, or whether a fertilizer sample really contains all of the potassium, phosphorus, and nitrogen it is supposed to have.

To do chemical arithmetic it is first necessary to have the correct chemical reaction. You have to know what is reacting (the reactants) and what is produced (the products). The next step is to balance the chemical equation. The correct molecular and atomic weights of all of the reactants and products must be known. It is necessary to know which reactant or product is being used as the basis for the calculation. For example, we may state that 2.00 g of P_2O_5 is produced, or that 0.500 g of O_2 is used in producing P_2O_5. With this information the weight of a particular reactant or product is calculated using the right proportion or the mole-ratio method.

Chapter Review Questions

The following questions are designed as a self-teaching tool to help you review Chapter 5. The answers to each question follow. See Chapter Review Questions for Chapter 1 for further instructions.

1. The name given to chemical arithmetic done by the chemist is _____.

2. The weight of a molecule of CO_2 is called its _____ and the weight of "one NaCl" (an ionic compound) is called _____ _____.

3. Given 40.1 for the atomic weight of Ca, 31.0 for the atomic weight of phosphorus, and 16 for the atomic weight of O, the formula weight of $Ca_3(PO_4)_2$ is _____.

4. In the laboratory the chemist normally weighs things in units of _____.

5. Exactly 150 g of magnesium chloride, $MgCl_2$, is dissolved in 1 liter of water. It is to be removed by adding sodium hydroxide, NaOH. The magnesium forms a precipitate of magnesium hydroxide, $Mg(OH)_2$, which can be filtered off. What is the balanced chemical equation for this chemical reaction?

6. The atomic weight of Mg is 24.3, that of chlorine is 35.5, that of Na is 23.0, that of O is 16.0, and that of H is 1.0. The formula weights of each of the following are: $MgCl_2$ _____, NaOH _____, $Mg(OH)_2$ _____, NaCl _____.

7. It is desired to calculate the weight of NaOH required to react with the 150 g of $MgCl_2$. From the balanced equation and the formula weights, one can say that 95.3 g of $MgCl_2$ react with _____ g of NaOH.

8. To calculate the number of grams of NaOH that react with 150 g of $MgCl_2$, multiply 150 times _____ and divide by _____ to give _____.

9. To calculate the amount of magnesium hydroxide in the product, first consider that 95.3 g of $MgCl_2$ yield _____ g of $Mg(OH)_2$.

10. To calculate how much $Mg(OH)_2$ is obtained from 150 g of magnesium chloride, multiply _____ times _____ and divide by _____ to get _____ g of $Mg(OH)_2$.

11. Exactly 95.3 g of $MgCl_2$ would yield _____ g of NaCl.

12. The weight of NaCl obtained from 150 g of $MgCl_2$ is obtained by multiplying _____ times _____ and dividing by _____ to yield _____ g of NaCl.

13. The weight of NaOH required to react with 150 g of $MgCl_2$ may also be calculated by the mole-ratio method. The mole ratio of NaOH to $MgCl_2$ is _____.

14. The number of moles of $MgCl_2$ is obtained by dividing _____ by _____ to yield _____ moles of $MgCl_2$.

15. The number of moles of NaOH is obtained by multiplying _____ times _____ to yield _____ moles of NaOH.

16. The weight of NaOH is obtained by multiplying _____ moles of NaOH times _____ g per mole, yielding _____ g of NaOH.

17. To calculate the weight of $Mg(OH)_2$ by the mole-ratio method, consider that the mole ratio of $Mg(OH)_2$ to $MgCl_2$ is _____, there are _____ moles of $MgCl_2$, _____ moles of $Mg(OH)_2$, yielding _____ g of $Mg(OH)_2$.

18. To calculate the weight of NaCl by the mole-ratio method, consider that the ratio of moles of NaCl to $MgCl_2$ is _____, so there are _____ moles of NaCl and _____ g of NaCl.

19. Sulfur trioxide with a chemical formula _____ reacts with water to form a compound called _____ with a chemical formula of _____.

20. A total of 36 g of water will react with SO_3 to produce _____ g of pure H_2SO_4.

21. Going back to the chemical reaction between NaOH and $MgCl_2$, suppose only 86 g of NaOH had been added to the 150 g of $MgCl_2$ dissolved in water. The number of g of $MgCl_2$ reacting with this amount of NaOH is _____ g, leaving an excess of _____ g of $MgCl_2$.

22. In 1975 a total of 61,180,000,000 lb of sulfuric acid was manufactured in the U.S. Production was lower than normal because it was a recession year. This very large number expressed to a power of 10 is $6.118 \times$ _____.

23. Phosphorus, P, is made by heating a mixture of _____, _____, and _____ in (a type of furnace) _____.

24. A mole of a compound contains _____ molecules, or formula units of the compound.

25. This very large number is called _____ number.

26. The number of grams of a compound in a mole is the same number as its _____.

Answers to Chapter Review Questions

1. stoichoimetry
2. molecular weight, its formula weight
3. 310.3
4. grams
5. $MgCl_2 + 2\,NaOH \rightarrow$
   $\qquad Mg(OH)_2\downarrow + 2\,NaCl$
6. 95.3, 40, 58.3, 58.5
7. 80
8. 80, 95.3, 125.9 g of NaOH
9. 58.3
10. 150, 58.3, 95.3, 91.8
11. 117
12. 150, 117, 95.3, 184.2
13. $\dfrac{2 \text{ moles NaOH}}{1 \text{ mole } Mg(OH)_2}$
14. 150, 95.3, 1.57
15. 1.57, 2, 3.18
16. 3.18, 40, 125.9
17. 1, 1.57, 1.57, 91.8
18. 2, 3.18, 184.2
19. SO_3, sulfuric acid, H_2SO_4
20. 196
21. 102.4, 47.6
22. 10^{10}
23. $Ca_5F(PO_4)_3$, coke, sand, an electrical arc furnace
24. 6.02×10^{23}
25. Avogadro's
26. molecular weight or formula weight

Exercises for Chapter 5

1. Small quantities of oxygen may be prepared in the laboratory by heating potassium chlorate, $KClO_3$. Balance the reaction:

$$KClO_3 \longrightarrow KCl + O_2$$

2. Given 39.1 for the atomic weight of K, 35.5 for the atomic weight of Cl, and 16 for the atomic weight of O, calculate the molecular weights of $KClO_3$, KCl, and O_2.

3. How many milligrams (mg) of $KClO_3$ must be broken down to produce 96 mg of O_2?

4. How many grams of CaO may be obtained by heating 42 g of $Ca(OH)_2$? The reaction is $Ca(OH)_2 \rightarrow CaO + H_2O$. (Atomic weights: Ca, 40; O, 16; H, 1.)

5. The atomic weight of sulfur is 32, that of oxygen is 16, and that of hydrogen is 1. When sulfur trioxide, SO_3, is mixed with water, H_2O, sulfuric acid is produced:

$$H_2O + SO_3 \longrightarrow H_2SO_4$$

If 40 g of H_2O are mixed with 12 g of SO_3, which will be left over? How much? How much H_2SO_4 will be produced?

6. HCl gas may be produced in the laboratory by heating NaCl with H_2SO_4. The unbalanced reaction is,

$$H_2SO_4 + NaCl \longrightarrow HCl + Na_2SO_4$$

and all of the atomic weights needed for the calculation have been given in previous questions except for that of Na, which is 23. How many grams of HCl may be obtained by treating 10 g of NaCl with excess H_2SO_4?

7. Carbon tetrachloride, CCl_4, is a chemical which was commonly used for cleaning and fire extinguishers until it was found to be toxic and damaging to the liver. One way of preparing CCl_4 is through the reaction of methane and chlorine by the following (unbalanced) equation:

$$CH_4 + Cl_2 \longrightarrow CCl_4 + HCl$$

How many pounds of methane are required for the preparation of 1 lb of carbon tetrachloride? (The atomic weights needed have been given in previous exercises.)

8. Hydrogen gas is produced when sodium is placed in water. The equation in words is the following:

sodium metal + water $\longrightarrow$ hydrogen gas + sodium hydroxide

Write the chemical reaction, balance it, and calculate how many mg of H_2 are produced from a 100 mg piece of Na.

9. What weight of NaOH is produced in Exercise 8?

10. How many grams of water are produced by the complete burning of 1 g of methane, CH_4? The unbalanced equation is

$$CH_4 + O_2 \longrightarrow CO_2 + H_2O$$

The atomic weight of carbon is 12.

11. The chemical formula of propane gas is C_3H_8. It burns in O_2 producing carbon dioxide and water. What are the chemical formulas of these two compounds? What is the weight of oxygen gas which reacts with 100 g of propane?

12. Suppose that the propane were burned without sufficient oxygen so that the products were carbon *mon*oxide (CO) and water. What weight of oxygen would be consumed?

13. The abbreviation *amu* was used frequently in this chapter. What does it mean?

14. What is the process called *calcination?* What is the chemical reaction for calcination?

15. The chemical compound that appears as a white fog between a beaker of ammonia and one of hydrochloric acid adjacent to each other was discussed in this chapter. A similar compound is formed by the chemical reaction of NH_3 and HF. What is the chemical formula of this compound? What is its electron-dot structure? What is it called?

16. Molecules of HCl are not present dissolved in water. What is produced when HCl gas is dissolved in water?

17. Write out the number, 4.91×10^5 showing all of the zeros.

18. The chemical formula of phosphoric acid is H_3PO_4. It may be prepared by the reaction of water and P_2O_5. What is the balanced chemical equation for this reaction?

19. From the above example, what is the mole ratio of H_2O to H_3PO_4?

Ocean water is a solution of sodium chloride and other salts. This photograph shows Bass Rocks off the coast of Gloucester, Mass. (Courtesy of the Massachusetts Dept. of Commerce and Development)

6

Solutions: Dissolved Chemicals and What They Do

6.1

What are Solutions? Why are They Important?

Draw some water from a water faucet into a glass and examine it. The water probably appears clear. Taste it. It probably tastes all right. Add a teaspoon of sugar and stir the contents of the glass. Notice that the sugar begins to disappear. The water around the sugar starts to appear cloudy or "streaky." With continued stirring the sugar disappears. Examine the glass of water again. It appears as clear as it did directly from the tap. Taste it. Now it has a sweet taste. Some of its properties have been changed by the addition of sugar.

The experiment illustrates several important characteristics of chemicals, how they affect us, and how we use them. Sugar **dissolves** in water. When this happens, a **solution** is formed. Where the sugar molecules were originally in the form of hard, rigid sugar crystals in water, the molecules break away from the crystals and spread throughout the liquid. The sugar is still there, but it is dissolved in the water **solvent**. The dissolved sugar is called the **solute**. It can no longer be seen, but it can be tasted. The water appears unchanged, but it is different. It has a different taste. Some of its other properties have changed too. For example, it now boils at a higher temperature, and freezes at a lower temperature than pure water.

There are many examples of important and useful solutions. Sugar, for example, must be dissolved before it can even be used by the body for food. Candy, which is sugar with added flavoring, dissolves in the mouth to form a solution of sugar with saliva. The coolant in an automobile's cooling system is a solution of antifreeze in water. This solution freezes at a much lower temperature than pure water. This prevents the water from freezing and cracking the engine block. A solution containing the simple sugar gluclose and some other things may be injected directly into the veins of an ill or injured person who cannot take food through the stomach. Chemists use many different kinds of solutions which undergo chemical reactions with other kinds of chemicals. By measuring how much of a solution is required to complete the reaction, the chemist can tell how much of a particular kind of chemical is in a solution.

One of the most important properties of solutions is their ability to allow chemical species to come into close contact so that they can react. For example, if perfectly dry crystals of calcium chloride, $CaCl_2$, were mixed with dry crystals of sodium fluoride, NaF, a chemical reaction would not occur. However, if each is dissolved in separate solutions which are then mixed, a *precipitation* reaction occurs.

$$CaCl_2 + 2\,NaF \longrightarrow CaF_2\downarrow + 2\,NaCl$$

This reaction takes place because in solution the Ca^{2+} ions (from dissolved $CaCl_2$) and the F^- ions (from dissolved NaF) move around and easily come together to form CaF_2. This calcium fluoride does not stay in solution and forms a precipitate. It is **insoluble**.

In other cases solutions enable chemical reactions to occur which result in materials being dissolved. Some of these reactions are very important geologically. An example is provided by limestone made of calcium carbonate, $CaCO_3$. Limestone does not react with CO_2 gas. Nor is it soluble in pure water. However, when water containing dissolved CO_2 contacts limestone a chemical reaction occurs.

$$CaCO_3 + CO_2(\text{dissolved in water}) + H_2O \longrightarrow Ca^{2+} + 2\,HCO_3^-$$

The calcium ion and the bicarbonate ion, HCO_3^-, remain dissolved in water. This dissolves the limestone leaving a cave or hole in the limestone formation. In some regions, such as parts of southern Missouri, this has occurred to such an extent that the whole area is underlain by limestone caves and potholes. These are called *karst* regions.

For living things the most important function of solutions is to carry molecules and ions to and from cells. Our body fluids consist of complex solutions. Digestion is largely a process of breaking down complex, insoluble, food molecules to simple soluble molecules which

SEC. 6.1

What are Solutions? Why are They Important?   143

Underground limestone caverns, formed by the action of dissolved CO_2 on the limestone, are used for office space in Kansas City, Missouri. (Courtesy of the Underground Development Corp.)

may be carried by the blood to the body cells which need them for energy and to make more cell material. On the return trip the blood carries waste products, such as carbon dioxide, which are eliminated from the body.

Solutions are widely used in industry. Many chemical reactions for the manufacture of important industrial chemicals occur in solutions. Brines are solutions found underground and in some special lakes. Brines are solutions containing a lot of dissolved material. Commercially valuable chemicals are recovered from brines. One such chemical is borax, a compound containing boron and oxygen which is used as an antiseptic, in making ceramics, and in some cleaning formulations. Solutions of detergents are used for cleaning. Some dyes are applied as solutions. Ammonia fertilizer may be added to the soil as a solution of NH_3 in water.

Let us reconsider clear tap water. As illustrated in Figure 6.1, it, too, is a solution containing many things. It has some dissolved oxygen and carbon dioxide in it. It almost certainly has some dissolved calcium making it "hard." There may be a small amount of iron present, which

FIGURE 6.1
Tap water is actually a solution, which contains, in small quantities, many things besides H_2O.

causes the water to stain clothing. It contains some chlorine added to kill bacteria. Unfortunately, it may contain some lead and cadmium dissolved from plumbing and the solder used to connect copper plumbing. These are toxic, heavy metals, which are very harmful to health. Many kinds of liquids that we use are solutions.

6.2

Solvents

Water is the solvent for most of the solutions discussed in this chapter. However, it should be mentioned that many other liquids are also used as solvents. Other than water, most solvents are organic (carbon-containing) liquids. Among the more important organic solvents are those shown in Table 6.1. Other solvents will be mentioned in Chapter 10 where organic chemicals are discussed.

TABLE 6.1
Important organic solvents.

Solvent	Solvent Use (may have many other nonsolvent uses)	Approximate U.S. Production, Millions of Pounds per Year
Benzene	Dissolve grease and other organic compounds	11,000
Carbon tetrachloride	Formerly used in dry cleaning, largely discontinued because of toxicity. Used for industrial degreasing.	1000
Perchloroethylene	Best solvent for dry cleaning, also used for degreasing metals and extraction of fats	700
Acetone	Solvent for spinning cellulose acetate fibers and for spreading paints and other protective coatings.	2000

There are many uses for **solvents**. Their role as media for chemical reactions to enable chemical species to actually get together has already been mentioned. In the chemical industry solvents are employed for purification, separation, and physical processing. Solvents are used for cleaners. One important example is the use of organic solvents to dissolve grease and oil from metal parts. The chemicals which make up synthetic fibers, such as rayon, are dissolved in solvents, then forced under very high pressure through small holes in a special dye to make individual filaments of the fibers. One of the most important uses for solvents is as **vehicles** for **coatings**. Paint is of course a typical coating. Other coatings include printing inks, lacquers, and anti-rust formulations.

In order to apply these coatings, it is necessary to dissolve them in a solvent so that they may be spread around on the surface to be coated. The solvent is a **volatile** liquid which **evaporates** to produce a vapor, leaving the coating behind as a thin, protective layer.

Fire and toxicity are major hazards associated with the use of many solvents. Some organic solvents, such as benzene, are even more of a fire hazard than gasoline. Interestingly, carbon tetrachloride does not burn and was even used in fire extinguishers to smother fires. The toxicity hazard of solvents arises from absorption through the skin and inhalation through the lungs. One solvent, dimethyl sulfoxide, is relatively harmless by itself but has the property of carrying solutes through the skin and into the body. Exposure to solvent vapor is limited by occupational health regulations which express a threshold limiting value (TLV). This is a measure of solvent vapor concentration in the atmosphere considered safe for exposure of healthy humans over a normal 40-hour work week schedule.

6.3

Water: The Champion Solvent

The remainder of this chapter deals with water as a solvent. Water is an extremely important compound. All of Chapter 8 deals with it in great detail. Here we summarize just those properties of water which relate directly to its characteristics as a solvent.

At room temperature H_2O is a colorless, tasteless, odorless liquid. It boils at 100°C (212°F) and freezes at 0°C (32°F). Water by itself is a very stable compound. It is very difficult to break up by heating. As explained in Chapter 4, water containing some ions that make it an electrical conductor can be broken up by an electrical current to produce hydrogen gas and oxygen gas.

Water is an excellent solvent for a variety of materials. These include many ionic compounds (acids, bases, salts). Some gases dissolve well in water, particularly those which react with it chemically. Sugars and many other biologically important compounds are soluble in water. Greases and oils generally are not soluble in water but dissolve in organic solvents instead.

Some of water's solvent properties can best be understood by considering the structure and bonding of the water molecule. The water molecule is made up of two hydrogen atoms bonded to an oxygen atom. The three atoms are not in a straight line. Instead, they form an angle of 105° as shown in the following diagram:

Because of this structure and the fact that the oxygen atom attracts the

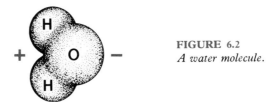

FIGURE 6.2
A water molecule.

negative electrons more strongly than do the hydrogen atoms, the water molecule behaves like a body having opposite electrical charges at either end or pole (see Figure 6.2). Such a body is called a *dipole*. Due to the fact that it has opposite charges at opposite ends, the water dipole may be attracted to either positive or negative electrically charged ions. Recall that NaCl dissolves in water to form positive Na^+ ions and negative Cl^- ions in solution. The positive sodium ions are surrounded by water molecules having their negative ends pointed at the ions, and the chloride ions are surrounded by water molecules with their positive ends pointing at the negative ions as shown in Figures 6.3 and 6.4. This kind of attraction for ions is the reason why water dissolves many ionic compounds and salts that do not dissolve in other liquids. Some noteworthy examples are sodium chloride in the ocean, the waste salts in our urine, calcium bicarbonate, which is very important in lakes and in geological processes, and widely used industrial acids (such as HNO_3, HCl, and H_2SO_4).

In addition to being a polar molecule, the water molecule has another important property which gives it many of its special characteristics. This is the ability to form **hydrogen bonds**. Hydrogen bonds

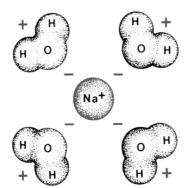

FIGURE 6.3
Na^+ *ion surrounded by polar molecules.*

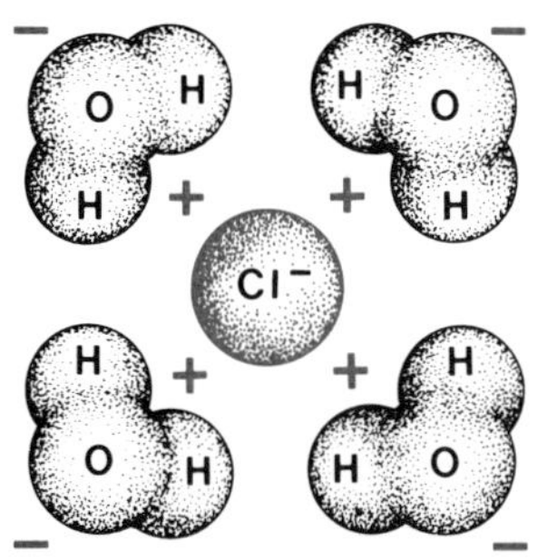

FIGURE 6.4
Cl^- *ions surrounded by polar molecules.*

are bonds that form between the hydrogen in one water molecule and the oxygen in another molecule. This bonding takes place because the oxygen has a partly negative charge and the hydrogen, a partly positive charge. Hydrogen bonds, shown in Figure 6.5 as dashed lines, hold the water molecules together in large groups.

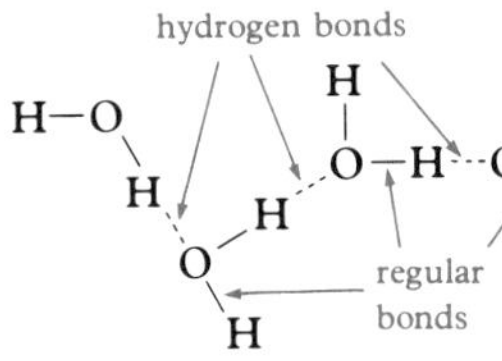

FIGURE 6.5
Hydrogen bonding between water molecules.

Likewise, hydrogen bonds help to hold some solute molecules or ions in solution. When this occurs, hydrogen bonds appear between the water molecules and hydrogen or oxygen atoms on the solute molecule (see Figure 6.6). Hydrogen bonding is one of the main reasons that some proteins can be put in water solution or held suspended in water as extremely small particles called *colloidal particles*.

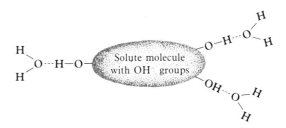

FIGURE 6.6
Hydrogen bonding of a solute molecule in solution.

6.4

What Happens When Something Goes into Solution?

Suppose that really pure water is shaken with air. Air is mostly N_2 and O_2. Small quantities of these gases dissolve in water. However, not very much happens to N_2 and O_2 in water. The molecules of nitrogen and oxygen mingle with the water molecules. If the water is heated, some of the gases are driven out of solution. This may be observed as small bubbles which appear in heated water just before it boils. A fish in water can extract some of the oxygen by "breathing" through its gills. Just 6 or 7 parts of oxygen in a million parts of water is all the oxygen that fish require. Water saturated with air at 25°C contains about 8 parts per million oxygen. Chapter 8 discusses how only a small amount of an oxygen-consuming substance can use up this small quantity of oxygen in water and kill fish.

Commercial granulated white sugar is another example of a solute. Its chemical formula is $C_{12}H_{22}O_{11}$. In its solid form large molecules of sugar group together in crystal patterns. When the sugar dissolves, the molecules leave the crystal shapes and spread out among the water molecules. Even though the sugar crystal has been broken up, the $C_{12}H_{22}O_{11}$ molecule has not changed a great deal.

The situation is much different when hydrogen chloride, HCl, dissolves in water. Hydrogen chloride is a gas. The molecule consists of a hydrogen atom bonded to a chlorine atom with a covalent bond. (Recall that covalent bonds are formed by sharing electrons between atoms.)

$$H : Cl :$$

Water has a huge appetite for hydrogen chloride. One hundred grams of water at 0°C will dissolve 82 g of this gas. When HCl dissolves in water, the solution is not simply hydrogen chloride molecules mixed with water molecules. The water has a strong effect upon the HCl molecule and breaks it into two parts. The 2 electrons in the chemical bond stay with the chlorine. This forms a positively charged hydrogen ion, H^+, and a negatively charged chloride ion, Cl^-.

Water cuts apart a   a hydrogen ion, H^+,   and a chloride ion, Cl^-.
hydrogen chloride
molecule to form

City sewage floating in water. Proper sewage treatment is a major environmental goal. (Courtesy of USDA, Soil Conservation Service; Douglas L. Pope, photographer)

In the water solution the chloride ion is surrounded by the positive ends of the water molecules, which are attracted to the negatively charged Cl^- ion. This kind of attraction of water molecules for a negative ion has already been shown in Figure 6.4. The H^+ ion from the HCl molecule does not remain in water as the bare ion. It attaches to an unshared electron pair on a water molecule. This water molecule with its extra hydrogen ion and extra positive charge now becomes a different ion with a formula of H_3O^+. It is called the **hydronium ion**. Although we will indicate a hydrogen ion in solution as H^+ for simplicity, it is really present as a hydronium ion.

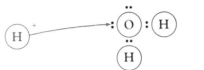

A hydrogen ion, H^+,   bonds to a water   to produce a hydronium
                                 molecule, H_2O,   ion, H_3O^+.

The solution of hydrogen chloride illustrates several important points. It demonstrates a case in which a neutral molecule dissolves and forms electrically charged ions in water. While this happens with many other substances dissolved in water, the hydrogen ion resulting when HCl is dissolved in water is particularly important. It is responsible for solutions which are *acids*. So, rather than say that we have a solution of hydrogen chloride, we call it a **hydrochloric acid** solution.

6.5

Concentration: How Much is in Solution?

In describing a solution it is necessary to know what ingredients are making it up. For example, we have already seen that HCl gas is the solute placed in water to form hydrochloric acid. It is also necessary to know what happens to the material when it dissolves. For example, one needs to know that hydrogen chloride molecules dissolved in water form H^+ ions and Cl^- ions. One of the most important things about a solution, though, is its **concentration**. The concentration of a solution is the *amount* of solute material dissolved in a particular amount of solution, or with a particular amount of solvent. Solution concentration may be expressed in a number of different ways. Solutions used in technical applications, such as for cleaning, are often made up of so many grams of solute per 100 ml (milliliters) of solution added. (The milliliter is a thousandth of a liter. It takes 946 ml, or nearly 1 liter, to make a quart.) A person involved in crop spraying may mix the required solution by adding several pounds of pesticide to a specified number of barrels of water.

The concentrations of water pollutants frequently are given in units of milligrams per liter (mg/l). Most of the chemicals that commonly

Oil that is spilled on water spreads rapidly. Some of it is evaporated; the rest eventually is dispersed in the water and is partially utilized by microorganisms at a very slow rate. Oil from an oil spill can suffocate marine animals, plants, and waterfowl that come in contact with it. (Courtesy of Massachusetts Audubon Society)

pollute water are harmful at such low levels that milligrams per liter of the water is the most convenient way of expressing their concentrations. For example, water containing more than about one-third of a milligram per liter of iron can stain clothing and bathroom fixtures. To get an idea of how little this quantity is, consider that a liter of water weighs 1 million milligrams. (Strictly speaking, that is the weight at 4°C. The difference is not great at other temperatures.) Water containing one-third part per million of iron contains only 1 mg of iron in 3 million milligrams (3 liters) of water. Because 1 liter of water weighs 1 million milligrams, 1 mg of a solute dissolved in a liter is a **part per million**. This is abbreviated **ppm**. The terms, *part per million* and *milligrams per liter* are both frequently used in reference to levels of pollutants in water.

Some pollutants are so poisonous that their concentrations are given in micrograms per liter (μg/liter). Any particle weighing a microgram is so small that it cannot be seen with the naked eye. A microgram is a millionth of a gram. A liter of water weighs 1 billion micrograms. So, 1 microgram per liter is 1 **part per billion (ppb)**. Sometimes it is necessary to think in terms of concentrations which are this low. In the case of pesticides, Endrin, when present in water at a concentration of two-thirds of a microgram per liter, will kill half of the fingerlings (young fish) in the water over a four-day period.

FIGURE 6.7

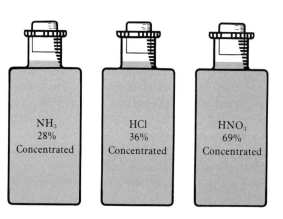

NH$_3$
28%
Concentrated

HCl
36%
Concentrated

HNO$_3$
69%
Concentrated

At the other end of the scale we may consider very high concentrations. These are often given as percent by weight. As indicated in Figure 6.7 the concentrations of commercial acids and bases are often expressed this way. For example, a solution of "concentrated ammonia" purchased for laboratory use is 28% by weight NH_3. This means that out of 100 g of the ammonia solution 28 g are NH_3 and 72 g are water. Commercial concentrated hydrochloric acid is about 36% by weight hydrogen chloride, HCl. Of 100 g of concentrated hydrochloric acid, 36 g are HCl and 64 g are water.

6.6

Molar Concentration

The weight of material in solution often does not tell us everything we need to know about its effect. For example, both a solution of NaCl and sodium iodide (NaI) will remove silver from a solution of silver nitrate ($AgNO_3$) when the solutions are mixed.

$$AgNO_3 + NaCl \longrightarrow NaNO_3(\text{stays in solution}) + AgCl\downarrow(\text{precipitates out})$$
$$AgNO_3 + NaI \longrightarrow NaNO_3 + AgI\downarrow$$

The formula weight of NaCl is 58.5 and the formula weight of NaI is 149.9. Therefore, to remove a given amount of silver requires a sodium iodide solution with a considerably higher concentration on the basis of percentage by weight. In chemical reactions such as these, it is the number of ions or molecules which is really important. It is very convenient to have ways of expressing concentrations where the numbers of molecules and ions in solution bear a definite relationship to the solution concentration. However, the number of molecules in even a milligram of a compound is so high, that it would involve working with huge, unwieldy numbers. Instead, the chemist normally works with *moles*. Recall from Section 5.5 that a mole is the weight in grams of the substance which has the same number as the molecular weight or formula weight. For example, it was mentioned above that the formula weight of NaCl is 58.5. A mole of NaCl weighs 58.5 g.

When moles are used as the quantity of solute in expressing solution concentration, the concentration is called a **molar concentration**. The molar concentration of a solution is the number of moles of solute dissolved in a liter of solution. A 1-molar (M) solution has 1 mole of solute dissolved in 1 liter of solution. To understand this concept better, consider the following:

The molecular weight of HCl is 36.5. A 1 M solution of HCl has 1 mole of HCl (36.5 g) dissolved in 1 liter of solution.

The molecular weight of NH_3 is 17. A 1 M solution of NH_3 has 1 mole of NH_3 (17 g) in 1 liter of solution.

The molecular weight of glucose, $C_6H_{12}O_6$, is 180. A 1 M solution of glucose has 1 mole of glucose (180 g) in 1 liter of solution

Of course, solutions are not always exactly 1 M in concentration. Once it is known how much of a solute is present in a liter of 1 M solution, it is easy to calculate how much is present in a solution of different molar concentration as shown in the following examples:

Example 1. A 2 M solution of HCl has 2 moles of HCl in 1 liter of solution:

$$
\begin{array}{rl}
36.5 & \text{g HCl in 1 liter of 2 } M \text{ solution} \\
\underline{\times\ 2} & \text{multiplied by 2} \\
73.0 & \text{g HCl in 1 liter of 2 } M \text{ solution}
\end{array}
$$

Example 2. A 3 M solution of HCl has 3 moles of HCl in 1 liter of solution:

$$
\begin{array}{rl}
36.5 & \text{g HCl in 1 liter of 1 } M \text{ solution} \\
\underline{\times\ 3} & \text{multiplied by 3} \\
109.5 & \text{g HCl in 1 liter of 3 } M \text{ solution}
\end{array}
$$

Example 3. A 1/2 (or 0.5) M solution of HCl has 0.5 moles of HCl in 1 liter of solution:

$$
\begin{array}{rl}
36.5 & \text{g HCl in 1 liter of 1 } M \text{ solution} \\
\underline{\times\ 0.5} & \text{multiplied by 0.5} \\
18.25 & \text{g HCl in 1 liter of 0.5 } M \text{ solution}
\end{array}
$$

So we see that to get the weight of a compound dissolved in 1 liter of a solution, which is not 1 M in concentration, the molecular weight of the compound is simply multiplied by the concentration of the solution. A 2 M solution has 2 moles in 1 liter, or 2 times the weight of a mole in grams; a 1/2 M solution has 0.5 moles in 1 liter, or 0.5 times the weight of a mole in grams.

Solutions do not always come in 1 liter quantities. The weight of material in solution varies, of course, with the volume of the solution. Let us consider again the HCl solutions of 1 M in concentration. We will find how much HCl is dissolved in various volumes of such solutions.

Example 4. Exactly 2 liters of 1 M HCl has 2 moles of HCl:

$$
\begin{array}{rl}
36.5 & \text{g HCl in 1 liter of 1 } M \text{ solution} \\
\underline{\times\ 2} & \text{multiplied by 2} \\
73.0 & \text{g HCl in 2 liters of 1 } M \text{ solution}
\end{array}
$$

Example 5. Exactly 3 liters of 1 M HCl has 3 moles of HCl:

$$
\begin{array}{rl}
36.5 & \text{g HCl in 1 liter of 1 } M \text{ solution} \\
\underline{\times\ 3} & \text{multiplied by 3} \\
109.5 & \text{g HCl in 3 liters of 1 } M \text{ solution}
\end{array}
$$

Example 6.   Exactly 0.5 liters of 1 M HCl has 0.5 moles of HCl:

$$
\begin{array}{ll}
36.5 & \text{g HCl in 1 liter of 1 } M \text{ solution} \\
\times 0.5 & \text{multiplied by 0.5} \\
\hline
18.25 & \text{g HCl in 0.5 liters of HCl}
\end{array}
$$

Finally, of course, most solutions are neither exactly 1 liter in volume nor 1 M in concentration. We can show by example how to calculate the weight of a compound dissolved in solutions which are neither 1 liter in volume nor 1 M concentration:

Example 7.   A 2 M solution of HCl has 2 moles of HCl in 1 liter of solution. In 2 liters of such a solution there are 2 multiplied by 2, or 4 moles of HCl. The weight of HCl dissolved to make 2 liters of 2 M solution is

$$
\begin{array}{ll}
36.5 & \text{g per mole} \\
\times 4 & \text{moles multiplied by 4} \\
\hline
146.0 & \text{g HCl dissolved in 2 liters of 2 } M \text{ solution}
\end{array}
$$

Example 8.   A 3 M solution of HCl has 3 moles of HCl in 1 liter of solution. In 0.5 liters of such a solution there are 0.5 multiplied by 3, or 1.5 moles of HCl. The weight of HCl dissolved to make 0.5 liters of 3 M solution is

$$
\begin{array}{ll}
36.5 & \text{g per mole} \\
1.5 & \text{moles multiplied by 1.5} \\
\hline
54.75 & \text{g HCl dissolved in 0.5 liters of 3 } M \text{ solution}
\end{array}
$$

Example 9.   A 0.5 M solution of HCl has 0.5 moles of HCl in a liter of solution. In 0.5 liters of such a solution there are 0.5 multiplied by 0.5, or 0.25 moles of HCl. The weight of HCl dissolved to make 0.5 liters of 0.5 M solution is

$$
\begin{array}{ll}
36.5 & \text{g per mole} \\
0.25 & \text{moles multiplied by 0.25} \\
\hline
9.125 & \text{g HCl dissolved in 0.5 liters of 0.5 } M \text{ solution}
\end{array}
$$

To summarize the steps involved in making up a certain quantity of a solution with a specified concentration, suppose you were given the task of making up 2 liters of 0.750 M NaCl. You would go through the following steps:

Step 1.   Calculate the weight of a mole of NaCl.

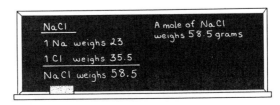

Step 2.   Calculate the number of moles of NaCl required.

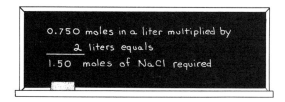

0.750 moles in a liter multiplied by
2 liters equals
1.50 moles of NaCl required

Step 3.   Calculate the weight of NaCl required.

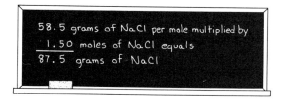

58.5 grams of NaCl per mole multiplied by
1.50 moles of NaCl equals
87.5 grams of NaCl

Step 4.   Weigh out the amount of NaCl required.

Step 5.   Add the NaCl to a container which has a mark at exactly 2 liters. This special container is a 2-liter **volumetric flask**.

Step 6. Add water and "swirl" to dissolve the NaCl. Keep adding water and shaking until the volume of the solution is exactly 2 liters.

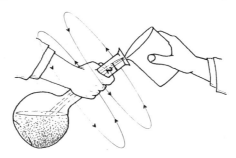

Step 7. The product is 2 liters of 0.750 *M* NaCl. It contains 1.50 moles, or 87.5 g of NaCl.

Often it is necessary to make a less concentrated solution from a more concentrated solution. This process is called **dilution**. Although a *dilute* solution may be what is needed, it is often more convenient to store more concentrated solutions in order to save shelf space. Laboratory acid solutions, such as those of hydrochloric acid, sulfuric acid, and phosphoric acid are almost always purchased as very concentrated solutions. These are more economical because there is more of the active ingredient in a bottle.

For example, the concentration of commerical concentrated hydrochloric acid is 12 *M*. A laboratory technician needs 1 liter of 1 *M* hydrochloric acid. How much of the concentrated acid is required? The key to this problem is to realize that when a volume of the concentrated acid is diluted with water, the total amount of acid, HCl, in the solution remains the same. The problem can then be solved as follows:

Step 1. Recognize that 1 liter of 1 *M* hydrochloric acid to be prepared contains 1 mole of HCl.

Step 2. Find the volume of concentrated hydrochloric acid containing 1 mole of HCl to be measured out: Exactly 1 liter of the 12 *M* hydrochloric acid contains 12 moles of HCl. Exactly 1 mole of HCl would be contained in 1/12 of a liter:

1/12 liter multiplied by 12 moles per liter = 1 mole HCl

Step 3. Measure out 1/12 of a liter of concentrated hydrochloric acid and dilute it with water to 1 liter to get the desired solution. Expressed in decimals, 1/12 of a liter is 0.083 liters. Volumes that small are generally measured as milliliters, each of which is 1/1000 of a liter. The required volume is 83 ml.

What if 2 liters of 1.5 M HCl were to be prepared from 12 M HCl? What volume of 12 M HCl would have to be diluted to 2 liters? The steps in solving this problem are the following:

Step 1. Consider how many moles of HCl are in 2 liters of 1.5 M HCl.

2 liters of HCl × 1.5 moles per liter = 3 moles of HCl

Step 2. Find the volume of 12 M HCl in the desired 3 moles of HCl.

$$\frac{3 \text{ moles of HCl}}{12 \text{ moles of HCl per liter}} = 0.25 \text{ liters of } 12 \text{ } M \text{ HCl}$$

Step 3. Express this in milliliters of HCl.

0.25 liters of HCl × 1000 mole per liter = 250 ml of HCl

Step 4. Dilute 250 ml of 12 M HCl to 2 liters to get the desired solution.

The same general approach used in solving these dilution problems may be used when concentrations are expressed in units other than molar concentration. As will be discussed in Chapter 12, concentrations of metals dissolved in water are frequently measured by a technique called atomic absorption spectroscopy. To measure the concentration of metal in an unknown solution, it is necessary to have a standard solution of known concentration. These are sold as solutions containing 1000 mg of the desired metal dissolved in 1 liter of standard solution. Suppose one had a standard solution of $CaCl_2$ containing 1000 mg of Ca^{2+} per liter of solution.

An atomic absorption spectrophotometer is used for the analysis of metals. (Courtesy of Instrumentation Laboratory, Inc., Analytical Instrument Division)

How would you dilute this solution to make 5 liters of a solution containing 20 mg of calcium per liter?

Step 1. Consider how many milligrams of calcium are in the desired 5 liters of solution containing 20 mg of calcium per liter.

$$5 \text{ liters} \times 20 \text{ mg of calcium per liter} = 100 \text{ mg of calcium}$$

Step 2. Find how much stock solution containing 1000 mg of calcium per liter contains 100 mg of calcium.

$$\frac{100 \text{ mg of calcium}}{1000 \text{ mg per liter}} = 0.100 \text{ liters}$$

Step 3. Dilute 0.100 liters (100 ml) of the stock calcium solution to 5 liters to obtain the desired solution containing 20 mg of calcium per liter.

6.7

Normal Concentrations

The concentrations of solutions used for chemical analysis are often expressed in terms of **normality** (N). Normality expresses the concentration of a particular reacting species, such as H^+ ion or OH^- ion. To understand this idea, first consider the chemical reactions of hydrochloric acid and sulfuric acid with sodium hydroxide, NaOH. Suppose that there is 1 liter of each acid and that the concentration of each acid is 1 M. The reaction of HCl and NaOH is

$$\text{HCl} \quad + \quad \text{NaOH} \quad \longrightarrow \quad \text{NaCl} + \text{H}_2\text{O}$$

One liter of 1 M hydrochloric acid contains 1 mole of HCl which reacts with exactly 1 mole of sodium hydroxide.

The reaction of sulfuric acid and NaOH is

$$\text{H}_2\text{SO}_4 \quad + \quad 2 \text{ NaOH} \quad \longrightarrow \quad \text{Na}_2\text{SO}_4 + 2 \text{ H}_2\text{O}$$

One liter of 1 M sulfuric acid contains 1 mole of H_2SO_4, but because of the *two* hydrogens it reacts with exactly *two* moles of sodium hydroxide.

From these examples we observe that when molar concentrations are used, a sulfuric acid solution is twice as powerful as a hydrochloric acid solution with the same concentration. This is because 1 mole of H_2SO_4 contains *two* moles of hydrogen ion. A mole of HCl contains only *one* mole of hydrogen ion.

It is convenient to have in the laboratory concentrations of acid solutions expressed in terms of the amount of base the acid will react with. When such is the case it is not necessary to consider whether the acid is hydrochloric acid or sulfuric acid. This can be done by using **normal concentrations** rather than molar concentrations. Normality is defined in terms of **equivalents** per liter, rather than moles per liter (mole/liter). What has to be taken into consideration is the type of reaction, such as an acid-base reaction.

Consider 1 mole of hydrogen chloride, HCl, dissolved in 1 liter of solution to make a 1 M solution. One H^+ ion is obtained from each HCl. In this case 1 equivalent is the same as 1 mole. A 1 M solution of hydrochloric acid is also a 1 normal (N) solution of HCl.

Next consider 1 mole of H_2SO_4 dissolved in 1 liter of solution to make 1 M sulfuric acid. *Two* H^+ ions are obtained from each HCl. In this case there are 2 equivalents per mole. A 1 M solution of sulfuric acid containing 1 mole of H_2SO_4 per liter is a 2 N solution containing 2 equivalents per liter.

Suppose that it is desired to have 1 liter each of solutions of HCl and H_2SO_4, both 1 N in concentration. In the case of HCl it is easy to compute because a 1 N solution is also 1 M. In the case of sulfuric acid, however, it is a little more complicated as shown by the following:

1 liter of 1 M sulfuric acid contains 1 mole of H_2SO_4 in 1 liter of solution	1 liter of 1 M sulfuric acid contains 2 equivalents of H_2SO_4 in 1 liter of solution, so it is 2 N.
1 liter of 0.5 M sulfuric acid contains 0.5 moles of H_2SO_4 in 1 liter of solution	1 liter of 0.5 M sulfuric acid contains 1 equivalent of H_2SO_4, so it is 1 N.

The desired 1 N solution of sulfuric acid is 0.5 M. The normality of a sulfuric acid solution is *twice* the molarity.

Normality can also apply to bases. Consider 1 M solutions of NaOH and $Ca(OH)_2$ involved in reactions with HCl.

$$NaOH \quad + \quad HCl \quad \longrightarrow \quad NaCl + H_2O$$

One liter of 1 M sodium hydroxide contains 1 mole of NaOH which reacts with

exactly 1 mole of HCl

$$Ca(OH)_2 \quad + \quad 2\,HCl \quad \longrightarrow \quad CaCl_2 + 2\,H_2O$$

One liter of 1 M calcium hydroxide contains 1 mole of $Ca(OH)_2$, but, because of the *two* hydroxides (OH^-), it reacts with

exactly *two* moles of HCl.

A 1 M solution of NaOH is also 1 N. However, a 1 M solution of $Ca(OH)_2$ is 2 N. A 1 N solution of $Ca(OH)_2$ is only 0.5 M.

6.8

Solubility

Suppose that you were doing a chemical analysis of a water sample for calcium and needed a solution containing calcium whose concentration was known. You might consider getting some pure calcium carbonate from the shelf, weighing out a mole of it, and dissolving it in a liter of water to get a 1 M solution of calcium carbonate. What would happen when the water was added to the calcium carbonate in the volumetric flask? Not much of anything would happen. You would not observe any calcium carbonate dissolving. Its **solubility** is very low. Only about 5 mg (just a small white "speck") of calcium carbonate will dissolve in a liter of water.

This illustrates an important point that people working in laboratories should keep in mind. When preparing a solution it is a good idea to look up the solubility of the compound being dissolved. Make sure that the solubility is high enough to give the concentration which is desired. Many futile hours of shaking of bottles have been spent trying to get something to dissolve whose solubility is just too low to make the desired solution.

A solution which has dissolved as much of a solute as possible is said to be **saturated** with regard to that solute. The concentration of the substance in the saturated solution is the solubility. Solubilities of different substances in water vary enormously. At the low end of the scale, even glass will dissolve a little bit in water. The concentration of the "glass" solution is very, very low. It can cause difficulties in the analysis of silicon (one of the elements in glass). The dissolved glass increases silicon in the water and adds error to the analysis. Antifreeze (an organic compound called ethylene glycol) is an example of a substance which is completely soluble in water. One could pour a cup of water into a barrel and keep adding antifreeze without ever getting a saturated solution of antifreeze in water even if the barrel filled to the point of overflowing.

On a hot summer day, lacking ice or a refrigerator, some people have been driven by thirst to open a bottle of warm beer. As the cap comes off, there is a loud pop; and the contents pour forth in a geyser

of foam. The person opening the warm bottle of beer has just encountered a supersaturated solution. The beer contains carbon dioxide, CO_2, which gives it a characteristic "tingle." The carbon dioxide is added to the cold beverage under pressure. When the beer becomes warm and the pressure is released by removing the bottle cap, the solution suddenly finds that it contains more CO_2 than it can tolerate. It is a supersaturated solution, and the escaping dissolved gas causes the bubbles of foam to spew from the bottle.

Solubility is affected by several factors. The preceding example has shown two of the most important effects on gas solubility, temperature and pressure. The solubilities of gases such as CO_2 decrease with increasing temperature. A gas is much less soluble in water just about hot enough to boil than it is in water just about cold enough to freeze. But once the solution freezes, the gas is not at all soluble in ice. This is sometimes illustrated vividly with soda beverages, which also contain carbon dioxide dissolved under pressure. A bottle of soda placed in the refrigerator freezer to cool quickly and then forgotten may burst from the pressure of the carbon dioxide coming out of solution as the liquid freezes.

The solubilities of most solids increase with rising temperature, although not in all cases. Sugar, for example, is much more soluble and easier to dissolve in a cup of hot tea than in a cold glass of fruit drink.

One of the most important things affecting solubility is a chemical reaction in solution. For example, CO_2 is really not very soluble in water. But, if the water already contains some NaOH (sodium hydroxide), the carbon dioxide is very soluble because of a chemical reaction between NaOH and CO_2 to form highly soluble sodium bicarbonate, $NaHCO_3$

$$NaOH + CO_2 \text{ (not very soluble)} \longrightarrow NaHCO_3 \text{ (very soluble)}$$

6.9

Solutions that Keep Water from Freezing, or Boiling

One of the most practical uses of solutions depends upon the effect which materials dissolved in water have upon the temperature at which the water, or the solution, freezes. Solutions freeze at lower temperatures than does water. Most automobiles are water-cooled, that is, water circulates through the engine picking up heat and then goes to a radiator where the excess heat is given off. If pure water were left in an engine at freezing temperatures, it would of course freeze. When water freezes, it expands so that the ice which is formed has a larger volume than the liquid from which it came. This increase in volume produces enormous forces which can crack the stoutest engine block as if it were an egg shell.

To keep water from freezing in the engine cooling system, we make use of antifreeze which is mixed with water. The chemical name of antifreeze is ethylene glycol, and it has the chemical formula, $C_2H_6O_2$.

A solution containing 40% by weight of ethylene glycol and 60% by weight of water freezes at 8° below zero Fahrenheit, or −22.2°C. (Recall that water freezes at 32°F and 0°C. It boils at 212°F and 100°C.) A solution containing exactly half ethylene glycol and half water by weight freezes at 29° below zero Fahrenheit.

Mixing permanent antifreeze, or other materials which do not boil easily, with water raises the boiling temperature. Because of the higher boiling temperature, a solution of antifreeze in water makes a good "summer coolant."

6.10

"Almost Solutions": Colloids

If one pours some fine sand into a bottle of water and swirls it around vigorously, the sand will "float" around in the water for a very brief time, then rapidly settle to the bottom. Particles like sand, which can be held briefly in water and then settle out readily are called **suspensions**. We have already seen that molecules or ions which dissolve in water and mingle individually with the water molecules make up *solutions*. Between these two extremes are particles which are much smaller than any we can see with the naked eye, but much larger than individual molecules. These are **colloidal particles**, and they are a characteristic of some important life processes, of many formations in nature, and of a large number of products in industry. Colloidal particles in water form **colloidal suspensions**. Unlike sand stirred in a jar, or soil granules carried by a vigorously running stream, the colloidal particles do not settle out of colloidal suspension by gravity alone.

Individual cells of bacteria are colloidal particles and can form colloidal suspensions in water. Many of the green algae in water are present as colloidal suspensions of individual cells of the algae. Milk,

Uncontrolled water carries enormous amounts of soils with it. Watersheds are designed to prevent erosion of land by surface water and to channel its flow into open ditches. (Courtesy of USDA, Soil Conservation Service; Clark A. Eacher, photographer)

mayonnaise and paint are colloidal suspensions. Colloids are used in making rubber, glue, plastics, and grease. The formation of a colloidal suspension of butter fat in milk is the process by which milk is *homogenized*, so that the cream does not rise to the top. The processes by which colloidal particles of minerals come together and settle out of water are crucial in the formation of mineral deposits. The colloidal suspension of bacteria which devour sewage at a sewage treatment plant must eventually be brought out of colloidal suspension to obtain purified water. Crude oil frequently comes out of the ground as a colloidal suspension in water. The colloidal particles of crude oil must be separated from the water before the crude oil can be refined. Colloids are so important and so common that this whole book could be filled with examples like those just mentioned.

What keeps colloidal particles suspended throughout a mass of water? Most of these particles have an electrical charge. Particles with the same electrical charge repel each other as shown in Figure 6.8. For example, "muddy" water is often the result of the colloidal clay particles suspended in it. These clay particles have a negative charge, which prevents them from coming together and settling from the suspension.

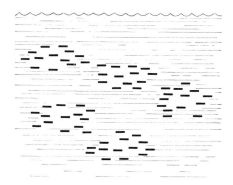

FIGURE 6.8
Some colloidal particles stay suspended in water because of their electrical charges, which keep them apart.

Colloidal particles which are kept in water suspension because of their electrical charges may be caused to clump together and settle. This is done by adding charged ions, such as Na^+ and Cl^- ions from sodium chloride. These charged ions tend to neutralize the electrical charges on the colloidal particles and allow them to come together. This process is called **coagulation**.

Electrical charge is not the only thing which will keep colloidal particles in suspension in water. Some colloids stay in water because they have a strong chemical attraction for the water. Good examples are proteins, such as the gelatin used to make Jell-O. The colloidal protein particles form chemical bonds with the water. These bonds can be strong enough to keep the particles apart. Another type of colloidal suspension is formed by soap. Soap forms "water-loving" colloidal particles, each made up of a number of soap ions. The soap ion consists of a long chain made up of an "oily" hydrocarbon chain, attached at one end to a chemical group having an electrical charge.

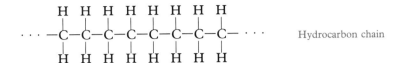

Hydrocarbon chain

The "oil-like" chains of several ions cluster together inside the colloidal particle. This is because "oil and water do not mix," so this inner group of ions avoids the water. The charged ends of the ions are attracted to the water (see Figure 6.9). Recall from Section 6.3 that water is attracted to charged groups because water is a dipole and because of hydrogen bonding.

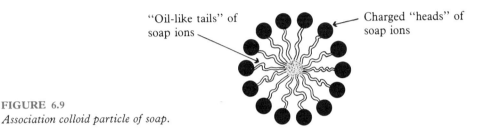

"Oil-like tails" of soap ions

Charged "heads" of soap ions

FIGURE 6.9
Association colloid particle of soap.

6.11

Nature's Pump: Osmosis

Blood consists chiefly of red blood cells suspended in a fairly concentrated solution. The dissolved material making up the solution is mostly sodium chloride at around 0.15 molar concentration. The red blood cells also contain a solution much like the **plasma** in which they float. If one were to take some blood, separate out the red cells by "spinning" in a centrifuge (a device which spins test tubes much like a ball on a string and causes denser material to settle out), and then place the cells in pure

Laboratory centrifuge. This device is used to make a precipitate settle from suspension. (Courtesy of Fisher Scientific Co., Pittsburg, Pa.)

water, a strange effect would be observed. When viewed under a microscope, the cells would be seen to swell and finally burst. This is an example of osmosis. Water can go through the membrane which holds the red blood cell together. When the cell is placed in pure water, the water tends to pass through the membrane to the more concentrated solution inside the cell. One way of looking at it is to say that the solution inside the cell has relatively less water, so that water from the outside has a tendency to enter the cell. Finally so much water gets in that it breaks the cell apart (Figure 6.10). However, when a blood cell is placed in a very concentrated solution of sodium chloride, the opposite effect is observed. Water passes from inside the cell to the more concentrated solution outside and the cell shrivels up (Figure 6.11).

Many biological membranes, such as the "wall" surrounding a red blood cell, allow material to go through. Water, dissolved molecules (such as sugar), and ions (such as the Na^+ and Cl^- in dissolved sodium chloride) sometimes pass through such membranes. These materials tend to go from regions of higher concentrations to regions of lower concentrations. Consider the CO_2 produced as a waste product by processes inside a cell. This CO_2 tends to migrate from the relatively concentrated solution of CO_2 in the cell to a relatively more dilute solution of CO_2 in the blood outside the cell. Oxygen in the blood tends

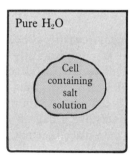 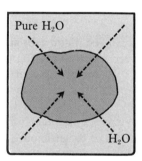 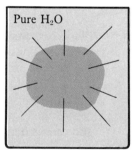

FIGURE 6.10 *Osmosis causes water from a container of pure water to be absorbed by a red blood cell, increasing the volume in the cell and causing it to burst.*

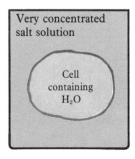 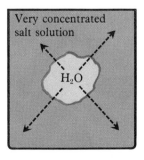 

FIGURE 6.11 *Osmosis causes water inside a red blood cell to pass out into a concentrated salt solution, causing the cell to shrivel.*

to go the other way, and is used up by life processes in the cell. Water in the ground tends to move through cell membranes in root cells and finally to plant leaves, where it evaporates to form water vapor in the atmosphere. Osmosis is a major part of the driving force behind these processes.

The concentration of a solution relative to another solution determines which solution water will have a tendency to enter. This can be particularly important in blood. Solutions injected into the veins for feeding, or to replace body fluids lost due to illness must be prepared so that water will neither move in or out of the cells by osmosis. Such a solution in which there is no tendency for osmosis to occur is called an **isotonic** solution. It is also sometimes referred to as a physiological solution. Its use prevents damage to blood cells by either shrinking or swelling.

Osmosis may result in the buildup of a very high pressure called **osmotic pressure**. It is this pressure which can get so high in a red blood cell suspended in water that the cell is caused to burst. Osmotic pressure can be as high as several times the pressure of the atmosphere around us.

Pure water tends to move by osmosis through a membrane to a more "contaminated" solution. Application of sufficient opposite pressure can "squeeze" water out of a contaminated solution, producing pure water. This process is called **reverse osmosis**. It is commonly used to purify small quantities of water.

Chapter Summary

When placed in some liquids, some substances seem to disappear. Their molecules or ions become intermixed with the molecules of liquid to form a *solution*. The substance is said to *dissolve*. The liquid is called a *solvent*. The substance which dissolves is called the *solute*.

There are many kinds of solutes and many solvents. *Organic solvents* are useful for dissolving many kinds of things. "Like dissolves like," so organic solvents are especially good for organic solutes. These solvents are used to remove grease, as *vehicles* for coatings such as paints, for dry cleaning, as solvents for spinning organic fibers and many other applications. Typical organic solvents include benzene, carbon tetrachloride, perchloroethylene, and acetone.

In Chapter 6 we have dealt primarily with solutions in which water is the solvent. Water is a "champion solvent" in that it dissolves many things much better than most other solvents. The solvent action of water is related to its chemical structure. For one thing, the water molecule is *polar*, with a negative end and a positive end. This makes it an especially good solvent for ionic compounds. Water molecules surround positive ions so that the negative ends of the water molecule cluster around the cation. Similarly, the positive ends of the water molecule surround anions. Another special quality of water which helps make it such a good solvent is its ability to form *hydrogen bonds.* Water molecules form hydrogen bonds with each other. They also form hydrogen bonds with some solute molecules in solution.

When a solute goes into solution in water, many different things can happen to it. Unreactive molecules, such as N_2 or O_2 remain simply as these molecules in solution. They do not dissolve very well in water. The ions in ionic compounds, such as sodium chloride, split apart from their rigid arrangement in the crystal and become dispersed about randomly in the water. (It should be mentioned that molecules of liquids and the species dissolved in liquids are in continual motion.) Some covalent compounds split up to form ions in water. A good example is hydrogen chloride, which exists in the pure form as molecules of HCl. When it dissolves in water, it is split into H^+ ion and Cl^- ion. This is responsible for the extremely high solubility of HCl in water. Such a solution is called *hydrochloric acid.* Chemical reaction in water can also increase tremendously the solubility of a compound. Carbon dioxide by itself is not very soluble in water. But, if the water contains sodium hydroxide, the solubility of CO_2 is increased by the reaction

$$CO_2 + NaOH \longrightarrow NaHCO_3$$

Hydrogen ion, H^+, is a very important species in water because it makes the water *acidic.* Although we refer to H^+ in solution, it is not there as the bare ion. Instead it is present as *hydronium ion,* H_3O^+. *Bases* in water have the hydroxide ion, OH^-.

The amount of solute in solution is the solution *concentration.* The maximum concentration of solute in solution is the *solubility.* There are many ways of expressing concentration. Included are percent by weight, milligrams per liter, molarity, and normality.

The idea of molar concentrations, or *molarity* is extremely important in chemistry. The molarity of a solution is the number of moles of solute per liter of *solution.* To calculate molarity it is necessary to

Mineral deposits, such as these ferromanganese nodules at the Pacific Ocean floor, cover the very deep ocean bottoms. These deposits were originally formed from dissolved metals in the ocean, which were taken out of solution probably by bacterial action. (Courtesy of Lamont-Geophysical Observatory)

know the weight of solute in a particular volume of solution. The number of moles of solute is calculated by dividing the number of grams of solute by the molecular weight, or formula weight. The number of moles of solute is then divided by the number of liters of solution to give the molar concentration.

Normality is a way of expressing solution concentrations so that solutions with the same normality have the same concentration of a particular species which may occur in a number of different chemical compounds. Therefore, 1 N solutions of HCl, H_2SO_4, and H_3PO_4 all have different molar concentrations, but have the same concentrations of ionizable hydrogen.

Colloids are very small particles suspended in a solvent. They are partly like true solutions and partly like suspensions.

Other important things considered in this chapter are the effects of solutes on *freezing* and *boiling temperatures,* and the important phenomenon of *osmosis.*

Chapter Review Questions

The following questions are designed as a self-teaching tool to help you review Chapter 6. The answers to each question follow. See Chapter Review Questions for Chapter 1 for further instructions.

1. A solid which disappears when stirred with water is said to _____. It forms a _____.

2. The substance which dissolves is called the _____, and the liquid in which it dissolves is the _____.

3. A substance which does not dissolve appreciably in a solvent is said to be _____.

4. Four typical organic solvents are _____, _____, _____, and _____.

5. Two things about water molecules which make water an excellent solvent for many substances are _____ and _____ _____.

6. When O_2 dissolves in water the oxygen molecules are in solution as _____; when NaCl dissolves, the species formed in solution are _____; and when HCl gas dissolves, it forms _____.

7. The actual form of H^+ in water solution is as _____.

8. The amount of solute in a particular amount of solution or of solvent is the solution_____.

9. Concentrations of pollutants are often expressed as parts per _____, abbreviated _____, or at even lower concentrations as _____ abbreviated _____.

10. The molar concentration of a solution is the number of _____ of solute per _____ of _____.

11. The molecular weight of NH_3 is _____, so a mole of ammonia weighs _____ (give units of weight).

12. The molar concentration of a solution prepared by dissolving 8.5 g of NH_3 gas in 2 liters of solution is _____ M.

13. The volume of 2 M HCl which must be diluted with water to make 5 liters of 1.5 M HCl is _____ liters.

14. A solution containing 1 equivalent of sulfuric acid per liter is said to be 1 _____.

15. A 0.25 M solution of $Ca(OH)_2$ is _____ N, and a 0.80 N solution of H_2SO_4 is _____ M.

16. The maximum amount of solute which dissolves in a particular amount of solution is called its _____.

17. A solution which has the maximum amount of solute which it can hold at equilibrium is said to be _____.

18. If the amount of solute in solution is higher than the saturation concentration, the solution is _____.

19. Solutes _____ the freezing temperature of water.

20. A solution of antifreeze in water boils at a _____ temperature than pure water.

21. Extremely small particles suspended uniformly in water form a _____ suspension.

22. Colloidal particles are stabilized in water by electrical _____ or attraction to _____.

23. Two foods which are colloidal suspensions are _____ and _____.

24. Water and solutes pass through certain membranes by a special process called _____.

25. Because of osmosis, red blood cells placed in pure water _____, and those placed in a solution containing a lot more salt than blood plasma contains will _____.

Answers to Chapter Review Questions

1. dissolve, solution
2. solute, solvent
3. insoluble
4. benzene, carbon tetrachloride, perchloroethylene, acetone
5. hydrogen bonding, the fact that the water molecules are dipoles
6. O_2 molecules, Na^+ and Cl^- ions, H^+ and Cl^- ions
7. H_3O^+ called hydronium ion
8. concentration
9. million, ppm, parts per billion, ppb
10. moles, liter, solution
11. 17, 17 g
12. 0.25
13. 3.75
14. normal
15. 0.50, 0.40
16. solubility
17. saturated
18. supersaturated
19. lower
20. higher
21. colloidal
22. charge, water
23. milk, mayonnaise
24. osmosis
25. swell, shrink

Exercises for Chapter 6

1. HCl and H_2 are both gases. What would you guess to be a big difference between them insofar as what happens when they dissolve?

2. What is meant by concentration in percent by *weight*?

3. What is meant by concentration in units of milligrams per liter? When is it desirable to express concentrations in that way?

4. What is a "mole" in chemistry?

5. What is meant by the molar concentration of a solution?

6. The molecular weight of ammonia, NH_3, is 17. How many grams of ammonia are in 1 liter of 2 M solution?

7. How many grams of ammonia are in 3 liters of 1 M solution?

8. How many grams of ammonia are in 3 liters of 2 M solution?

9. It is desired to prepare 2 liters of 1.2 M NaCl. How many liters of 2 M NaCl would be required for 2 liters of 1.2 M NaCl?

10. How much of a stock solution of standard sodium containing 1000 mg of Na^+ per liter should be taken to prepare 5 liters of a standard sodium solution containing 10 mg of sodium per liter?

11. What is meant by a supersaturated solution?

12. Although syrup can get very thick in the winter, why does it not ever freeze?

13. Recall the discussion of osmosis. What might happen to a sea fish suddenly placed in fresh water?

14. What kinds of things keep colloidal particles from coming together?

15. Describe the general process by which a solid such as sugar goes into solution. Where do the sugar molecules go as the sugar crystals disappear?

16. Fish live well in water by "breathing" water which is only 6–7 ppm oxygen by weight. From what you know about the composition of air, how many parts per million of oxygen do we breathe in air? You may not be able to give an exact answer to this question until the gas laws have been studied in Chapter 9, but a rough estimate should be possible.

17. Exactly 1.50 liters of 2.00 M HCl was added to a 2.00 liter volumetric flask, and the volume brought to 2.00 liters with water. What was the molar concentration of HCl in the resulting solution?

18. Exactly 1.00 liter of 1.00 M HCl was added to a 2.00 liter volumetric flask. A total of 0.25 moles of solid NaOH was added. After the chemical reaction between the HCl and the NaOH was complete, water was added to bring the total volume to 2.00 liters. What chemical reaction occurred when the HCl was added? How many moles of HCl were left after this reaction occurred? What was the molar concentration of HCl after the solution was diluted to 2.00 liters?

19. A total of 2.50 liters of 0.100 M NaCl was mixed with 3.00 liters 0.0800 M NaCl. Assume that the volumes of solutions add together to give 5.50 liters (volumes may not be additive with more concentrated solutions). What was the molar concentration of NaCl in the final solution?

The hot lavas emitted by an erupting volcano change in grade from basic into intermediate and end with acidic. The lavas are classified into these types according to the amounts of silica they contain: acid lavas have 70% or more silica; intermediate, 60–65%; and basic, less than 50%. (Courtesy of the Naval Photographic Center)

7

Acids, Bases, Salts, and Ions

7.1

What are Acids, Bases, Salts, and Ions?

Almost all inorganic compounds and many organic compounds can be classified as acids, bases, or salts. Such substances have been mentioned to some extent in the preceding chapters. In Chapter 7 we go into greater detail.

Among acids, bases, and salts are some of the chemicals that are essential to life processes, agriculture, and industry. Of the top five chemicals produced each year, one, sulfuric acid, is an acid; two are bases, ammonia and sodium hydroxide; and two are salts, potassium chloride and sodium chloride. You may recall that potassium chloride is the major source of essential potassium fertilizer and sodium carbonate is used for water purification.

The salt content and the acid-base balance of blood must stay within very narrow limits to keep a person healthy, or even alive. Soil with too much acid or too much base will not support good crop growth. Too much salt in irrigation water may prevent crops from growing.

This is a major problem for farmers in California's Imperial Valley and other parts of the world.

From the above discussion, it is seen that acids, bases, and salts are very important compounds to human health and modern welfare. This chapter discusses their preparation, properties, and naming.

Recall that an ion is an atom or group of atoms having an electrical charge. In discussing acids and bases two very important ions are involved. One of these is the **hydrogen ion**, H^+. It is always produced by **acids**. The other is the **hydroxide ion**, OH^-. It is always produced by **bases**. These two ions react together,

$$H^+ + OH^- \longrightarrow H_2O$$

to produce water. This is called a **neutralization reaction**. It is one of the most important of all chemical reactions.

An acid is a substance which produces hydrogen ions. For example, HCl in water is entirely in the form of H^+ ions and Cl^- ions. These two ions in water form hydrochloric acid. Acetic acid, which is present in vinegar, also produces hydrogen ions in water.

acetic acid
CH_3CO_2H

acetate ion

Acetic acid demonstrates two important characteristics of acids. First, many acids contain H which is not released by the acid molecule to form H^+. Of the 4 hydrogens in CH_3CO_2H, only the one bonded to oxygen is **ionizable** to form H^+. The second important point about acetic acid has to do with how much of it is ionized to form H^+ and acetate ion, $CH_3CO_2^-$. Most of the acetic acid remains as molecules of CH_3CO_2H in solution. In a 1 *M* (molar) solution of acetic acid only about 0.5% of the acid is **ionized** to produce an acetate ion and a hydrogen ion. Of a thousand molecules of acetic acid, 995 remain as unionized CH_3CO_2H. Therefore, acetic acid is said to be a **weak acid**. This term will be discussed later in the chapter.

A base is a substance which produces an hydroxide ion. When solid sodium hydroxide is placed in water, the NaOH goes completely to Na^+ ions and OH^- ions. Ammonia gas bubbled into water produces a few hydroxide ions:

$$NH_3 + H_2O \longrightarrow NH_4^+ + OH^-$$

ammonia   water   ammonium   hydroxide
                          ion   ion

Most of the ammonia remains as molecules of NH_3 in solution. Only about 0.5% of the ammonia in a 1 *M* solution goes to the ammonium ion and to the hydroxide ion. It is a **weak base**.

Observe from the examples just given that whenever an acid produces a hydrogen ion, a negative ion is also produced. Hydrochloric acid produces a chloride ion, Cl^-. Whenever a base produces a hydroxide ion, a positive ion is also a product. Sodium hydroxide, NaOH, in water has Na^+ as the positive ion. It has also been seen that H^+ ion and OH^- ion react together to form water. Whenever an acid and a base are brought together, water is always a product. But a negative ion from the acid and a positive ion from the base are always left over as shown in the following reaction:

$$H^+ + Cl^- + Na^+ + OH^- \longrightarrow Na^+ + Cl^- + H_2O$$

hydrochloric   sodium   sodium chloride   water
acid   hydroxide   (salt)

Sodium chloride dissolved in water is a solution of a **salt**. A salt is made up of a positively charged ion called a **cation** and a negatively charged ion called an **anion**. If the water were evaporated, the solid salt made up of cations and anions would remain as crystals. *A salt is a chemical compound made up of a cation (other than H^+) and an anion (other than OH^-).*

Acids have a sour taste. Acetic acid in vinegar gives it the stinging sensation that makes its use to flavor some foods so desirable. Hydrochloric acid from the stomach contributes to the repulsive taste of vomit. Bases have a soapy feeling and a bitter taste. Drinking water that has a high lime content may taste bitter. Of course, this is not to say that you should taste unknown materials to see if they are acids or bases! Various indicators have been developed for such a purpose. They consist of dyes that have different colors in acids and bases. One of the oldest of these is litmus. It is commonly used as a dye on paper, referred to as litmus paper. Litmus is red in acid and blue in base.

Some substances can act both as an acid and a base. The simplest example is water. Water can split apart to form a hydrogen ion and a hydroxide ion.

$$H_2O = H^+ + OH^-$$

Since it produces a hydrogen ion, water is an acid. However, the fact that it produces a hydroxide ion also makes it a base. This reaction occurs only to a very small extent. In pure water only one out of 10 million molecules of water is in the form of H^+ and OH^-. Except for this very low concentration of these two ions that can exist together, H^+ and OH^- react strongly with each other to form water.

Another important substance that can be either an acid or base is glycine. Glycine is one of the amino acids that is essential in composition of the body's protein. It can give off a hydrogen ion or it can react with water to release a hydroxide ion from the water:

$$\text{H:O:C:C:N:} + \text{H:O:} \longrightarrow \text{H:O:C:C:N:H}^+ + \text{OH}^-$$

Substances which can be either acids or bases are termed **amphoteric**.

Some metal ions are acids. As an example consider iron(III) ion, Fe^{3+}. This ion is commonly called a ferric ion. When ferric chloride, $FeCl_3$, is dissolved in water,

$$FeCl_3 + 6 H_2O = Fe(H_2O)_6^{3+} + 3 Cl^-$$

it produces chloride ions and ferric ions. Each ferric ion is bonded to 6 water molecules. The ferric ion surrounded by water is called a **hydrated** ion. This hydrated ferric ion can lose hydrogen ions and form a slimey brown precipitate of iron(III) hydroxide, $Fe(OH)_3$:

$$Fe(H_2O)_6^{3+} \longrightarrow Fe(OH)_3\downarrow + 3 H_2O + 3 H^+$$

It is this reaction that is partly responsible for the acid in iron-rich acid mine water. It is also used to purify drinking water. The gooey $Fe(OH)_3$ settles out, carrying the impurities to the bottom of the container, and the water clears up.

Some salts which are not really acids or bases themselves react with water to produce hydroxide ions. The most widely used of these is sodium carbonate, Na_2CO_3, which is commonly known as soda ash. Millions of pounds of soda ash are produced each year for the removal of hardness from boiler water, for the treatment of waste acid, and for many other industrial processes. Sodium carbonate reacts in water

$$2 Na^+ + CO_3^{2-} + H_2O \longrightarrow Na^+ + HCO_3^- + Na^+ + OH^-$$

| sodium carbonate | sodium bicarbonate | sodium hydroxide |

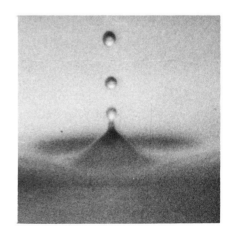

Salt dissolved in small droplets of water enter the atmosphere by the bursting of bubbles on the ocean's surface as shown in this photo. These droplets are carried into the atmosphere by wind, where the water evaporates, leaving small salt crystals. These crystals make up "condensation nuclei" around which raindrops form. (Courtesy of Duncan C. Blanchard, SUNY at Albany)

to produce a hydroxide ion. If a hydrogen ion, such as that from hydro-chloric acid, is already present in the water, sodium carbonate reacts with it as follows:

$$2\,Na^+ + CO_3^{2-} + H^+ + Cl^- \longrightarrow Na^+ + Cl^- + Na^+ + HCO_3^-$$

| sodium carbonate | hydrochloric acid | sodium chloride | sodium bicarbonate |

Some salts act as acids. Salts that act as acids react with hydroxide ions. Ammonium chloride, NH_4Cl, is such a salt. This salt is also called "sal ammoniac," and it provides the acid which cleans metal surfaces and is used as a "flux" in soldering automobile radiators or copper plumbing. In the presence of a base NH_4Cl reacts with the hydroxide ion

$$NH_4^+ + Cl^- + Na^+ + OH^- \longrightarrow NH_3\uparrow + H_2O + Na^+ + Cl^-$$

| ammonium chloride | sodium hydroxide | sodium chloride |

to produce ammonia gas and water.

A hydrogen ion in water is strongly attracted to water molecules. When the hydrogen ion is written as H^+, it does not mean that the ion is floating around in the water by itself. The bonding of hydrogen ion to water is shown by the equation

$$H^+ + H_2O = H_3O^+$$

The H_3O^+ ion is called the **hydronium** ion. The electron-dot structure of the hydronium ion was given in Section 6.4. The hydrogen ion in water is frequently shown as H_3O^+. In this book, however, we will simply indicate it by H^+.

7.2

The Effect of Electricity on Acids, Bases, and Salts in Solution

In Section 7.1 we saw that when acids, bases, or salts are dissolved in water, charged ions are formed. When HCl gas is dissolved in water,

$$HCl\ (gas) \xrightarrow{\text{water}} H^+ + Cl^-$$

all of it goes to H^+ and Cl^- ions. Acetic acid in water also forms a few ions,

$$CH_3CO_2H \longrightarrow H^+ + CH_3CO_2^-$$

but most of it stays as CH_3CO_2H. NaOH in water is all in the form of Na^+ and OH^- ions. The salt, NaCl, in water is all present as Na^+ and Cl^- ions.

One of the most important properties of ions is that they conduct electricity in water. Water containing ions from an acid, base, or salt will conduct electricity much like a metal wire. Consider what would happen if very pure distilled water were made part of an electrical circuit as shown in Figure 7.1. The light bulb would not glow at all. This is because pure water does not conduct electricity. However, if a solution of salt water, such as brine from a jar of pickles, is substituted for the distilled water, the bulb will glow brightly as shown in Figure 7.2. Salty water conducts electricity because of the ions that it contains. Even tap water has some ions dissolved in it, which is why one may experience a painful, even fatal, electrical shock by touching an electrical fixture while bathing.

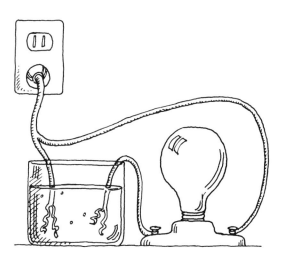

FIGURE 7.1
Pure distilled water does not conduct electricity when it is made part of an electrical circuit.

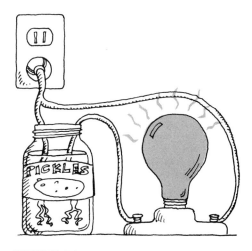

FIGURE 7.2
Water containing dissolved NaCl does conduct electricity.

Materials which conduct electricity in water are called **electrolytes**. These materials form ions in water. The charged ions allow the electrical current to flow through the water. Materials, such as sugar, that do not form ions in water are called **nonelectrolytes**. Solutions of nonelectrolytes in water do not conduct electricity. Electrolytes vary in how well they conduct electricity. A solution of brine from the pickle jar conducts electricity very well because it contains NaCl. All of the NaCl in the water is in the form of Na^+ and Cl^-. The NaCl is completely ionized, and it is a **strong electrolyte**. An ammonia water solution (used for washing windows) does not conduct electricity very well. That is because only a small fraction of the NH_3 molecules react,

$$NH_3 + H_2O \longrightarrow NH_4^+ + OH^-$$

to form the ions which let electricity pass through the water. Ammonia is a **weak electrolyte**. (Recall that it is also a weak base.) Nitric acid, HNO_3 is a strong electrolyte because it is completely ionized to H^+ and NO_3^- ions. Acetic acid is a weak electrolyte, as well as a weak acid. The base, sodium hydroxide, is a strong electrolyte. All salts are strong electrolytes because they are always completely ionized in water. Acids and bases may be weak or strong electrolytes.

In the laboratory the strength of an electrolyte is measured by how well it conducts electricity in solution as shown in Figure 7.3. The ability of a solution to conduct electrical current is called its **conductivity**.

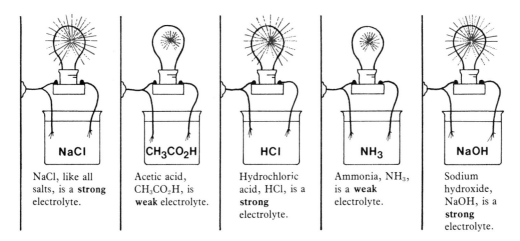

| NaCl | CH₃CO₂H | HCl | NH₃ | NaOH |

NaCl, like all salts, is a **strong** electrolyte.

Acetic acid, CH_3CO_2H, is **weak** electrolyte.

Hydrochloric acid, HCl, is a **strong** electrolyte.

Ammonia, NH_3, is a **weak** electrolyte.

Sodium hydroxide, NaOH, is a **strong** electrolyte.

FIGURE 7.3 *The electrical conductivity of a solution can be determined by placing the solution in an electrical circuit and observing how well electricity goes through it. Strong electrolytes conduct electricity well. Weak electrolytes do it poorly. This principle is used by water analysts to determine total salt concentrations in water.*

The passage of electricity through a solution is widely used in industry to separate and purify materials. When a direct current (one which always flows in one direction) is passed through a solution containing a metal ion, the pure metal may be deposited on the negative $(-)$ electrode. It is possible then to remove the metal from solution and to get it in a pure form. This process is used in the electroplating industry for chrome plating automobile bumpers and many other applications.

One of the most common uses of electricity in chemistry is in the preparation of NaOH and Cl_2 by passing electricity through a solution of NaCl. Sodium hydroxide ranks fourth in the production of industrial chemicals. Chlorine ranks fifth. These two chemicals may be made in an apparatus like the one shown in Figure 7.4. Notice that the negative

FIGURE 7.4
Electrolysis of
sodium chloride.

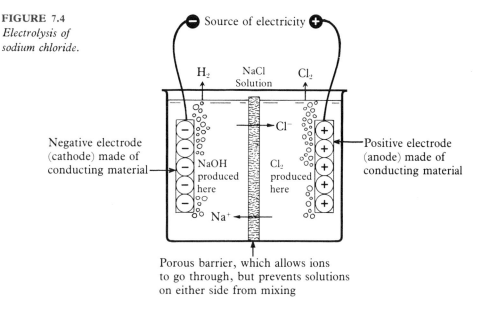

electrode has an excess of electrons, indicated by e⁻ in chemical reactions. These electrons react with water

$$2 \, H_2O + 2 \, e^- \longrightarrow H_2\uparrow + 2 \, OH^-$$

to produce hydrogen gas and hydroxide ion. The positive electrode lacks electrons. It takes them away from chloride ions

$$2 \, Cl^- \longrightarrow Cl_2\uparrow + 2 \, e^-$$

to produce chlorine gas. The negative electrode where water is **reduced** by giving it electrons is called the **cathode**. The positive electrode where chloride ion is **oxidized** by taking away its electrons is called the **anode**. (Recall the discussion of oxidation and reduction from Chapter 3.) The reduction reaction adds negative ions—hydroxide ions—on one side of the apparatus. The oxidation reaction removes negative ions—chloride ions—at the anode. The electrical charge must be balanced on both sides of the apparatus. This is done by positive ions (Na^+) migrating through the porous barrier toward the cathode and by negative chloride ions migrating the other way toward the anode. We can add the two chemical reactions in the experiment in Figure 7.4 to compute the total process that occurs:

$$2 \, H_2O + 2 \, Na^+ + 2 \, Cl^- \longrightarrow H_2\uparrow + \boxed{2 \, Na^+ + 2 \, OH^-} + Cl_2\uparrow$$

sodium   chlorine gas
hydroxide   product
product

A sodium hydroxide solution is isolated on one side. The water may be boiled off to give pure, solid sodium hydroxide. Chlorine gas is collected on the other side.

7.3

Acids and Bases Coming Apart in Water

It has already been seen that acids and bases come apart in water to form ions. When acetic acid splits up in water,

$$CH_3CO_2H \longrightarrow CH_3CO_2^- + H^+$$

it forms hydrogen ions and acetate ions. The process of forming ions is called **ionization**. Another term is commonly employed. When the acetic acid molecule comes apart, it is said to **dissociate**. The process is called **dissociation**.

There is a great difference in how much various acids and bases dissociate. Some, like HCl or NaOH, are completely dissociated in water. Because of this hydrochloric acid is called a **strong acid**. Sodium hydroxide is a **strong base**. Some acids such as acetic acid are only partly dissociated in water. They are called **weak acids**. Ammonia, NH_3, reacts only a little bit in water to form an ammonium ion (NH_4^+) and a hydroxide ion (OH^-). It is a **weak base**.

The extent of dissociation is a very important property of an acid or base. The 3 % or so acetic acid solution used to make up oil and vinegar salad dressing lends a pleasant taste to the lettuce and tomatoes. There is not much of the H^+ ion in the acetic acid. If 3 % HCl had been used instead, the unfortunate diner would spit out the greens and reach for the water glass. All of the H in HCl is in the form of H^+, and a 3 % solution of hydrochloric acid is very sour, indeed. Similarly, a several percent solution of NH_3 in water makes a good window wash, helping to dissolve the grease and grime of auto exhausts and factory smoke as well as the incredible assortment of sticky materials left from children's handprints. If a similar concentration of the base, sodium hydroxide, were used to clean windows, they would soon become permanently fogged because the OH^- in the strong base eventually reacts with glass and etches it. However, sodium hydroxide solutions are used to clean ovens. Incredibly, this cleaning solution can be purchased in spray aerosol cans. A faceful of this spray can severely damage eyes and lungs.

Table 7.1 shows some acids and the degree to which they are dissociated. It allows comparison of the strengths of these acids.

Discharges of chemical wastes dumped at the plant are not only unsightly but present a real hazard to youngsters who may happen to play near this urban location. (Courtesy of Massachusetts Audubon Society; Daniel S. Brody, photographer)

TABLE 7.1
Dissociation of acids.

Acid Formula	Acid Name	Common Uses	Percent Dissociated in 1 M Solution	Strength
H_2SO_4	Sulfuric	Industrial chemical	100	Strong
HNO_3	Nitric	Industrial chemical	100	Strong
H_3PO_4	Phosphoric	Making fertilizer	8	Moderately weak
$H_3C_6H_8O_7$	Citric	Fruit drinks	3	Weak
CH_3CO_2H	Acetic	Foods, industry	0.4	Weak
$HOCl$	Hypochlorous	Disinfectant	0.02	Weak
HCN	Hydrocyanic	Industrial chemical, very poisonous	0.002	Weak
H_3BO_3	Boric acid	Antiseptic, ceramics	0.002	Weak

The percentage of acid molecules which are dissociated depends upon the concentration of the acid. The lower the concentration, the higher the percentage of dissociated molecules. This may be understood by looking at the reaction

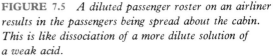

$$CH_3CO_2H \longrightarrow H^+ + CH_3CO_2^-$$

for the dissociation of acetic acid. At high concentrations there will be more crowding together of H^+ and $CH_3CO_2^-$ ions. This forces them back together to form CH_3CO_2H again. At low concentrations there are fewer H^+ and $CH_3CO_2^-$ ions. They are more free to roam around the solution alone, and there is less pressure for them to form $HC_2H_3O_2$. It is somewhat like the seating which occurs on an airplane. If there are few passengers, they will spread around the cabin and not sit next to each other (Figure 7.5). If there are many passengers, they will of course have to occupy adjacent seats (Figure 7.6).

FIGURE 7.5 *A diluted passenger roster on an airliner results in the passengers being spread about the cabin. This is like dissociation of a more dilute solution of a weak acid.*

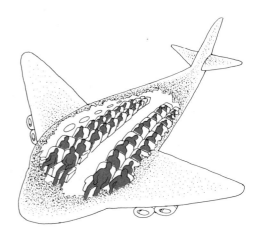

FIGURE 7.6 *Passengers in a crowded airplane cabin must pair up in seats, just as the ions from a weak acid tend to stay in the undissociated form in a concentrated solution.*

An idea of the effect of concentration upon the dissociation of a weak acid can be obtained from the percentage of acid molecules that have dissociated to ions at several different concentrations. This is shown for acetic acid in Table 7.2.

TABLE 7.2

Total Acetic Acid Concentration	Percent Dissociated to H^+ and $CH_3CO_2^-$
1 mole/liter	0.4
0.1 mole/liter	1.3
0.01 mole/liter	4.1
0.001 mole/liter	12
0.0001 mole/liter	34
0.00001 mole/liter	71
0.000001 mole/liter	95
0.0000001 mole/liter	99

Table 7.2 shows that in a 1 M solution less than 1% of acetic acid is dissociated. In a one-thousandth M (0.001 M) solution 12 out of 100 molecules of acetic acid are in the form of H^+ and acetate ions. In a one-millionth M (0.000001 M) solution only 5 out of 100 acetic acid molecules are present as CH_3CO_2H.

It is important to know the difference between the *strength* of an acid or base in solution and the *concentration* of the solution. A strong acid is one which is all in the form of H^+ ions and anions. It may be very concentrated or very dilute. A weak acid does not give off much H^+ to water solution. It may also range in concentration from a very dilute solution to a very concentrated one. Similar arguments apply to bases.

7.4

The Hydrogen Ion Concentration and Buffers

It is important to make the distinction between the concentration of H^+ and the concentration of an acid. To show this difference, compare 1 M solutions of acetic acid and hydrochloric acid. The concentration of H^+ in a 1 M solution of CH_3CO_2H is only 0.0042 mole/liter. The concentration of H^+ in a 1 M solution of HCl is 1 mole/liter. A liter of a 1 M solution of HCl contains two hundred and fifty times as many H^+ ions as a liter of a 1 M solution of acetic acid.

Consider, however, the amount of NaOH which will react with 1.00 liter of 1.00 M acetic acid. The reaction is

$$CH_3CO_2H + Na^+ + OH^- \longrightarrow Na^+ + CH_3CO_2^- + H_2O$$

acetic acid   sodium hydroxide   sodium acetate

Exactly 1.00 mole of NaOH reacts with the 1.00 mole of acetic acid contained in a liter of a 1.00 M solution of this acid. Exactly the same amount of NaOH reacts with the HCl in 1.00 liter of 1.00 M HCl.

$$H^+ + Cl^- \ + \ Na^+ + OH^- \ \longrightarrow \ Na^+ + Cl^- \ + H_2O$$

| hydrochloric | sodium | sodium |
| acid | hydroxide | chloride |

Therefore, even though acetic acid is a weaker acid than hydrochloric acid, *equal volumes of each, with the same molar concentration, will react with the same number of moles of base.*

In many systems the concentration of H^+ is very important. For a person to remain healthy the H^+ concentration in blood must stay within a very narrow range. If the H^+ concentration is too high in a boiler system, the pipes may be corroded through in a short time. If the H^+ concentration becomes too high in a fermentation process for the preparation of yogurt from milk, different microorganisms will grow in the mix and ruin the product.

Fortunately, there are mixtures of chemicals which keep the H^+ concentration of a solution relatively constant. Reasonable quantities of acid or base added to such solutions do not cause large changes in H^+ concentration. Solutions that resist changes in H^+ concentration are called **buffers**. (Be sure to remember that important term.)

To understand how a buffer works, consider a typical buffer system. A solution containing both acetic acid and sodium acetate is a good buffer. The acetic acid in the solution is present as undissociated CH_3CO_2H. The H^+, which is in solution, is there because a very small amount of the CH_3CO_2H has dissociated to H^+ and $CH_3CO_2^-$ ions. The sodium acetate is present as Na^+ ion and $CH_3CO_2^-$ ion. If some base, such as NaOH, is added, some of the acetic acid reacts.

$$CH_3CO_2H \ + \ Na^+ + OH^- \ \longrightarrow \ Na^+ + CH_3CO_2^- \ + H_2O$$

| acetic acid | sodium hydroxide | sodium acetate |

This reaction changes some of the acetic acid to sodium acetate, *but it does not change the hydrogen ion concentration much.* If a small amount of hydrochloric acid is added to the buffer mixture of acetic acid and sodium acetate, some of the sodium acetate is changed to acetic acid.

$$Na^+ + CH_3CO_2^- \ + \ H^+ + Cl^- \ \longrightarrow \ CH_3CO_2H + Na^+ + Cl^-$$

| sodium acetate | hydrochloric acid | acetic acid |

The acetate ion acts like a sponge for H^+ and prevents the concentration of the added hydrogen ion from becoming too high.

Buffers can also be made from a mixture of a weak base and a salt of the base. A mixture of NH_3 and NH_4Cl is such a buffer. Mixtures of two salts can be buffers. A mixture of NaH_2PO_4 and Na_2HPO_4 is a buffer made from salts. This is one of the very common phosphate buffers. It occurs in living cells. Fairly concentrated solutions of strong acids act as buffers. Small amounts of base are neutralized by these acids, and the addition of small amounts of acid does not change the acid concentration much, because it is already so high. Similarly, solutions of strong bases are buffers.

7.5

pH and the Relationship Between Hydrogen Ion Concentration and Hydroxide Ion Concentration

Because of the fact that water, itself, produces both hydrogen ion and hydroxide ion,

$$H_2O \longrightarrow H^+ + OH^-$$

there is always *some* H^+ and *some* OH^- in any solution. Of course, in an acid solution the concentration of OH^- must be very low. In a solution of base the concentration of H^+ is very low. There is a definite relationship between the concentration of H^+ and the concentration of OH^-. It varies a little with temperature. At 25°C (about room temperature) the following rule applies: *The concentration of hydroxide ion is obtained by dividing 0.00000000000001 by the concentration of hydrogen ion. The concentration of a hydrogen ion is obtained by dividing 0.00000000000001 by the concentration of a hydroxide ion.* The number with all of the zeroes is difficult to handle. It is easy to misplace a zero or two. It can be written instead as 1×10^{-14}. This sort of notation was discussed before in Section 5.7. To understand where the minus fourteen comes from, take the number 1 and move the decimal to the left 14 times:

1. with the decimal moved 14 spaces to the left is

$$0 \underbrace{.0\,0\,0\,0\,0\,0\,0\,0\,0\,0\,0\,0\,0\,1}_{14\ 13\ 12\ 11\ 10\ 9\ 8\ 7\ 6\ 5\ 4\ 3\ 2\ 1}. \quad \text{or} \quad 0.00000000000001$$

What is the concentration of OH^- in a solution of 0.01 M HCl?

$$OH^- \text{ concentration} = \frac{0.00000000000001}{0.01} = 0.000000000001 \ M$$

Another way of showing the calculation is

$$OH^- \text{ concentration} = \frac{1 \times 10^{-14}}{1 \times 10^{-2}} = 1 \times 10^{-12} \ M$$

What is the concentration of H^+ in 0.005 M NaOH?

$$H^+ \text{ concentration} = \frac{0.00000000000001}{0.005} = 0.000000000002 \ M$$

Or

$$H^+ \text{ concentration} = \frac{1 \times 10^{-14}}{5 \times 10^{-3}} = 2 \times 10^{-12} \ M$$

In referring to hydrogen ion concentrations, it is very inconvenient to be using numbers such as 0.00000000001. In water the hydrogen ion concentration may be different by many powers of ten with differences of a thousand, a million, a billion, or more. For that reason it is convenient to talk of the hydrogen ion in terms of pH. *The pH of a solution is the negative logarithm of the hydrogen ion concentration.* If you have not been exposed to logarithms before, that definition may be a little hard to work with. However, even without a knowledge of logarithms, you can get a good idea of pH by looking at Table 7.3.

TABLE 7.3

Hydrogen Ion Concentration, Mole/liter		pH	Typical Solution
1, or 1×10^0	(Very acidic)	0	1 M HNO$_3$
0.1, or 1×10^{-1}		1	
0.01, or 1×10^{-2}		2	
0.001, or 1×10^{-3}	(Acidic)	3	Acid mine water, vinegar
0.0001, or 1×10^{-4}		4	
0.00001, or 1×10^{-5}		5	
0.000001, or 1×10^{-6}		6	
0.0000001, or 1×10^{-7}	(Neutral)	7	Pure water
0.00000001, or 1×10^{-8}		8	
0.000000001, or 1×10^{-9}		9	
0.0000000001, or 1×10^{-10}		10	
0.00000000001, or 1×10^{-11}	(Basic)	11	Laundry detergent
0.000000000001, or 1×10^{-12}		12	
0.0000000000001, or 1×10^{-13}		13	
0.00000000000001, or 1×10^{-14}	(Very basic)	14	1 M NaOH

7.6

Preparation of Acids

Acids can be prepared in several ways. In discussing the preparation of acids, it is important to keep in mind that acids usually contain nonmetals. And, of course, all acids contain hydrogen. Furthermore, the hydrogen has to be ionizable; it must have the ability to form H^+ ion. Finally, more often than not, acids contain oxygen.

A simple way to make an acid is to react hydrogen with a nonmetal.

Hydrochloric acid can be made by reacting hydrogen and chlorine

$$H_2 + Cl_2 \longrightarrow 2\,HCl$$

$$\downarrow \text{water}$$

$$H^+ + Cl^-$$

hydrochloric
acid

and adding the hydrogen chloride product to water. Other acids which consist of hydrogen combined with a nonmetal are HF, HBr, HI, and H_2S. Hydrocyanic acid, HCN, is an "honorary member" of this family of acids, even though it contains three elements.

Sometimes a nonmetal reacts directly with water to produce acids. The best example of this is the reaction of chlorine with water,

$$Cl_2 + H_2O = HCl + HClO$$

to produce hydrochloric acid and hypochlorous acid.

Many very important acids are produced when nonmetal oxides react with water. One of the best examples is the reaction of sulfur trioxide with water

$$SO_3 + H_2O = H_2SO_4$$

to produce sulfuric acid. Other examples are shown in Table 7.4.

TABLE 7.4
Important acids produced when nonmetal oxides react with water.

Acid Formula	Acid Name	Oxide	Use of Acid
H_2SO_4	Sulfuric	SO_3	Many industrial uses
H_2SO_3	Sulfurous	SO_2	Paper making
HNO_3	Nitric	N_2O_5	Synthesis of chemicals
HNO_2	Nitrous	N_2O_3	Unstable, few uses
H_3PO_4	Phosphoric	P_2O_5	Fertilizer, chemical synthesis

Volatile acids, those which evaporate easily, can be made from salts and nonvolatile acids. The most common nonvolatile acid so used is sulfuric acid, H_2SO_4. When NaCl is heated with sulfuric acid,

Acid mine water drainage from an abandoned coal mine in W. Virgina pollutes the stream in the foreground. This is the result of surface water running through old mine openings and exiting as acid drainage. (Courtesy of USDA, Soil Conservation Service; E. V. Wickline, photographer)

$$2\,NaCl + H_2SO_4 = 2\,HCl\uparrow + Na_2SO_4$$

HCl gas is given off. This gas can be collected in water to make hydrochloric acid. Similarly when calcium sulfite is heated with sulfuric acid,

$$CaSO_3 + H_2SO_4 = CaSO_4 + SO_2\uparrow + H_2O$$

sulfur dioxide is given off as a gas. It can be collected in water to produce sulfurous acid, H_2SO_3.

Organic acids, such as acetic acid, CH_3CO_2H, have the group,

$$\begin{array}{c} O \\ \parallel \\ -C-OH \end{array}$$

attached to a hydrocarbon group. These **carboxylic acids** are discussed in detail in Section 10.10.

7.7

Preparation of Bases

Bases can be prepared in several ways. Many bases contain metals. They either contain the hydroxide ion, OH^-, or are capable of producing it in water.

Some metals react directly with water to produce a solution of base. Lithium, sodium, and potassium react very vigorously with water to produce their hydroxides:

$$2\,K + 2\,H_2O \longrightarrow \boxed{2\,K^+ + 2\,OH^-} + H_2\uparrow$$

potassium hydroxide
(strong base)

Many metal oxides form bases when they are dissolved in water. When waste liquor (a concentrated solution of salts and materials extracted from wood) from the sulfite paper-making process is burned to produce energy and reclaim magnesium hydroxide, the magnesium in the ash is recovered as MgO. This is added to water

$$MgO + H_2O = Mg(OH)_2$$

to produce the magnesium hydroxide used with other chemicals to break down the wood and produce paper fibers. Other important bases and the metal oxides from which they are prepared are given in Table 7.5.

Many important bases cannot be isolated as the hydroxides but produce OH^- ion in water. A very good example is ammonia, NH_3. Ammonium hydroxide, NH_4OH, cannot be obtained in a pure form. Even when ammonia is dissolved in water, very little NH_4OH is present in the

TABLE 7.5
Important bases and corresponding metal oxides.

Base Formula	Base Name	Oxide	Use of Base
LiOH	Lithium hydroxide	Li_2O	Lubricating greases
NaOH	Sodium hydroxide	Na_2O	10 million tons for U.S. industry each year, soap making and many other uses
KOH	Potassium hydroxide	K_2O	Alkaline batteries
$Mg(OH)_2$	Magnesium hydroxide	MgO	Paper making, medicine
$Ca(OH)_2$	Calcium hydroxide	CaO	Water purification, soil treatment to decrease soil acidity

solution. However, ammonia does react with water,

$$NH_3 + H_2O \longrightarrow NH_4^+ + OH^-$$

to give an ammonium ion and a hydroxide ion. Only a small percentage of the ammonia molecules react this way. Recall that ammonia is a weak base.

Many salts that do not themselves contain hydroxide ions react with water to produce it. Sodium carbonate, Na_2CO_3, is the most widely used of these salts. Around 14 billion pounds of this soda ash are produced for industrial use in the U.S. each year. When sodium carbonate is placed in water, it forms sodium ions and carbonate ions. The carbonate ion reacts with water

$$CO_3^{2-} + H_2O \longrightarrow HCO_3^- + OH^-$$

to form a hydroxide ion and a bicarbonate ion, HCO_3^-. Soda ash is used very widely for neutralizing acid in water treatment and other applications. It is used in phosphate-free detergents. It is a much easier base to handle and use than sodium hydroxide. Sodium hydroxide rapidly absorbs enough water from the atmosphere to dissolve itself. It is very harmful to the skin. Sodium carbonate does not absorb water nearly so readily. It is not quite as dangerous to the skin.

Trisodium phosphate, Na_3PO_4, is an even stronger base than sodium carbonate. The phosphate ion reacts with water

$$PO_4^{3-} + H_2O \longrightarrow HPO_4^{2-} + OH^-$$

to yield a high concentration of hydroxide ions. This kind of reaction with water is called a **hydrolysis** reaction.

Many organic compounds are bases. Most of these contain nitrogen. One of these is trimethylamine, $(CH_3)_3N$. This compound is one of several that give dead fish their foul smell. It reacts with water

$$(CH_3)_3N + H_2O \longrightarrow (CH_3)_3NH^+ + OH^-$$

to produce hydroxide ion. Like most organic bases it is a weak base.

7.8

Titration

Titration is one of the most common operations which a chemist performs. It is an important part of chemical analysis and will be discussed in detail in Chapter 12. Here it is discussed as it applies to the reactions of acids and bases.

Titration consists of measuring the amount of **standard solution** that reacts with a sample. The object of the operation is to find out how much of something is in the sample. The standard solution is one with a known concentration. Suppose, for example, that a hospital incinerator system for the burning of trash is equipped with a water scrubbing system to scrub smoke and other pollutants out of the exhaust. It is found that the scrub water product is rich in hydrochloric acid produced when chlorine-containing plastics are burned. This acid scrub water eats through the iron drain pipes. The problem can be eliminated by adding calcium hydroxide to the scrub water to neutralize the acid, but the amount of base needed must be known. This can be determined by taking a measured volume of the waste water and titrating it with a standard solution of sodium hydroxide as shown in Figure 7.7. The reaction is

$$H^+ + Cl^- \;+\; Na^+ + OH^- \quad\longrightarrow\quad Na^+ + Cl^- + H_2O$$

hydrochloric   sodium
acid   hydroxide

It is continued until just enough sodium hydroxide has been added to

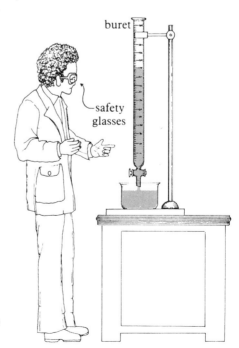

FIGURE 7.7

A long glass tube with marks on it called a ***buret*** *is used to measure the standard solution added to a sample during titration.*

react with all of the hydrochloric acid in the sample. This is called the **end point**. It is shown by a dye called an **indicator**. This dye changes color when the hydrogen ion concentration decreases to the point when all of the hydrochloric acid has been neutralized. Litmus, mentioned in Section 7.1, is such an indicator substance.

The mathematical calculations involved in titrations will be covered in detail in Chapter 12. Suppose, though, that exactly 50 ml of waste water were titrated and that it required 40 ml of 0.01 M standard sodium hydroxide to neutralize the HCl in the waste water sample. The volume of the NaOH required is less than that of the sample. This information tells us that the concentration of HCl in the sample is less than the concentration of NaOH in the standard solution. The concentration of HCl in the sample is given by the calculation

$$\frac{40 \text{ ml NaOH}}{50 \text{ ml of sample}} \times (0.01 \ M \text{ NaOH}) = 0.008 \ M \text{ HCl}$$

The concentration of HCl in the sample is 0.008 M.

7.9

Preparation of Salts

Many salts are important industrial chemicals. Others are used in food preparation or medicine. The huge quantity of Na_2CO_3 used each year, largely to treat water and to neutralize acid, has been mentioned already. Over 1.5 million tons of Na_2SO_4 are used in applications such as inert filler in powdered detergents. Approximately 60 million pounds of sodium thiosulfate, $Na_2S_2O_3$, are used each year in developing photographic film and in other applications. Canadian mines produce more than 10 million tons of KCl each year for use as fertilizer. Lithium carbonate, Li_2CO_3, is used as a medicine to treat some kinds of manic-depressive illnesses. Many other examples of the importance of salts could be given.

Whenever possible, salts are obtained by simply mining them. Many kinds of salts can be obtained by evaporating water from a few salt-rich inland sea waters or from brines pumped from beneath the ground. However, most salts cannot be obtained so directly and must be made by chemical processes. Some of these processes will be discussed.

One way of making salts has already been discussed in this chapter. That method is to react an acid and a base to produce a salt and water. Calcium propionate which is used to preserve bread could be made by reacting calcium hydroxide and propionic acid, $HC_3H_5O_2$.

$$Ca(OH)_2 + 2 \ HC_3H_5O_2 \longrightarrow Ca(C_3H_5O_2)_2 + 2 \ H_2O$$

calcium propionate

Almost any salt can be made this way if the right acids and bases are available.

Salt, deposited from evaporation of water in ancient seas, is being mined. There are vast salt deposits in the U.S. (Courtesy of the Salt Institute)

In some cases a metal and a nonmetal will react directly to make a salt. If a strip of magnesium burns (explodes would be a better description) in an atmosphere of chlorine gas,

$$Mg + Cl_2 \longrightarrow MgCl_2$$

magnesium chloride salt is produced.

Metals react with acids to produce a salt and hydrogen gas. Calcium placed in sulfuric acid will yield calcium sulfate.

$$Ca + H_2SO_4 \longrightarrow H_2\uparrow + CaSO_4$$

Some metals react with strong bases to produce salts. Aluminum metals reacts with sodium hydroxide to yield sodium aluminate, Na_3AlO_3.

$$2\,Al + 6\,NaOH \longrightarrow 2\,Na_3AlO_3 + 3\,H_2\uparrow$$

In cases where a metal forms an insoluble hydroxide, addition of a base to a salt of that metal can result in the formation of a new salt. If potassium hydroxide is added to a solution of magnesium sulfate

$$2\,KOH + MgSO_4 \longrightarrow Mg(OH)_2\downarrow + K_2SO_4$$

the insoluble magnesium hydroxide precipitates out of the solution leaving potassium sulfate salt in solution.

If the anion in a salt can form a volatile acid, a new salt can be formed by adding a nonvolatile acid. If nonvolatile sulfuric acid is heated with NaCl,

$$H_2SO_4 + 2\,NaCl \longrightarrow 2\,HCl\uparrow + Na_2SO_4$$

HCl gas is given off and sodium sulfate remains behind.

Some metals will displace other metals from a salt. If magnesium metal is added to a solution of copper sulfate,

$$Mg + CuSO_4 \longrightarrow Cu + MgSO_4$$

solid copper metal and a new salt, magnesium sulfate, are formed.

Finally there are many special commercial processes for making specific salts. One such example is the widely used Solvay Process for making sodium bicarbonate and sodium carbonate. In this process a sodium chloride solution is saturated with ammonia gas, then saturated with carbon dioxide and finally cooled. The reaction which occurs is

$$NaCl + NH_3 + CO_2 + H_2O \longrightarrow NaHCO_3\downarrow + NH_4Cl$$

and sodium bicarbonate (baking soda) precipitates from the cooled sodium chloride solution is saturated with ammonia gas, then saturated with carbon dioxide and finally cooled. The reaction which occurs is

$$2\,NaHCO_3 + heat \longrightarrow Na_2CO_3 + H_2O\uparrow + CO_2\uparrow$$

7.10

Acid Salts and Basic Salts

Some compounds are crosses between acids and salts. Other salts are really crosses between bases and salts. The acid salts contain hydrogen ion. This hydrogen ion can react with bases. One example of this is sodium hydrogen sulfate, $NaHSO_4$, which reacts with sodium hydroxide,

$$NaHSO_4 + NaOH = Na_2SO_4 + H_2O$$

to give sodium sulfate and water. Some other examples of acid salts are shown in Table 7.6.

TABLE 7.6
Examples of acid salts.

Acid Salt Formula	Acid Salt Name	Typical Use
$NaHCO_3$	Sodium hydrogen carbonate	Food preparation (baking soda)
NaH_2PO_4	Sodium dihydrogen phosphate	Prepare buffers
Na_2HPO_4	Disodium hydrogen phosphate	Prepare buffers
$KHC_4H_4O_6$	Potassium hydrogen tartrate	Dry acid in baking powder*

* Cream of tartar baking powder consists of a mixture of potassium hydrogen tartrate and sodium hydrogen carbonate. When this mixture contacts water in a batch of biscuit dough the reaction,

$$KHC_4H_4O_6 + NaHCO_3 \longrightarrow KNaC_4H_4O_6 + H_2O + CO_2\uparrow$$

occurs producing small bubbles of carbon dioxide which cause the dough to rise.

Some salts contain hydroxide ions. These are known as basic salts. One example is aluminum hydroxyacetate, $Al(OH)(C_2H_3O_2)_2$. The heavier metals in particular form basic salts. Many rock-forming minerals are basic salts.

7.11

Water of Hydration

Many salts have a very strong appetite for water. Magnesium perchlorate is one such salt, which takes water out of humid air. It is used to keep air dry in sealed containers where materials are placed to keep them dry. These containers are called *desiccators*. The chemical that removes the water is called the *desiccant*. Desiccators are widely used in chemical analysis to keep samples dry for very accurate weighing.

Sometimes water reacts with a salt to produce a product with a specific number of water molecules. Copper sulfate is a good example of such a salt. In the dry form $CuSO_4$ is a light blue, almost white material. When it absorbs water, it becomes intense blue in color. The product is copper sulfate pentahydrate. The formula is $CuSO_4 \cdot 5\ H_2O$. The dot indicates that the water is **water of hydration**. The 5 shows that there are five waters of hydration for each $CuSO_4$.

7.12

Names of Chemical Compounds

The names of many chemical compounds have already been given in this book. Many of these are now familiar to you. You have seen the names of acids, bases, and salts. Names have been given to oxides which react with water to make acids and bases. Obviously, the naming of chemical compounds is very important to chemists. This part of chemistry is called **chemical nomenclature**. The remainder of this chapter discusses chemical nomenclature.

Widely used chemicals generally have **common names**. They do not follow any formal rules for naming chemicals. Most of these names were established long before rules were developed for naming compounds. The baker calls $NaHCO_3$ baking soda, rather than using its official name of sodium hydrogen carbonate. The pre-mix cement company orders $CaCO_3$ as crushed limestone, instead of calcium carbonate. The hardy soul in need of a laxative asks the druggist for $MgSO_4 \cdot 7H_2O$ by the name of epsom salts, rather than magnesium sulfate heptahydrate.

Since it is impossible to use common names for all of the several million known chemical compounds, **systematic names** have been developed. These names follow rules of **nomenclature**. The following sections discuss nomenclature of inorganic compounds. The naming of organic compounds is discussed in Chapter 10.

7.13

Compounds Containing Two Elements

A large number of simple compounds are made up of only two elements. Many examples of these including table salt (NaCl), water (H_2O), and calcium oxide (CaO) have already been given. These compounds are bonded together in two ways. Ionic bonding occurs when one element donates one or more electrons to another. This happens, for example, in the formation of sodium chloride.

$$Na \cdot \ + \ \cdot \ddot{\underset{\cdot\cdot}{Cl}} \colon \ = \ Na^+ \colon \ddot{\underset{\cdot\cdot}{Cl}} \colon^-$$

When this compound is formed, the sodium atom becomes a *positive ion*. The chlorine atom becomes a *negative ion*. In naming an ionic compound made up of two elements like this one, the positive ion name is given first. The negative ion name is given second. This name ends in "ide." Therefore, the official name of table salt is sodium chloride:

NaCl
↗ ↖
sodium chloride

In the case of an ionic compound it is easy to decide which part of the name goes first. It is the element that has lost electrons. Since metals most readily lose electrons, the name of the metal comes first. What is done, though, in the case of a compound where electrons are shared to join two atoms together? For example HCl gas is made by the combination of hydrogen atoms and chlorine atoms:

$$H \cdot \ + \ \cdot \ddot{\underset{\cdot\cdot}{Cl}} \colon \ = \ H \colon \ddot{\underset{\cdot\cdot}{Cl}} \colon$$

↑
two shared electrons
making up a
chemical bond

Although 2 electrons are shared in the chemical bond between hydrogen and chlorine, the sharing is not equal. In this case the chlorine atom has a stronger attraction for the two shared electrons than does the hydrogen atom. This leaves the hydrogen atom with a small shortage of electrons and the chlorine atom with a slight excess of electrons. Because the electrons spend slightly more time around the chlorine atom, the end of the molecule containing chlorine has a small negative charge. The hydrogen end of the molecule is slightly positive. The more positive element is given first in the name. For that reason the name given to HCl gas is hydrogen chloride.

In some compounds a particular element may be more positive than its partner, and in other compounds this same element may be more negative. Hydrogen frequently behaves that way. It has just been seen that hydrogen is relatively more positive when combined with chlorine so that the formula of the compound is HCl, and it is called hydrogen chloride. When hydrogen combines with sodium

$$Na \cdot + \cdot H = Na^+ H \colon ^-$$

hydrogen gets a negative charge. The compound that is produced is called sodium hydride. It is used for taking scale off of metal surfaces.

A large number of common inorganic compounds containing only two elements and having names ending in "ide" exist. Some of these are given in Table 7.7.

TABLE 7.7
Common inorganic compounds with names that end in "ide."

Compound Formula	Compound Name	Significance
$BeCl_2$	Beryllium chloride	Ingredient of cell baths for electrorefining of beryllium metal
$MgCl_2$	Magnesium chloride	Treatment of leaves for fire resistance and to prevent drying
H_2S	Hydrogen sulfide	Poisonous compound with a bad odor found in sour natural gas
CaC_2	Calcium carbide	Reacts with water to produce acetylene gas.
NaF	Sodium fluoride	Added to drinking water to prevent tooth decay
$AlCl_3$	Aluminum chloride	Used in water treatment

Some metals lose different numbers of electrons when they react with nonmetals. Iron is the best example. It may lose either 2 or 3 electrons. The officially accepted way of showing how many electrons are lost by a metal is to use a roman numeral in parentheses after the metal name. Using this system $FeCl_2$ is named iron(II) chloride. This name is pronounced "iron two chloride." It shows that the iron atom has lost an electron to each of two chlorine atoms. When iron loses 3 electrons to chlorine forming $FeCl_3$, the compound is called iron(III) chloride.

Another system for naming compounds in which different numbers of electrons have been lost from the metal is the "ous-ic" system. It gives the name of ferrous chloride to $FeCl_2$ and ferric chloride to $FeCl_3$. The "fer-" part of the name comes from the Latin word for iron, *ferrum*. The "-ous" is used for the iron compound in which only 2 electrons have been lost and "-ic" where 3 electrons have been lost. Both ferrous chloride and ferric chloride are used to treat drinking water. These compounds react with water to form sticky hydroxide compounds, which settle out and carry very fine suspended solid particles along. This makes the water clear.

Mercury is another metal which can lose different numbers of electrons. When a mercury atom loses *one* electron to a chlorine atom, the compound commonly called calomel is formed. Its simplest formula is HgCl. However, the molecule contains 2 mercury atoms and 2 chlorine atoms, so the actual formula is Hg_2Cl_2. Its official name is mercury(I) chloride, or mercur*ous* chloride. The loss of *two* electrons from a mercury atom in combining with chlorine produces $HgCl_2$. This compound is called mercury(II) chloride or mercur*ic* chloride. Mercury(I) chloride, calomel, has been widely used in medicine to kill worms in the intestines and for other purposes. Mercury(II) chloride, on the other hand, is a violent poison.

In naming chemical compounds *prefixes* are often put in front of words to designate the number of atoms or groups of atoms of a particular kind in the compound. These prefixes are given as follows:

1 -mono	6 -hexa
2 -di	7 -hepta
3 -tri	8 -octa
4 -tetra	9 -nona
5 -penta	10 -deca

Using these prefixes, CO is called carbon monoxide (one oxygen) and CO_2 is called carbon dioxide (two oxygens). The 'laughing gas" anesthetic N_2O is called dinitrogen oxide (two nitrogens). Its toxic cousin NO_2 is called nitrogen dioxide (two oxygens). The NO given off from an automobile exhaust is called nitrogen oxide. These prefixes are very useful in telling the chemical formula of a compound from its name.

The "-ide" ending is also used in naming some compounds that contain three elements. Compounds containing the negatively charged OH^- groups are called **hydroxides**. Thus, the lye used in making soap has the chemical formula, NaOH, and is called sodium hydroxide. The lime, $Ca(OH)_2$, used in plaster is calcium hydroxide. Compounds containing the negative ion, CN^-, are named **cyanides**. The deadly HCN gas used in fumigation to kill insects and rodents is called hydrogen cyanide. Compounds containing the positive ammonium ion, NH_4^+, may end in "-ide." Ammonium chloride, NH_4Cl, is an example.

7.14

Compounds Containing Three Elements: Acids

As has been discussed previously, acids are compounds which form hydrogen ion, H^+, in water. Normally the name of an acid ends in "-ic." An example is acet*ic* acid. Vinegar contains about 4% acetic acid dissolved in water. The chemical formula of acetic acid is written as CH_3CO_2H. Only one hydrogen can come off to form H^+ in water. This hydrogen is bonded to the acetic acid molecule in a way that is different from the other three hydrogens:

Ionizable hydrogen, which can come off to form H^+

acetic acid molecule

Some other examples of "-ic" acids are given in Table 7.8.

TABLE 7.8
Some acids with names that end in "ic."

Acid Formula	Acid Name	Significance
HCO_2H	Formic acid	Produces one H^+, given off by ants causing painful stings
HNO_3	Nitric acid	Widely used industrial and laboratory chemical, causes yellow color when spilled on skin
$HC_7H_5O_2$	Benzoic acid	Produces one H^+ per molecule used to preserve some foods.
$H_2C_2O_4$	Oxalic acid	Used in dyeing cloth

Acids very frequently contain oxygen. Sometimes the same element will combine with different numbers of oxygen atoms to produce more than one kind of acid. An example is provided by two acids formed when oxygen combines with sulfur and the sulfur oxides are dissolved in water. Sulfur trioxide, SO_3, is produced in the catalytic converters of some automobiles. It may then react with moisture in the air to produce sulfuric acid, H_2SO_4.

$$H_2O + SO_3 \longrightarrow H_2SO_4$$

There is some concern that this sulfuric acid may be as harmful to the lungs as the automobile exhaust pollutants which the catalytic converter removes. A chemical cousin of sulfuric acid is also a common air pollutant. It is formed, for example, when high sulfur residual fuel oil (a black tar-like material) is burned in power plants.

$$S \text{ (in residual fuel oil)} + O_2 \longrightarrow SO_2$$

The product of burning sulfur is sulfur dioxide gas, SO_2, which goes out the power plant stack. Sulfur dioxide gas dissolves in water (including raindrops)

$$H_2O + SO_2 \longrightarrow H_2SO_3$$

to form an acid with the formula H_2SO_3. This acid cannot be called sulfur*ic* acid because that name has already been given to H_2SO_4. Instead, H_2SO_3 is called sulfur*ous* acid. *An "-ous" acid always has fewer oxygens than the "-ic" acid of the same element.*

In a few cases a whole series of acids can be formed from the same element that has combined with different amounts of oxygen. Acids containing chlorine provide the best example. The first of these acids is formed when chlorine gas is bubbled into water,

$$Cl_2 + H_2O \longrightarrow HCl + HClO$$

to disinfect it for drinking or for use in a swimming pool. The hydrochloric acid, HCl, which is formed has already been discussed. The other product is HClO, a compound which is itself a very good disinfectant. It is called *hypo*chlor*ous* acid.

The chlorine atom can be bonded to as many as four oxygen atoms. This occurs in *perchlor*ic acid, $HClO_4$. Cold perchloric acid is a very inactive substance. When heated, though, it readily gives its oxygen to anything that will accept it. Hot perchloric acid is a strong **oxidizing agent**. It is widely used to oxidize completely and to dissolve biological tissue and plant material for chemical analysis. The "digested" sample can be analyzed for dangerous metals such as lead, or for other elements. The "digestion" of organic samples in hot perchloric acid can be dangerous because the mixture becomes explosive if too much organic matter is present. Even some "explosion proof" laboratory hoods have acquired gaping holes in their sides because of perchloric acid explosions.

In between HClO and $HClO_4$ are two other "oxy-acids" of chlorine. These are $HClO_2$ and $HClO_3$. Chlorous acid is the name given to $HClO_2$, and chloric acid is the name of $HClO_3$. The names for the oxy-acids of chlorine are summarized in Table 7.9.

TABLE 7.9
Oxy-Acids of Chlorine.

Acid Formula	Acid Name
HClO	*Hypo*chlor*ous* acid
$HClO_2$	Chlor*ous* acid
$HClO_3$	Chlor*ic* acid
$HClO_4$	*Per*chlor*ic* acid

Table 7.9 shows how a series of oxygen-containing acids is named. Each name contains "*chlor*" to show that it is a compound with a chlorine atom. The acid with the least amount of oxygen has "hypo-ous" in the name. The addition of a second oxygen atom produces an "-ous" acid. Further addition of oxygen yields the "-ic" acid. The acid with the most oxygen is a "per-ic" acid.

Another example of this system of naming is provided by the oxygen-containing acids of phosphorous. The phosphorous oxy-acid with a formula of H_3PO_2 is called *hypo*phosphor*ous* acid. The acid with a formula of H_3PO_3 is called phosphor*ous* acid. Phosphor*ic* acid is the name given to H_3PO_4. Phosphoric acid is an extremely important chemical. It is used in making essential phosphorous-containing fertilizers; for removing scale from metal surfaces (a process called pickling); as an ingredient of soft drinks and preserves; and in many other applications.

7.15

Bases

As we have seen, bases are chemical compounds which either contain hydroxide (OH^-) ion, or produce it in solution. An example of the latter type of compound is ammonia, which produces hydroxide ion by reacting with water.

$$H_2O + NH_3 \longrightarrow NH_4^+ + OH^-$$

Bases are named very simply with the name of the positive ion followed by the word, **hydroxide**. For example, LiOH is called lithium hydroxide. Some bases and their purposes are given in Table 7.10.

TABLE 7.10
Some bases and their significance.

Base Formula	Base Name	Significance
NaOH	Sodium hydroxide	Fourth in production among U.S. industrial chemicals, over 10 million tons per year
$Mg(OH)_2$	Magnesium hydroxide	Widely used in industry, sugar processing and medicine ("milk of magnesia")
KOH	Potassium hydroxide	Used to prepare other potassium compounds and in some alkaline batteries
$Ca(OH)_2$	Calcium hydroxide	A very inexpensive source of base, used to neutralize acid and has many other applications

7.16

Compounds Containing Three Elements: Salts

A **salt** is formed when the hydrogen in an acid is replaced by a metal or by a positive ion such as NH_4^+. If a piece of magnesium metal is placed in sulfuric acid,

$$Mg + H_2SO_4 \longrightarrow MgSO_4 + H_2\uparrow$$

the H in the H_2SO_4 is changed to H_2 gas and $MgSO_4$ is produced. The $MgSO_4$ salt is called magnesium sulf*ate*. An "-ic" acid (sulfuric acid) produces an "-ate" salt (magnesium sulfate). If magnesium reacts with sulfur*ous* acid,

$$Mg + H_2SO_3 \longrightarrow MgSO_3 + H_2\uparrow$$

$MgSO_3$ is a product. This salt is called magnesium sulf*ite*. An "-ous" acid (sulfurous acid) produces an "-ite" salt (magnesium sulfite).

Additional rules for naming salts can be seen from the salts of chlorine oxy-acids. When sodium hydroxide reacts with hypochlorous acid,

$$NaOH + HClO \longrightarrow NaClO + H_2O$$

the NaClO salt formed is called sodium *hypo*chlor*ite*. This salt is an important bleaching compound used as a laundry bleach. A "hypo-ous" acid forms a "hypo-ite" salt. The reaction of chlorous acid with sodium hydroxide,

$$NaOH + HClO_2 \longrightarrow NaClO_2 + H_2O$$

produces sodium chlor*ite*, $NaClO_2$. The reaction of chloric acid with sodium hydroxide,

$$NaOH + HClO_3 \longrightarrow NaClO_3 + H_2O$$

yields sodium chlor*ate*, $NaClO_3$. Finally, the reaction of perchloric acid and sodium hydroxide yields sodium *per*chlor*ate*, $NaClO_4$. In this example a "per-ic" acid yields a "per-ate" salt.

TABLE 7.11
Some salts and the acids from which they are formed.

Acid Formula	Acid Name	Salt Formula	Salt Name
H_3PO_2	Hypophosphorous acid	Na_3PO_2	Sodium hypophosphite
H_3PO_3	Phosphorous acid	Na_3PO_3	Sodium phosphite
H_3PO_4	Phosphoric acid	Na_3PO_4	Sodium phosphate
HNO_2	Nitrous acid	KNO_2	Potassium nitrite
HNO_3	Nitric acid	KNO_3	Potassium nitrate
H_3BO_3	Boric acid	Na_3BO_3	Sodium borate
$H_2C_2O_4$	Oxalic acid	$Na_2C_2O_4$	Sodium oxalate
H_2CO_3	Carbonic acid	$CaCO_3$	Calcium carbonate
HCl	Hydrochloric acid	NaCl	Sodium chloride

Table 7.11 gives some examples of salts and their names. It also gives the formulas and names of the acids from which these salts are formed. Several important acids do not contain oxygen and are named "hydro-ic" acids. Hydrochloric acid, HCl, is one important example.

These acids react with bases to form salts and water as shown in the following examples:

$$HCl + NaOH \longrightarrow NaCl + H_2O$$

*hydro*chloric acid   sodium hydroxide   sodium chlor*ide*

$$2\,HF + Ca(OH)_2 \longrightarrow CaF_2 + 2\,H_2O$$

*hydro*fluoric acid   calcium hydroxide   calcium fluor*ide*

$$HCN + KOH \longrightarrow KCN + H_2O$$

*hydro*cyanic acid   potassium hydroxide   potassium cyan*ide*

$$H_2S + 2\,NaOH \longrightarrow Na_2S + 2\,H_2O$$

*hydro*sulfuric acid   sodium hydroxide   sodium sulf*ide*

From these examples it is seen that "hydro-ic" acids form "-ide" salts.

7.17

Salts with Two Positive Ions

A number of important salts have two positive ions. For example, if one phthalic acid, $H_2C_8H_4O_4$, reacts with one potassium hydroxide,

$$H_2C_8H_4O_4 + KOH \longrightarrow KHC_8H_4O_4 + H_2O$$

only one of the two hydrogens reacts. The product is called potassium hydrogen phthalate.

This compound is very important in analytical chemistry because it reacts further with base and can be prepared in a very pure form. It is weighed out very accurately and reacts with solutions of sodium hydroxide,

$$KHC_8H_4O_4 + NaOH \longrightarrow KNaC_8H_4O_4 + H_2O$$

to **standardize** the sodium hydroxide. This is accomplished by the *titration* technique discussed in Section 7.8. The resulting sodium hydroxide solution, which has been determined very accurately, can be used to react with unknown acid solutions (titration). The analytical chemist calls potassium hydrogen phthalate by the name of KHP. Since it can be weighed out very accurately and used to measure the concentration of a solution used in chemical analysis, it is called a **primary standard**.

Many other examples of salts containing hydrogen ion as one of the positive ions may be given. Baking soda, $NaHCO_3$, is called sodium hydrogen carbonate. It is also called sodium bicarbonate. The "bi-" is often used to name a compound formed by the replacement of one hydrogen in an acid having two hydrogens. Sodium bicarbonate is formed when one sodium hydroxide reacts with one carbonic acid,

$$NaOH + H_2CO_3 \longrightarrow NaHCO_3 + H_2O$$

and a sodium ion replaces one of the hydrogens in the carbonic acid.

In cases where the acid from which a salt is formed has three hydrogens, the name of the salt has to indicate how many hydrogen ions are present. For example, phosphoric acid may react partly with sodium hydroxide to form either NaH_2PO_4 or Na_2HPO_4. The name sodium *di*hydrogen phosphate is given to NaH_2PO_4 to show that it contains two hydrogens and one sodium. The salt, Na_2HPO_4 is called *di*sodium hydrogen phosphate. The "di-" indicates that the salt has two sodiums.

Some salts are formed in which two metals are present. One example is "potash alum" $KAl(SO_4)_2$. It is called potassium aluminum sulfate to show that both potassium and aluminum are present. This salt is used to treat water. It reacts with water to form a jelly-like material that traps fine particles floating in the water and carries them to the bottom. Magnesium ammonium phosphate, $MgNH_4PO_4$ is another example of a salt with two different cations. This salt can be precipitated out of solution when magnesium salts and diammonium hydrogen phosphate react:

$$MgCl_2 + (NH_4)_2HPO_4 \longrightarrow MgNH_4PO_4\downarrow + NH_4Cl + HCl$$

The $MgNH_4PO_4$ precipitate can be washed with water in a filter, dried, and weighed to determine how much magnesium was present in the original solution.

Chapter Summary

Most inorganic compounds may be classified as *acids*, *bases*, or *salts*. Oxides do not fall strictly into these classifications, although many oxides form acids or bases with water.

Acids are compounds that have or produce hydrogen ion, H^+. Bases are compounds which have or produce hydroxide ion, OH^-. Acids react with bases to produce salts. A salt consists of an ionic compound containing a *cation other than* H^+ and an *anion other than* OH^-.

The properties of acids, bases, and salts in water solution are particularly interesting. Salts exist as ions in solution. Solutions of salts

Electroplating is often used to enhance the appearance of an object, as shown in this photo of silver-plated objects. (Courtesy of Shreve, Crump, and Low, Boston, Mass.)

conduct electricity well because the ions are capable of carrying an electrical current. Strong acids that are more or less completely ionized in solution also conduct electricity. Weak acids do not produce high concentrations of ions and their solutions do not conduct electricity well. Similarly, solutions of strong bases conduct electricity well; but solutions of weak bases do not. Compounds that conduct electricity well in water are called *electrolytes*.

The degree to which an acid or base *dissociates in solution* is a very important property. Strong acids dissociate 100% to H^+ ion and an anion. Weak acids may hardly dissociate at all. Some acids lie in between these two extremes. The distinction must be made between the degree of dissociation, or strength, of an acid and its concentration.

Buffers are solutions that resist changes in hydrogen ion concentration. They frequently consist of a mixture of a weak acid and one of its salts.

Titration is a common operation for measuring how much acid (or base) is required to react with a given volume of base (or acid). It is a widely performed operation in chemical analysis.

Chemists have devised systematic systems for naming chemical compounds. This aspect of chemistry is called *nomenclature*. Although naming chemicals comes naturally with experience, it is helpful to study the rules of nomenclature. These rules are summarized in the latter part of the chapter.

Chapter Review Questions

The following questions are designed as a self-teaching tool to help you review Chapter 6. The answers to each question follow. See Chapter Review Questions for Chapter 1 for further instructions.

1. An acid contains, or produces _____ in water; and a base contains or produces _____.

2. The chemical reaction between an acid and a base is a _____ reaction which produces a _____.

3. Acetic acid exists mostly as undissociated $HC_2H_3O_2$ in solution. It is therefore a _____ acid.

4. In acids the color of litmus is _____ and in bases it is _____ .

5. Substances which can act as either acids or bases are said to be _____ .

6. The formula of the hydronium ion is _____ .

7. An acid, base, or salt which is completely ionized in solution and conducts electricity extremely well is called a _____ .

8. When an electrical current (direct current) is passed through a solution of sodium chloride, water is _____ at the electrode called the _____ and chloride ion is _____ at the _____ .

9. In terms of acid strength, sulfuric acid is _____ ; hydrocyanic acid is _____ ; and phosphoric acid is _____ .

10. At a total concentration of 0.00001 mole/liter, acetic acid is _____% ionized, and at 0.1 mole/liter it is _____% ionized.

11. A solution which resists changes in hydrogen ion concentration is called a _____ .

12. A buffer solution may contain a mixture of a weak acid and _____ _____ .

13. Solutions of 0.100 M HCl and 0.100 M acetic acid will have different concentrations of _____ but will still react with the same amount of _____ .

14. Many acids such as sulfuric acid are made when _____ oxides react with water.

15. The reaction of many metal oxides and water produces _____ .

16. A base which is among the top five industrial chemicals is _____ , and an acid in the same group is _____ .

17. The process by which a measured amount of acid reacts with a measured amount of base to the point of neutralization is called _____ .

18. The reaction of an anion from a salt to produce OH^- ion is called _____ .

19. In water the molar concentration of H^+ ion multiplied by the molar concentration of OH^- ion has the value, _____ .

20. A salt such as $NaHCO_3$ which contains a hydrogen ion is called an _____ .

21. Salts containing OH^- in addition to some other anion are called _____ .

22. Two general types of names for chemical compounds are _____ names and _____ names.

23. The process of naming compounds is called _____ .

24. The compound, $FeCl_2$, may be called _____ or _____ .

25. An "-ous" acid always has _____ oxygens than an "-ic" acid of the same element.

Answers to Chapter Review Questions

1. hydrogen ion, H^+, hydroxide ion, OH^-

2. neutralization, salt

3. weak

4. red, blue

5. amphoteric
6. H_3O^+
7. strong electrolyte
8. reduced, cathode, oxidized, anode
9. strong, weak, moderately weak
10. 71, 1.3
11. buffer
12. one of its salts
13. H^+ ion, base
14. nonmetal
15. bases
16. sodium hydroxide, sulfuric acid
17. titration
18. hydrolysis
19. 1×10^{-14}
20. acid salt
21. basic salts
22. common, systematic
23. nomenclature
24. ferrous chloride, iron(II) chloride
25. fewer

Exercises for Chapter 7

1. Dry $CaSO_4$ absorbs water to produce a product with a specific number of waters of hydration. Exactly 136 g of $CaSO_4$ exposed to humid air gained enough water to weigh 172 g. What is the formula of the product with the waters of hydration?

2. Give the formulas of each of the following:

   Magnesium acetate _____

   Calcium monohydrogen phosphate _____

   Aluminum sulfate _____

   Calcium hypochlorite _____

3. A 25-ml sample of acetic acid was titrated with 0.1 M sodium hydroxide. A total of 37.5 ml of the NaOH solution was required to neutralize the acetic acid. What was the concentration of acetic acid?

4. A common error in speaking the chemical language is to confuse acidic (pronounced uh-sid-ik) with acetic (pronounced uh-seat-ik). What is the correct meaning of each of these terms? What is the difference between ammonia and ammonium?

5. The following is a list which contains the names of three cations and three anions: hypochlorite, hydrogen, sodium, sulfate, calcium, nitrate. List the three cations. List the three anions. Give the formulas of nine compounds that can be made by various combinations of these.

6. Write a chemical reaction in which $NaHCO_3$ acts as an acid. Write another in which it acts as a base, remembering that if H_2CO_3 is produced in solution it largely goes to carbon dioxide gas and water.

7. Write the electron-dot structure of the hydronium ion, H_3O^+.

8. Explain by chemical reactions how a mixture of $NaHCO_3$ and Na_2CO_3 in water would act as a buffer.

9. What would be the chemical reaction at the cathode if an electrical current were passed through a solution of $CuCl_2$? What would be the reaction at the anode?

10. Formulas of some chemical compounds are given in the lefthand column. Match the formula of each compound with its correct name in the righthand column.

CaO   Potassium sulfide
SiO_2 Dinitrogen pentoxide
K_2S Nitrogen dioxide
$AlCl_3$ Silicon dioxide
NO_2 Potassium bromide
N_2O_5 Sodium iodide
NaI   Calcium oxide
KBr   Magnesium fluoride
MgF_2 Calcium fluoride
CaF_2 Aluminum chloride

11.   Match the names in the right column with the formulas in the left column.

Na_2CO_3 Calcium sulfate
$CaSO_3$ Potassium perchlorate
$Al(OH)_3$ Sodium carbonate
$CaSO_4$ Calcium phosphate
$NaNO_2$ Aluminum hydroxide
$Ca_3(PO_4)_2$ Calcium sulfite
$NaNO_3$ Calcium hypochlorite
$Ca(ClO)_2$ Sodium nitrate
$KClO_4$ Sodium nitrite
$Ca_2(PO_3)_2$ Calcium phosphite

12.   Match the names in the right column with the formulas in the left column.

K_2HPO_4 Sodium hydrogen sulfate
$KHCO_3$ Sodium hydrogen oxalate
$NaHSO_4$ Dipotassium hydrogen phosphate
KH_2PO_4 Sodium hydrogen phthalate
$NaHC_8H_4O_4$ Potassium hydrogen carbonate
$NaHC_2O_4$ Potassium dihydrogen phosphate

13.   Fill in each of the following blanks with the number corresponding to the meaning of each of the prefixes. The first one is done for you as an example.

___4___tetra-   _____mono-   _____octa-   _____deca-   _____di-
_____penta-   _____hepta-   _____tri-   _____nona-   _____sexa-

14.   Give the correct name to each of the following compounds. The first one is done for you as an example.

N_2O_5 _dinitrogen pentoxide_____ N_2O_4 _____
NO_2 _____ N_2O_3 _____
NO _____ N_2O _____

15.   Iron in a compound can also be designated as ferrous or ferric. Similarly copper (Cu) may be called cuprous or cupric. Tin (Sn) may be called stannous or stannic. Name each of the following compounds with two acceptable names. The first one is done for you as an example.

$FeCl_2$ _____ferrous chloride_____ or _____iron(II) chloride_____
$FeCl_3$ _____ or _____
CuCl _____ or _____
$CuCl_2$ _____ or _____
$SnCl_2$ _____ or _____
$SnCl_4$ _____ or _____

16. In each of the following chemical reactions fill in the formula of the missing compound. The rest of the chemical equation is balanced.

$2 N_2 + 3 O_2 =$ _____ (dinitrogen trioxide)

$KOH + SO_2 =$ _____ (potassium hydrogen sulfite)

$KOH + H_3PO_4 =$ _____ (potassium dihydrogen phosphate)

17. Give one or two examples of compounds in which each of the following is used.

-ic	acetic acid	hydrochloric acid
ide-		
-ous		
hypo-		
per-		
-ite		
-ate		

Water occupies more than 70% of the Earth's surface and is essential to all forms of life for transporting nutrients through soil and bodies of living things. Water also provides for all sorts of recreational activities. (Courtesy of USDA, National Park Service; Richard Frear, photographer)

8

Water and Water Pollution

8.1

What is Water?

Water, H_2O, has one of the more commonly known chemical formulas. Even persons who have never had a chemistry course know what is meant by "H-two-Oh." Despite a rather simple formula, water is really a very complicated substance. It has a number of important properties which make it quite different from all other substances. These special qualities combined with the abundance of water make it a key material for geological processes, energy production, mining, industrial operations, agriculture, transportation, and life, itself. Water is the solvent in which all life processes are carried out. It was in the watery soup making up the Earth's oceans that life originated millions of years ago.

The living material in both plants and animals is made up largely of water. Our bodies are about 70% water by weight. Water dissolves the salts, gases, sugars, and proteins that must be carried to and from living cells as they function and grow. The water in streams, lakes, oceans, and sewage treatment plants contains plants and animals that get their nutrients from material dissolved in water. The water also carries away the waste products from these plants and animals.

Considering the large quantities used for irrigation, industry, and municipal water supplies, water is by far the most commonly used chemical. Throughout history the quality and quantity of available water have been big factors determining the rise and fall of whole civilizations. As recently as the early 1970's, changes in climate including drastically decreased rainfall produced deserts in African countries which once supported flourishing civilizations. Thousands of people starved in Ethiopia and other African nations as a result. Great plagues of typhoid, cholera, and other water-carried diseases sentenced millions to agonizing deaths in times past. An ominous annual increase in cancer deaths suggests that man-made chemicals that get into drinking water may be causing millions of equally agonizing deaths in the U.S. and other industrialized nations. It is easy to see that water is a very important substance. That is why a whole chapter is devoted to water and water pollution.

8.2

Properties of Water

Water has a number of special properties that give it a unique place among chemical compounds. These were discussed in Section 6.3 in connection with water's solvent action. Recall that water is a colorless, tasteless, odorless liquid. It boils at 100°C (212°F) and freezes at 0°C (32°F). It is in general a stable chemical compound, which is hard to break down into hydrogen and oxygen. It does react chemically with many substances, however.

Water is an excellent solvent for many compounds. It is an especially good solvent for many acids, bases, and salts. It also dissolves sugars very well but is a poor solvent for many organic compounds such as oils and greases. Gases dissolve in water. Those gases which react with water, or with other things dissolved in water, may dissolve particularly well.

The solvent behavior of water is related to the chemical nature of the water molecule. Recall that this molecule is a *dipole* with a positive and negative end. Therefore, the molecules of water can cluster around both cations and anions in solution. In addition water forms *hydrogen bonds*. Hydrogen bonding exerts a strong influence on the structure of water in the liquid and solid form. As a result substances that can form hydrogen bonds dissolve.

8.3

Heating and Cooling of Water

"A watched pot never boils." Anybody who has to have a cup of coffee in the morning to pull the mental processes together has experienced the frustration of getting up too late and waiting for the water in the coffee pot to boil while rush hour traffic builds up outside. It takes a lot of heat to make water hot. Water is said to have a high **heat capacity**. This means that it is necessary to put a lot of heat energy into water to raise its temperature. Heat energy is measured as **calories**. *One gram of water requires 1 calorie (cal) of heat to raise its temperature 1°C.* (Water weighing 1 g has a volume about the same as that of a sugar cube.) This **heat capacity** is much higher than that of alcohol, gasoline, or other common liquids. The high heat capacity of water is largely due to the fact that during heating so much of the energy is used up in breaking hydrogen bonds.

The high heat capacity of water is very useful. In a building cooling system water can be cooled to near freezing, then circulated through a large building. In going through the building the water picks up a lot of heat before it warms up and is returned for cooling to complete the cycle.

Fish and other living things in water have little control over their own temperatures. They are just as hot or as cold as the surrounding water. Because of its high heat capacity, however, water resists changes in the temperature of its surroundings. When a warm fall day suddenly turns bitterly cold, the temperature of a large body of water changes very little. Because of water's high heat capacity, the water of a pond or lake loses its heat only slowly to the surrounding cold air. If this were not the case, the fish, turtles, and frogs would suffer severe temperature changes which would possibly destroy them.

Water's high heat capacity makes it excellent for use in automobile cooling systems. A relatively small volume of water picks up heat from the engine block and head and transfers the heat to the radiator where it is lost to the air circulating over the radiator surface.

8.4

Boiling Water

Although it takes a lot of heat energy to make water warmer, truly huge quantities of heat are required to make water boil. To make water boil it must be heated so much that the molecules become completely separated and fly away from one another as a gas (steam). All of the hydrogen bonds must be broken and all of the attraction between the negative and positive ends of the water molecules must be overcome. Water boils at a temperature of 100°C. The steam which comes off of the boiling water is also at 100°C. However, a total of 540 cal of heat are required to change 1 g of liquid water to steam at 100°C. Although

Geysers of Sonoma County, California are being tapped by the Pacific Gas and Electric Company to generate electricity. The steam wells in the photograph extract the steam and hot water from the hot springs that are used to produce power at the electrical plant. (Courtesy of Pacific Gas and Electric Co.)

its temperature is not higher than boiling water, the steam contains 540 more calories of heat energy per gram. This is called the **heat of vaporization** of water. It is an enormous amount of heat considering that 1 cal is required to increase the temperature of 1 g of water by 1°C, or that it takes only 100 cal to go from ice water to water hot enough to boil. When 1 g of steam at 100°C changes (condenses) to liquid water at 100°C, 540 cal of heat are **released**.

The tremendous amounts of energy transferred when water changes back and forth between steam and liquid water are very important in nature and widely used in industry. Steam is frequently used to transfer heat in industrial processes and in heating buildings. An efficient way to heat a large building is to generate steam in a boiler, carry it to rooms through pipes insulated to prevent heat loss, and condense it to liquid water in radiators in the rooms. The large amounts of heat released when the steam condenses heats the rooms.

Steam is widely used to provide heat needed for industrial processes whenever extremely high temperatures are not required. One example is the use of steam carried through pipes to dry a powdered product. It is often more convenient and safer to pipe steam to an industrial process than to use heat directly from a flame.

Water does not have to be at its boiling temperature of 100°C to form water vapor (observe Figure 8.1). This is because even at lower

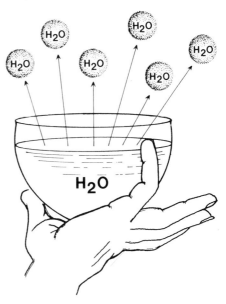

FIGURE 8.1
Water evaporates at room temperature.

temperatures water molecules are in motion from heat, and some of the molecules escape from the liquid surface as a vapor. Wet clothes dry out on a clothesline, and sweat evaporates from our bodies at temperatures

far below boiling. When 1 g of water evaporates at a temperature below boiling, more than 540 cal of heat are absorbed from the surroundings. As a result, the evaporation has a cooling effect. This is why wet clothes on a clothesline feel cold and clammy, even on a warm day. It is also the reason that evaporating sweat cools our bodies. Similarly, when water evaporates from a lake or stream, heat is taken from the body of water, which cools it. For that reason a lake is seldom as warm as the surrounding air on a hot summer day.

The tendency of water to evaporate is called **vapor pressure**. Vapor pressure is less at lower temperatures. That is why clothes do not dry so rapidly on a cool day as on a warm day.

8.5

Freezing Water

When water freezes, two important things happen. The water gives off a lot of heat, and it expands. When 1 g of water freezes at 0°C it gives off 80 cal of heat. This large amount of heat must be taken up by the surroundings. It explains why a considerable time is required for a tray of ice cubes to freeze in a refrigerator. When a gram of ice thaws, 80 cal of heat must be absorbed from the surroundings. A small amount of ice absorbs a lot of heat while thawing, which makes ice an excellent cooler. A 6-pack of warm beer or a ripe watermelon covered with crushed ice quickly cools to 0°C and remains at that temperature until all of the ice has melted.

Whenever liquid water and ice are in contact at equilibrium, both are at 0°C. When liquid water freezes, the temperature of both the ice and the water stay at 0°C until all of the liquid has frozen. After all the water has frozen, the ice may reach temperatures below 0°C. Similarly, when ice changes to liquid, the ice stays at 0°C until it has all thawed.

The heat given off when water freezes, or absorbed when ice thaws, keeps the temperature of the water in lakes and reservoirs at around 0°C in colder regions during the winter. When water freezes, the molecules form hydrogen bonds which hold the ice in a very rigid structure. As a result, ice expands and occupies more space than does liquid water. The less dense ice floats. It acts as an insulating material on the surface of a body of water and slows further freezing. Fish survive in the cold water below the ice.

The expansion of ice is not so fortunate for the forgetful automobile owner who neglects to put antifreeze in his auto cooling system. The expansion of ice in the engine can crack the engine block. The unlucky home owner whose furnace fails during a midwinter vacation may return home to face a huge plumbing bill because of pipes burst by ice. Wet, freezing soil can also crack building foundations, basement walls, and street pavements. These effects are taken into account by engineers when they construct buildings and estimate costs of street maintenance in cold climates. (Figure 8.2)

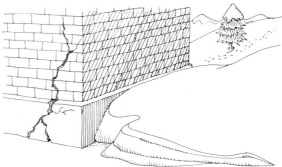

FIGURE 8.2
The tremendous forces of expansion from freezing water must be considered in building construction.

8.6

The Things that Water Dissolves

Dissolved substances (solutes) are very important in considering the role of water in the environment and in living systems. Water dissolves many substances that are not soluble in other common liquids. Ionic compounds, such as salts and minerals, are particularly important. So are dissolved gases, such as oxygen. These dissolved substances are involved with the formation of mineral deposits, the carrying out of life processes, and many industrial operations. The fact that water molecules have positive and negative ends and attract ions has already been explained. Many of the materials which take part in processes in the body are ions. Blood and urine contain dissolved NaCl. Calcium ions, Ca^{2+}, and hydrogen phosphate ions, HPO_4^{2-}, must be transported through the body to form bone. Potassium ions, K^+, move across nerve cell membranes to transmit nerve signals in the body. Poisonous cadmium ion, Cd^{2+}, picked up from plumbing in almost all drinking water systems is carried by water in the body where it damages kidneys and other body organs.

Many common minerals have formed from the combination of ions in water. Limestone deposits were formed in ancient sea beds by the combination of calcium and carbonate ions in water.

$$Ca^{2+} + CO_3^{2-} \longrightarrow CaCO_3\downarrow$$

Iron ores were formed by the combination of ferric ion and hydroxide ions,

$$Fe^{3+} + 3\,OH^- \longrightarrow Fe(OH)_3\downarrow$$

which produces ferric hydroxide. This material later lost water to form iron oxide.

$$2\,Fe(OH)_3 \longrightarrow Fe_2O_3 + 3\,H_2O$$

Some minerals are mined with water. Water can be pumped into a formation of NaCl (called a salt dome) through a well drilled into it (Figure 8.3). The **brine** containing dissolved NaCl is pumped out, and the water evaporated to yield solid salt. Some salt lakes and salt marshes are "mined" for their salts. The water from Searles Lake,

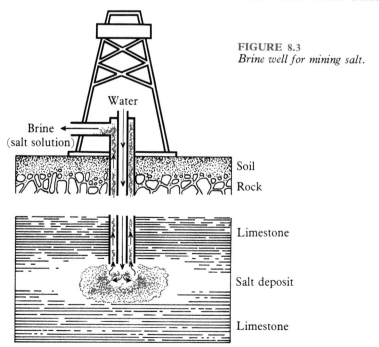

FIGURE 8.3
Brine well for mining salt.

Marshlands provide sanctuary for many forms of wildlife. The ability of marshes to support life can be threatened by water pollution caused by poisoning from chemicals. (Courtesy of the National Park Service, U.S. Dept of the Interior)

California, is about one-third dissolved salts. These are mostly NaCl, KCl, Na_2CO_3, and Na_2SO_4. This lake water is evaporated to produce KCl.

Gases dissolved in water are important for life processes, geological changes, and other things. For example, in the equation describing the formation of limestone the carbonate ion, CO_3^{2-}, dissolved in water reacts with calcium ion to form the limestone. The carbonate ion is produced when carbon dioxide gas dissolved in water reacts with hydroxide ion.

$$CO_2 + 2\,OH^- \longrightarrow CO_3^{2-} + H_2O$$

Release of dissolved carbon dioxide causes soft drinks to fizz and gives them their stinging taste. Carbon dioxide dissolved in blood is carried away from cells in the body. The carbon dioxide is produced by cells as "exhaust gas" from energy-producing chemical processes.

Oxygen dissolved in water is absorbed by the gills of fish. Water transports dissolved oxygen away from algae (microscopic plants that grow in water). Algae produce oxygen as a waste product from photosynthesis (the process by which carbon dioxide is turned into biological material with the aid of energy from sunlight).

Nitrogen dissolved in blood under the high pressure in a diving suit can come out of solution when the diver comes to the surface. Little bubbles are formed in the blood causing the painful condition called the "bends."

The amount of gas that dissolves in water increases with increasing pressure. If the pressure of the gas doubles, the amount of gas that dissolves also doubles. Soft drinks are bottled under pressure from carbon dioxide. When the bottle is opened the pressure is released, and some of the CO_2 comes out of solution as bubbles or foam.

8.7

Water in Other Compounds

Many compounds have a strong thirst for water. In the case of salts, this water is frequently bound to the molecule as **water of hydration**. The example of copper sulfate containing water of hydration was given in Section 7.11. Powdered calcium sulfate reacts with water to form a rigid solid,

$$CaSO_4 + 2H_2O = CaSO_4 \cdot 2H_2O$$

in which two molecules of water are chemically bound to each $CaSO_4$. The product is **hydrated** calcium sulfate. The *waters of hydration* are shown in the formula by a dot. Calcium sulfate with no water is an **anhydrous** (without water) salt. Powdered calcium sulfate containing only about one water molecule for each two $CaSO_4$'s is marketed as plaster of Paris. It is mixed with water and poured into molds where it hardens into a solid, $CaSO_4 \cdot 2H_2O$. The process is used in making little statues, wall plaques, industrial molds, and casts for broken bones.

Sodium carbonate decahydrate,

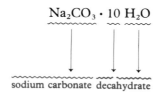

$$Na_2CO_3 \cdot 10H_2O$$

sodium carbonate decahydrate

is another important hydrated salt. It is used in detergents, as a household cleaner, and for water softening. When this salt is dissolved in water, it reacts with the water and makes it very basic by producing hydroxide ions, OH^-. This is one reason why it is used in detergents, because most of the common detergents work best in a basic solution. Basic solutions dissolve grease pretty well, which makes a solution of sodium carbonate decahydrate a pretty good cleaner around the kitchen. The carbonate ion from this salt reacts with calcium ion (which causes water hardness)

$$Ca^{2+} + CO_3^{2-} \longrightarrow CaCO_3\downarrow$$

and removes hardness from water by producing solid calcium carbonate, $CaCO_3$. For that reason sodium carbonate decahydrate is a good water softener (removes hardness). The water softening property is another reason why $Na_2CO_3 \cdot 10H_2O$ is used in detergents. Calcium and magnesium ions, responsible for water hardness, interfere with the action of detergents. Anhydrous sodium carbonate, Na_2CO_3, should not be used in powdered detergents because of its strong attraction for water. If a child should accidentally put some detergent containing Na_2CO_3 in its mouth, water would be drawn from tissue in the mouth and throat, greatly increasing the damage.

Many anhydrous salts and other anhydrous compounds have such a strong attraction for water that they will take it from humid air. Some anhydrous salts are used as **drying agents** (desiccating agents). Electronic components, switches, and fine metal parts are sometimes packed for shipment with little packets of anhydrous $CaSO_4$. The calcium sulfate absorbs moisture from the air in the container. This dries the air and keeps moisture away from the contents. Corrosion (rusting), which requires moisture, is prevented.

Compounds which absorb moisture from the air are said to be **hygroscopic**. Some compounds will absorb enough moisture to dissolve themselves. This can be seen by observing a pellet of sodium hydroxide, which is often sold for use in the laboratory and is about the size and shape of a pea cut in half. When one of these pellets is exposed to the atmosphere, the surface soon becomes shiny due to absorbed water. If the pellet is allowed to remain in the open air for a few days, nothing will be left but a small puddle of very concentrated NaOH solution. Acids such as H_2SO_4 or H_3PO_4 are also frequently very hygroscopic. Materials that remove enough water from the air to dissolve themselves are said to be **deliquescent**.

Some materials lose their water of hydration when exposed to the air. One of these is lignite, a low grade of coal found in hundreds of billions of tons in North Dakota. When freshly mined, lignite is a shiny, black, reasonably hard material containing about 30% water. The water is necessary to maintain lignite in a hard, crystal-like form. When lignite is exposed to air, it loses water and large chunks of it turn to a gray powder sometimes called "bug dust." This can happen in the open cars of a freight train used to transport lignite. The "bug dust" readily blows off to the displeasure of persons along the railroad. Such a loss of water is called **efflorescence**. Very frequently when a substance in the form of a nicely shaped crystal undergoes efflorescence, the crystal crumbles and loses its shape.

8.8

What is Natural Water?

Water occurs throughout the world in oceans, streams, lakes, under the ground, and in the atmosphere. About five-sevenths of the Earth's surface is covered by water, sometimes as ice or snow a mile or more deep. The movement of water through these places is described by the hydrologic cycle shown in Figure 8.4.

Water found in lakes, streams, and reservoirs is called surface water. Water under the ground is called ground water. Water without much salt dissolved in it is called fresh water. The water which man uses is primarily fresh surface water and ground water. In arid (low rainfall) regions near the ocean (such as Southern California) some ocean water is now used. The dissolved salt has to be removed by a process called

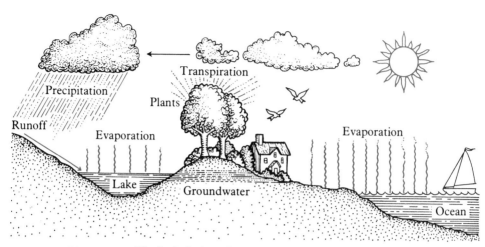

FIGURE 8.4   *The hydrologic cycle.*

desalination. This source is likely to become more important as the demand for fresh water increases. Ground waters in some areas also contain salt and are sometimes desalinated for use.

Ground water and surface water may have different characteristics. Many substances either dissolve in surface water or become suspended in it on its path to the ocean. Water in a lake or reservoir may contain the fertilizer materials needed for the growth of plants which float in the water (algae). Water may contain a lot of organic material from sewage, crop residues, or feedlot wastes. This water normally contains many bacteria which feed on the organic material. All of these things have a strong effect upon the quality of surface water.

Ground water dissolves minerals from the formations through which it passes. Most bacteria originally present in ground water are gradually filtered out as the water seeps through the ground. Sometimes the salt content becomes too high for use. Generally, though, ground water is a better source of drinking water than is surface water. This is partly because man's influence is limited below ground.

In the continental U.S., an average of approximately 3,900,000,000,000 gallons of water fall as precipitation each day. This amounts to 30 in. of rainfall per year. About two-thirds of this water is lost by evaporation and transpiration (loss of water vapor by plants). Much of the remainder is available for use. As shown in Figure 8.5, uneven distribution of precipitation is a major water supply problem in the U.S. Some of greatest demand for water occurs in areas of low rainfall, for example, Southern California and Arizona.

About 46% of the water used in the U.S. is taken by agriculture, mostly for irrigation. About the same amount is required by industry, mostly as cooling water to get rid of waste heat. Municipal water works account for about 8% of the water. The demand for water continues to increase. Particularly in areas having a low supply of water, more efficient ways of using it must be developed. In some of the rapidly growing regions in the southwestern U.S., water soon may have to be purified to remove some of the dissolved salts, then reused.

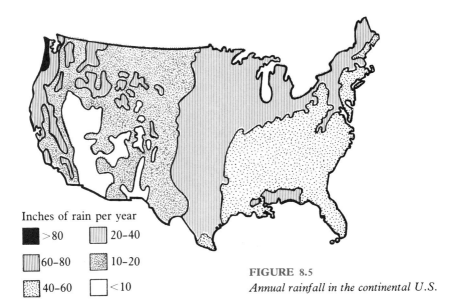

Inches of rain per year

■ >80   ▥ 20–40

▥ 60–80   ▨ 10–20

▨ 40–60   □ <10

FIGURE 8.5
Annual rainfall in the continental U.S.

Bodies of water behave in ways that affect the quality of the water. Water **stratification** is the best example of this. It occurs because warm water is less dense than colder water. A particular volume of water at 20°C weighs less than the same volume of water at 4°C. Water is most dense at 4°C. Below that temperature water expands until it freezes. Relatively warm, lighter water floats on top of colder water forming layers in lakes and reservoirs. The stratification phenomenon of water is illustrated in Figure 8.6. During the summer months a surface layer, the **epilimnion**, is heated by the sun and floats upon the bottom layer, or

FIGURE 8.6

Stratification of a lake. CH_2O is used to designate the "chemical formula" of biomass produced by photosynthesis.

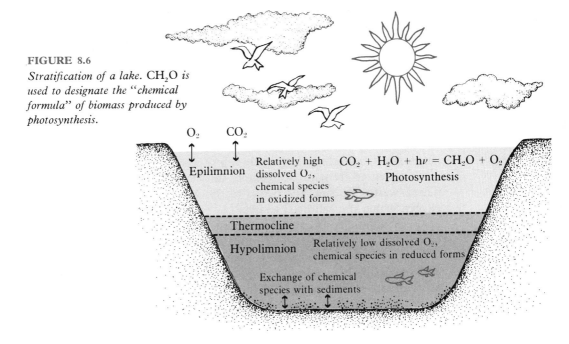

O_2 CO_2

Epilimnion   Relatively high dissolved O_2, chemical species in oxidized forms $CO_2 + H_2O + h\nu = CH_2O + O_2$
Photosynthesis

Thermocline

Hypolimnion   Relatively low dissolved O_2, chemical species in reduced forms

Exchange of chemical species with sediments

hypolimnion. The thin layer in between is the thermocline. These layers do not mix much. Their chemistry and biology are different. The epilimnion, which is exposed to sunlight, may have a heavy growth of algae. The epilimnion dissolves oxygen from the atmosphere. For that reason the water in the epilimnion is said to be **aerobic.** Generally, little sunlight penetrates to the hypolimnion. In the hypolimnion, bacteria feed on organic matter and use up most of the dissolved oxygen. When this happens, the water becomes **anaerobic.** As the water cools during the fall of the year, the water in the upper layer becomes more dense, and it sinks. This causes mixing known as **overturn.**

Living things affect the chemistry of bodies of water. Algae and bacteria are mostly responsible for these effects. As mentioned previously, algae are very small green plants which are suspended in the water. They use sunlight and carbon dioxide dissolved in the water to manufacture living material. The process is called **photosynthesis.** The organic matter manufactured by the algae may be represented by the simplified formula, $[CH_2O]$. It is placed in brackets to show that it is a simplification of the real formula. The photosynthesis reaction carried out by algae is

$$CO_2 + H_2O + \text{sunlight} \longrightarrow [CH_2O] + O_2\uparrow$$

The photosynthesis process gives off oxygen. It also produces the organic matter used as food by animals in water. This organic matter is essential for fish. If algae grow too well in water, too much organic material is produced. Bacteria decay this material and use up dissolved oxygen in the water. This kills fish and gives the water a bad odor. Such a condition is called **eutrophication.** It happens when water contains too much fertilizer from sewage, detergent phosphates, or farmland runoff. This fertilizer causes the algae to grow too well.

Bacteria are very small single-celled organisms that cannot perform photosynthesis. They consume many kinds of waste materials for food. In effect, they function as "waste disposals" for nature. They decompose organic matter, $[CH_2O]$, in water by the reaction,

$$[CH_2O] + O_2 \xrightarrow{\text{bacteria}} CO_2\uparrow + H_2O$$

which is the reverse of photosynthesis. This reaction uses up oxygen. When too much organic waste gets into water, the bacteria use up all the dissolved oxygen to decompose the organic matter. The water can no longer support fish life. Frequently fish kills result when heavy rains wash organic matter from cattle feedlots into lakes, streams, or reservoirs. These wastes do not kill fish directly, but their decay uses up the oxygen which the fish need to live.

Acids and bases can be important in natural waters. If too much of either gets into water, it is harmful to living things in the water and makes it unsuitable for drinking. **Acid mine water** is the most common acid pollutant. It results when special kinds of bacteria convert sulfur-containing minerals into H_2SO_4 in coal mines.

Many of the water-bearing geological formations in the western U.S. have too much base in them. The water from these formations is called **alkali water** because of the base content. This kind of water is undesirable for livestock or for irrigation.

Alkalinity is one of the most important characteristics of water. It is frequently measured at the water treatment plant or by the fisheries biologist. Alkalinity is the capacity of water to react with acid. It is normally due to bicarbonate ion, HCO_3^-, present along with Mg^{2+} or Ca^{2+}. Bicarbonate ion reacts with hydrogen ion from acids.

$$H^+ + HCO_3^- \longrightarrow H_2O + CO_2\uparrow$$

Hydroxide ion, OH^-, and carbonate ion, CO_3^{2-}, also contribute to alkalinity.

Alkalinity is important in water treatment because many of the chemicals used to treat water are acids. One such chemical is aluminum sulfate, $Al_2(SO_4)_3$. Aluminum sulfate reacts in water,

$$Al_2(SO_4)_3 + 6\,H_2O \longrightarrow 2\,Al(OH)_3\downarrow + 6\,H^+ + 3\,SO_4^{2-}$$

to produce aluminum hydroxide and hydrogen ion. The $Al(OH)_3$ is a jelly-like material which settles from the water and carries very fine particles with it. This clarifies the water (makes it clear). The H^+ ion must be removed, or it will cause the water to become too acidic and will stop the formation of more $Al(OH)_3$. Normally the hydrogen ion reacts with alkalinity in the water.

$$H^+ + HCO_3^- \longrightarrow H_2O + CO_2\uparrow$$

If enough alkalinity is not present naturally it must be put in, usually by adding Na_2CO_3.

Water hardness, mentioned in Section 8.7, is another important characteristic of water. It is due to the presence of Ca^{2+} and Mg^{2+} ions. These ions in water react with soap to form a solid, curdy, useless form of soap. This is the infamous bathtub ring. Enough soap must be added to the hard water to react with all of the hardness before any suds are obtained. Hard water also causes deposits of scale to form inside water pipes. This occurs when calcium ion and carbonate ion react,

$$Ca^{2+} + CO_3^{2-} \longrightarrow CaCO_3\downarrow$$

to form deposits of calcium carbonate. Since the CO_3^{2-} comes from water alkalinity, the alkalinity-hardness relationship is an important one. A little bit of scale in pipes is a good thing. It slows down corrosion and prevents the water from dissolving toxic heavy metals from the pipe. Too much scale clogs the pipes and is a major problem in water distribution systems.

The content of dissolved oxygen is important in water. The dissolved oxygen content of a natural water determines how well the water supports fish life. It is an overall measure of water quality, because water with a low oxygen content frequently contains too much organic matter and bacteria and can support few fish. A liter of water in contact with air at 25°C can contain up to 8 mg of oxygen. This increases to 15 mg at

0°C. The amount of oxygen actually found in water is usually less than the maximum because bacteria use it up faster than it dissolves from air. This is a more serious problem in a stagnant pond than in a free-running stream where water is stirred with air.

Dissolved oxygen is undesirable in boiler feedwater and water used for cooling or heat transfer systems because it causes corrosion. It can be removed by sodium sulfite,

$$2\,Na_2SO_3 + O_2 \longrightarrow 2\,Na_2SO_4$$

or hydrazine, N_2H_4:

$$N_2H_4 + O_2 \longrightarrow 2\,H_2O + N_2\uparrow$$

When used in this way, these compounds are called **oxygen scavengers**.

Potassium ion, K^+, and compounds of nitrogen and phosphorus are fertilizers in water. They are needed for the growth of plants. The contribution of fertilizers in water to excess growth of algae, causing eutrophication, has already been mentioned. Nitrogen is normally found in water as nitrate ion, NO_3^-. Phosphorus occurs as monohydrogen phosphate, HPO_4^{2-}, or dihydrogen phosphate, $H_2PO_4^-$.

Salts of sulfate ion, SO_4^{2-}, are found in water. Generally, sulfate comes from dissolved calcium sulfate, $CaSO_4$. Too much calcium sulfate dissolved in water gives it a bitter taste. Such water is called gypsum water from the name of the $CaSO_4$ mineral.

Chloride ion, Cl^-, is always found in natural water. If too much chloride ion is present, it indicates salt water pollution. In many areas, irrigation waters frequently dissolve too much salt. This makes the water unfit for further irrigation or drinking. Chloride salts are used widely in industry, and hundreds of tons of sodium chloride and calcium chloride are used each year for street de-icing. Chloride from these sources eventually gets into natural waters. Chlorine disinfectant added to water is eventually converted to chloride ion. Domestic wastes contribute an appreciable amount of chloride to sewage water.

Fluoride ion, F^-, is an important and controversial species in drinking water. Around 1930 it was shown that fluoride affects bone and tooth structure development. It prevents tooth decay at a level of approximately 1 ppm (part per million) in water. Too much fluoride can cause brown spots on teeth and deterioration of bones. Like almost any other chemical, it has been accused of causing cancer. The deliberate addition of fluoride to water, known as water fluoridation, is practiced in many domestic water systems. This practice has caused much hoop-la in cities where it has been started or proposed.

Two elements in water are particularly important because of staining and coloring. These are iron and manganese. When found in water, iron is normally present as ferrous ion, Fe^{2+}. When water containing ferrous ion is exposed to air, the oxygen in the air oxidizes the Fe^{2+},

$$4\,Fe^{2+} + O_2 + 10\,H_2O \longrightarrow 4\,Fe(OH)_3\downarrow + 8\,H^+$$

Sludge removed by filter drums, which separate solids from water, is usually disposed of in landfills. In some cases, it can also be dried for use as fertilizer. (Courtesy of The Maytag Co.)

to red-brown solid $Fe(OH)_3$. This substance deposits on bathroom fixtures and clothing. It is very difficult to remove. Similarly, manganese is found in water as Mn^{2+} ion. It reacts with oxygen in air,

$$2\,Mn^{2+} + O_2 + 2\,H_2O \longrightarrow 2\,MnO_2 + 4\,H^+$$

to yield black MnO_2. This substance leaves intense, black stains on things. For this reason, the allowable limits for dissolved manganese in water are very low.

8.9

Water Pollution

Throughout history the pollution of water has been a factor in determining mankind's welfare. Drinking water polluted by human feces has caused diseases that have killed most of the people in some cities. Bad water polluted by natural sources has caused great hardship for the people forced to drink it or use it for irrigation.

Even today there are occasional epidemics of diseases carried by water. Some water supplies still have unsafe levels of bacteria. One cannot even trust the safety of water in a tempting, sparkling mountain brook—there may be a campsite toilet along its banks a few hundred yards upstream. In general, though, diseases carried by water have been extremely well controlled during the last 40 or 50 years.

What about poisonous chemicals in water, though? As the danger from bacteria has decreased, the possibility of chemical contamination has increased. This has resulted from the tremendous increase in industrial chemical production, metal plating, pesticide use, and other activities that contribute to water pollution. Consider that approximately 9000 different man-made organic compounds are produced commercially. Over 100 billion pounds of these chemicals are manufactured each year. Many of them are "exotic" compounds never made in nature. Many are persistent; they do not decay by the action of bacteria. Because of their widespread use, these chemicals get into water used for municipal water supplies. Some are not completely removed by water treatment processes. Other toxic chemicals, particularly lead ion and cadmium ion, are leached (dissolved) in water from plumbing. We have good reason to be concerned about the safety of drinking water in some areas.

A water pollutant is anything in the water that causes it to be harmful to plants, animals, or materials. Water pollutants may be placed in several different classes. These classes will be discussed separately.

Many of our waterways have been abused so that the water is no longer healthy for human consumption or for recreation. (Courtesy of Massachusetts Audubon Society; Daniel S. Brody, photographer)

8.10

Toxic Trace Elements and Heavy Metals

Some of the elements are harmful at levels of a part per million or less in water. These are sometimes called trace elements because only "traces" of them are found. The effects that traces of iron and manganese have in water have been mentioned. This section discusses some other trace elements and their effects in water.

Heavy metals are those with atomic weights greater than that of calcium. Several of these elements are dangerous water pollutants. The "big three" pollutant heavy metals are cadmium, lead, and mercury. Cadmium ion, Cd^{2+}, gets into water from industrial discharges, mining waste, metal plating operations, and from solder in water pipes. It has been related to high blood pressure, kidney failure, and destruction of red blood cells. Acute cadmium poisoning is a horrible condition characterized by greatly weakened bones. Mercury enters water from industrial wastes, mining, pesticides, and as a product from the burning of coal. Mercury primarily attacks the nervous system. Mercury in water is converted to soluble monomethylmercury ion, CH_3Hg^+, by the action of bacteria. The same bacteria can convert mercury to dimethylmercury, $(CH_3)_2Hg$, which forms a vapor. These dangerous mercury compounds can be produced from insoluble, harmless mercury compounds. Lead gets into water from industrial wastes, mining, plumbing, and the burning of coal and leaded gasoline. It causes anemia, kidney disease, and damage to the nervous system. Chromium is another heavy metal that is thought to be undesirable in water. It is used in metal plating and as a cooling tower water additive.

One of the light metals, beryllium, Be, is toxic and must not be present in drinking water.

Some nonmetals are classified as water pollutants. Arsenic, As, is one of these. It is used in some pesticides and is found in mine tailings. Boron, B, is toxic to some plants. Boron compounds are used in some detergents. Selenium, Se, is toxic to animals at high levels and should not be present in drinking water.

8.11

Inorganic Pollutants

Some simple inorganic compounds and ions are considered to be water pollutants. Acidity, alkalinity, and salt in water come from dissolved inorganic compounds. These have already been discussed. The fertilizer elements—potassium, nitrogen, and phosphorus—have also been discussed. This leaves some other inorganic pollutants of which cyanide ion, CN^-, is the most dangerous. Others are ammonia, carbon dioxide, hydrogen sulfide, nitrite, and sulfite.

Cyanide is a deadly poison, which exists in water as hydrocyanic acid, HCN. Gaseous HCN is very toxic. It was used to kill 521 convicted persons in gas chambers in the U.S. between 1940 and 1967. Cyanide is widely used in industry, especially for metal cleaning and electroplating (a process by which an electrical current is used to put a thin layer of one metal onto another metal). It is one of the main pollutants in water that has been used to wash coke (coal heated to remove liquids and gases). Until very recently, at least one gold mine in the U.S. used almost $1\frac{1}{4}$ tons of cyanide per day to leach gold from a daily output of 5000 tons of ore. About 75 pounds of cyanide was dumped into a nearby creek each day. Fish were not found downstream and the water was not recommended as a source of drinking water!

Ammonia occurs in water as NH_3 or as ammonium ion, NH_4^+. It

Fertilizers, insecticides, and other toxic materials from industrial wastes and land runoff often cause heavy fish kills. (Courtesy of Massachusetts Audubon Society; Daniel S. Brody, photographer)

is formed when wastes containing nitrogen (protein wastes) decay. It is sometimes added to drinking water. It reacts with chlorine in drinking water,

$$NH_3 + Cl_2 \longrightarrow NH_2Cl + HCl$$

to form monochloramine, NH_2Cl. Dichloramine, $NHCl_2$, and trichloramine, NCl_3, may also be formed. Like chlorine, the chloramines kill bacteria. They last a long time in water pipes and keep bacteria from growing.

Hydrogen sulfide, H_2S, is produced from sulfur compounds when bacteria act in the absence of oxygen. Wastes from chemical plants, paper mills, textile mills, and tanneries may also contain H_2S. It has a very bad rotten egg odor and is toxic.

High concentrations of carbon dioxide, CO_2, are produced in water by the decay of organic matter. It is sometimes added to water that has been treated with lime. It prevents $CaCO_3$ from depositing on pipes because of the following reaction:

$$CaCO_3 + H_2O + CO_2 \longrightarrow Ca^{2+} + 2 HCO_3^-$$

Too much carbon dioxide in water causes metal to corrode and harms fish.

Nitrite ion, NO_2^-, is sometimes produced by bacteria from other compounds that contain nitrogen. It is added to some industrial process water to prevent corrosion. Nitrite ion can bind to the hemoglobin in blood. Hemoglobin, which is bound to nitrite ion, cannot carry oxygen in the bloodstream. The reaction of nitrite with hemoglobin causes methemoglobinemia. The victims of this condition, like those suffering from some kinds of heart defects, are called "blue babies" because of their blue skin color.

8.12

Oxygen-Demanding Substances in Water

Substances that use up oxygen in water are harmful water pollutants. These are normally some form of organic matter. Showing organic matter by the simplified formula $[CH_2O]$, the reaction by which bacteria use up oxygen in the decay of organic matter is

$$[CH_2O] + O_2 \xrightarrow{\text{bacteria}} CO_2\uparrow + H_2O$$

The amount of oxygen used up by bacteria in the decay of the organic matter in a particular volume of water is called the biological (biochemical) oxygen demand. It is abbreviated BOD. In measuring BOD, the amount of oxygen used by bacteria in a five-day period is determined.

8.13

Detergents in Water

Detergents are chemical compounds which actually make water wetter so that it is a better solvent for dirt and grease. This is done with a compound called a surface active agent. The surface of water behaves much like the surface of a balloon filled with water. It is possible to press the balloon up against an object, but the water inside cannot make the object wet. A surface active agent reduces the effect of the water surface. The most common surface active agent is LAS (linear alkyl sulfonate), which has the structure

linear alkyl sulfonate
(LAS)

The advantage of using LAS is that it is **biodegradable**, meaning that bacteria break it down easily. Before LAS came into use, a chemical relative with a branched, rather than straight, chain of hydrocarbons was used. It was called ABS (alkyl aryl sulfonate). Since bacteria did not break it down, ABS got into wells which received sewage water. Water from these wells often had a head of foam in the glass. Great beds of foam sometimes covered sewage treatment plants. These problems went away after LAS came into wide use.

Most of the water pollution problems from detergents come from the builders added to the surface active agent. The most common such builder is sodium tripolyphosphate, $Na_5P_3O_{10}$. This compound contains 3 phosphorus atoms with oxygen atoms connecting them. It makes the detergent solution basic, reacts with water hardness (Ca^{2+} and Mg^{2+}), and helps loosen dirt in clothes. Eventually it reacts with water to form HPO_4^{2-} and $H_2PO_4^-$. These ions act as fertilizers for algae and cause it to grow too much. This causes eutrophication, which has already been discussed.

8.14

Pesticides and Other Organic Compounds in Water

Even drinking water that has been carefully treated may contain very low concentrations of organic compounds, including pesticides. The two major types of pesticides are chlorinated hydrocarbons and organic phosphates. DDT

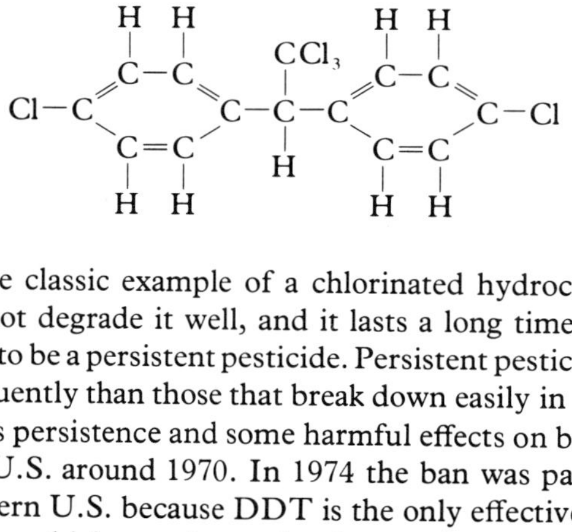

DDT,
a chlorinated
hydrocarbon pesticide

is the classic example of a chlorinated hydrocarbon pesticide. Bacteria do not degrade it well, and it lasts a long time in the environment. It is said to be a persistent pesticide. Persistent pesticides need to be applied less frequently than those that break down easily in the environment. Because of its persistence and some harmful effects on birds, its use was banned in the U.S. around 1970. In 1974 the ban was partially lifted in the northwestern U.S. because DDT is the only effective pesticide against tussock moth, which was destroying forests there.

Parathion

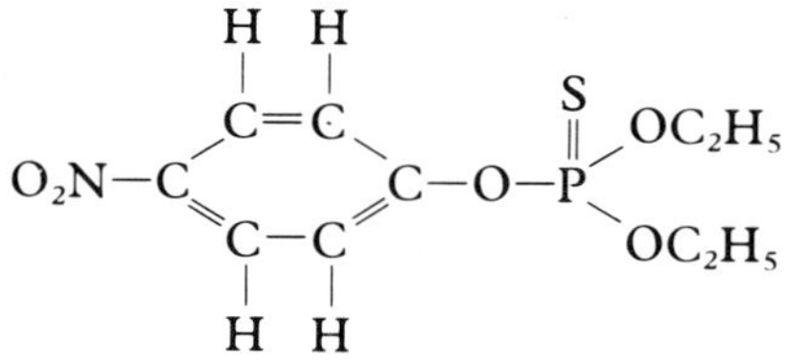

parathion,
an organophosphorus pesticide

is an example of an organophosphorus pesticide. These compounds are related to nerve gases. Bacteria degrade most of them pretty easily. They are not likely to be found in drinking water.

PCB (polychlorinated biphenyls), such as

PCB,
polychlorinated
biphenyls

are often found when samples of water, sediment, birds, or fish are analyzed for chlorinated pesticides. There are 210 PCB compounds consisting of two rings of carbon atoms with chlorines bonded to them. They do not burn or decay. They are very persistent in the environment. They have been widely used as cooling fluids in electrical transformers, although their use has now been banned.

8.15

Municipal Water Treatment

The municipal water treatment plant is one of the major triumphs of modern chemistry and sanitary engineering. The clear, safe, even tasteful water that comes from the faucet may have started as a murky liquid pumped from a muddy, polluted river swarming with bacteria. Or it may have been well water, much too hard for household use and containing too much iron and manganese. The water treatment plant operator makes sure that the product from the plant is of high quality.

The type of treatment which water gets depends upon the qualities of the water. Usually the water undergoes **aeration** in an **aerator**. This consists of squirting the water into the air in a fountain or pumping air through it. It takes out dissolved gases such as H_2S, CO_2, and CH_4. It also removes some of the organic compounds which cause odor in water.

Boston's first reservoir, called The Conduit, built near Dock Square in 1652 is shown in this early drawing. The reservoir's main purpose at the time was to provide water for fire fighting. (Courtesy of the Metropolitan District Commission, Boston, Mass.)

The oxygen in the air reacts chemically with some of the things dissolved in water. Ferrous ion reacts with oxygen,

$$4\ Fe^{2+} + O_2 + 10\ H_2O \longrightarrow 4\ Fe(OH)_3\downarrow + 8\ H^+$$

to produce ferric hydroxide, $Fe(OH)_3$. This compound is not soluble, so iron is removed from the water.

Lime, $Ca(OH)_2$, is often added to remove Ca^{2+}, which causes water hardness. Usually the calcium is present along with bicarbonate ion so that the reaction for calcium removal is

$$Ca^{2+} + 2\ HCO_3^- + Ca(OH)_2 \longrightarrow 2\ CaCO_3\downarrow + 2\ H_2O$$

This reaction is interesting because a calcium compound is added to *remove* calcium from the water.

Large solid particles are removed by allowing them to settle and by filtration. Particles that are roughly 1 micron (one-millionth of a meter) across are much harder to remove. These are called colloidal particles and were discussed in Chapter 6. Bacteria in water are colloidal particles. These particles require the addition of a **coagulant** which causes them to stick together and settle out. Filter alum, aluminum sulfate with 18 waters of hydration, is often used. The formula of this compound is $Al_2(SO_4)_3 \cdot 18\ H_2O$. The use of aluminum sulfate to purify water by forming jelly-like aluminum hydroxide that pulls suspended impurities out of water was discussed in Section 8.8.

Before going to the water mains, water must be **disinfected**. Chlorine, Cl_2, is usually used as a **disinfectant**. When added to water, chlorine reacts,

$$Cl_2 + H_2O \longrightarrow H^+ + Cl^- + HOCl$$

FIGURE 8.7

A typical municipal water treatment plant layout.

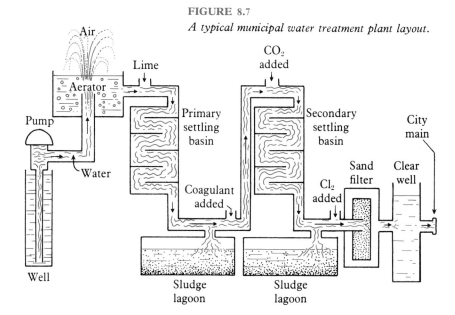

to form hypochlorous acid, HOCl. The hypochlorous acid kills bacteria that might cause disease. There is now some evidence to suggest that chlorine reacts with organic compounds in water to produce dangerous chlorinated organics. Chlorine gas is dangerous to handle. Sometimes calcium hypochlorite $Ca(OCl)_2$, is used instead. This compound is the calcium salt of hypochlorous acid.

Figure 8.7 shows a typical water treatment plant layout. These treatments vary with the particular type of water and processes used.

8.16

Sewage Treatment

Most of the water that goes through a water distribution system ends up as sewage. This must be treated before it can be returned to streams to prevent pollution. Sewage first receives primary treatment. This is a simple process in which solid material settles from the sewage and scum is skimmed from the sewage surface. It removes grit, cooking oil, socks, and all the other incredible kinds of objects that get flushed down the sewer.

After primary treatment the sewage goes to secondary treatment. The main object of secondary treatment is to reduce the biological oxygen demand (BOD) of the water. As discussed in Section 8.13, BOD is a measure of how much oxygen will be consumed when bacteria use the organic waste in the water for food. Most secondary treatment processes speed up the process by which bacteria would eat the organic matter in the water in streams. The best of the biological treatment systems is the activated sludge process shown in Figure 8.8. In this process sewage flows into a big aeration tank. Air is

FIGURE 8.8
Activated sludge process for secondary waste treatment. CH_2O *designates organic matter.*

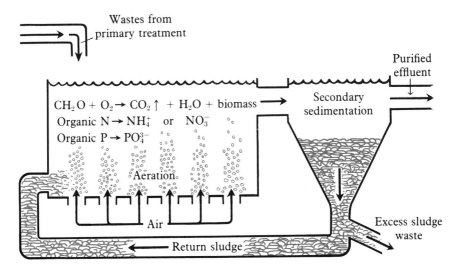

pumped into the aeration tank from the bottom. This air provides the oxygen which bacteria need and keeps the sewage stirring. Bacteria in the aeration tank convert organic matter in the sewage to CO_2, water, and new bacteria. The nitrogen in sewage is changed to NH_4^+ and NO_3^-. The phosphorous in the organic compounds is changed to HPO_4^{2-} and $H_2PO_4^-$. From the aeration tank the sewage goes to a settler. The bacteria settle out and the treated, clear water is discharged to a stream. Next comes the trick that makes the activated sludge process work so well. The settled mass of bacteria, called sewage sludge, is pumped back to the front of the aeration tank. Large quantities of hungry bacteria contact fresh sewage and eat it rapidly. For that reason the activated sludge process accomplishes in a few hours what would take many days in a stream.

Water from secondary waste treatment is clean enough to put in a reasonably large stream. However, it contains nutrients that cause algae to grow, resulting in eutrophication. If it is discharged to a lake or reservoir, or if it is likely to go into another municipal water system, sewage effluent should be given further treatment. The most common advanced treatment is phosphate removal by addition of lime.

$$5 \, Ca(OH)_2 + 3 \, HPO_4^{2-} = Ca_5OH(PO_4)_3\downarrow + 6 \, OH^- + 3 \, H_2O$$

The phosphate-containing precipitate is $Ca_5OH(PO_4)_3$, which is called hydroxyapatite. It settles out and is removed as sludge. Phosphate removal is particularly important because phosphate is such a good nutrient for algae.

Chapter Summary

Water is an extremely important substance in agriculture, industry, living systems, and elsewhere in our surroundings. Shortages of water, particularly for irrigation, threaten many parts of the world.

Water has a number of special properties which, along with its abundance, make it so important. One of the most important of these is *its ability to dissolve many substances not dissolved by other common liquids.* Another particularly important property of water is *its capacity to accept large quantities of heat energy* as its temperature is raised, as ice melts, or as liquid water evaporates. When the reverse processes occur, large quantities of heat are given off.

Water occurs as *water of hydration* in many chemical compounds. Compounds that absorb water from air are said to be *hygroscopic*. Those which absorb enough water to become dissolved are called *deliquescent*. The loss of water of hydration is called *efflorescence*.

"Natural water" is water found in streams, lakes, reservoirs, in the oceans, and underground. The circulation of this water from the oceans, to the atmosphere as vapor, back to the Earth's surface as precipitation, and finally returning to the ocean as runoff is described by the *hydrologic cycle*.

An activated sludge municipal sewage treatment plant converts sewage to harmless solids and carbon dioxide. (Courtesy of Massachusetts Audubon Society; Daniel S. Brody, photographer)

The relationship between water temperature and density results in the formation of layers with different temperatures in bodies of water. This is called *water stratification*. It has a strong influence upon the chemistry and biology of lakes and reservoirs. Frequently, the bottom layer of water loses most of its dissolved oxygen and becomes anaerobic. Water that contains appreciable amounts of dissolved oxygen is *aerobic*.

The biological productivity of a body of water is one of its most important characteristics. This is the ability of the water to support the growth of algae so that these small plants may use energy from the sun to convert carbon dioxide, water, and nutrients to biological material. The process is called *photosynthesis*. If too much photosynthesis occurs as a result of too many nutrients in the water, the water will accumulate an excess of plant material. This then rots in the water. The overall condition is called *eutrophication*.

Water may contain too much acid. The most common such water is acid mine water produced in some coal mining operations. The capacity of water to neutralize acid added to it is the *alkalinity* of the water. The level of salts dissolved in water is the water *salinity*. Water hardness results from the presence of calcium and magnesium ion. Some water hardness is desirable in drinking water, but too much can cause scaling of pipes and prevent soaps and detergents from working properly.

Water pollution is one of our most important environmental problems. Many types of substances can cause water pollution. Iron and manganese in water cause staining. Other heavy metals such as lead, mercury, or cadmium are very toxic. Dissolved organic compounds in water can be toxic. Other organic materials in water are not directly toxic, but their decay in water uses up oxygen needed by fish. Ammonia, carbon dioxide, hydrogen sulfide, nitrite ion, sulfite ion, and cyanide can be toxic in water.

Treatment of water for municipal use is an important, and often complicated process. Suspended matter, dissolved gases, and sometimes hardness and iron are removed in municipal water treatment. Sewage treatment has removal of biological oxygen demand as its main objective. Advanced sewage treatment to remove algal nutrients and other undesirable materials is being practiced more commonly.

Chapter Review Questions

The following questions are designed as a self-teaching tool to help you review Chapter 8. The answers to each question follow. See Chapter Review Questions for Chapter 1 for further instructions.

1. Water freezes at_____°C and boils at _____°C.

2. The water molecule is a _____ having a positive end and a negative end. Water molecules form _____ bonds with each other and with solute molecules.

3. The number of calories of heat required to raise the temperature of 1 g of water 1°C is _____. A total of _____ cal are required to melt 1 g of ice, and a total of _____ cal are required to change 1 g of water at 100°C to 1 g of steam at 100°C.

4. The density of ice is _____ than the density of liquid water.

5. In the compound $Na_2CO_3 \cdot 10\,H_2O$, the water is called _____.

6. Chemical compounds which absorb water from the air are said to be _____, and those which absorb enough water to dissolve are _____.

7. The loss of water of hydration is called _____.

8. The fraction of the Earth's surface covered by water is approximately _____, and our own bodies are about _____ % water by weight.

9. The fraction of water falling on the continental U.S. that is lost by evaporation and transpiration is approximately _____.

10. Of the water actually used in the U.S., approximately _____% is used for irrigation, _____ % is used by industry, largely for cooling, and _____ % is used by municipal water works.

11. The process of a body of water forming layers in the summer is called _____. The highest layer is the _____ and the lowest layer is the _____.

12. The chemical reaction by which algae make organic matter is _____ _____, and the process is called _____.

13. When bacteria decompose organic matter in water, dissolved _____ needed by fish is also removed.

14. The most common acid pollutant found in water is _____.

15. The capacity of a natural water to neutralize acid is called its _____.

16. Water hardness is due to _____ ions and _____ ions.

17. Two chemical compounds which act as oxygen scavengers are _____ and _____.

18. The three fertilizer pollutants in water are the _____ ion and compounds of _____ and _____.

19. The presence of _____ ion in water indicates salt water pollution.

20. _____ ions in water at about 1 ppm help prevent tooth decay.

21. Some examples of undesirable metals in water are _____ and _____ which cause staining, and _____, _____, and _____, which are very toxic.

22. Chlorine and ammonia react to form _____, _____, and _____.

23. Methemoglobinemia may be caused by _____ in water.

24. The amount of oxygen used up by bacteria in decaying organic matter in a water sample is a measure of _____.

25. Regarding the length of time which it lasts in the environment, DDT is classified as a _____ pesticide.

26. A sewage treatment process in which bacteria are settled and recirculated to an aeration tank is the _____.

Answers to Chapter Review Questions

1. 0, 100
2. dipole, hydrogen
3. 1, 80, 540
4. less
5. water of hydration
6. hygroscopic, deliquescent
7. efflorescence
8. five-sevenths, 70
9. two-thirds
10. 46, 46, 8
11. stratification, epilimnion, hypolimnion
12. $CO_2 + H_2O + sunlight \longrightarrow [CH_2O] + O_2\uparrow$, photosynthesis
13. oxygen
14. acid mine water
15. alkalinity
16. calcium, magnesium
17. Na_2SO_3, N_2H_4
18. K^+, phosphorus, nitrogen
19. chloride
20. fluoride
21. iron, manganese, lead, cadmium, mercury
22. monochloramine, dichloramine, trichloramine
23. nitrite
24. biological oxygen demand
25. persistent
26. activated sludge process

Exercises for Chapter 8

1. Show how ammonia, NH_3, dissolved in water might form hydrogen bonds with the water.

2. What process requires:
   a. 1 cal/g of water,   b. 540 cal/g,   c. 80 cal/g?

3. How does hydrogen bonding increase the heat capacity of water?

4. If steam is to be used to heat a room, should the steam go through the radiator as a gas or should it condense to form water? Why?

5. Several cans of a soda beverage were cooled by placing them in 2000 g of liquid water originally at 0°C. After the cans lost heat to the water, both the cans and the water were at 5°C. This was done in an insulated container so that no heat was gained or lost to the surroundings. The amount of ice at 0°C which would have been required for the same cooling is:
   a. 2000 g,   b. 1 g,   c. 125 g,   d. 752 g,   e. 355 g.

6. A thermometer is dipped several centimeters into a pond at 0°C. What is the thermometer reading after the first centimeter of ice has formed on the surface?

7. Describe two chemical reactions by which mineral deposits were formed in water.

8. What property of gas solubility explains why a hot soda fizzes more than a cold one when the bottle is opened?

9. Define the following: water of hydration, hydrated, anhydrous, hygroscopic, deliquescent, hygroscopic, efflorescence.

10. List some of the things that surface water or ground water may contain, and explain how they affect the properties and uses of the water.

11. What is meant by desalination? Where is water desalinated in the hydrologic cycle?

12. Approximately how many millions of gallons of water are lost by evaporation and transpiration in the continental U.S. each year?

13. Within limits bacteria work faster with increasing temperatures. Give two reasons why water heated by waste heat from a power plant may have less dissolved oxygen than water which has not been used for this purpose.

14. What is the difference between the concentration of dissolved oxygen and BOD?

15. Explain what is meant by water stratification, epilimnion, hypolimnion, aerobic, anaerobic, and overturn.

16. Write the chemical reaction by which bacteria use up organic matter and the chemical reaction for photosynthesis.

17. Exactly 45 ml of 0.05 M HCl were required to titrate the alkalinity in 1.00 liter of water.
    a. If the alkalinity was due to a bicarbonate ion, what was its reaction with HCl?
    b. What was the alkalinity as moles of HCO_3^- per liter?

18. What are two undesirable effects of too much water hardness?

19. Explain how bacteria increase the danger of mercury pollution in water.

20. What does ammonia dissolved in water usually indicate?

21. Write a chemical reaction which shows how carbon dioxide in water dissolves calcium carbonate coated on the inside of a pipe.

22. Explain, using chemical reactions when possible, how each of the following is used in water treatment:
    a. air,   **b.** filter alum,   **c.** calcium hydroxide,   **d.** chlorine.

23. The two hydrogen atoms in a water molecule form almost a right angle with the oxygen atom. Explain what this has to do with making the water molecule a dipole.

Spiraling winds of a hurricane circulate at 100 mi/hr near Florida. The bright spot in the center is known as the eye of the hurricane. This small, round area produces relatively mild weather, that is, few clouds, no rain, and only light winds. The photograph was taken by a NASA synchronous meteorological satellite. (Courtesy of NASA)

9

Gases and the Atmosphere

9.1

What is a Gas?

Most gases are without color and cannot be seen. Many do not have an odor nor a taste. Despite this unobtrusiveness, gases are very important. The air around us making up the atmosphere is gas. Oxygen gas is required to keep our bodies alive. Carbon dioxide is a gas given off as a waste by animals and used as a raw material by plants. Methane gas is used to fire our furnaces. Nitrogen and hydrogen gases are combined to make fertilizer. The product of this reaction is another gas, ammonia. Argon is used in some specialized types of welding. Acetylene gas is used in welding torches and for cutting steel. Oxygen gas is given to hospital patients who have weak hearts or difficulty breathing. Gas in the form of compressed air holds up tires and stops trains (air brakes).

It is easy to see that gases are important. What, though, is a gas? It is one of three forms of matter. It is the "loosest" form. Solids have a definite shape and volume. A solid, such as a brick, cannot be made to change shape without breaking it. If you squeeze it, nothing happens. The volume of the brick cannot be changed by squeezing. In solids all of the atoms and molecules are in particular locations that do not change. A liquid is a second form of matter. If you fill a balloon with water, its shape changes easily when it is pushed around. If you try to make the total volume smaller by squeezing, it doesn't work. Squeezed in one place, the balloon must bulge out in another. The molecules of a liquid stick together but still move around one another. For that reason a particular amount of liquid will keep the same volume, but will change shape very easily. However, when a balloon is filled with a gas such as air, it changes shape easily just like a liquid. If you wrap both hands firmly around a small air-filled balloon and squeeze hard, the balloon actually becomes smaller. The gas inside it is **compressed**. If you put air into a bicycle tire with a small hand pump, many volumes of air equal to that of the pump can be forced into the tire. The tire doesn't get much larger. It just gets harder as the air in it becomes more compressed.

Why does a gas behave like it does? The molecules or atoms in a gas have hardly any attraction for each other. They bounce around like Ping-pong balls rebounding from container walls and from each other. They move very rapidly. At 0°C the average molecule of hydrogen gas moves at 3600 mi/h, 6 or 7 times as fast as a jet passenger plane. The molecules bump into each other frequently. For that reason gas molecules are always trying to get away from each other and spread out. If a rotten egg is broken on one side of a room, the people on the other side soon know it because the molecules of stinking H_2S gas spread out (diffuse) very quickly. There is a lot of space between molecules of gas. At 100°C a mole (18 g) of water occupies a little more than 18 ml of volume. That is equivalent to just a few teaspoonsful. When the water is heated and changed to gaseous steam at 100°C, the volume is about 30,600 ml. This is 1700 times the original volume. It is the great distance between gas molecules that allows gas to be compressed (pushed together). Squeezing the molecules a little closer together when they are so far apart does not make much difference. Figures 9.1, 9.2, and 9.3 show the differences between solids, liquids, and gases. Water is used as an example.

The fact that gas molecules are so far apart, bounce around at a furious rate, and bump into each other and their container walls explains two of the most important properties of gases. These properties are **diffusion** and **pressure**.

Diffusion of gas refers to the way that it moves or spreads on its own. Diffusion of gas is sometimes demonstrated to the careless individual who takes a pan of gasoline to the basement to clean up grease. The gasoline easily evaporates, going into the gas, or vapor, form. The molecules of gasoline vapor keep bumping into other molecules until they have spread far from the source. If the gasoline vapor reaches a water heater pilot light, a disastrous explosion and fire can result.

FIGURE 9.1
The molecules of solid water (ice) are touching each other and have definite positions. The ice is very hard to compress and does not change shape.

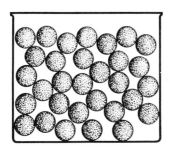

FIGURE 9.2
The molecules of liquid water touch each other but can slide around one another. The water changes shape easily but cannot be compressed.

FIGURE 9.3
The molecules of gaseous water (steam) are far apart and bounce around. A body of steam changes shape easily and can be compressed.

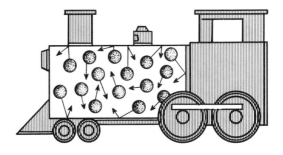

Pressure comes from gas molecules bumping into a container wall and pushing it. Pressure increases with the amount of gas in the container and with its temperature. If you keep pumping air into a bicycle tire you know that the tire gets harder and harder as more and more molecules bump against the inside surface of the tire. Generally you get tired and stop pumping before the tire gets too hard. But, if you take the bicycle to a service station where an electric pump can do all of the work, it is very easy to force too much air into the tire. A blowout frequently results. All of the air molecules pushing against the tire wall push a hole right through it.

Air pressure, as well as the pressure of other gases, may be measured with a column of mercury. Mercury is a heavy liquid metal. A long glass tube is sealed at one end and tipped upside-down in a bowl of mercury metal. Air pushes on the mercury in the bowl, which pushes on the mercury in the tube, as shown in Figure 9.4. The length of the mercury that is held up in the tube measures the pressure of the air. At sea level this is about 760 mm of mercury, a column that is a little less than a yard long.

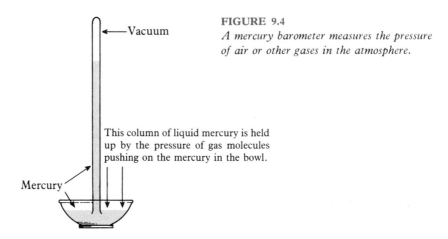

FIGURE 9.4

A mercury barometer measures the pressure of air or other gases in the atmosphere.

←—Vacuum

This column of liquid mercury is held up by the pressure of gas molecules pushing on the mercury in the bowl.

Mercury

The pressure of air in the atmosphere changes with altitude, and varies slightly with weather conditions. The average pressure at sea level is 1.00 atmosphere (atm). This is sufficient pressure to hold up a 760-mm column of mercury. At mile-high Denver, though, the average pressure is only 0.83 atm. The reason for this is that at lower altitudes there are more air molecules above that push down and create the pressure. Very sensitive barometers are used in airplanes to measure altitude. The pressure of the atmosphere changes with changing weather. Low atmospheric pressure frequently indicates rainy, stormy weather. Clear, sunny days generally occur along with high pressure (see Figure 9.5).

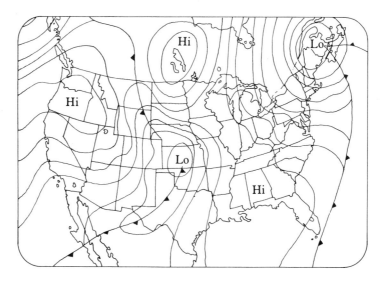

FIGURE 9.5

Variations in air pressure play an important role in weather changes.

We have noted that pressure may be expressed in millimeters of mercury, or atmospheres. Weather forecasters in the U.S. frequently use inches of mercury, where 29.92 in. corresponds to 760 mm. Another

 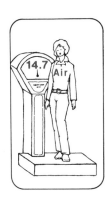

FIGURE 9.6
The box shown is 1 cubic inch and has a vacuum inside. In the air at 1 atm pressure, the box has 14.7 lb of air pressure pushing at each side.

common measure of pressure is pounds per square inch (psi). Gauges on tanks of compressed gas are usually expressed in pounds per square inch. A pressure of 1.00 atm is 14.7 psi as shown in Figure 9.6.

9.2

Effect of Pressure on Gas Volume

When a purchasing agent buys a liquid chemical, the amount is often given as a volume. A 55 gal barrel of dry cleaning fluid contains the same amount of fluid, regardless of whether it is delivered in a blizzard or during a heat wave. This is not the case, though, for the welder buying a tank of compressed oxygen. The old tank, with just a "hiss-worth" of oxygen in it, has the same volume of oxygen as the new "full" tank.

Oxygen therapy is administered to patients suffering from asphyxia, asthma, pulmonary diseases, heart diseases, and anemia. Treatment of different oxygen concentrations can be provided by means of a nasal catheter; a face mask, such as shown in the photograph; or an oxygen tent. (Courtesy of Massachusetts General Hospital)

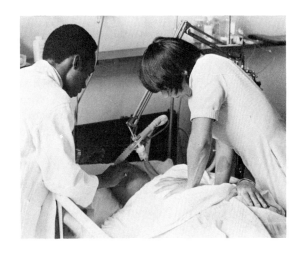

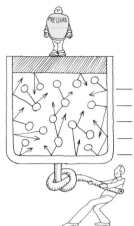

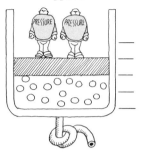

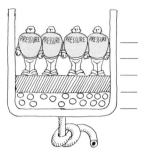

FIGURE 9.7

To decrease the volume of a gas at a particular temperature, more pressure must be applied.

The piston of a pump that is not being forced has 1 atm pressure on it from the outside air.

To make the volume half as great, twice as much pressure must be applied.

To make the volume half again as much, the pressure must be doubled again. This makes it 4 times the original pressure.

But there are many more oxygen molecules in the new tank. It has a higher pressure. It also weighs more.

Because there is so much room between gas molecules, it is possible to keep forcing more gas into a container until the gas either turns to a liquid or the container breaks. That is why it is necessary to know the volume, pressure, and temperature of gas to know how much is present. The relationship of pressure and volume at constant temperature is considered in this section. The effect of temperature will be explained next.

Consider a foot pump such as those used to inflate air mattresses as shown in Figure 9.7. Suppose that it starts out filled with air, but that the outlet is plugged up so that no air can get out. The air in the pump is under 1 atm of pressure from the surrounding air outside the pump. Now imagine that the pump is pushed in half-way. The air molecules are now in half as much space. It is reasonable to suppose that they will push on the pump piston twice as hard. The pressure has doubled. Now imagine that the piston is forced down half of the remaining distance. The air molecules are in half again as much space. (They occupy only one-fourth the original space.) The pressure has again doubled. It is four times the original pressure. This example shows that an increase in pressure causes the volume of a gas to decrease. At constant temperature, if the pressure of a known volume of gas is changed, the new volume can be figured out easily. Suppose that the volume of air originally in the air mattress pump was 1.00 liter. It was under a pressure of 1.00 atm from the outside air. If the pressure is increased to 4.00 atm the new volume is given by:

$$\frac{1.00 \text{ atm}}{4.00 \text{ atm}} \times 1.00 \text{ liters} = 0.25 \text{ liters (new volume)}$$

Multiplying by this decreases the volume.

This calculation shows that increasing the pressure on a gas from 1.00 atm to 4.00 atm causes the volume to become one-fourth of the original volume.

If the pressure on a gas is *decreased*, the volume *increases*. Suppose that 1.50 liters of gas is under a pressure of 2.50 atm. If the pressure is decreased to 0.75 atm, what is the new volume?

$$\frac{2.50 \text{ atm}}{0.75 \text{ atm}} \times 1.50 \text{ liters} = 5.00 \text{ liters (new volume)}$$

Multiplying by this
increases the volume.

We have just shown that **at constant temperature, the volume of a gas is inversely proportional to pressure**. This is an important relationship known as **Boyle's Law**.

9.3

Effect of Temperature on Gas Volume

A basketball left out of doors on a freezing night may become very limp and bounce poorly. Bring it indoors by the fireplace, and it soon becomes round and firm. The cold basketball contains the same weight of air as the warm one. But the volume of the cold air is less. When gas kept at the same pressure is heated, the volume becomes larger. This may be understood by considering what happens to molecules of gas when they are heated. Gas molecules are always moving around, bouncing off of each other and off container walls. The rate at which they bounce around is a measure of the temperature. When they are heated up, the molecules of gas bounce around faster. If they are heated under a constant pressure, such as in a partly filled ball or a cylinder with a piston, they spread out; and the total volume of the gas becomes larger as shown in Figure 9.8.

The effect of temperature upon the volume of gas can be calculated using arithmetic. But first it is necessary to talk about temperature in

FIGURE 9.8
Heating a gas increases its volume.

Molecules of gas in a cold inflated ball move around and bounce off of each other and off the walls of the ball.

When the gas is heated up, the molecules move faster and spread out, increasing the volume of the gas.

different terms. In this book temperature has been given as degrees Celsius (°C). Water freezes at 0°C. The temperature can be a negative value lower than 0°C. In calculating gas volumes it is necessary to use a temperature scale that cannot go lower than zero degrees. Such a temperature is called absolute temperature. It is expressed as degrees Kelvin (°K). The Kelvin stands for the name of the man who invented the absolute temperature scale. To change degrees Celsius to absolute temperature, add 273. A temperature of 0°C is 273°K. A temperature of 21°C (about room temperature) is 293°K. A temperature of 0°K is a cold −273°C.

At constant pressure the volume of a gas increases directly with increases in the absolute temperature. This statement is known as **Charles' Law**. To see how it works, consider gas in a cylinder (Figure 9.9) with a piston at one end placed in a deep freeze at 200°K (−73°C). Suppose that the gas has a volume of 1.00 liter. Now suppose that the cylinder is taken from the deep freeze and heated to 400°K (127°C). The absolute temperature is doubled. This also doubles the volume. The new volume is 2.00 liters.

Example 1. Exactly 1.50 liters of gas at 25°C is heated to 350°C. The pressure remains the same. What is the new volume? The first thing to do is to change the temperatures to absolute temperatures.

$$25°C \text{ is } 25 + 273 = 298°K$$
$$350°C \text{ is } 350 + 273 = 623°K$$

The temperature increases so the volume increases, too.

$$\frac{623°K}{298°K} \times 1.50 \text{ liters} = 3.14 \text{ liters (new volume)}$$

Multiplying by this
increases volume.

FIGURE 9.9
Increasing the temperature of gas at constant pressure increases the volume.

Gas in a cylinder equipped
with a piston and at 200°K has
a volume of 1.00 liter.

Heating the gas to 400°K
causes the gas to expand.
The new volume is 2.00 liter.

In doing this calculation, one of the temperatures goes at the top and one at the bottom. Since the volume must *increase,* the *higher* temperature goes on top.

Example 2.   The volume of gas at 210°C is 2.60 liters. What is the volume at − 10°C if the pressure is the same?

210°C is 210 + 273 = 483°K

− 10°C is − 10 + 273 = 263°K   (Adding a − 10 to 273 is the same as subtracting 10 from 273.)

The temperature goes down, so the volume becomes smaller.

$$\frac{263°K}{483°K} \times 2.60 \text{ liters} = 1.42 \text{ liters (new volume)}$$

Multiplying by this
decreases the volume.

9.4

Changes in Gas Volume When Both Pressure and Temperature are Changed

Frequently both the temperature and pressure of a quantity of gas change. It is easy to figure out the new volume of gas by considering the effect of the temperature change and the effect of the pressure change separately. Just remember the following:

1.   A higher pressure squeezes the gas and makes its volume smaller.

A lower pressure allows the gas to expand and fill a larger volume.

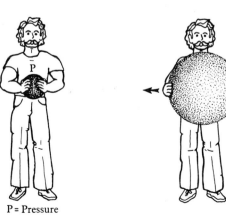

P = Pressure

2.   A higher temperature moves the molecules of gas around much faster and makes the volume larger.

A lower temperature causes the molecules of gas to move less vigorously, so they take up less volume.

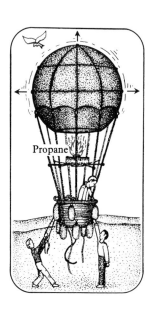

To calculate the effect of pressure, one pressure must be divided by the other. If the pressure has increased, this division must make a smaller number. If the pressure has become less, the division must make a larger number.

To calculate the effect of temperature, one temperature must be divided by the other. If the temperature has increased, this division must make a larger number. If the temperature has become less, this division must make a smaller number.

The explanation above can be shown with several examples. Exactly 1.00 liter of gas is at a pressure of 1.80 atm and a temperature of 300°K. The pressure is changed to 0.90 atm and the temperature to 400°K. What is the new volume? The pressure has become less. This increases the volume. The temperature has become greater. This also increases the volume. The new volume is given by the following calculation:

$$\frac{1.80 \text{ atm}}{0.90 \text{ atm}} \times \frac{400°\text{K}}{300°\text{K}} \times 1.00 \text{ liters} = 2.67 \text{ liters (new volume)}$$

Multiplying by   Multiplying by
this increases   this increases
the volume.   the volume.

Example 1.   What is the new volume when 1.40 liters of gas at 0.80 atm pressure and 20°C is changed to 1.50 atm pressure and 110°C?

$$20°C \text{ is } 20 + 273 = 293°K$$

$$110°C \text{ is } 110 + 273 = 383°K$$

1.   The temperature has become larger. This makes the volume larger. Divide 383°K by 293°K.

2.   The pressure has become higher. This makes the volume smaller. Divide 0.80 atm by 1.50 atm.

$$\frac{0.80 \text{ atm}}{1.50 \text{ atm}} \times \frac{383°K}{293°K} \times 1.40 \text{ liters} = 0.98 \text{ liters (new volume)}$$

Multiplying by   Multiplying by
this decreases   this increases
the volume.   the volume.

Example 2.   Exactly 12 liters of gas has a pressure of 2.00 atm and a temperature of 100°C. The pressure is changed to 1.20 atm and the temperature to 0°C. What is the new volume?

$$100°C \text{ is } 100 + 273 = 373°K$$

$$0°C \text{ is } 0 + 273 = 273°K$$

1.   The temperature has become less. This makes the volume smaller. Divide 273° by 373°.

2.   The pressure has become less. This makes the volume larger. Divide 2.00 atm by 1.20 atm.

$$\frac{2.00 \text{ atm}}{1.20 \text{ atm}} \times \frac{273°K}{373°K} \times 12 \text{ liters} = 14.6 \text{ liters (new volume)}$$

Multiplying by   Multiplying by
this increases   this decreases
the volume.   the volume.

9.5

The Weight of a Gas

The weight of a quantity of gas is related to its volume, temperature, and pressure. At a specified temperature and pressure, a particular volume of any gas contains the same number of molecules. This leads to a very important relationship, which can be used in calculations involving the weights of gases. Consider exactly 1 mole of gas. A mole of gas contains 6.02×10^{23} (602,000,000,000,000,000,000,000) molecules of gas. Recall from Section 5.5 that this is *Avogadro's number*. Recall also that a mole of any substance is the same number of grams as its molecular weight.

A mole of gas occupies a definite volume at a particular temperature and pressure. **A mole of any gas at 0°C and 1.00 atm pressure occupies a volume of 22.4 liters**. This volume is the same as that of a cube whose sides are each about the length of a sheet of typing paper (11 in.). According to this law 1 mole of hydrogen, H_2, weighing 2 g occupies the same 22.4 liter volume as 1 mole of chlorine, Cl_2, weighing 71 g. Observe Figure 9.10. A balloon filled with 1 mole of hydrogen weighs less than the air displaced, so the balloon floats. A balloon filled with 1 mole of Cl_2 weighs much more than the air displaced, so the balloon falls rapidly. Of course, the lightweight H_2 molecules have to move a lot faster and work a lot harder than the heavyweight chlorine molecules in order to occupy the same volume.

FIGURE 9.10
At STP, both 1 mole of Cl_2 and 1 mole of H_2 occupy 22.4 liters.

It should be pointed out that conditions of 0°C temperature and 1.00 atm pressure are special. They are called **standard temperature and pressure**. This is abbreviated as **STP**. A gas at 0°C and 1.00 atm of pressure is said to be under **standard conditions**.

Knowing the volume, temperature, and pressure of a gas, it is possible to calculate the weight of the gas. For example, what is the weight of fluorine gas, F_2, contained in 44.8 liters at STP? The atomic weight of fluorine is 19. The molecular weight of fluorine is 38. At STP a mole, 38 g, of fluorine occupies 22.4 liters. A volume of 44.8 liters is twice 22.4 liters. It contains 2 moles of fluorine or 76 g. The key to working this problem is to find out how many moles of the gas were present. This was done by dividing the volume in liters by 22.4 liters per mole:

$$\frac{44.8 \text{ liters}}{22.4 \text{ liters/mole}} = 2 \text{ moles, or } 76 \text{ g of } F_2$$

Example 1. The atomic weight of carbon is 12 and that of hydrogen is 1. What is the weight of 10.0 liters of methane, CH_4, at STP?

Step 1. Calculate the molecular weight of CH_4.

1 carbon atom weighing 12 + 4 hydrogen atoms weighing 1 each

$$= 1 \; CH_4 \; \text{molecule weighing 16}$$

Step 2.   Since the molecular weight of methane is 16, a mole of CH_4 weighs 16 g.

Step 3.   The number of moles of methane in 10.0 liters at STP is

$$\frac{10.0 \; \text{liters}}{22.4 \; \text{liters/mole}} = 0.446 \; \text{moles}$$

Step 4.   Multiply the number of moles by the number of grams in a mole.

$$0.446 \; \text{moles} \times 16 \; \text{g/mole} = 7.14 \; \text{g}$$

If the volume of the gas that is given is not at STP, it must be changed to STP. Then the weight of the gas can be calculated. This can be shown by some examples. Suppose that some methane gas occupies 16.0 liters at 0°C and 0.75 atm of pressure. What does the methane weigh? Standard temperature is 0°C so no correction will have to be made for temperature. But, standard pressure is 1.00 atm, so the volume of the gas at 1.00 atm must be found:

$$\frac{0.75 \; \text{atm}}{1.00 \; \text{atm}} \times 16.0 \; \text{liters} = 12 \; \text{liters (volume of methane at STP)}$$

The next step is to calculate the number of moles of methane at STP.

$$\frac{12 \; \text{liters}}{22.4 \; \text{liters/mole}} = 0.536 \; \text{moles}$$

Finally the weight of methane is calculated.

$$0.536 \; \text{moles multiplied by 16 g/mole} = 8.57 \; \text{g}$$

Example 2.   What is the weight of 15.0 liters of ammonia, NH_3, at 30°C and 1.20 atm of pressure? The molecular weight of NH_3 is 17, so a mole of NH_3 weighs 17 g.

Step 1.   What would be the volume of the NH_3 at STP?

$$\frac{1.20 \; \text{atm}}{1.00 \; \text{atm}} \times \frac{273°K}{303°K} \times 15.0 \; \text{liters} = 16.2 \; \text{liters}$$

Step 2.   The number of moles of ammonia in 16.2 liters at STP is

$$\frac{16.2 \; \text{liters}}{22.4 \; \text{moles/liter}} = 0.723 \; \text{moles}$$

Step 3.   The number of grams in 0.723 moles is

$$0.723 \; \text{moles} \times 17 \; \text{g/mole} = 12.3 \; \text{g}$$

9.6 omit

Volumes of Gases in Chemical Reactions

Volumes of gases produced or consumed in chemical reactions can be calculated directly. For example, consider the production of hydrogen gas by the reaction of magnesium and sulfuric acid.

$$Mg + H_2SO_4 = H_2\uparrow + MgSO_4$$

This reaction shows that 1 mole of magnesium reacts with 1 mole of sulfuric acid to produce 1 mole of hydrogen gas and 1 mole of magnesium sulfate. At STP, 1 mole of H_2 occupies 22.4 liters. How many liters of hydrogen at STP would be produced by the reaction of 2 moles of Mg with excess H_2SO_4? The 2 moles of Mg produce 2 moles of H_2. Since 1 mole of H_2 occupies 22.4 liters at STP, 2 moles occupy twice as much volume, or 44.8 liters.

Example 1.   How many liters of H_2 at STP are produced by the reaction of 0.75 moles of Mg with excess H_2SO_4?

Step 1.   The number of moles of H_2 produced is the same as the number of moles of Mg added, or 0.75 moles.

Step 2.   The volume of H_2 is

$$0.75 \text{ moles} \times 22.4 \text{ liters/mole} = 16.8 \text{ liters}$$

Example 2.   How many liters of H_2 at 20°C (293°K) and 0.90 atm of pressure are produced by the reaction of 0.75 moles of Mg with excess H_2SO_4?

Step 1.   From the above example it was seen that 0.75 moles of Mg produce 16.8 liters of H_2 at STP (273°K and 1.00 atm of pressure).

Step 2.   Convert the volume at STP to the volume at 293°K and 0.90 atm of pressure

$$\frac{1.00 \text{ atm}}{0.90 \text{ atm}} \times \frac{293°K}{273°K} \times 16.8 \text{ liters} = 20.0 \text{ liters}$$

Oxygen gas is sometimes made in the laboratory by heating $KClO_3$.

$$2 \text{ KClO}_3 + \text{heat} \longrightarrow 2 \text{ KCl} + 3 \text{ O}_2\uparrow$$

From this reaction it is seen that 2 moles of $KClO_3$ produce 3 moles of O_2. The molecular weight of $KClO_3$ is 122.5.

Example 3.   How many liters of oxygen at STP could be produced from 65.0 g of $KClO_3$?

Step 1.   The number of moles of $KClO_3$ is

$$\frac{65.0 \text{ g}}{122.5 \text{ g/mole}} = 0.531 \text{ moles}$$

Step 2.   The number of moles of O_2 produced from 0.531 moles of $KClO_3$ is

$$0.531 \text{ moles of } KClO_3 \times \frac{3 \text{ moles of } O_2}{2 \text{ moles of } KClO_3} = 0.797 \text{ moles of } O_2$$

$$0.797 \text{ moles} \times 22.4 \text{ liters/mole} = 17.9 \text{ liters}$$

9.7

Gases in Industry

Gases are very important in industry. Of the top five chemicals produced in the U.S., three are gases. These are ammonia (17 million tons in 1976), oxygen (16 million tons) and chlorine (11 million tons). Other major gases are nitrogen (almost 11 million tons) and carbon dioxide (1.8 million tons). With increasing demand for nitrogen-containing fertilizer to increase food production, it is likely that the output of ammonia will continue to increase. The increased use of oxygen for steel production, sewage treatment, and other applications will increase the demand for this gas. The development of a major synthetic fuels industry to manufacture synthetic natural gas and gasoline from coal would require vast production of hydrogen and oxygen.

Air is one of the major sources of industrial gases. Both oxygen and nitrogen as well as several less important gases are isolated from air. Dry air consists of 78.0% nitrogen by volume, 21.0% oxygen, and 0.94% argon. These gases are separated from liquid air as follows. First air is filtered and compressed to a high pressure. It is then cooled to produce liquid air. Nitrogen, which boils at $-195.8°C$, is separated from oxygen boiling at $-183°C$ by a distillation process that depends upon their different boiling temperatures. Argon, which is used to fill light bulbs and to prevent metals from burning during arc welding, is also separated out if there is a market for it. Neon may also be removed for use in neon lights. Formerly these were widely used for advertising signs.

9.8

The Air Around Us

We live at the bottom of a sea of air, the atmosphere. It is thin compared to the diameter of the Earth. The atmosphere provides the oxygen needed by animals and the carbon dioxide required by plants. It is the source of nitrogen, which nitrogen-fixing plants and ammonia manufacturers use to produce essential fertilizer. The atmosphere shields living things from the hostile high energy particles and cancer-causing ultraviolet light in outer space. The atmosphere carries moisture from the oceans and spreads it over the land as life-giving rain. It is a basic part of the hydrologic cycle (see Chapter 8).

The atmosphere is essential in maintaining the Earth's heat balance. Air absorbs infrared and ultraviolet radiation emitted by the sun. It also absorbs energy re-emitted from the Earth in the form of infrared radiation. Because of this, the atmosphere stabilizes the surface temperature of the Earth. It prevents the tremendous temperature extremes that occur on planets and moons which do not have much or any atmosphere.

Unfortunately, the atmosphere has become a dumping ground for many pollutant materials such as sulfur dioxide, aerosol can Freon, and the exhaust from supersonic transport planes. These materials, and the changes which they cause, can damage vegetation and materials. Human life can be shortened, and the characteristics of the atmosphere itself may be changed. Most important, the Earth's whole climate may be changed by pollutants in the atmosphere. This could have bad consequences for man.

The normal atmosphere contains a number of different gases as shown in Table 9.1. In addition to the gases shown, air may contain from 0.1 to 5% water on a volume basis, with a normal range of 1 to 3%.

TABLE 9.1

Components in pollution-free dry air at ground level expressed as percent by volume.

Major components	Volume percent
Nitrogen	78.08
Oxygen	20.95
Minor components	
Argon	9.34×10^{-1}
Carbon dioxide	3.14×10^{-2}
Trace components	
Neon	1.818×10^{-3}
Helium	5.24×10^{-4}
Methane	2×10^{-4}
Krypton	1.14×10^{-4}
Nitrous oxide	2.5×10^{-5}
Hydrogen	5×10^{-5}
Xenon	$0–8.7 \times 10^{-6}$
Sulfur dioxide	$0–1 \times 10^{-4}$
Ozone	$0–2 \times 10^{-6}$
Nitrogen dioxide	$0–2 \times 10^{-6}$
Ammonia	0–trace
Carbon monoxide	0–trace
Iodine	0–trace

9.9

Major Regions of the Atmosphere

Before each flight in a commercial airliner, the passengers are shown the location of oxygen masks, and the operation of this device is explained. The passengers normally pay little attention. However, if the pressure system in the airplane were to fail, they would quickly grab for the masks and the pilot would dive for the thicker air at lower altitudes, just like a swimmer quickly comes to the surface when he is out of breath. This is because most of the Earth's atmosphere is located below even the 5 or 6 mi of altitude where airliners normally fly.

One of the major characteristics of the atmosphere is that the density of air and the air pressure decrease very rapidly with increasing altitude. More than 99% of the atmosphere is below a 20-mile altitude. The atmosphere is divided into four distinct layers based upon temperature variations at certain distances from the Earth. These regions are shown in Figure 9.11.

Closest to the Earth is a thin layer going up roughly 7 mi known as the **troposphere.** The temperature becomes lower with increasing altitude in the troposphere. People who drive to the top of Pike's Peak

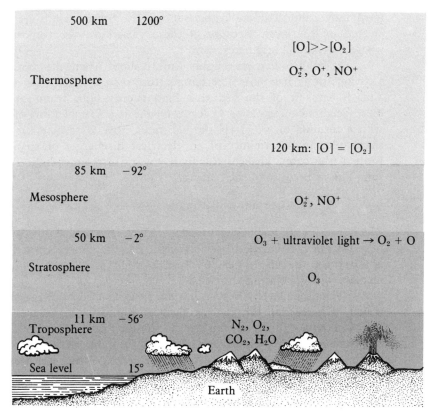

FIGURE 9.11
Major regions of the atmosphere (not to scale).

The atmosphere forms a gaseous envelope above the surface of the Earth. (Courtesy of NASA)

on even an August day notice this effect. The reason for this temperature decrease is that the Earth's surface is always giving off heat. It has to get rid of all the heat energy received from the sun. As the distance up from the "hot" Earth's surface increases, the temperature becomes lower. The troposphere shows considerable variations in temperature, pressure, and moisture content. These differ with location and with time. Clouds form, move, and dissipate in the troposphere. Strong winds are likewise created in this layer. Because of these variations, the troposphere is where "weather" originates.

At an altitude from roughly 7 mi to about 30 mi (the stratosphere) a curious thing happens. The temperature *increases* at higher altitudes. This is a result of the fact that high energy light from the sun at these heights causes ozone to form. Ozone is a special form of oxygen with a formula of O_3. It is the substance that is responsible for the sharp odor in the vicinity of an electrical discharge, or spark. Once formed, the ozone absorbs the high energy ultraviolet light from the sun. This is because of the reaction,

$$O_3 + \text{ultraviolet light} \longrightarrow O_2 + O$$

which breaks up the ozone molecule. This reaction requires energy, which is taken from the ultraviolet light. As the energy from the light is absorbed, the air is heated. This is what causes the temperature increase with increasing altitude.

The ozone layer is very important to us. It absorbs ultraviolet light, which, if it reached the Earth's surface, would cause severe sunburn and skin cancer. There is considerable concern that pollutants added to the atmosphere may be causing chemical reactions which decrease the concentration of ozone in the ozone layer. Two of the potential culprits are the supersonic transport plane and Freon aerosol cans. The SST has to fly in the thin air found at high altitudes to prevent friction from the air from heating up the wing surfaces too much. Products from the SST exhaust enter the ozone layer and may cause chemical reactions that destroy O_3. These exhaust products are oxides of nitrogen.

Aerosol cans are not used at such great altitudes. However, those that use Freon as the force behind their "squirt" add Freon to the atmosphere. Freon is the name given to several different chemical compounds. The chemical formula of a common form is CCl_2F_2. Freon does not react chemically with much of anything, which is one reason that it is so useful. When it is released to the atmosphere, it stays around for years. So much Freon has been put into the atmosphere from aerosol cans and refrigeration equipment that it can be detected in an air sample anywhere on Earth. Eventually the Freon released to the air at the surface of the Earth drifts up to the stratosphere. There it comes into contact with the high-energy, ultraviolet light from the sun. This sunlight knocks Cl atoms off of the Freon molecule. These atoms then enter the chain reaction,

$$Cl + O_3 = ClO + O_2$$
$$O_3 + \text{ultraviolet light} = O_2 + O$$
$$ClO + O = Cl + O_2$$

which rapidly breaks down the ozone molecules.

At altitudes above the stratosphere, the atmosphere again becomes cooler with increasing distance from the hot Earth. This occurs in the region known as the mesosphere. Finally, in the thermosphere the temperature becomes very high because of direct exposure to intense sunlight. Actually at this altitude, there is essentially no air left and the idea of temperature does not really apply very well. At these altitudes it is extremely cold in the shade and extremely hot in the sunlight.

9.10

The Earth's Heat Balance

The Earth is constantly receiving light energy from the sun. This energy is sent back from the Earth's surface so the Earth's surface does not become too hot. The amount of energy involved is enormous. As shown in Figure 9.12, a panel of 1-m (approximately 1 yard) sides exposed directly to the sun above the Earth's atmosphere receives light energy at a rate of 1340 watts. The area of such a panel is smaller than a typical desk top. Consider that the incandescent light bulb in the

FIGURE 9.12

A square meter exposed to sunlight above the Earth's atmosphere receives energy at a rate of 1340 watts.

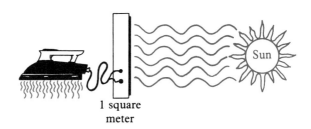

1 square
meter

desk lamp is probably no larger than a 100-watt bulb. But the bulb feels hot. This gives you some idea of the amount of light energy that the Earth's surface receives. Just one square meter receives enough energy to heat an electrical iron, fry a hamburger, or power a soldering iron. These examples demonstrate the potential of solar energy as an energy source.

Most of the energy received from the sun is in the form of visible radiation. This is light which we can see. Not all of this energy actually reaches the Earth's surface. Some is scattered back by air in the atmosphere and by clouds. Some of the light energy is reflected back from the Earth's surface. However, about half of the sunlight energy is absorbed by the Earth. This causes the surface to become warm. A warm object, such as the Earth's surface, gives off energy in the form of infrared radiation. This "invisible light" carries energy from the Earth's surface back through the atmosphere. Some of the infrared radiation is absorbed by the atmosphere, but eventually it leaves the atmosphere and goes out into space (see Figure 9.13).

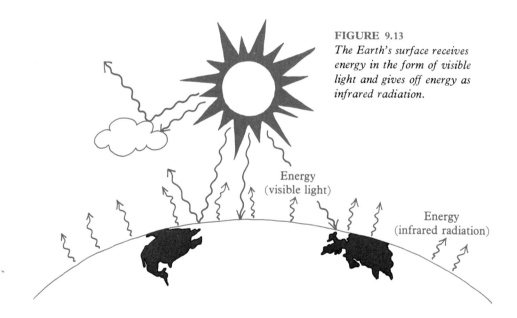

FIGURE 9.13
The Earth's surface receives energy in the form of visible light and gives off energy as infrared radiation.

Energy (visible light)

Energy (infrared radiation)

The heat balance of the Earth is very important to our well-being. The delicate balance between solar energy received and infrared radiation energy given off by the Earth's surface determines the average temperature of the Earth. If that balance varies much at all, the climate changes a lot. The Earth's average temperature during the last Ice Age— which was really a very recent occurrence—was only a few degrees colder than present average temperatures. If the Earth's average temperature were to increase by only about two degrees, the great ice caps at the North and South Poles would start to melt. Eventually the water produced would cover most of the world's large cities.

Man's activities are doing things which may be changing this delicate heat balance. One of the most important of these is the addition of carbon dioxide to the atmosphere from the burning of fuels containing carbon. Carbon dioxide (as well as water vapor) reabsorbs some of the infrared radiation given off from the Earth. The burning of fuels has increased the carbon dioxide level in the atmosphere by a significant amount since the 1800's. As more carbon dioxide absorbs more infrared radiation, the effect is to make the Earth hotter. This is called the **greenhouse effect**.

Another effect (albedo effect), which may work in the opposite direction from that of increased CO_2, is the formation of clouds. Clouds are made up of very tiny droplets of water, which have formed from water vapor in the atmosphere. These droplets are formed around very small particles in the atmosphere known as **condensation nuclei**. Condensation nuclei may be particles from evaporated salt from sea spray, smoke from forest fires, and other natural sources. They may also come from the particulate matter emitted by factories, automobiles, and other pollutant sources. In addition, sulfuric acid from the burning of sulfur-containing fuel causes cloud formation. Clouds reflect light coming from the sun. An increase in cloud cover resulting from air pollution could cause the Earth's average temperature to decrease.

9.11

Sulfur Dioxide in the Atmosphere

Sulfur dioxide, SO_2, is probably the most serious air pollutant at the present time. As shown in the atmospheric sulfur cycle in Figure 9.14, sulfur occurs in several forms in the atmosphere. It comes from a number of different sources, most of which are natural sources. The major problem with sulfur dioxide in the atmosphere is that it is produced at high concentrations in small areas where it can have a big impact. As supplies of clean fossil fuels such as natural gas become diminished, we will have to rely more upon "dirty" fuels, particularly coal. Most of the available coal contains several percent of sulfur, which will either have to be tolerated as a pollutant or removed.

Sulfur dioxide, and the sulfuric acid which it produces, is considered to be damaging to human health. It is believed to cause problems with the respiratory tract. Sulfur dioxide is thought to have been partly responsible for killing people in several cases of severe air pollution. One of these incidents occurred when weather conditions caused the accumulation in the atmosphere of waste products from industrial plants in a narrow valley along the Meuse River in Belgium in 1930. A total of 60 people died. In 1948 over 40% of the population of Donora, Pennsylvania (a town near Pittsburgh) became ill during a

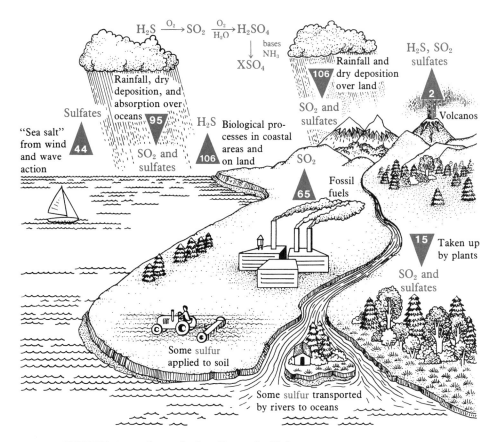

FIGURE 9.14 *Atmospheric sulfur cycle. Values are in millions of tons (teregrams) of S as estimated by James P. Friend, "The Global Sulfur Cycle," in* Chemistry of the Lower Atmosphere, *S. I. Rasool, Ed., Plenum Press, N.Y., N.Y., 1973, Chap. 4.*

similar incident and 20 died. Mortality records in London during a five-day period in December, 1952, when sulfur dioxide reached high levels showed an excess of 3500 to 4000 deaths over those that normally would have occurred.

Sulfur dioxide in the atmosphere is harmful to plants. Acute exposure to high levels of the gas kills leaf tissue (leaf necrosis). The edges of the leaves and the areas between leaf veins are particularly damaged. Chronic exposure to low levels of SO_2 causes chlorosis, a bleaching or yellowing of the normally green portions of the leaf.

Sulfur dioxide reacts with oxygen and water in the atmosphere,

$$2\,SO_2 + O_2 + 2\,H_2O \longrightarrow 2\,H_2SO_4$$

to produce sulfuric acid. This forms as very small droplets, or **aerosols**. Sulfuric acid aerosols are harmful to plants. Such damage appears as small spots where the sulfuric acid droplets have landed on the plant leaves. Sulfuric acid aerosols are also very damaging to materials. For example, electrical relay contacts are rapidly corroded by sulfuric acid in the atmosphere.

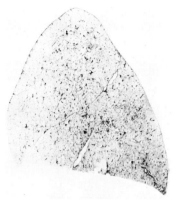

Normal

Magnification of the cells in lung tissue taken from a normal person and those suffering from emphysema and lung cancer. These conditions may be caused by exposure to pollutants over a long period of time. (Courtesy of Massachusetts Audubon Society; John Mitchell, photographer)

Emphysema

Carcinoma

9.12

Nitrogen Oxides and Smog in the Atmosphere

Nitric oxide, NO, is produced at the very high temperatures which occur during combustion in an automobile engine.

$$N_2 + O_2 \text{ (high temperature)} \longrightarrow 2\,NO$$

It is also produced when fuels containing nitrogen are burned in furnaces. In the atmosphere NO reacts with O_2,

$$2\,NO + O_2 \longrightarrow 2\,NO_2$$

to produce nitrogen dioxide, NO_2. The reaction is not so simple as shown. It is actually a complicated series of steps involving sunlight and often organic compounds in the atmosphere. Nitrogen dioxide is a toxic gas with a bad odor and a reddish-brown color. However, even in polluted air, it is not normally present at a high enough concentration to damage human health. It does absorb light and cut down on visibility.

The most important effect of nitrogen dioxide in the atmosphere comes from its chemical reaction when exposed to light. This reaction,

$$NO_2 + \text{high energy sunlight} \longrightarrow NO + O$$

produces oxygen atoms, O. It is called a photochemical dissociation. The oxygen atom reacts violently with other things in the atmosphere. It particularly reacts with compounds of hydrogen and carbon (hydrocarbons) such as those which enter the atmosphere from the incomplete burning of gasoline. The first products of this reaction are unstable species called **free radicals**. These go through a complicated series of reactions which produce more free radicals and ozone. Eventually these reactions convert any NO present back to NO_2. Aldehydes, such as formaldehyde,

$$\begin{matrix} & O \\ & \| \\ H-&C&-H \end{matrix} \quad \text{formaldehyde}$$

are produced. Compounds called **oxidants** are also produced. These compounds add oxygen to other compounds more vigorously and at lower temperatures than does O_2. Ozone, O_3, is an oxidant. Peroxyacetyl nitrate (PAN)

$$\begin{matrix} H & O \\ | & \| \\ H-C-&C&-O-O-NO_2 \\ | \\ H \end{matrix} \quad \text{peroxyacetyl nitrate (PAN)}$$

is another oxidant formed in the atmosphere. Oxidants are very irritating to the eyes and nose. They cause damage to plants. Pine trees are particularly damaged by oxidants. Oxidants also harm materials. They cause rubber to crack and become brittle.

As a result of the very complicated processes, which begin with the breakdown of NO_2 by sunlight followed by reactions of hydrocarbons, very small particles of organic material are formed. These scatter sunlight and reduce visibility. The aldehydes, ozone, and PAN in the atmosphere make people's eyes water and their noses burn. The air has a bad, choking odor. Plants do not grow well and materials are damaged. These conditions result in **photochemical smog**. This is the infamous smog which causes so much grief in Los Angeles and some other cities.

Although the reactions that cause smog to form are too complicated to cover here, and are not even completely understood, the general scheme of smog formation can be shown (see Figure 9.15). Because of the role played by sunlight in smog formation, the process varies with the time of day. The changing concentrations of the species in a smoggy atmosphere during the course of one day are shown in Figure 9.16.

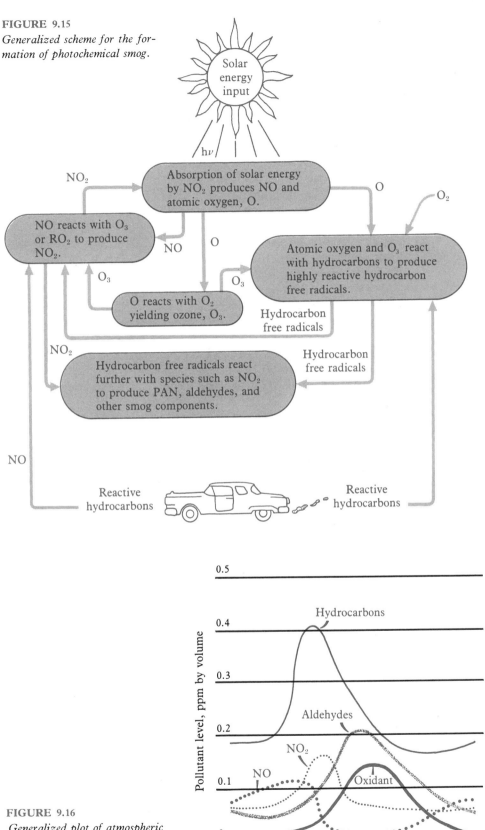

FIGURE 9.15

Generalized scheme for the formation of photochemical smog.

Solar energy input

$h\nu$

NO_2

Absorption of solar energy by NO_2 produces NO and atomic oxygen, O.

O

O_2

NO reacts with O_3 or RO_2 to produce NO_2.

NO

O

Atomic oxygen and O_3 react with hydrocarbons to produce highly reactive hydrocarbon free radicals.

O_3

O_3

O reacts with O_2 yielding ozone, O_3.

Hydrocarbon free radicals

NO_2

Hydrocarbon free radicals

Hydrocarbon free radicals react further with species such as NO_2 to produce PAN, aldehydes, and other smog components.

NO

Reactive hydrocarbons

Reactive hydrocarbons

FIGURE 9.16

Generalized plot of atmospheric concentrations of species involved in smog formation as a function of time of day.

Pollutant level, ppm by volume

0.5

0.4   Hydrocarbons

0.3

0.2   Aldehydes

NO_2

0.1   NO   Oxidant

0

Mid-night   4 A.M.   8 A.M.   Noon   4 P.M.   8 P.M.   Mid-night

Time of day

9.13

Particles in the Atmosphere

Even clear air contains small particles. Particles in the atmosphere ranging in size from about 0.5 mm down to clusters of a few molecules are made of a large variety of materials and specific objects. They may consist of solids or of liquid droplets. The term "aerosols" refers to extremely small particles the size of colloidal particles discussed in Chapter 6.

Very small solid particles include carbon black, silver iodide (used for "rain making"), soot from burning fuel, and sea salt left over when ocean spray evaporates. Larger particles include cement dust, windblown soil dust, foundry dust, and pulverized coal. Liquid particulate matter, generally called mist, includes rain drops, fog, and sulfuric acid mist. Some particles are biological materials such as viruses, bacteria, spores from bacteria, spores from fungi, and pollen.

Particles may affect climate. They can damage human health and increase the harmful effects of gaseous air pollutants such as sulfur dioxide. They damage materials, reduce visibility, and give the atmosphere an unpleasing appearance.

Chapter Summary

Gases are one of the three main physical forms of matter. A body of gas changes shape and can be compressed or expanded. This is because gas molecules are not attracted to each other and are always in motion. They move very rapidly. When a substance changes from the liquid to the gas form (evaporates), it takes up a much greater volume.

The three things which determine the volume of a quantity of gas are *pressure, temperature,* and *number of molecules.* The volume decreases with increasing pressure and increases with decreasing pressure. The volume increases with increasing temperature and decreases with decreasing temperature. These volume changes may be calculated mathematically. In doing these calculations the temperature must be expressed as absolute temperature (degrees Kelvin). Standard temperature and pressure (STP) are defined as 0°C (273°K) and 1 atm of pressure. At STP 1 mole of gas has a volume of 22.4 liters. It contains Avogadro's number (6.02×10^{23}) molecules of gas.

Many gases are very important industrial chemicals. Three of the top five chemicals produced in the U.S. are gases. These are ammonia, oxygen, and chlorine. Oxygen, nitrogen, argon, and neon are distilled from liquid air.

The atmosphere above us is a protective blanket, which serves many of our needs. It provides oxygen for animals and carbon dioxide for plant growth. It is the source of nitrogen which is fixed in chemical compounds for plant growth and industrial use. It carries water which

Three photographs taken of a business district in Boston, Mass. illustrate the effects of automobile and industrial stack emissions in the course of one day. (Courtesy of Massachusetts Audubon Society; Allen Morgan, photographer)

later falls as precipitation. It filters out harmful ultraviolet rays from the sun and serves to maintain the Earth's heat balance. A large number of gases are found as normal components of the atmosphere. By far the most common of these are nitrogen (78%) and oxygen (21%). The atmosphere is divided into layers based upon temperature.

Ozone in the upper atmosphere is very important. It filters out harmful ultraviolet rays from the sun. The ozone layer is in danger of being disturbed by chemical reactions involving nitrogen oxides from high flying supersonic planes and Freon.

The Earth's heat balance is maintained by the atmospheric absorption of infrared radiation given off from the Earth's surface. Water vapor and carbon dioxide are responsible for the absorption of this radiation. An increase in the concentration of carbon dioxide in the atmosphere brought on by increased burning of fossil fuels could result in an increase in the average temperature of the Earth. The opposite effect occurs with increased cloud cover because of reflection of sunlight from clouds.

Sulfur dioxide, SO_2, is one of the more harmful air pollutants. It is produced by the burning of high sulfur fuels. Nitrogen oxides are also harmful. Nitrogen dioxide absorbs energy from sunlight and starts the complicated series of reactions, which result in the formation of photochemical smog.

Particles in the atmosphere are called *aerosols*. They may be solids, such as sea salt crystals, or liquids, such as sulfuric acid droplets. These particles can damage human health, increase the effects of gaseous air pollutants, and reduce visibility.

Chapter Review Questions

The following questions are designed as a self-teaching tool to help you review Chapter 9. The answers to each question follow. See Chapter Review Questions for Chapter 1 for further instructions.

1. A gas is a form of matter in which there is no attraction between the molecules so that both the _____ and _____ of a body of gas change readily.

2. What may be said regarding the motion of gas molecules? _____
   _____.

3. When a liquid such as water goes into the gaseous (vapor) form at the boiling temperature of the liquid, what may be said about the change in volume? _____
   _____.

4. The constant rapid movement of gas molecules is responsible for the _____ exerted by the gas, and the phenomenon causing an unrestrained gas to spread out known as _____.

5. An air pressure of 1 atm is the average pressure of the atmosphere at _____.

6. An air pressure of 1 atm will hold up a column of mercury _____ mm high.

7. A pressure of 1 atm is also equivalent to _____ pounds per _____.

8. The volume of a gas at a particular temperature _____ with increasing pressure, and a volume of a gas at a particular pressure _____ with increasing temperature.

9. A quantity of gas which occupies 2.00 liters at 1.00 atm of pressure occupies _____ liters at 0.50 atm of pressure, if the temperature does not change.

10. A temperature of 25°C is _____°K, which is calculated by adding _____ to 25.

11. At constant pressure, a gas that occupies 1.00 liter at −10°C will occupy _____ liters at 150°C (remember to change °C to °K).

12. A temperature of 0°C and a pressure of 1.00 atm are called conditions of _____, which is abbreviated _____.

13. A mole of any gas at STP occupies a volume of _____ liters.

14. The number of liters of hydrogen at STP produced by the reaction of 2.50 moles of Mg with sulfuric acid is _____ liters.

15. Five gases produced in very large quantities in the U.S. are _____, _____, _____, _____, and _____.

16. The four gases produced by distilling liquid air are _____, _____, _____, and _____.

17. Air provides _____ needed by animals and _____ required by plants.

18. Air absorbs _____ radiation given off by the Earth's surface, largely because of _____ and _____ in the air.

19. With increasing altitude, the four major regions of the atmosphere are the _____, _____, _____, and _____.

20. The compound which occurs several miles up in the atmosphere and which filters out harmful ultraviolet radiation is called _____, and its chemical formula is _____.

21. Two kinds of substances which may be threatening the ozone layer are _____ and _____.

22. Cloud cover tends to have a _____ effect upon the Earth's temperature.

23. The gaseous air pollutant which enters the atmosphere from burning of "dirty" coal is _____.

24. Automobile engines produce pollutant _____ oxide gas.

25. A combination of nitrogen oxides, organic matter, and sunlight in the atmosphere produces _____, a very troublesome air pollution problem.

Answers to Chapter Review Questions

1. volume, shape

2. They are in constant and rapid motion.

3. The volume of the gas is many times greater.

4. pressure, diffusion

5. sea level

6. 760

7. 14.7, square inch

8. decreases, increases

9. 4.00
10. 298, 273
11. 1.61
12. standard temperature and pressure, STP
13. 22.4
14. 56
15. carbon dioxide, oxygen, ammonia, chlorine, nitrogen
16. oxygen, nitrogen, argon, neon
17. oxygen, carbon dioxide
18. infrared, water vapor, carbon dioxide
19. troposphere, stratosphere, mesosphere, thermosphere
20. ozone, O_3
21. nitrogen oxides from supersonic aircraft exhausts, Freon
22. cooling
23. sulfur dioxide
24. nitric
25. photochemical smog

Exercises for Chapter 9

1. Why is there some concern about the increasing carbon dioxide concentration in the atmosphere?

2. The total mass of the Earth's atmosphere is given as 5.5×10^{15} tons. It is 20.95% oxygen by volume. How many tons of coal (assuming it to be pure carbon) would have to be burned to consume half of this oxygen?

3. What is the chemical reaction of NO_2 that triggers the smog-forming process?

4. Match the gas in the left column with the use in the right column.

    | nitrogen | fill light bulbs |
    | oxygen | required by plants |
    | argon | make ammonia |
    | carbon dioxide | convert coal to hydrocarbons |
    | hydrogen | required by animals |

5. What are two properties of gases which are explained by the fact that gas molecules are far apart, move around rapidly, and are constantly bouncing into each other and their container walls?

6. To how many millimeters of mercury is exactly one-half atmosphere pressure equivalent?

7. Write a chemical reaction that explains the temperature maximum found at the boundary of the stratosphere and mesosphere.

8. Why would an order for "10 gal of oxygen" not have any meaning?

9. A volume of 5 liters of gas at 10°C and 0.50 atm of pressure is changed to 150°C and 1.50 atm of pressure. What is the new volume?

10. A pure gas weighing 12.0 g has a volume of 5.6 liters at STP. What is the molecular weight of the gas?

11. What volume of H_2 gas at STP is produced when a gram of aluminum (atomic weight 27) reacts with excess H_2SO_4 to produce H_2? and $Al_2(SO_4)_3$?

12. One type of airplane altimeter depends upon a very common characteristic of gases. From what you have learned about changes in the atmosphere with increasing altitude, explain what this property is.

13. It was stated in the text that changing liquid water at 100°C to steam at 100°C results in an increase in volume by 1700 times that of the liquid. If the final temperature of the steam were 473°C instead of 100°C, by how many times would the volume increase compared to the original liquid?

14. Match each pressure in the left column with the same pressure (but different units) on the right.

3.00 atm	2.00 atm
76 mm of mercury	44.1 psi
29.4 psi	0.100 atm

15. A volume of 22.4 liters of air weighs 28.8 g at STP. Assume that a balloon, which by itself weighs 0.8 g, is filled with 22.4 liters of helium gas at STP. What is the maximum weight of an object which the balloon could lift?

16. What is Charles' law?

17. Explain why a balloon filled with neon would rise in the air, while one filled with fluorine gas (which has a lower *atomic* weight) would not.

18. Explain the effect upon the Earth of an increase in the average temperature of only two or three degrees Celsius for a long period of time.

19. From Figure 9.14, which shows the atmospheric sulfur cycle, what is the greatest single source of sulfur in the atmosphere? Why are man's pollutant sources so much more troublesome than this one?

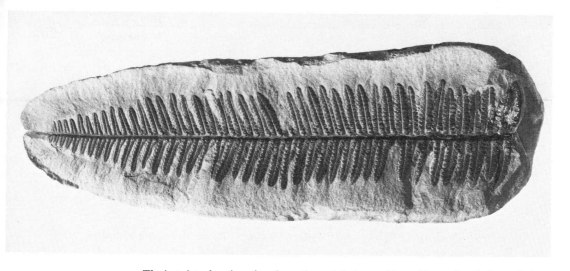

The imprint of a giant fern in a piece of shale provides evidence that fuels result from the burial and accumulation of organic deposits millions of years ago. (Courtesy of the Smithsonian Institution)

10

Organic Chemistry

10.1

What is So Special About Carbon?

The carbon atom occupies a very special place in chemistry, industry, medicine, and our own bodies. This is because carbon atoms bond to other carbon atoms. These bonds are covalent bonds in which carbon's 4 bonding electrons

4 bonding electrons

The carbon atom has a nucleus with 6 protons and 6 neutrons. The atomic number of carbon is 6, and the atomic weight is 12.

are shared with electrons from other atoms. By bonding with each other, carbon atoms form a wide variety of structures. These may take the form of straight chains, branched chains, and rings.

As can be seen in Figure 10.1, groups of carbon atoms bonded together can form a variety of structures. Of course, carbon atoms can

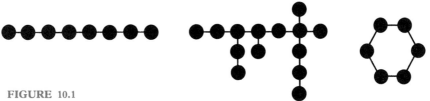

FIGURE 10.1

Carbon atoms bond with each other to form arrangements of straight chains, branched chains, and rings.

bond to other kinds of atoms such as oxygen, nitrogen, or sulfur. Considering all of the bonding arrangements, it is possible to have literally millions of compounds containing carbon. Carbon-containing compounds are generally classified as **organic compounds**. More than 3 million organic compounds have been identified by chemists. With the exception of ionic carbonate, bicarbonate, and cyanide compounds, practically all chemicals containing carbon are organic compounds. The study of these compounds is called **organic chemistry**. Because there are so many organic compounds, which are useful for so many different things, more chemists deal with organic chemistry than any other branch of chemistry. This whole chapter is devoted to organic chemistry. For those planning to study chemistry in more detail, whole courses are taught about organic chemistry.

A great variety of organic chemicals occur in living systems. Our bodies are made up of organic chemicals. Many of these are extremely complicated. The food we eat consists of organic chemicals manufactured by plants and animals. We also eat organic chemicals in the form of food additives (see Chapter 15). The effects of these organic chemicals in our diet may not all be good. The organic chemicals involved in life processes are the subject of a special branch of chemistry called **biochemistry**. That topic is discussed in Chapter 11.

10.2

Alkanes: Fuel for Heating, Transportation, and Industry

Many organic chemicals are made up of only carbon and hydrogen. These are called **hydrocarbons**. They will be discussed first because they are fairly simple and can be used to show some important things about the structure and naming of organic compounds. Hydrocarbons are produced and used in tremendous quantities. Petroleum is a mixture of hydrocarbons. The U.S. uses almost 20 *million* barrels of petroleum *per day*.

Alkanes, also called **paraffins**, are the most common type of hydrocarbons. These are compounds of carbon and hydrogen in which the carbon atoms are joined by only single bonds, each made up of 2 electrons. Other hydrocarbons having double bonds made up of 4 electrons or triple bonds consisting of 6 electrons are discussed later in this chapter.

One of the ways coal is mined is by removing overburden, which is the soil and rock on top of coal deposits, with a giant dragline and then excavating the coal from an open trench. This process is called "strip-mining." (Courtesy of USDA, Forest Service; J. Prater, photographer)

The simplest alkane is methane, CH_4. The electron-dot formula for methane is

$$H:\overset{\displaystyle \cdot\cdot}{\underset{\displaystyle \cdot\cdot}{C}}:H \qquad \text{methane}$$

in which each of the pairs of dots represents a covalent single bond made up of a pair of electrons. More complicated formulas may have so many dots that they would be extremely confusing. For that reason a dashed line, —, is often used to represent a pair of electrons in a single bond. This gives the following structure for methane:

$$H-\overset{\displaystyle H}{\underset{\displaystyle H}{C}}-H \qquad \text{methane}$$

In addition to being the simplest alkane, methane is the most important. It is a stable, colorless, odorless gas which becomes a liquid at a very low −161.5°C and freezes at −183.2°C. Methane is not very poisonous by itself. Toxicologically, it is considered to be a simple asphyxiant. This means that it harms the body by depriving it of oxygen.

Methane is produced by bacteria acting in the absence of oxygen. Millions of tons of methane enter the atmosphere from this source each year. It is produced by bacteria in land fills containing buried garbage. Some of this methane is now tapped for commercial use.

Methane makes up the bulk of natural gas used for fuel and for chemical synthesis. Over 60 billion cubic feet of natural gas are produced in the U.S. each year. Methane burns cleanly to yield only carbon dioxide and water. Because methane is such an ideal, nonpolluting fuel and raw material, the supply of natural gas is becoming quite limited. Substitutes will have to be found soon.

The most important industrial use of methane is the production of hydrogen. This occurs by the reaction of pressurized steam and methane,

$$CH_4 + H_2O \longrightarrow CO + 3\,H_2$$

at 700 to 870°C over a nickel oxide catalyst. The hydrogen produced is used in large quantities to make ammonia by the reaction

$$N_2 + 3\,H_2 \longrightarrow 2\,NH_3$$

Hydrogen produced from methane is also used for upgrading gasoline in petroleum refining and for the manufacture of a number of kinds of chemicals.

All of the alkanes other than methane have chemical bonds between carbon atoms. The arrangement of carbon atoms may be in the form of straight chains, branched chains, or rings. Molecules with the ring arrangement are called **cycloalkanes**.

The straight-chain alkanes can be used to show two key points about organic chemistry. These are **structure** and **nomenclature.** Structure describes the arrangement of the atoms in an organic compound. Two molecules may have the same number of each kind of atoms, but different structures. Because of differences in structure their behavior may be very different. This is particularly true of molecules in living systems. Nomenclature is very important to the organic chemist for identifying particular organic compounds. The name of an organic compound may describe its structure.

Table 10.1 gives the names and structures of the first 10 straight-chain alkanes. In cases where it is important to designate that the alkane is a straight chain, the name may have an "*n*-" in front of it, such as *n*-butane or *n*-hexane.

Ethane, propane, and butane are gases. Ethane occurs to a certain extent in natural gas. It is used as a fuel and to make other chemicals. Propane can be extracted from natural gas and from petroleum. It can be compressed to form a liquid, which is stored in pressurized tanks. It is widely used as a fuel on farms (including tractors) and in other locations where piped gas is not available. Automobile engines modified to run on propane are especially pollution-free. Butane is produced from petroleum. It is the main ingredient of liquefied petroleum gas, LPG, used as a fuel. It is also used for the manufacture of synthetic rubber.

Propane and butane are commonly used as fuels in remote locations where piped natural gas is not available.

TABLE 10.1
The first ten straight-chain alkanes.

Alkane name	Structure	Formula
Methane	$H-\overset{\displaystyle H}{\underset{\displaystyle H}{C}}-H$	CH_4
Ethane	$H-\overset{H}{\underset{H}{C}}-\overset{H}{\underset{H}{C}}-H$	C_2H_6
Propane	$H-\overset{H}{\underset{H}{C}}-\overset{H}{\underset{H}{C}}-\overset{H}{\underset{H}{C}}-H$	C_3H_8
Butane	$H-\overset{H}{\underset{H}{C}}-\overset{H}{\underset{H}{C}}-\overset{H}{\underset{H}{C}}-\overset{H}{\underset{H}{C}}-H$	C_4H_{10}
Pentane	$H-C-C-C-C-C-H$ (with H above and below each C)	C_5H_{12}
Hexane	$H-C-C-C-C-C-C-H$ (with H above and below each C)	C_6H_{14}
Heptane	$H-C-C-C-C-C-C-C-H$ (with H above and below each C)	C_7H_{16}
Octane	$H-C-C-C-C-C-C-C-C-H$ (with H above and below each C)	C_8H_{18}
Nonane	$H-C-C-C-C-C-C-C-C-C-H$ (with H above and below each C)	C_9H_{20}
Decane	$H-C-C-C-C-C-C-C-C-C-C-H$ (with H above and below each C)	$C_{10}H_{22}$

The other alkanes shown in Table 10.1 are colorless liquids at room temperature. The lighter ones, particularly, evaporate very easily. They are said to be **volatile**. These gasoline-like compounds burn very vigorously. This, along with their volatile nature makes them quite a fire hazard.

Now we may consider some things about structure and naming of alkanes. Straight-chain octane has the structure,

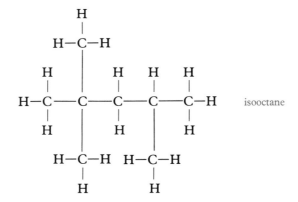

It is called normal octane (*n*-octane) to show that all carbons are in one chain. It can be used as gasoline. However, an engine running on *n*-octane would knock terribly and would soon be ruined because this alkane burns with explosive force in the engine cylinder. The atoms in octane can be arranged to give isooctane

in which the carbon atoms are in a branched structure, rather than a straight chain. This compound burns so smoothly in an engine that it is used to define the antiknock quality of gasoline. The ability of gasoline to resist knocking is expressed as an **octane number**. Pure isooctane has an octane number of 100, which is higher than that of even premium gasoline.

What are the chemical formulas of *n*-octane and isooctane? Each compound contains 8 carbon atoms and 18 hydrogen atoms. Therefore, the chemical formula of each is C_8H_{18}. These two compounds have the same chemical formula. However, they act very differently when used as gasoline. This shows the importance of structure in organic chemistry. It is not enough to know that the chemical formula is C_8H_{18}. The way that the atoms are put together—the structure—must be known also.

There is a definite relationship between the number of carbon atoms and the number of hydrogen atoms in straight-chain and branched-chain alkanes. Examining the chemical formulas in Table 10.1 shows that each compound has two hydrogen atoms for each carbon atom, and in addition to that two more hydrogens. For example, methane has 1 carbon atom and 2 + 2 hydrogens. Ethane has 2 carbons and 4 + 2 hydrogens. Propane has 3 carbons and 6 + 2 hydrogens. If we let *x* represent the number of carbons, a general formula for these alkanes becomes C_xH_{2x+2}. This formula indicates that a 10-carbon alkane has 20 + 2, or 22, hydrogens. Note from Table 10.1 that the formula of decane is in fact $C_{10}H_{22}$.

In the case of octane and isooctane it was shown that two alkanes may exist having the same formulas but different structures. This illustrates the very important idea of **isomerism**. Isooctane and *n*-octane are **isomers** of each other. Butane is the simplest alkane in which isomers are possible. Its 4 carbons can be in one chain, or 3 in a chain with the fourth attached as a branch to the chain. Both *n*-butane and

<table>
<tr><td>
H H H H
| | | |
H—C—C—C—C—H
| | | |
H H H H
</td></tr>
</table>

H
|
H—C—H

H   H
| |
H—C———C———C—H
| | |
H   H   H

n-butane

isobutane,
or 2-methylpropane

isobutane have the same formula, C_4H_{10}. But they are put together differently and are said to be isomers of each other. Because of their differences in structure, these two isomers have somewhat different properties. For example, *n*-butane boils at −0.5°C compared to −11.7°C for isobutane. They have some differences in chemical behavior also.

Note that another name for isobutane is 2-methylpropane. This is a name given according to a system approved by the International Union of Pure and Applied Chemistry, IUPAC. The IUPAC name describes the structure of the organic compound. This system of nomenclature (naming) is relatively easy to understand for alkanes. Examine again the structure of 2-methylpropane.

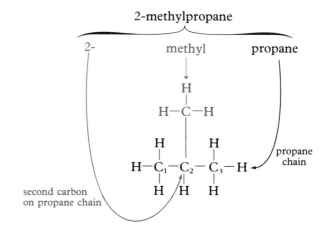

Notice that the longest continuous chain of carbon atoms is made up of 3 carbon atoms. From Table 10.1, you can see that the alkane with 3 carbon atoms is propane. This is where we get the "propane" part of the 2-methylpropane name. The $-CH_3$ group attached to the second carbon atom in the chain is called the **methyl** group. That name comes from the alkane with 1 carbon, which is methane. The methyl group is attached to the second carbon on the propane chain. Thus, the IUPAC name is 2-methylpropane.

It is possible to have other groups besides the methyl group attached as branches on a carbon chain. Some of these are shown as follows.

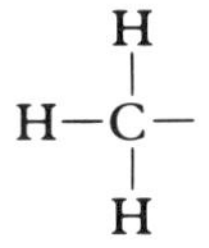

$$
\begin{array}{c}
H \\
| \\
H-C- \\
| \\
H
\end{array}
\qquad \textit{meth}yl \text{ group (from } \textit{meth}\text{ane)}
$$

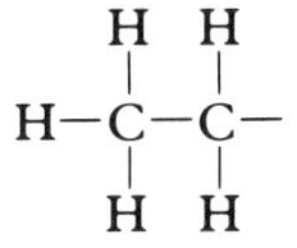

$$
\begin{array}{cc}
H & H \\
| & | \\
H-C-C- \\
| & | \\
H & H
\end{array}
\qquad \textit{eth}yl \text{ group (from } \textit{eth}\text{ane)}
$$

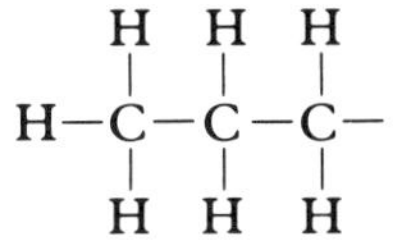

$$
\begin{array}{ccc}
H & H & H \\
| & | & | \\
H-C-C-C- \\
| & | & | \\
H & H & H
\end{array}
\qquad \textit{prop}yl \text{ group (from } \textit{prop}\text{ane)}
$$

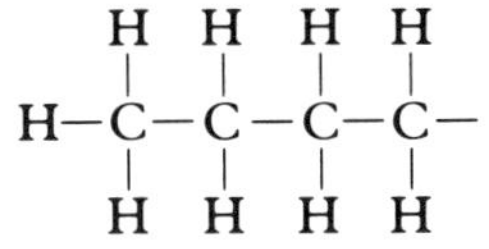

$$
\begin{array}{cccc}
H & H & H & H \\
| & | & | & | \\
H-C-C-C-C- \\
| & | & | & | \\
H & H & H & H
\end{array}
\qquad \textit{n-but}yl \text{ group (from } \textit{n-but}\text{ane)}
$$

Butane has only two isomers. As the number of carbons increases, the number of possible isomers increases very rapidly. This is shown clearly for the 7-carbon alkane, heptane. Heptane has all of the isomers shown in Figure 10.2. In naming all of the isomers in Figure 10.2 the longest chain of carbon atoms is taken as the basis for the name. Those isomers for which 6 carbons may be shown in a row have "*hexane*" as the root of the name. For these isomers of heptane only one methyl group may be attached. It may be bonded to either the second or third carbon from the end to give 2-methylhexane or 3-methylhexane. The most highly branched of the structures shown above is that of 2,2-dimethyl-3-methylbutane. Here the longest possible chain has 4 carbon atoms giving the "butane" part of the name. The "2,2" indicates that groups are substituted onto the second carbon atom. The "dimethyl" shows that there are 2 methyl groups on that atom. The "3-methyl" part of the name shows that there is one methyl group on

FIGURE 10.2
Possible isomers of the 7-carbon alkane, heptane.

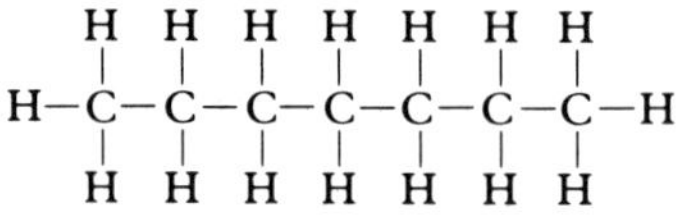

n-heptane

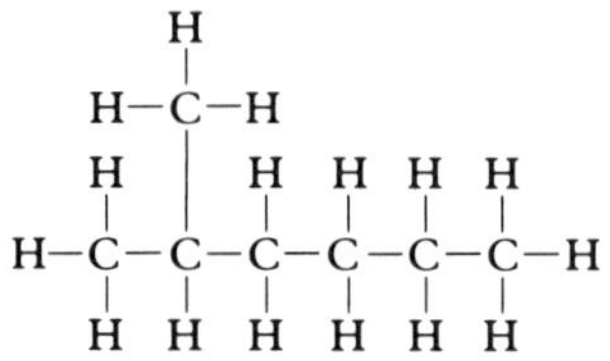

2-methylhexane

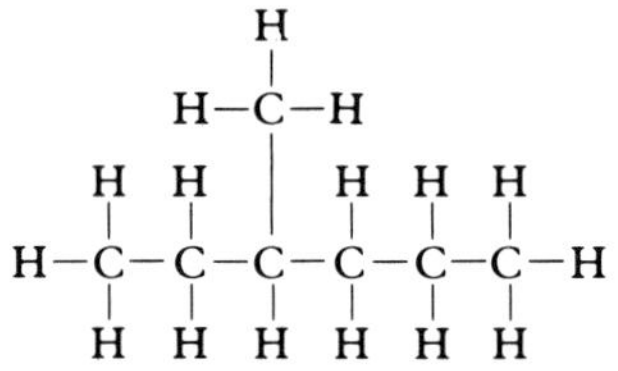

3-methylhexane

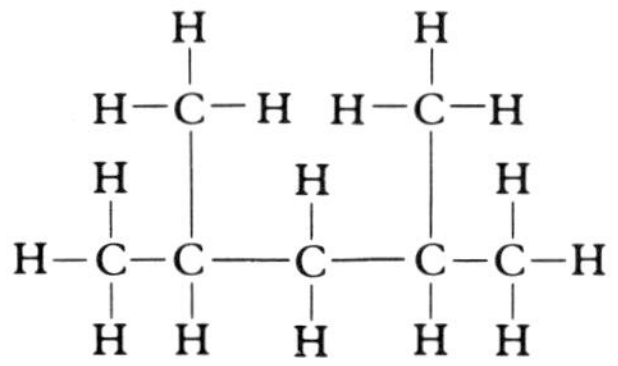

2,4-dimethylpentane

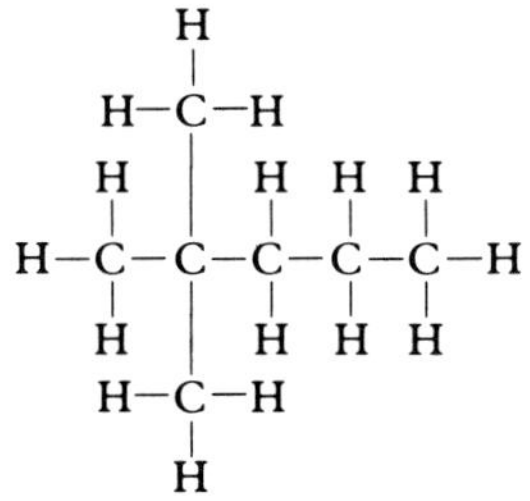

2,2-dimethylpentane

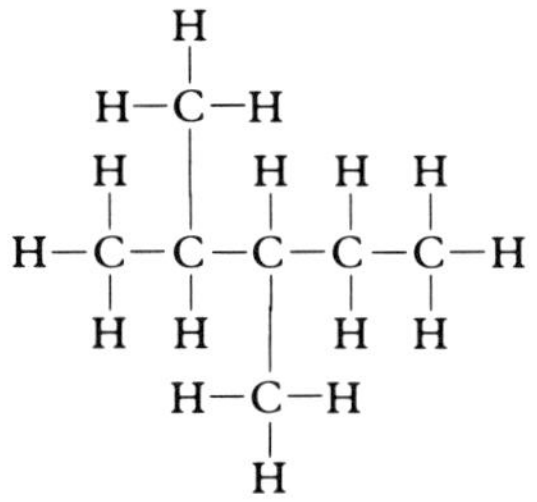

2,3-dimethylpentane

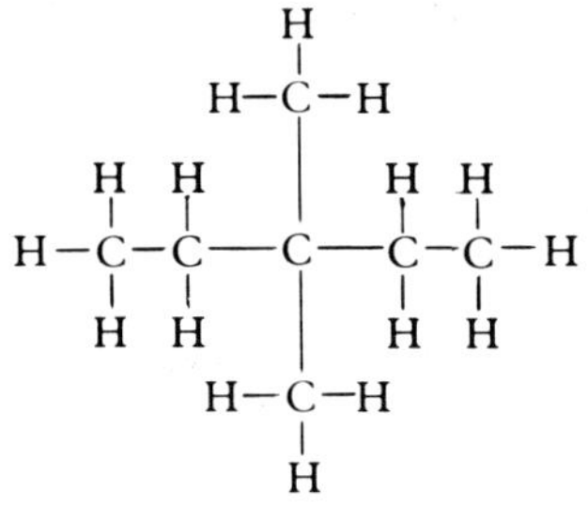

3,3-dimethylpentane

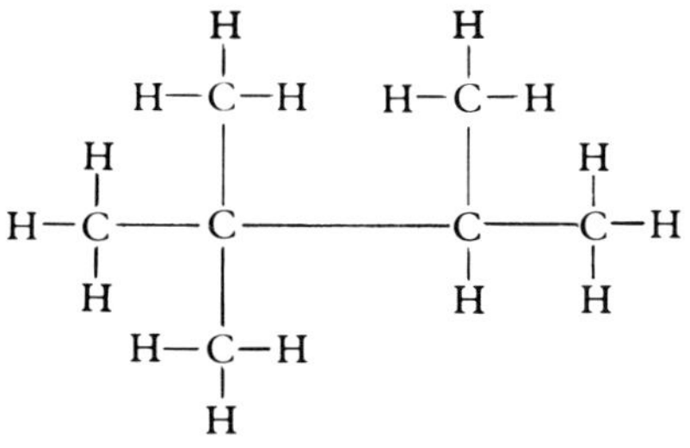

2,2-dimethyl-3-methylbutane

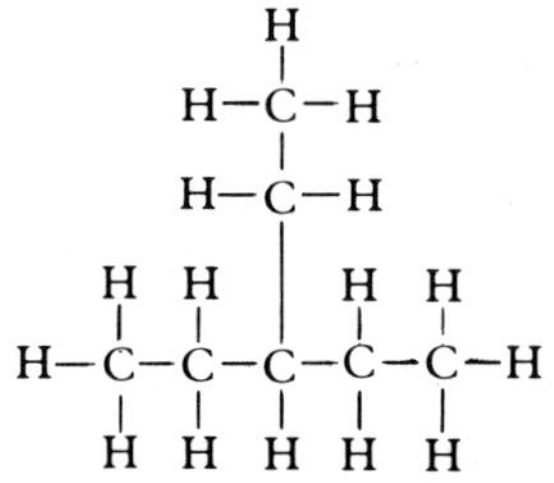

3-ethylpentane

the third carbon atom of the butane chain. In order to understand the names given in the rest of the chapter, it will be useful to spend some time figuring out the IUPAC names of the other isomers shown in Figure 10.2.

A total of 75 isomers of decane, $C_{10}H_{22}$, are possible. For alkanes above 30 carbons, the number of possible isomers is in the millions for each chemical formula. Alkanes higher than methane are normally obtained from the distillation and chemical modification of crude oil. Pentanes, hexanes, and heptanes make up the mixture of low-boiling hydrocarbons called **petroleum ethers**. These highly flammable low-boiling liquids are used as solvents to dissolve grease and fats, as dry cleaning agents, and as paint and varnish thinners. **Gasoline** contains alkanes and other hydrocarbons containing from 4 to 12 carbon atoms. **Kerosene** is made up of alkanes with 12 to 15 carbon atoms. Formerly widely used for home cooking and lamps, it is now used for jet airplane fuel. Alkanes containing more than 15 carbon atoms are used as fuel oil for oil-burning furnaces and as fuel for diesel engines. Lubricating oils have 20 or more carbon atoms. Paraffin wax is made up of straight-chain alkanes with 26 to 30 carbon atoms in the chain.

Kerosene, formly used in lamps and cooking stoves, is now widely employed as jet fuel. It is much less flammable than the high octane gasoline used in aircraft powered by piston engines.

Distillation of crude oil yields the products just described. Distillation is accomplished in a tall device called a **fractionating tower** as shown in Figure 10.3. The crude oil is vaporized by heating at the bottom of the tower, and it becomes progressively cooler as it goes to the top. In the fractionating tower, portions of the crude oil vapor form liquids which collect on trays in the tower. The hydrocarbons that are most volatile (have the lowest boiling point) in the crude oil go farthest up the tower before forming liquids. The trays upon which the liquids condense are arranged so that the heated vapors bubble up through the liquid in the trays. This gives an efficient separation of the crude oil into fractions based upon the temperatures at which the hydrocarbons boil.

The combination of alkanes with oxygen to yield carbon dioxide and water,

FIGURE 10.3
*Fractional distillation column
used in petroleum refining.*

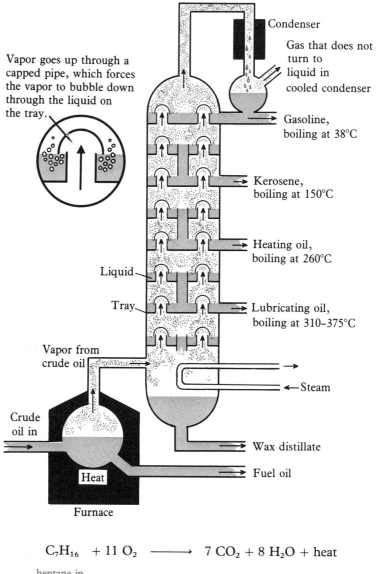

Vapor goes up through a
capped pipe, which forces
the vapor to bubble down
through the liquid on
the tray.

Condenser

Gas that does not
turn to
liquid in
cooled condenser

Gasoline,
boiling at 38°C

Kerosene,
boiling at 150°C

Heating oil,
boiling at 260°C

Liquid

Lubricating oil,
boiling at 310–375°C

Tray

Vapor from
crude oil

Steam

Crude
oil in

Wax distillate

Fuel oil

Heat

Furnace

$$C_7H_{16} + 11 O_2 \longrightarrow 7 CO_2 + 8 H_2O + heat$$

heptane in
gasoline

is the most common type of chemical reaction for which these hydrocarbons are used. The **combustion** of hydrocarbons is used to obtain heat
and mechanical energy. Unfortunately, some undesirable byproducts
result from this kind of reaction, particularly when it is carried out in an
internal combustion (piston) engine. The automobile engine produces
toxic carbon monoxide, CO. This air pollutant is discussed in Chapter 9.
In addition, not all of the hydrocarbon burns. Organic molecules are
produced that are very reactive (chemically active). These are introduced

into the atmosphere from automobile exhausts. Sunlight provides the energy that enables these hydrocarbon molecules to react with nitrogen oxides and oxygen in the atmosphere to form photochemical smog.

As supplies of natural gas and petroleum become tighter, the use of alkanes as fuel will become more expensive. These hydrocarbons are valuable for making other chemicals and eventually will be used almost exclusively for such **chemical synthesis**. There is not room here to discuss in detail the chemical reactions that alkanes undergo in various types of chemical synthesis. The most common of these reactions are **substitution reactions**. These are the replacement of hydrogen with some other atom or group of atoms. A typical simple reaction of this type is that between methane and chlorine,

$$CH_4 + Cl_2 \longrightarrow CH_3Cl + HCl$$

to produce methyl chloride, CH_3Cl. Methyl chloride is a **chlorinated hydrocarbon**. These make up a large class of compounds discussed in Section 10.6. Methyl chloride is used to make other chemicals, such as silicones employed as high temperature lubricants and caulking.

Several alkanes have ring structures. The most common of these is cyclohexane,

cyclohexane

which has a chemical formula of C_6H_{12}. A ring of 6 carbon atoms is about the most stable size for a cyclic compound. Smaller rings are strained. About 400 million gallons of cyclohexane are produced in the U.S. each year. About two-thirds of this production goes for the manufacture of nylon. Cyclohexane is also employed as a solvent and as a paint remover.

10.3

Alkenes: Raw Materials for Making Polyethylene Bottles and Many Other Things

Some hydrocarbons contain one or more double bonds in which 4 electrons make up the chemical bond. The simplest of these hydrocarbons is ethylene, C_2H_4.

ethylene

It is also one of the most important, with about 12 million tons produced in the U.S. each year. Hydrocarbons with double bonds are called **alkenes** or **olefins**.

The identity of a particular alkene molecule depends upon the location of the double bond. One or more double bonds can be located in a number of places along a chain of carbon atoms so that alkenes form even more isomers than alkanes. It was shown that butane exists as two isomers, *n*-butane and isobutane. If two hydrogens are removed from butane,

$$
\begin{array}{c}
\underset{\text{\textit{n}-butane}}{
H-\overset{\displaystyle H}{\underset{\displaystyle H}{C}}-\overset{\displaystyle H}{\underset{\displaystyle H}{C}}-\overset{\displaystyle H}{\underset{\displaystyle H}{C}}-\overset{\displaystyle H}{\underset{\displaystyle H}{C}}-H
}
\longrightarrow
H_2 +
\underset{\text{1-butene}}{
H-\overset{\displaystyle H}{\underset{\displaystyle H}{C}}-\overset{\displaystyle H}{\underset{\displaystyle H}{C}}-\overset{\displaystyle H}{C}=C\begin{smallmatrix} H \\ \\ H \end{smallmatrix}
}
\quad \text{or} \quad
\underset{\text{2-butene}}{
H-\overset{\displaystyle H}{\underset{\displaystyle H}{C}}-\overset{\displaystyle H}{C}=\overset{\displaystyle H}{C}-\overset{\displaystyle H}{\underset{\displaystyle H}{C}}-H
}
\end{array}
$$

either 1-butene, with the double bond on an end carbon atom, or 2-butene, with the double bond on the *second* carbon atom from the end may be formed.

Double bonds enable the formation of another type of isomer called **geometrical isomers**. There are two geometrical isomers possible for 2-butene. To understand why this is so, we have to know that atoms held together by a *single bond* can rotate in relation to each other.

FIGURE 10.4

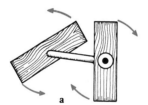

a

Two boards mounted on a single shaft can rotate freely in opposite directions.

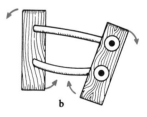

b

Two boards mounted on two parallel shafts cannot rotate in opposite directions without breaking or twisting the shafts.

Observe the analogy in Figure 10.4. The single bond acts much like it is a shaft to which the atoms are connected by roller bearings. However, rotation of atoms around a *double bond* is not possible. This makes it possible to have two structures for 2-butene. If we designate each of the two $-\overset{\displaystyle H}{\underset{\displaystyle H}{C}}-$H groups in 2-butene as methyl groups, these $-CH_3$ groups may be either on the same side (*cis*) or on opposite sides (*trans*). These are different compounds and have somewhat different properties.

$$
\underset{\textit{cis}\text{-2-butene}}{
\begin{smallmatrix} CH_3 \\ \\ H \end{smallmatrix} \! C=C \! \begin{smallmatrix} CH_3 \\ \\ H \end{smallmatrix}
}
\qquad\qquad
\underset{\textit{trans}\text{-2-butene}}{
\begin{smallmatrix} H \\ \\ CH_3 \end{smallmatrix} \! C=C \! \begin{smallmatrix} CH_3 \\ \\ H \end{smallmatrix}
}
$$

One other isomer of butene,

$$\underset{H}{\overset{H}{\diagdown}}C=C\underset{CH_3}{\overset{CH_3}{\diagup}}$$

2-methylpropene,
an isomer of butene

is possible. It is a branched chain alkene, which may be compared to 2-methylpropane, a branched chain alkane. There are no geometrical isomers of 2-methylpropene because switching the two hydrogens around or doing the same with the two methyl groups would produce the same compound.

An alkene may have more than one double bond. One common example is butadiene,

$$\underset{H}{\overset{H}{\diagdown}}C=\overset{\overset{H}{|}}{C}-\overset{\overset{H}{|}}{C}=C\underset{H}{\overset{H}{\diagup}}\qquad \text{butadiene}$$

widely used to make the common type of synthetic rubber.

It was shown at the beginning of this section that alkanes undergo substitution reactions in which hydrogen is removed and replaced by another kind of atom. The most common reactions of alkenes are **addition reactions** in which a chemical adds to the molecule. This is possible with alkenes because of the double bond. Alkenes are said to be **unsaturated**. (It is because of the presence of double bonds that some fats and oils are called unsaturated.) A double bond has 4 electrons, but a single bond containing only 2 electrons is sufficient to hold 2 carbon atoms together. That leaves 2 extra electrons to form more bonds with other atoms. Therefore, when chlorine gas reacts with ethylene,

$$Cl-Cl \;+\; \underset{H}{\overset{H}{\diagdown}}C=C\underset{H}{\overset{H}{\diagup}} \;\longrightarrow\; H-\overset{\overset{Cl}{|}}{\underset{\underset{H}{|}}{C}}-\overset{\overset{Cl}{|}}{\underset{\underset{H}{|}}{C}}-H$$

molecule of   ethylene   ethylene dichloride,
chlorine, Cl_2 or 1,2-dichloroethane

a chlorine atom does not replace a hydrogen atom. Instead, both chlorine atoms from the chlorine molecule add to the ethylene molecule to form 1,2-dichloroethane.

Largely because of their ability to undergo addition reactions, alkenes are more reactive (chemically active) than alkanes. Two other addition reactions that may occur are addition of hydrogen chloride,

$$\underset{H}{\overset{H}{\diagdown}}C=C\underset{H}{\overset{H}{\diagup}} \;+\; HCl \;\longrightarrow\; H-\overset{\overset{Cl}{|}}{\underset{\underset{H}{|}}{C}}-\overset{\overset{H}{|}}{\underset{\underset{H}{|}}{C}}-H$$

ethylene   ethyl chloride and addition of hydrogen:

$$H_2C=CH_2 + H_2 \longrightarrow H_3C-CH_3$$

ethylene   ethane

The addition of hydrogen is called **hydrogenation**. Vegetable oils (unsaturated fats) containing double bonds in their structures are hydrogenated to produce solid hydrogenated margarines and cooking fats.

One addition reaction is especially important because it makes possible our vast synthetic textiles, plastics, and synthetic rubber industry. This is the addition of alkene molecules to each other. The combination of many small molecules to form a large molecule is called **polymerization**. The small molecules are called **monomers** and the product is a **polymer**. An important example is the polymerization of ethylene. Two ethylene molecules add to each other to produce another alkene,

$$H_2C=CH_2 + H_2C=CH_2 \longrightarrow H_3C-CH_2-CH=CH_2$$

which in turn can add another ethylene molecule,

$$H_3C-CH_2-CH=CH_2 + H_2C=CH_2 \longrightarrow H_3C-CH_2-CH_2-CH_2-CH=CH_2$$

and the process continues until very long chains are formed.

This polyethylene film used in packaging is made from ethylene gas. (Courtesy of Exxon Chemical Co., Inc.)

$$\cdots\overset{\displaystyle H}{\underset{\displaystyle H}{C}}-\overset{\displaystyle H}{\underset{\displaystyle H}{C}}-\overset{\displaystyle H}{\underset{\displaystyle H}{C}}-\overset{\displaystyle H}{\underset{\displaystyle H}{C}}-\overset{\displaystyle H}{\underset{\displaystyle H}{C}}-\overset{\displaystyle H}{\underset{\displaystyle H}{C}}-\overset{\displaystyle H}{\underset{\displaystyle H}{C}}-\overset{\displaystyle H}{\underset{\displaystyle H}{C}}-\overset{\displaystyle H}{\underset{\displaystyle H}{C}}\cdots$$

polyethylene

This long-chain polymer of ethylene is called **polyethylene**. It is the familiar substance used to make plastic bags, flexible bottles, and many other plastic articles.

10.4

Alkynes

Alkynes are hydrocarbons such as acetylene,

$$H-C\equiv C-H \qquad \text{acetylene}$$

which have triple bonds containing 6 electrons. Alkynes are very reactive. Acetylene is used as a high-energy fuel in cutting torches and welding. It and other alkynes are used to manufacture other chemicals.

The reaction of calcium carbide and water

$$CaC_2 + 2\,H_2O \longrightarrow C_2H_2\uparrow + Ca(OH)_2$$

calcium   acetylene
carbide

produces acetylene. Acetylene can also be prepared by removing hydrogen from other hydrocarbons at very high temperatures.

$$\overset{\displaystyle H}{\underset{\displaystyle H}{\diagdown}}C=C\overset{\displaystyle H}{\underset{\displaystyle H}{\diagup}} \quad + \quad \text{heat} \longrightarrow H-C\equiv C-H \; + \; H_2$$

ethylene   acetylene

$$2\,CH_4 \; + \; \text{heat} \longrightarrow H-C\equiv C-H \; + \; 3\,H_2$$

methane   acetylene

Like alkenes, the main chemical reactions of alkynes are addition reactions. Typical of such reactions are the addition of hydrogen,

$$H-C\equiv C-H \; + \; H_2 \longrightarrow \overset{\displaystyle H}{\underset{\displaystyle H}{\diagdown}}C=C\overset{\displaystyle H}{\underset{\displaystyle H}{\diagup}}$$

acetylene   ethylene

$$\overset{\displaystyle H}{\underset{\displaystyle H}{\diagdown}}C=C\overset{\displaystyle H}{\underset{\displaystyle H}{\diagup}} \; + \; H_2 \longrightarrow H-\overset{\displaystyle H}{\underset{\displaystyle H}{C}}-\overset{\displaystyle H}{\underset{\displaystyle H}{C}}-H$$

ethylene   ethane

addition of halogens such as bromine,

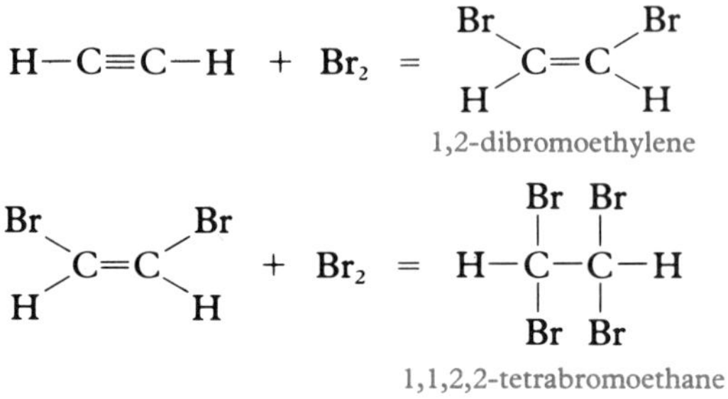

$$H-C\equiv C-H \ + \ Br_2 \ = \ \underset{\underset{H}{|}}{Br}C=C\underset{\underset{H}{|}}{Br}$$

1,2-dibromoethylene

$$\underset{\underset{H}{|}}{Br}C=C\underset{\underset{H}{|}}{Br} \ + \ Br_2 \ = \ H-\underset{\underset{Br}{|}}{\overset{\overset{Br}{|}}{C}}-\underset{\underset{Br}{|}}{\overset{\overset{Br}{|}}{C}}-H$$

1,1,2,2-tetrabromoethane

and addition of hydrogen halides such as HCl:

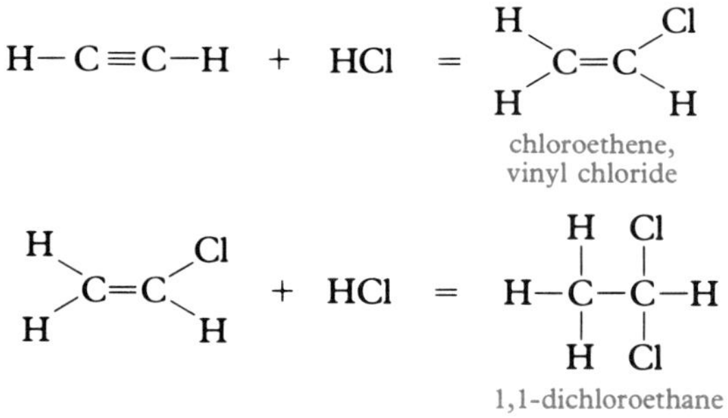

$$H-C\equiv C-H \ + \ HCl \ = \ \underset{\underset{H}{|}}{H}C=C\underset{\underset{H}{|}}{Cl}$$

chloroethene,
vinyl chloride

$$\underset{\underset{H}{|}}{H}C=C\underset{\underset{H}{|}}{Cl} \ + \ HCl \ = \ H-\underset{\underset{H}{|}}{\overset{\overset{H}{|}}{C}}-\underset{\underset{Cl}{|}}{\overset{\overset{Cl}{|}}{C}}-H$$

1,1-dichloroethane

10.5

Super-Strong Carbon Rings: Aromatic Compounds

Benzene is the simplest molecule of a large group of very important
organic compounds known as aromatic hydrocarbons. Its chemical
formula is C_6H_6. Benzene consists of a ring of 6 carbon atoms, each
attached to 1 hydrogen atom as shown in Figure 10.5 Notice that the

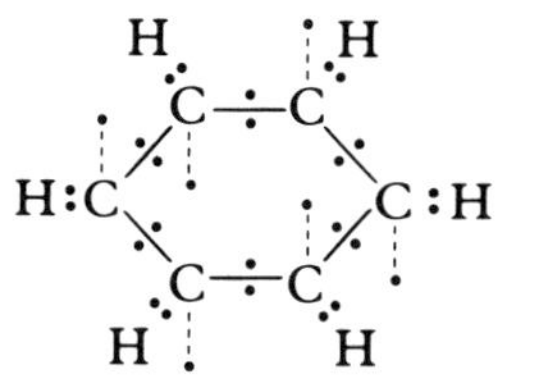

FIGURE 10.5

Benzene rings showing electrons.

electrons are represented by dots and chemical bonds by pairs of dots.
Each carbon atom is joined to two adjacent carbon atoms in the ring by an
electron-pair bond. In addition, each hydrogen is joined to a carbon on the
ring by such a chemical bond. However, each carbon has 1 electron left
over. For purposes of illustration only, it is shown as a dot at the end of a
dashed line either above or below the carbon atom. Actually each of these

extra electrons may be found either above or below the ring of carbon atoms. They do not stay attached to any particular carbon atom but form two doughnut-shaped clouds of electrons on either side of the ring as can be seen in Figure 10.6. This kind of chemical bond is especially stable. It is called π (pronounced "pie") bonding. The electrons making up the electron clouds are called π electrons. Since these electrons are not attached to any one carbon, they are said to be **delocalized**.

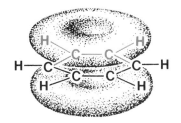

FIGURE 10.6
A molecule of benzene, C_6H_6, showing doughnut-shaped "clouds" of π electrons above and below the molecule.

The 6-carbon ring of atoms is so common in chemistry that its structure is shown as a hexagon in which each of the 6 corners represents a carbon atom. The π electron bonding is shown as a circle in the ring. The 1 hydrogen atom attached to each carbon is omitted for simplicity. Thus, the following figure

benzene

stands for benzene, C_6H_6. Sometimes benzene rings are shown as

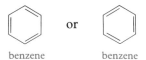

or

benzene   benzene

This can be misleading, though, because it implies that benzene is simply a ring-shaped alkene with three double bonds. In fact, benzene and all aromatic compounds are much more stable than alkenes and react chemically in very different ways.

Many aromatic compounds contain clusters of two or more rings.

No hydrogens attached where rings join.

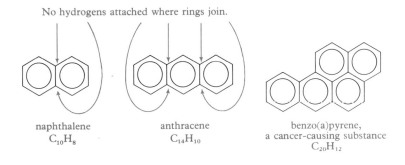

naphthalene   anthracene   benzo(a)pyrene,
$C_{10}H_8$ $C_{14}H_{10}$ a cancer-causing substance
                                              $C_{20}H_{12}$

Such compounds with several rings are called **polycyclic aromatic hydrocarbons**, PAH. Some of these are carcinogens (cancer-causing agents). Benzo(a)pyrene is a strong carcinogen found in cigarette smoke, coal tar, charcoal-broiled meat, and other sources. It should be noted that no hydrogens can be bonded to carbons shared between rings so that the proportion of carbon increases with the number of rings.

The first aromatic compounds discovered were those in natural scents and flavors including oils from cinnamon, cloves, vanilla, and wintergreen. Because of their pleasant odor, these compounds were called "aromatic." It was an unfortunate choice because many of the aromatic compounds found later stink.

The most important chemical reaction of benzene and other aromatic compounds is substitution. For example, in the presence of an iron catalyst, bromine reacts with benzene, to produce bromobenzene and hydrogen bromide gas (see Figure 10.7). If benzene were an alkene, the Br_2 would have *added* to the benzene.

FIGURE 10.7

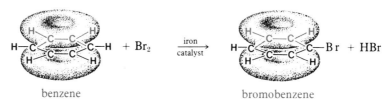

benzene   bromobenzene

Benzene is one of the most widely used organic chemicals. Approximately 1.5 billion gallons of this chemical are produced in the U.S. each year. Most of it comes from petroleum refining, but some is produced as a byproduct of the coking of coal. (Coke is used to make steel. It is prepared by heating coal to drive off liquids, such as benzene, leaving a residue of carbon called coke.)

Some of the most important aromatic compounds are those in which some other atom or group of atoms has been substituted for one or more of the hydrogens in benzene. Some of these and their uses are given in Table 10.2.

When two groups are substituted onto benzene, they can be in different locations relative to each other on the benzene ring. To show this, consider that toluene is a benzene ring with one $-CH_3$ group substituted for a hydrogen. If a nitro group, $-NO_2$, is also attached, the product is nitrotoluene. There are three places on the ring where the $-NO_2$ group can be attached in relation to the $-CH_3$ group. These three locations are called *ortho*,

CH₃ ... CH₃ NO₂ ... CH₃ NO₂ ... CH₃ NO₂

toluene   o-nitrotoluene   m-nitrotoluene   p-nitrotoluene

TABLE 10.2
Important aromatic compounds and their uses.

Aromatic Compound Name	Compound Structure	Uses and Importance
Toluene	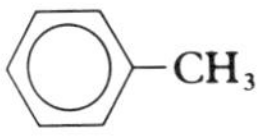 —CH$_3$	Used mostly for the manufacture of other chemicals such as trinitro-toluene (TNT), phenol, polyurethane resins, and as a solvent.
Chlorobenzene	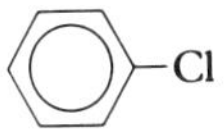 —Cl	Manufacture of phenol and aniline.
Phenol	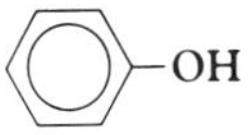 —OH	Manufacture of phenolic resins (plastics) such as Bakelite, synthesis of other chemicals, disinfectant. It is mostly synthesized from chlorobenzene, but is a major constituent of coal tars from coke ovens and coal liquefaction.
Aniline	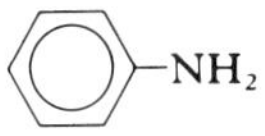 —NH$_2$	Used in large quantities in rubber to promote its formation (vulcanization) and prevent its oxidation. Also used in making dyes and drugs.
Cumene	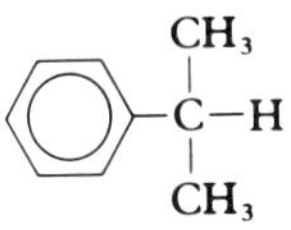	Widely used to make phenol with acetone as an important byproduct: 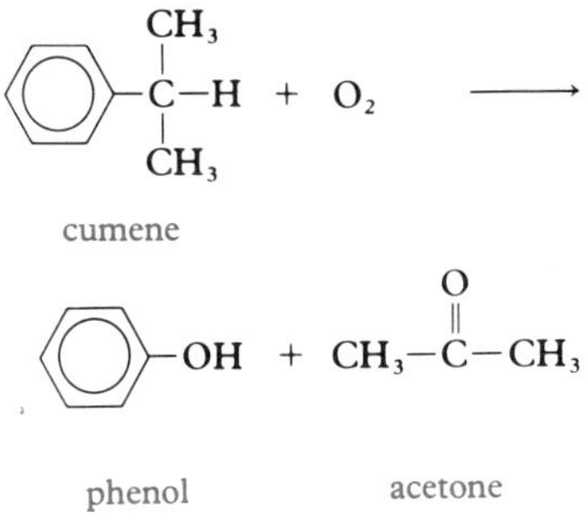
Nitrobenzene	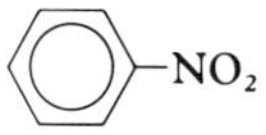 —NO$_2$	Used mostly in dye manufacture.
Styrene	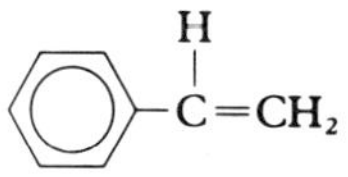	Used for plastics manufacture (polystyrene).

Cumene structure:
$$\text{C}_6\text{H}_5-\overset{\displaystyle CH_3}{\underset{\displaystyle CH_3}{\overset{|}{\underset{|}{C}}}}-H$$

Reaction:

cumene

phenol   acetone

About 1.5 million tons of cumene are produced in the U.S. for this purpose each year.

TABLE 10.2 *(continued)*

Aromatic Compound Name	Compound Structure	Uses and Importance
Benzoic acid	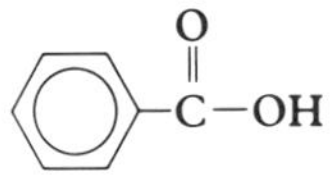	Byproduct of the manufacture of other chemicals (phthalates), intermediate in the manufacture of phenol from toluene.
Aspirin	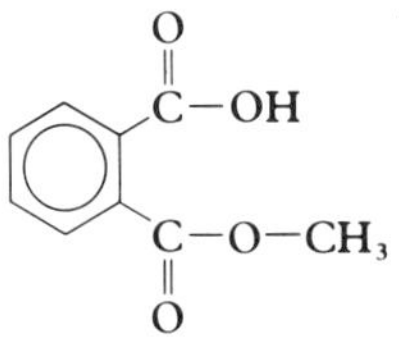	Widely used pain reliever and over-the-counter drug.

meta, and *para.* The names of the corresponding compounds shown above are *ortho*-nitrotoluene, *meta*-nitrotoluene, and *para*-nitrotoluene. Even more nitro groups can be put on a toluene molecule. The well-known explosive, trinitrotoluene (TNT) contains three nitro groups.

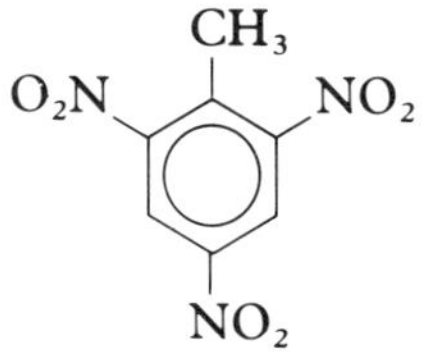

trinitrotoluene (TNT)

10.6

Organohalides

Atoms of fluorine, chlorine, bromine, or iodine may be substituted for hydrogen on hydrocarbons. These make up the class of compounds known as **organohalides**. If the hydrocarbon portion is an aromatic group, such as a benzene ring, the compound is called an **aryl halide**. If the hydrocarbon portion is not aromatic, the halide is an **alkyl halide**. The organohalide compounds are widely used for solvents, industrial chemicals, pesticides, and have many other applications.

Alkyl and aryl halides may be prepared by substitution reactions. These involve the reaction of a halogen, such as Cl_2, with a hydrocarbon to produce an organohalide. The other product is a hydrogen halide such as HCl. The preparation of methyl chloride by this route is shown in Section 10.2. The chemical synthesis of bromobenzene by substitution is given in Section 10.5. Addition reactions between unsaturated hydrocarbons and halogens or hydrogen halides also produce organohalides. The synthesis of 1,2-dichloroethane and ethyl chloride by addition are shown in Section 10.3.

Organohalides are among the compounds which concern us most

as environmental pollutants. Contamination of livestock feed by poly-brominated biphenyl compounds (PBB's) has caused millions of dollars of loss in farm income in Michigan. Concern exists over chloroform in drinking water. Freons from spray cans may be damaging the Earth's protective ozone layer. Some of these organohalides, their uses, and their effects are listed in Table 10.3.

TABLE 10.3
Some organohalides, their uses, and their effects.

Compound Name	Organohalide Structure	Uses and Significance
Chloroform	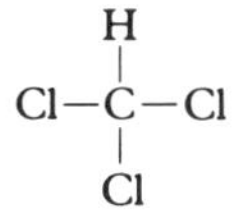	Used mostly to manufacture fluorocarbon refrigerants and spray can propellants, found as drinking water contaminant.
Typical polybrominated biphenyl	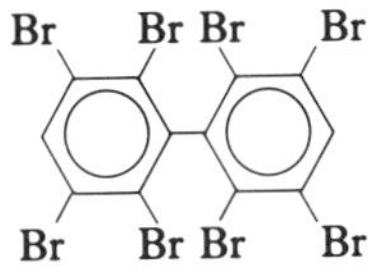	Fire retardant, livestock feed contaminant.
Freon	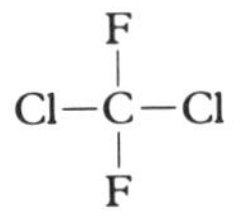	Refrigerant fluid, atmospheric pollutant, which may be undergoing reactions damaging the atmosphere's protective ozone layer.
DDT	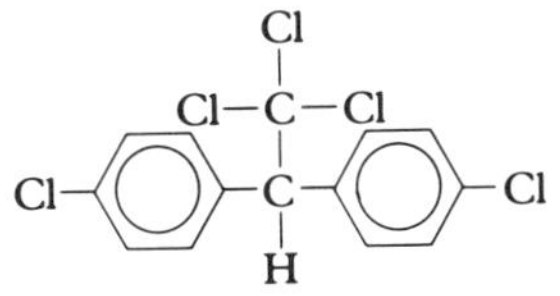	Insecticide, use now banned in in U.S. because of environmental effects and persistence.

One of the most widely produced organohalides is vinyl chloride, which has the formula

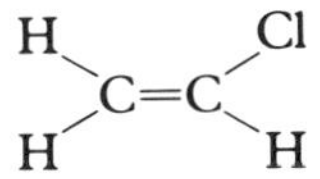

vinyl chloride

Approximately 3 million tons of vinyl chloride are manufactured in the U.S. each year. Most of this product goes into the manufacture of polyvinyl chloride (PVC). The basic structure of this plastic material is shown as follows.

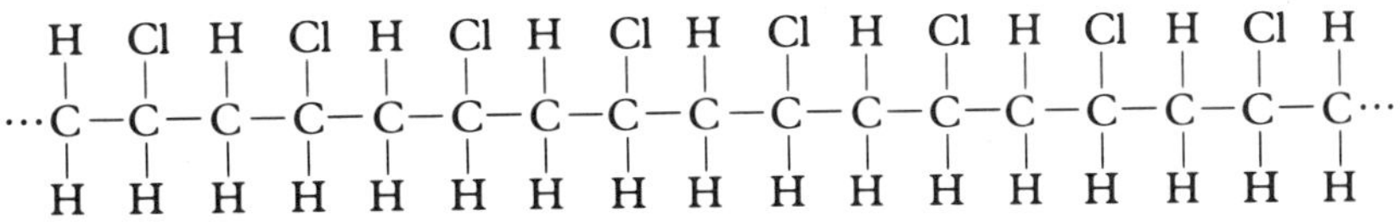

polyvinyl chloride (PVC)

Note that the structure of this polymer is very similar to that of polyethylene (Section 10.3) except that Cl atoms have been substituted for H atoms.

Polyvinyl chloride is a tough plastic and can be made very hard. It is widely used in making molded plastic objects, water pipes, water hoses, and similar materials.

The air in factories producing PVC used to be highly contaminated with vinyl chloride. Levels of as high as 500 ppm of vinyl chloride were common in the air that workers breathed. No harmful effects were noted until the early 1970's when it was found that some workers who had been exposed to vinyl chloride over periods of 14 to 27 years developed angiosarcoma, a rare form of liver cancer. Many other workers have been exposed to this chemical and may develop liver cancer as a result. Even the general public has been exposed because of the use of vinyl chloride as a spray can propellant. Measures have now been taken to reduce worker exposure and to remove spray cans containing vinyl chloride from the market.

10.7

Alcohols

Atoms other than carbon and hydrogen are often found attached to organic molecules as groups with special structures and properties. These are called **functional groups**. There are several important classes of organic compounds which have functional groups containing oxygen. The main ones are alcohols, ethers, aldehydes, ketones, carboxylic acids, and esters. Each of these is discussed separately in the remainder of this chapter.

Alcohols contain the hydroxyl functional group, —OH, attached to a hydrocarbon. The simplest alcohol is **methanol**,

$$
\begin{array}{ccc}
& \overset{\displaystyle H}{\underset{\displaystyle H}{\text{H}-\text{C}-\text{OH}}} & \\
\text{hydrocarbon (methyl)} & & \text{hydroxyl group} \\
\text{group} & &
\end{array}
$$

or methyl alcohol. It is also called "wood alcohol" because it can be prepared by heating wood to a high temperature in the absence of air. It is interesting to note that the structure of methanol is just like that of methane

$$
\overset{\displaystyle H}{\underset{\displaystyle H}{\text{H}-\text{C}-\text{H}}} \quad \text{methane}
$$

except that the —OH group has been substituted for one of the H atoms. The two compounds have entirely different properties, however. Methane is a gas at room temperature and must be cooled to very low temperatures to make a liquid of it. Liquid methane boils at an extremely cold − 162°C and freezes at − 182°C. Methanol, on the other hand, is a liquid at room temperature and boils at a relatively warm + 65°C. It freezes at − 97°C. Methane hardly dissolves at all in water. Methanol dissolves completely in water, and mixtures of methanol and water can be prepared ranging all the way from pure water to pure methanol. A major reason for this difference in properties is that with the oxygen present, methanol can form hydrogen bonds (see Chapter 8) with itself and with water molecules as shown in Figure 10.8.

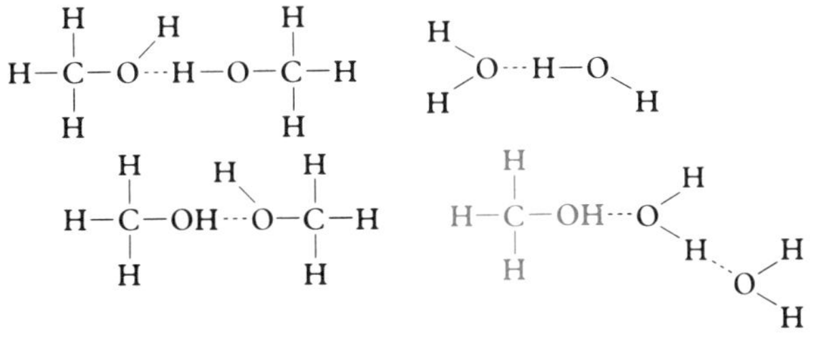

pure methanol

Hydrogen bonds
shown by dashed lines.

methanol (in color)

Dissolved in water showing
hydrogen bonding to water.

FIGURE 10.8   *Formation of hydrogen bonds between methanol molecules and between methanol and water.*

The commercial production of methanol is now accomplished mostly by the reaction of carbon monoxide and hydrogen

$$CO + 2\ H_2 \xrightarrow[\text{chromium oxide catalyst}]{\text{mixed zinc oxide and}} CH_3OH$$

at temperatures from 300°C to 400°C and very high pressures from 275 atm to 360 atm. Methanol is a convenient, nonpolluting fuel. When up to 15 % of it is added to gasoline, it even slightly improves the performance of automobiles. Methanol is being seriously considered as a petroleum substitute since it can be used as a liquid fuel without drastic changes in present production, distribution, and consumption facilities. At the present time the most important uses of methanol are as a solvent, antifreeze, and for the synthesis of other chemicals. It is used in large quantities to make formaldehyde, which is used to manufacture plastics. Methanol is very toxic and causes blindness if taken internally.

The next higher alcohol is ethanol, or ethyl alcohol,

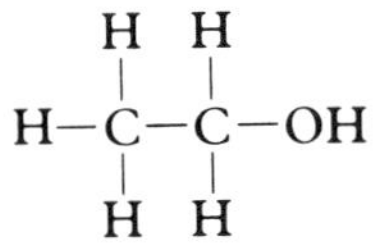

which is the alcohol contained in beer, whiskey, and other alcoholic beverages. Ethanol is easily made by the fermentation of sugars by yeasts and has been known throughout the history of civilization. The chemical reaction for the production of ethanol by fermentation is

$$C_6H_{12}O_6 \xrightarrow[\text{by yeasts}]{\text{fermentation}} 2\ C_2H_5OH + CO_2\uparrow$$

Fermentation produces a dilute solution of ethanol in water. This solution can be distilled to produce more concentrated solutions.

Fermentation is too expensive to make alcohol for industrial use. Instead, the chemical addition of water to ethylene

is now used to make most non-beverage alcohol.

Aside from its use as a beverage, ethanol is employed to make other chemicals including acetaldehyde, acetic acid, ethyl ether, ethyl chloride, ethyl bromide, and esters. It is a very common solvent for such products as food flavors, perfumes, and cosmetics.

The alcohol with 3 carbon atoms, propanol, can exist in two forms,

depending upon whether the —OH group is attached to an end carbon or to the one in the middle. The first of these alcohols, 1-propanol, is called a **primary** alcohol, and 2-propanol is a **secondary** alcohol. "Rubbing alcohol" is a concentrated solution of 2-propanol in water.

There are two especially important alcohols having more than one —OH group on each molecule. One of these is *ethylene glycol*,

widely used as an antifreeze and coolant. A little more than 1.5 million tons of this important chemical are produced in the U.S. each year. This colorless, syrupy liquid freezes at −12.7°C; and mixtures of it with water freeze at much lower temperatures. It boils at a very high 197.6°C, which makes it a very useful summer coolant in auto and truck cooling systems.

On an industrial scale it is made from ethylene in a two-step process in which ethylene oxide is formed

$$
\underset{\text{ethylene}}{\begin{array}{c}H\\ \diagdown\\ H\diagup\end{array}C=C\begin{array}{c}\diagup H\\ \diagdown H\end{array}} \;+\; O_2 \;\xrightarrow{\;\text{catalyst}\;}\; \underset{\text{ethylene oxide}}{\begin{array}{c}H\\ \diagdown\\ H\diagup\end{array}\overset{O}{C-C}\begin{array}{c}\diagup H\\ \diagdown H\end{array}}
$$

then reacted with water

$$
\underset{\text{ethylene oxide}}{\begin{array}{c}H\\ \diagdown\\ H\diagup\end{array}\overset{O}{C-C}\begin{array}{c}\diagup H\\ \diagdown H\end{array}} \;+\; H_2O \;\longrightarrow\; \underset{\text{ethylene glycol}}{H-\overset{\overset{\displaystyle OH}{|}}{\underset{\underset{\displaystyle H}{|}}{C}}-\overset{\overset{\displaystyle OH}{|}}{\underset{\underset{\displaystyle H}{|}}{C}}-H}
$$

to produce ethylene glycol.

The other major alcohol having more than one —OH group is glycerol,

$$
H-\overset{\overset{\displaystyle OH}{|}}{\underset{\underset{\displaystyle H}{|}}{C}}-\overset{\overset{\displaystyle OH}{|}}{\underset{\underset{\displaystyle H}{|}}{C}}-\overset{\overset{\displaystyle OH}{|}}{\underset{\underset{\displaystyle H}{|}}{C}}-H \qquad \text{glycerol}
$$

a clear, thick liquid with no odor and a sweet taste. Glycerol, sometimes called glycerin, is part of the chemical structure of all natural fats and oils in plants and animals. It can be prepared from these natural substances but is now largely made by chemical reactions starting with hydrocarbons.

Glycerol has many uses, many of which depend upon the fact that it is nontoxic compared to other materials that could otherwise be used. It serves as a humectant (to keep materials moist) in food, tobacco, cosmetics, and other products. It is also used as a base for ointments and medicinal syrups, as a softening agent for plastics, in brake fluids, and as an ingredient in various coatings, varnishes, and paints. The most spectacular use of glycerol is for the manufacture of nitroglycerin,

$$
\begin{array}{c}
H-\overset{\overset{\displaystyle H}{|}}{\underset{|}{C}}-ONO_2\\
H-\overset{|}{\underset{|}{C}}-ONO_2\\
H-\overset{|}{\underset{\underset{\displaystyle H}{|}}{C}}-ONO_2
\end{array} \qquad \text{nitroglycerin}
$$

a colorless liquid which explodes with great, shattering force when subjected to a slight shock. The explosion occurs with a great release of heat accompanied by an expansion of about 10,000 times in volume. Mixtures of nitroglycerin with wood powder and certain other materials are relatively safe to handle. These mixtures are called **dynamite**. Dynamite was developed by Alfred Nobel in 1867. He later established the various Nobel prizes.

When the hydrocarbon group to which the hydroxyl is attached is aromatic, the properties of the compounds are much different from those of the alcohols discussed above. These aromatic compounds are classified as **phenols**, rather than alcohols. The simplest of them is phenol,

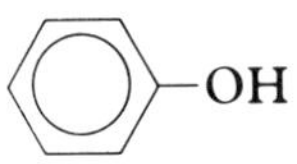

$$\langle\bigcirc\rangle\text{—OH} \qquad \text{phenol}$$

which has one hydroxyl group bonded to a benzene ring. Many phenols are toxic and can be used to kill bacteria. Phenol, under the name of *carbolic acid*, was the first disinfectant to be used. Phenols are acids and react with bases

$$\langle\bigcirc\rangle\text{—OH} + \text{Na}^+\text{OH}^- \longrightarrow \langle\bigcirc\rangle\text{—O}^-\text{Na}^+ + \text{H}_2\text{O}$$

phenol,   sodium hydroxide,   sodium phenoxide,
a weak acid   a base   a salt

to form salts. This reaction is used to extract phenols from coal tar or petroleum. The ionic salt product is water-soluble and can be extracted into a solution of sodium hydroxide. When acid is added to the solution of phenoxides, the phenols are regenerated; and they separate from the water. The greatest use for phenols is in the manufacture of plastics. One of the first synthetic plastics, Bakelite, is made by the reaction of heated phenol and formaldehyde (Figure 10.9). About 1.25 million tons of phenol are made in the U.S. each year.

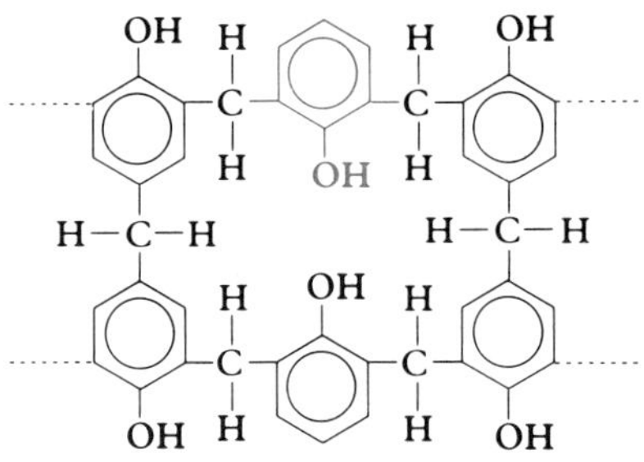

FIGURE 10.9 *Structure of Bakelite with phenol in color.*

Some of the most important chemical reactions of alcohols will be discussed later in the chapter along with esters, aldehydes, ketones, and carboxylic acids. The loss of water and the formation of alkyl halides are considered here.

If some alcohols are heated with a substance, such as sulfuric acid, which has a strong "thirst" for water,

$$H-\underset{\underset{\displaystyle H}{|}}{\overset{\overset{\displaystyle H}{|}}{C}}-\underset{\underset{\displaystyle H}{|}}{\overset{\overset{\displaystyle H}{|}}{C}}-OH \xrightarrow[180°C]{\text{concentrated } H_2SO_4} \overset{H}{\underset{H}{}}C=C\overset{H}{\underset{H}{}} + H_2O \text{ (in water)}$$

ethanol,
an alcohol

ethylene,
an alkene

H_2O is split off from the alcohol and an alkene remains. Because of the loss of water, this is called a **dehydration reaction**. Dehydration reactions are very important in organic chemistry and biochemistry.

Alcohols commonly undergo **replacement** reactions. These occur when the —OH group is replaced by some other group such as a halide (Cl, Br, I). A typical replacement reaction is

$$H-\underset{\underset{\displaystyle H}{|}}{\overset{\overset{\displaystyle H}{|}}{C}}-\underset{\underset{\displaystyle H}{|}}{\overset{\overset{\displaystyle H}{|}}{C}}-OH + HCl \xrightarrow[\text{catalyst}]{ZnCl_2} H-\underset{\underset{\displaystyle H}{|}}{\overset{\overset{\displaystyle H}{|}}{C}}-\underset{\underset{\displaystyle H}{|}}{\overset{\overset{\displaystyle H}{|}}{C}}-Cl + H_2O$$

ethanol

hydrogen
chloride gas

ethyl chloride,
an alkyl halide

Recall that ethyl chloride can also be made by the reaction of an alkane with Cl_2.

10.8

Ethers

Oxygen atoms can serve to link two hydrocarbon groups together. Such compounds are known as **ethers**. The most common of these is diethyl ether, once the most commonly used general anesthetic (a substance used to make a person unconscious during surgery). It is now widely used as a solvent to extract fats and other materials.

$$H-\underset{\underset{\displaystyle H}{|}}{\overset{\overset{\displaystyle H}{|}}{C}}-\underset{\underset{\displaystyle H}{|}}{\overset{\overset{\displaystyle H}{|}}{C}}-O-\underset{\underset{\displaystyle H}{|}}{\overset{\overset{\displaystyle H}{|}}{C}}-\underset{\underset{\displaystyle H}{|}}{\overset{\overset{\displaystyle H}{|}}{C}}-H \qquad \text{diethyl ether}$$

The ether inhaler used by Dr. W. T. G. Morton on October 16, 1846 when he first demonstrated the properties of ether as a surgical anesthetic. (Courtesy of Massachusetts General Hospital)

The two C_2H_5 groups in the diethyl ether structure are called **ethyl** groups; the fact that they are linked by an oxygen atom makes the compound an ether.

Diethyl ether boils at 34.6°C, and it evaporates easily at room temperature. It burns violently. Ether vapor is very dangerous because it is heavier than air and spreads like an invisible blanket along laboratory table tops and floors. If the vapor contacts a spark or flame, an explosion or fire results.

Another danger is presented by liquid ethers in contact with air. They react with oxygen in the air to form **peroxides**. These

$$
\begin{array}{ccccccc}
 & H & H & & & H & H \\
 & | & | & & & | & | \\
H- & C- & C- & O- & O- & C- & C-H \\
 & | & | & & & | & | \\
 & H & H & & & H & H \\
\end{array}
$$

peroxide formed from diethyl ether

compounds are violently explosive. They are often present in old containers of ether. One should always beware of this possibility in handling containers of ether. The likelihood of peroxide formation, combined with the ability of diethyl ether to make one unconscious, and its overall toxicity, make it a very dangerous compound. Its chemical relatives, such as dimethyl ether and di-isopropyl ether,

$$
\begin{array}{cccc}
H & & H & \\
| & & | & \\
H-C-O-C-H & & \\
| & & | & \\
H & & H & \\
\end{array}
$$

dimethyl ether   di-isopropyl ether

are equally dangerous (di-isopropyl ether forms explosive peroxides *very* easily). *All ethers must be handled with great caution.*

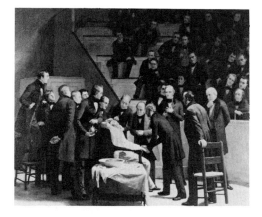

The Hinckley painting commemorating Dr. W. T. G. Morton's introduction of ether as a general anesthetic. Standing to the left of the patient and holding the ether inhaler is Dr. Morton. Dr. J. C. Warren is performing the operation. (Courtesy of Massachusetts General Hospital)

10.9

Aldehydes and Ketones

Oxygen atoms can form double bonds with carbon. Each of these double bonds involves *four* electrons. This gives rise to two kinds of compounds containing the carbonyl, C=O, group bonded to carbon or hydrogen. If the carbon atom is in the middle of a carbon chain, the compound is a **ketone**.

$$
\begin{array}{c}
\text{H} \\
| \\
\text{H---C---H} \\
| \\
\text{C=O} \\
| \\
\text{H---C---H} \\
| \\
\text{H}
\end{array}
\qquad
\begin{array}{c}
\text{H} \\
\text{H:}\overset{\cdot\cdot}{\text{C}}\text{:H} \\
\text{C::}\overset{\cdot\cdot}{\underset{\cdot\cdot}{\text{O}}}\text{:} \\
\text{H:}\overset{\cdot\cdot}{\underset{\cdot\cdot}{\text{C}}}\text{:H} \\
\text{H}
\end{array}
$$

acetone

Acetone is a ketone in which oxygen is bonded to carbon with a double bond. The electron-dot formula shows that the carbon attached to oxygen has 8 electrons around it when it is bonded to a total of only 3 atoms. If the carbon atom to which the oxygen is bonded is an end carbon and is also bonded to hydrogen, the compound is an **aldehyde**. Acetaldehyde

$$
\begin{array}{c}
\text{H} \quad \text{H} \\
| \quad\; | \\
\text{H---C---C=O} \\
| \\
\text{H}
\end{array}
\qquad \text{acetaldehyde}
$$

is a typical aldehyde in which the carbon bonded to oxygen is also bonded to H. Some aldehydes and ketones are listed in Tables 10.4 and 10.5 along with their uses.

   Aldehydes and ketones can be prepared from the oxidation of alcohols. Aldehydes are made from primary alcohols in which the —OH group is attached to an end carbon. The reaction for the preparation of propionaldehyde is

$$
\begin{array}{c}
\text{H} \; \text{H} \; \text{H} \\
| \;\; | \;\; | \\
\text{H---C---C---C---OH} \\
| \;\; | \;\; | \\
\text{H} \; \text{H} \; \text{H}
\end{array}
\xrightarrow[\substack{\text{distillation} \\ \text{at } 70°C}]{\text{KMnO}_4, \, \text{H}_2\text{SO}_4}
\begin{array}{c}
\text{H} \; \text{H} \; \text{H} \\
| \;\; | \;\; | \\
\text{H---C---C---C=O} \\
| \;\; | \\
\text{H} \; \text{H}
\end{array}
$$

n-propanol
boiling at 97°C

propionaldehyde
boiling at 49°C

in which the *n*-propanol is oxidized with $KMnO_4$. The more volatile aldehyde is distilled off before it is oxidized to propionic acid.

Ketones are made from secondary alcohols in which the —OH group is attached to a carbon atom, which, in turn, is attached to two other carbons. It is not possible to add more than one oxygen to such a carbon without breaking a carbon-carbon bond, so the oxidation is easy to stop with formation of ketone. Acetone, for example, is readily formed by an oxidation reaction

$$
\begin{array}{ccc}
\text{H OH H} & & \text{H O H} \\
| \ | \ | & & | \ \| \ | \\
\text{H}-\text{C}-\text{C}-\text{C}-\text{H} + [\text{O}] \longrightarrow & & \text{H}-\text{C}-\text{C}-\text{C}-\text{H} + \text{H}_2\text{O} \\
| \ | \ | & & | \ \ \ | \\
\text{H H H} & & \text{H H}
\end{array}
$$

isopropyl alcohol,   reactive oxygen   acetone,
a secondary alcohol   from an   a ketone
oxidizing agent

in which an oxidizing agent such as $KMnO_4$ is used as a source of O. On an industrial scale aldehydes and ketones are formed by a variety of processes. Formaldehyde is manufactured by a controlled air oxidation of methanol vapor

TABLE 10.4
Some aldehydes and their uses.

Aldehyde Name	Structural Formula	Uses
Formaldehyde	$$\begin{array}{c} \text{O} \\ \| \\ \text{H}-\text{C}-\text{H} \end{array}$$	Widely used in the manufacture of plastics, resins, lacquers, dyes, and explosives. As a 37 % solution in water, it is employed to preserve tissue samples and as an embalming fluid.
Acetaldehyde	$$\begin{array}{c} \text{H H} \\ | \ | \\ \text{H}-\text{C}-\text{C}=\text{O} \\ | \\ \text{H} \end{array}$$	Used in the manufacture of acetic acid, plastics, and other materials.
Benzaldehyde	$$\bigcirc\!\!-\!\!\begin{array}{c}\text{H}\\|\\\text{C}=\text{O}\end{array}$$	Known as "the oil of bitter almonds." Because of its almond taste and odor, it is widely used in flavors, perfumes, and soaps.
Vanillin	$$\begin{array}{c}\text{H}\\|\\\text{C}=\text{O}\\ \bigcirc \!\!-\!\!\text{OCH}_3 \\ \text{OH}\end{array}$$	This is the compound that gives vanilla ice cream and some other foods their characteristic odor and flavor. In addition to its use for flavoring foods, this compound is added to some rubber and plastic products to cover up their natural bad odor.

$$2\,H\!-\!\underset{\underset{\textstyle H}{|}}{\overset{\overset{\textstyle H}{|}}{C}}\!-\!OH + O_2 \longrightarrow 2\,\underset{\underset{\textstyle H}{|}}{\overset{\overset{\textstyle H}{|}}{C}}\!=\!O \;+\; 2\,H_2O$$

methanol   formaldehyde

with a metal catalyst at 400 to 500°C. Formaldehyde is not stable when pure and is normally sold as a 37 % solution in water.

Acetone, a very important industrial chemical, is made by a number of industrial processes. One of the best of these is the passage of 2-propanol over a copper catalyst at 400°C,

TABLE 10.5
Some ketones and their uses.

Ketone Name	Structural Formula	Uses
Acetone	$H-\overset{H}{\underset{H}{C}}-\overset{O}{C}-\overset{H}{\underset{H}{C}}-H$	About 2 billion pounds produced each year in the U.S. for solvents and applications in the rubber, leather, and plastics industry. Acetone dissolves 18 times its volume of acetylene and tanks of this gas contain acetone solvent. Acetone is produced in the bodies of persons suffering from *diabetes mellitus*, and its odor can be detected in the breaths of some diabetics.
Methyl ethyl ketone	$H-\overset{H}{\underset{H}{C}}-\overset{O}{C}-\overset{H}{\underset{H}{C}}-\overset{H}{\underset{H}{C}}-H$	This compound is employed as a low boiling solvent for coatings and adhesives and for the synthesis of other organic chemicals.
Progesterone		The major female sex hormone (steroid).
Testosterone

ketone functional groups | | The major male sex hormone (steroid). |

* Each "corner," or place where lines connect, in these structures represents the location of a carbon atom. The number of H atoms bonded to each C is 4 minus the number of bonds shown. For example there are two H's bonded to the carbon represented by ⌒; one bonded to the carbon represented by ⌒ or ⋏, and none bonded to the carbon represented by ⅄.

$$
\begin{array}{ccc}
\text{H} & \text{OH} & \text{H} \\
| & | & | \\
\text{H}-\text{C}-\text{C}-\!\!-\text{C}-\text{H} \\
| & | & | \\
\text{H} & \text{H} & \text{H}
\end{array}
\longrightarrow
\begin{array}{ccc}
\text{H} & \text{O} & \text{H} \\
| & \| & | \\
\text{H}-\text{C}-\text{C}-\text{C}-\text{H} + \text{H}_2 \\
| & & | \\
\text{H} & & \text{H}
\end{array}
$$

2-propanol   acetone

which yields valuable hydrogen gas as a byproduct.

Aldehydes and ketones undergo a large variety of chemical reactions. The most important of these are addition reactions in which a species adds to the $>\!\!C\!=\!O$ bond. For example, addition of hydrogen cyanide (HCN)

$$
\begin{array}{ccc}
\text{H} & \text{O} & \text{H} \\
| & \| & | \\
\text{H}-\text{C}-\text{C}-\text{C}-\text{H} + \text{H}-\text{C}\!\equiv\!\text{N} \\
| & & | \\
\text{H} & & \text{H}
\end{array}
\longrightarrow
\begin{array}{ccc}
& \text{N} & \\
& \| & \\
\text{H} & \text{C} & \text{H} \\
| & | & | \\
\text{H}-\text{C}-\text{C}-\!\!-\text{C}-\text{H} \\
| & | & | \\
\text{H} & \text{OH} & \text{H}
\end{array}
$$

acetone   acetone cyanohydrin

forms cyanohydrins, which are very useful in synthesizing other chemicals.

The fact that aldehydes add oxygen readily is used to test for the presence of aldehydes. One such test employs *Fehling's solution,* which contains cupric ion, Cu^{2+}. The reaction with an aldehyde is

$$
\begin{array}{cc}
\text{H} & \text{H} \\
| & | \\
\text{H}-\text{C}-\text{C}\!=\!\text{O} + 2\,\text{Cu}^{2+} + 2\,\text{Na}^+\text{OH}^- \\
| & \\
\text{H} &
\end{array}
\longrightarrow
\begin{array}{cc}
\text{H} & \text{O} \\
| & \| \\
\text{H}-\text{C}-\text{C}-\text{O}^-\text{Na}^+ + \text{Cu}_2\text{O}\!\downarrow \\
| & \\
\text{H} &
\end{array}
$$

acetaldehyde   sodium acetate,   cuprous oxide,
the sodium salt   a red
of acetic acid   precipitate

which produces a visible precipitate of red cuprous oxide. This shows the presence of the aldehyde. The sugar, glucose, has an

$$
\begin{array}{l}
\quad\;\;\text{H} \\
\quad\;\;| \\
\quad\;\;\text{C}\!=\!\text{O} \\
\quad\;\;| \\
\text{H}-\text{C}-\text{OH} \\
\quad\;\;| \\
\text{HO}-\text{C}-\text{H} \\
\quad\;\;| \\
\text{H}-\text{C}-\text{OH} \\
\quad\;\;| \\
\text{H}-\text{C}-\text{OH} \\
\quad\;\;| \\
\text{H}-\text{C}-\text{OH} \\
\quad\;\;| \\
\quad\;\;\text{H}
\end{array}
$$

glucose,
in an aldehyde form

aldehyde group. Fehling's solution can be used to test for sugar in urine; a positive test may indicate diabetes.

10.10

Carboxylic Acids

Organic compounds containing the $-\overset{\overset{O}{\|}}{C}-OH$ group are called **carboxylic acids**. One of the most common examples is acetic acid. Organic acids react with bases such as sodium hydroxide

$$H-\overset{\overset{\displaystyle H}{|}}{\underset{\underset{\displaystyle H}{|}}{C}}-\overset{\overset{\displaystyle O}{\|}}{C}-OH + Na^+OH^- \longrightarrow H-\overset{\overset{\displaystyle H}{|}}{\underset{\underset{\displaystyle H}{|}}{C}}-\overset{\overset{\displaystyle O}{\|}}{C}-O^-Na^+ + H_2O$$

acetic acid   sodium hydroxide   sodium acetate

to form salts whose names end in "-ate." Another example of such a salt is calcium propionate,

$$2\ H-\overset{\overset{\displaystyle H}{|}}{\underset{\underset{\displaystyle H}{|}}{C}}-\overset{\overset{\displaystyle H}{|}}{\underset{\underset{\displaystyle H}{|}}{C}}-\overset{\overset{\displaystyle O}{\|}}{C}-OH + Ca(OH)_2 \longrightarrow Ca(C_3H_5O_2)_2 + 2\ H_2O$$

propionic acid   calcium hydroxide   calcium propionate

which is formed by the reaction of propionic acid and calcium hydroxide. The calcium propionate salt is commonly added to bread and other foods as a preservative. Some common carboxylic acids are given in Table 10.6.

TABLE 10.6

Carboxylic acids and their uses.

Carboxylic Acid Name	Structural Formula	Uses and Significance
Formic	$H-\overset{\overset{\displaystyle O}{\|}}{C}-OH$	Many of its uses come from the fact that it is an inexpensive acid. It is used as an acid in the textile industry, in dyeing, and in tanneries. It is a good disinfectent and is employed to kill bacteria in casks and vats in the food and brewery industries.

TABLE 10.6   *(continued)*

Carboxylic Acid Name	Structural Formula	Uses and Significance
Acetic	H—C—C—OH (with H's and =O)	A major organic chemical with about 1.25 million tons produced in the U.S. each year. In the pure form (glacial acetic acid), it is a clear colorless liquid that boils at 118°C and forms a solid at 16.7°C. Vinegar is about 4% acetic acid. Greatest industrial use is to form acetate polymers, particularly cellulose acetate and vinyl acetate.
Propionic	H—C—C—C—OH (with H's and =O)	Found in many natural products, such as fruits, plants, sweat, and cheese. It is used as a food preservative and in making plastics.
n-butyric	H—C—C—C—C—OH (with H's and =O)	This is the acid that gives rancid butter its pungent odor. It is also found in sweat and some fruits. It is commonly prepared by the action of bacteria, such as *Clostridium butylicum*, on milk sugar (in whey) or molasses. It is used mostly to make esters (see Section 10.11), which are used as solvents and artificial food aromas.
Oxalic	HO—C—C—OH (with two =O)	This is a dicarboxylic acid (two acid groups). Salts of this acid are found in some plants (rhubarb), mammal urine, and kidney stones. It is used as a chemical reagent and as a bleaching agent.
Benzoic	(benzene ring)—C—OH (with =O)	A stable white powder melting at 122°C. The acid and its sodium salt are used as food preservatives. Its greatest use is in making other chemicals such as phenol.
Phthalic	(benzene ring)—C—OH and —C—OH (with =O's)	The greatest use is in making plasticizers, which are additives that give plastics desirable properties.
Salicylic	(benzene ring)—C—OH and —OH (with =O)	This organic acid has a hydroxyl group on the benzene ring. It is used as a food preservative and to make aspirin and other chemicals.

10.11

Esters

Some important types of organic compounds are formed by the combination of some of the compounds discussed previously in this chapter. **Esters** make up such a type of compound. These are made by the reaction of a carboxylic acid and an alcohol

$$H-\overset{\overset{\displaystyle H}{|}}{\underset{\underset{\displaystyle H}{|}}{C}}-\overset{\overset{\displaystyle O}{||}}{C}-OH + HO-\overset{\overset{\displaystyle H}{|}}{\underset{\underset{\displaystyle H}{|}}{C}}-\overset{\overset{\displaystyle H}{|}}{\underset{\underset{\displaystyle H}{|}}{C}}-H \xrightarrow{H_2SO_4} H-\overset{\overset{\displaystyle H}{|}}{\underset{\underset{\displaystyle H}{|}}{C}}-\overset{\overset{\displaystyle O}{||}}{C}-O-\overset{\overset{\displaystyle H}{|}}{\underset{\underset{\displaystyle H}{|}}{C}}-\overset{\overset{\displaystyle H}{|}}{\underset{\underset{\displaystyle H}{|}}{C}}-H + H_2O$$

  acetic acid   ethanol   ethyl acetate

in the presence of an acid catalyst such as sulfuric acid. The reaction involves the loss of a water molecule from the two reacting species. It is called a **condensation** reaction. Esters occur throughout nature. The pleasant odors of some esters are partly responsible for the fragrance of flowers, fruits, and essential oils (discussed in Chapter 15). Esters are widely used in artificial flavors and perfumes. Fats and oils from plants and animals are esters.

The ethyl acetate ester that has just been shown is a colorless liquid with an odor like that of apples. Found in several fruits, it is used in perfumes and flavors. It is also used as a solvent in the manufacture of plastics, rayon, and artificial leather.

Methyl acetate

$$H-\overset{\overset{\displaystyle H}{|}}{\underset{\underset{\displaystyle H}{|}}{C}}-\overset{\overset{\displaystyle O}{||}}{C}-O-\overset{\overset{\displaystyle H}{|}}{\underset{\underset{\displaystyle H}{|}}{C}}-H \qquad \text{methyl acetate}$$

is an excellent solvent. It has a pleasant fruit odor. The synthetic product may contain some methanol, which can make it toxic. At low concentrations methyl acetate is used in fruit flavors.

Methyl salicylate,

$$\overset{\overset{\displaystyle O}{||}}{C}-O-\overset{\overset{\displaystyle H}{|}}{\underset{\underset{\displaystyle H}{|}}{C}}-H \qquad \text{methyl salicylate,}$$
$$-OH \qquad\qquad \text{oil of wintergreen}$$

is also known as oil of wintergreen. It is used to imitate fruit flavors, such as grape and strawberry. Although only a small quantity of this ester is needed for flavoring, a larger quantity is toxic.

Esters readily undergo **hydrolysis**. This is the reverse of the condensation reaction. Hydrolysis is a process in which water is added to form the original acid and alcohol. Bases, which form a salt with the acid

product of ester hydrolysis

$$H\underset{\underset{H}{|}}{\overset{\overset{H}{|}}{C}}\!-\!\underset{}{\overset{\overset{O}{\|}}{C}}\!-\!O\!-\!\underset{\underset{H}{|}}{\overset{\overset{H}{|}}{C}}\!-\!H + Na^+OH^- \longrightarrow H\underset{\underset{H}{|}}{\overset{\overset{H}{|}}{C}}\!-\!\overset{\overset{O}{\|}}{C}\!-\!O^-Na^+ + HO\!-\!\underset{\underset{H}{|}}{\overset{\overset{H}{|}}{C}}\!-\!H$$

methyl acetate   sodium acetate   methanol

readily cause esters to hydrolyze.

10.12

Fats and Oils

Esters of the alcohol, glycerol,

$$\underset{\underset{H}{|}}{\overset{\overset{H}{|}}{H\!-\!C\!-\!OH}}$$
$$H\!-\!C\!-\!OH$$
$$H\!-\!C\!-\!OH$$ glycerol
$$|$$
$$H$$

are especially important in plants and animals. These esters are the fats and oils found throughout living systems. The acids attached to glycerol in these esters usually have long, straight carbon chains. Some of these carbon chains may have double bonds, in which case the ester is said to be **unsaturated**. These unsaturated esters are normally oils at room temperature. The fats, which are solid at room temperature, are made up mostly of saturated esters (no double bonds between carbons). Addition of H_2 to these double bonds forms saturated fats and converts the liquid oils to solids.

One of the most common organic acids found in animal fat is stearic acid,

$$HO\!-\!\overset{\overset{O}{\|}}{C}\!-\!C\!-\!C\!-\!C\!-\!C\!-\!C\!-\!C\!-\!C\!-\!C\!-\!C\!-\!C\!-\!C\!-\!C\!-\!C\!-\!C\!-\!C\!-\!C\!-\!C\!-\!H$$

stearic acid

which can be written in an abbreviated form as $HO\!-\!\overset{\overset{O}{\|}}{C}\!-\!C_{17}H_{35}$. Such a long-chain acid is called a **fatty acid**. Fatty acids from natural sources contain an even number of carbon atoms (2 to 22). The ester of stearic acid and glycerol

$$H-\underset{\underset{H}{|}}{\overset{\overset{H}{|}}{C}}-O-\overset{\overset{O}{||}}{C}-C_{17}H_{35}$$

$$H-\overset{|}{C}-O-\overset{\overset{O}{||}}{C}-C_{17}H_{35} \qquad \text{tristearin}$$

$$H-\underset{\underset{H}{|}}{\overset{|}{C}}-O-\overset{\overset{O}{||}}{C}-C_{17}H_{35}$$

is a fat called tristearin. Such an ester with three fatty acids attached belongs to the general class of compounds called triglycerides. Blood is routinely tested for triglycerides as a measure of the potential for fat accumulation. Most triglycerides contain more than one type of fatty acid attached to glycerol.

An unsaturated fatty acid, oleic acid,

$$HO-\overset{\overset{O}{||}}{C}-\overset{\overset{H}{|}}{\underset{\underset{H}{|}}{C}}-\overset{\overset{H}{|}}{\underset{\underset{H}{|}}{C}}-\overset{\overset{H}{|}}{\underset{\underset{H}{|}}{C}}-\overset{\overset{H}{|}}{\underset{\underset{H}{|}}{C}}-\overset{\overset{H}{|}}{\underset{\underset{H}{|}}{C}}-\overset{\overset{H}{|}}{\underset{\underset{H}{|}}{C}}-\overset{\overset{H}{|}}{\underset{\underset{H}{|}}{C}}-\overset{\overset{H}{|}}{C}=\overset{\overset{H}{|}}{C}-\overset{\overset{H}{|}}{\underset{\underset{H}{|}}{C}}-\overset{\overset{H}{|}}{\underset{\underset{H}{|}}{C}}-\overset{\overset{H}{|}}{\underset{\underset{H}{|}}{C}}-\overset{\overset{H}{|}}{\underset{\underset{H}{|}}{C}}-\overset{\overset{H}{|}}{\underset{\underset{H}{|}}{C}}-\overset{\overset{H}{|}}{\underset{\underset{H}{|}}{C}}-\overset{\overset{H}{|}}{\underset{\underset{H}{|}}{C}}-\overset{\overset{H}{|}}{\underset{\underset{H}{|}}{C}}-H$$

oleic acid

is probably the most abundant fatty acid in nature. Glycerol esters of this acid are found in all vegetable oils and in the fats of all ocean animals.

Like all esters, fats and oils undergo hydrolysis, the addition of water to form the original fatty acid and glycerol. This is the first step in the digestion of fats and oils in the body, and is accomplished by the action of a biological catalyst (enzyme), **lipase**. On an industrial scale hydrolysis is often accomplished with superheated steam. A special case of hydrolysis is **saponification**, in which a base reacts with the fat to give glycerol and a salt of the fatty acid. The reaction of tristearin and sodium hydroxide

$$H-\underset{\underset{H}{|}}{\overset{\overset{H}{|}}{C}}-O-\overset{\overset{O}{||}}{C}-C_{17}H_{35} \qquad\qquad H-\overset{\overset{H}{|}}{C}-OH$$

$$H-\overset{|}{C}-O-\overset{\overset{O}{||}}{C}-C_{17}H_{35} + 3\,Na^+OH^- = H-\overset{|}{C}-OH + 3\,Na^{+\,-}O-\overset{\overset{O}{||}}{C}-C_{17}H_{35}$$

$$H-\underset{\underset{H}{|}}{\overset{|}{C}}-O-\overset{\overset{O}{||}}{C}-C_{17}H_{35} \qquad\qquad H-\underset{\underset{H}{|}}{\overset{|}{C}}-OH$$

strong base

sodium stearate, a salt of stearic acid that is a soap

tristearin, a fat

glycerol, an alcohol

produces glycerol and the sodium salt of stearic acid, sodium stearate. Salts of fatty acids, such as sodium stearate, are **soaps**.

The cleaning properties of soap may be explained by the special properties of anions, such as sodium stearate, which have long hydrocarbon chains. These ions have a sort of a "split personality" because the charged $-\overset{\overset{\displaystyle O}{\|}}{C}-O^-$ group is attracted strongly to polar water, and the $-C_{17}H_{35}$ group wants nothing to do with water (see Figure 10.10). As a result, as many as 100 of these anions cluster together in balls. The charged carboxylate groups are on the surface of these tiny colloidal particles. These charged groups have a strong attraction

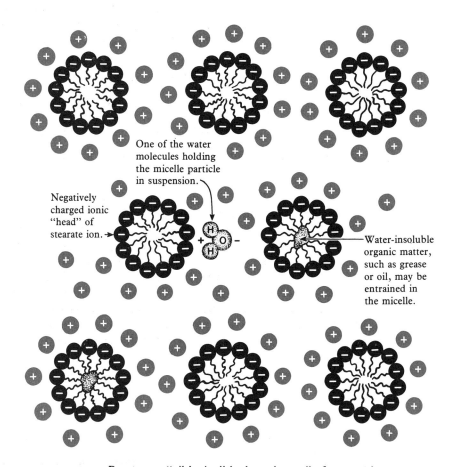

One of the water molecules holding the micelle particle in suspension.

Negatively charged ionic "head" of stearate ion. →

Water-insoluble organic matter, such as grease or oil, may be entrained in the micelle.

〜〜 Represents "oil-loving" hydrocarbon tail of stearate ion.

FIGURE 10.10

Colloidal soap micelles, some of which have entrained grease particles. The hydrocarbon-like "tails" of stearate ions cluster together inside the micelle particle. The charged $\overset{\overset{\displaystyle O}{\|}}{C}-O^-$ "heads" surround the outside of the particle and keep it suspended in water.

for water. The hydrocarbon "tails" of the fatty acid anions cluster together inside the colloidal particle, away from water. A group of associated ions such as this is called an **association colloid**. The inside of the small particle is "oil-loving" and can entrap small particles of grease or oil. This is one of the main properties that makes soap so effective for cleaning.

10.13

Nitrogen-Containing Organic Compounds

Amines and amides are two important classes of organic compounds that contain nitrogen. Nitrogen is especially important in biological compounds such as proteins (Chapter 11).

Amides are compounds containing the $-\overset{\overset{\displaystyle O}{\|}}{C}-NH_2$ group. They can be prepared by heating ammonium salts of carboxylic acids

$$H-\overset{\overset{\displaystyle H}{|}}{\underset{\underset{\displaystyle H}{|}}{C}}-\overset{\overset{\displaystyle O}{\|}}{C}-O^-\ ^+NH_4 \xrightarrow{\text{heating}} H-\overset{\overset{\displaystyle H}{|}}{\underset{\underset{\displaystyle H}{|}}{C}}-\overset{\overset{\displaystyle O}{\|}}{C}-NH_2 + H_2O$$

ammonium acetate   acetamide

The amide having greatest commercial importance is dimethylformamide

$$H-\overset{\overset{\displaystyle O}{\|}}{C}-N\overset{\nearrow CH_3}{\searrow CH_3}$$ dimethylformamide (DMF)

abbreviated DMF. It is an excellent solvent, especially for the synthetic polymer, polyacrylonitrile (the chemical name of Orlon and Acrylan). DMF is a "spinning" solvent. The polyacrylonitrile is dissolved in it, then forced out of small holes in a special die to make threads as illustrated in Figure 10.11.

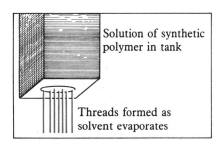

Solution of synthetic polymer in tank

Threads formed as solvent evaporates

FIGURE 10.11
Threads of synthetic fibers such as orlon are formed when a solution of the polymer is forced through small holes.

Amines make up a large variety of compounds in which one or more of the hydrogen atoms in NH_3 have been replaced by carbon. Some typical simple amines are shown in Figure 10.12.

FIGURE 10.12

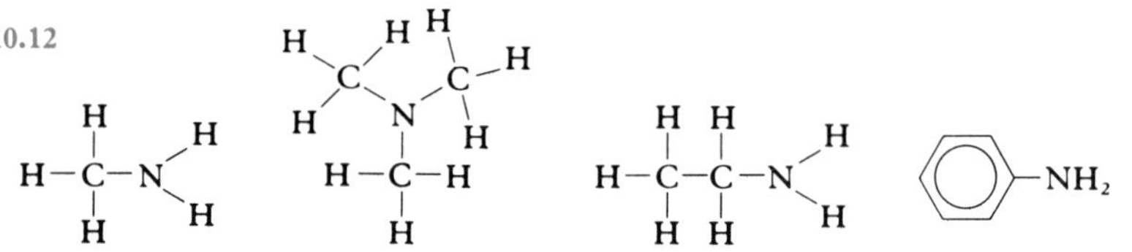

boils at $-6°C$ boils at $+3°C$ boils at $+17°C$ boils at $+184°C$

methylamine   trimethylamine   ethylamine   aniline,
                                                                                            an aromatic amine

Amines with lower molecular weights are volatile. Some have bad odors, like rotten fish. Aniline is the most important aromatic amine. This toxic chemical is used in the manufacture of dyes, amides, photographic chemicals, and drugs. Several dangerous carcinogens (cancer-causing agents) are amines. Included among these are benzidine,

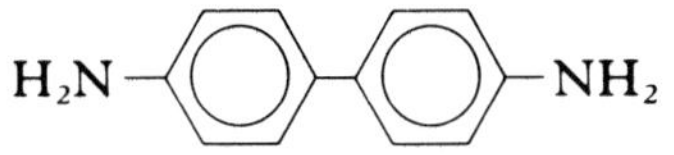

benzidine

used in the manufacture of dyes, and *beta*-naphthylamine,

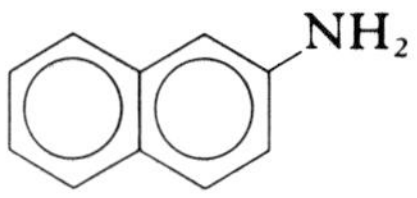

beta-naphthylamine

used as a laboratory reagent and to manufacture other chemicals. Both of these compounds cause bladder cancer.

Nitro compounds containing the $-NO_2$ group bonded to an organic molecule are common nitrogen-containing organics. Nitrobenzene, manufactured by the reaction of nitric acid and benzene,

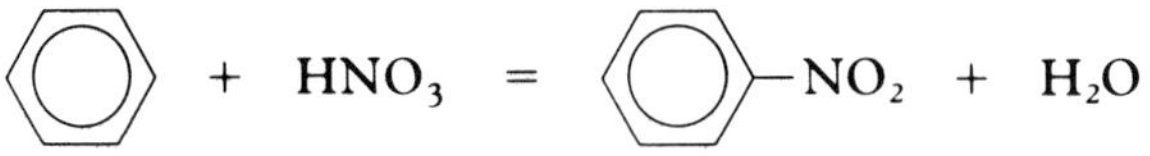

benzene   nitric acid   nitrobenzene

is one of the most widely produced of these. It is used mostly to make dyes. It is a dangerous chemical, causing irritation and reddening of the skin. If taken into the body it can damage the liver and produce jaundice and anemia.

The nitrile group, $-C\equiv N$, (also referred to as the cyanide group) is found in many significant nitrogen-containing organics. The simplest organic nitrile is acetonitrile,

$$H-\underset{\underset{H}{|}}{\overset{\overset{H}{|}}{C}}-C\equiv N \quad \text{acetonitrile}$$

used to remove tar and other impurities from crude oil and to extract fatty acids from vegetable and animal oils. It is interesting to observe that, although acetonitrile is a relatively safe compound, its inorganic chemical cousin, hydrogen cyanide (HCN), is a very toxic gas.

The most important commercial nitrile is acrylonitrile. It is manufactured by the reaction of oxygen and ammonia with propylene

$$2\ \underset{H}{\overset{H}{>}}C=\underset{\overset{|}{H}}{\overset{\overset{H}{|}}{C}}-\underset{\overset{|}{H}}{\overset{\overset{H}{|}}{C}}-H\ +\ 3\,O_2\ +\ 2\,NH_3\ =\ 2\ \underset{H}{\overset{H}{>}}C=\underset{}{\overset{\overset{H}{|}}{C}}-C\equiv N\ +\ 6\,H_2O$$

propylene,
an alkene
or olefin

acrylonitrile

at 500°C. The most important use of acrylonitrile is to make synthetic fibers of polyacrylonitrile (Figure 10.9).

10.14

The Names of Organic Compounds

From the discussion of organic chemistry in this chapter, it is easy to see that there are vast numbers of organic compounds. They are put together in orderly arrangements of straight chains, branched chains, and rings. Many of these compounds have **common names**, such as carbolic acid for phenol, or wood alcohol for methanol. Such names by themselves tell nothing about the chemical structure of the compounds. But, they are useful because they have been accepted for many years and are part of the vocabularies of persons dealing with these products. On the other hand, it is not possible to remember a common name for each chemical compound. It is also desirable for the name of a compound to tell what its chemical structure is. For that reason official naming systems have been worked out. The system approved by the IUPAC was discussed in Section 10.2 in connection with the naming of alkanes.

The naming of chemical compounds is called **nomenclature**. Having introduced the nomenclature of organic compounds earlier, we may now review it and extend it to other compounds besides alkanes. The nomenclature of organic compounds is based upon a numbering system used to show locations on the "backbone" of the compound. For example, the C atoms on a 5-carbon pentane chain are numbered from 1 to 5, and the numbers are used to show the carbon atom upon which

$$H-\underset{\underset{H}{|}}{\overset{\overset{H}{|}}{C_1}}-\underset{\underset{H}{|}}{\overset{\overset{H}{|}}{C_2}}-\underset{\underset{H}{|}}{\overset{\overset{H}{|}}{C_3}}-\underset{\underset{H}{|}}{\overset{\overset{H}{|}}{C_4}}-\underset{\underset{H}{|}}{\overset{\overset{H}{|}}{C_5}}-H \qquad \text{5-carbon pentane chain}$$

atoms or groups of atoms are substituted for hydrogen. Carbon atoms 1 and 5 are equivalent and 2 and 4 are equivalent. There are two different places to attach a methyl group to give a branched alkane. These are shown with their IUPAC names:

2-methylpentane   3-methylpentane

In addition to the methyl group, many other groups are possible, which may be substituted onto a hydrocarbon chain. The ethyl (2-carbon), propyl (3-carbon), and *n*-butyl (4-carbon) groups were described in Section 10.2. Another common group is that consisting of a benzene ring without one of its hydrogens. This is the **phenyl** group with the formula C_6H_5 shown in Figure 10.13.

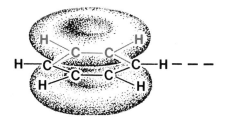

FIGURE 10.13
Phenyl group, C_6H_5.

Non-hydrocarbon organic compounds are named so that numbers indicate the location of the functional groups. This can be illustrated for halogenated hydrocarbons containing F (fluoro group), Cl (chloro), Br (bromo), or I (iodo) groups. Some compounds and their IUPAC names are given as follows.

1-chloropropane   2-chloropropane

$$\text{Cl}-\underset{\underset{\text{H}}{|}}{\overset{\overset{\text{H}}{|}}{\text{C}}}-\underset{\underset{\text{H}}{|}}{\overset{\overset{\text{H}}{|}}{\text{C}}}-\underset{\underset{\text{H}}{|}}{\overset{\overset{\text{F}}{|}}{\text{C}}}-\underset{\underset{\text{H}}{|}}{\overset{\overset{\text{H}}{|}}{\text{C}}}-\text{H}$$

1-chloro-3-fluorobutane

$$\text{H}-\underset{\underset{\text{H}}{|}}{\overset{\overset{\text{H}}{|}}{\text{C}}}-\underset{\underset{\text{H}}{|}}{\overset{\overset{\text{Br}}{|}}{\text{C}}}-\underset{\underset{\text{H}}{|}}{\overset{\overset{\text{Br}}{|}}{\text{C}}}-\underset{\underset{\text{H}}{|}}{\overset{\overset{\text{H}}{|}}{\text{C}}}-\text{H}$$

2,3-dibromobutane

In the cases of alcohols and ketones a number is used to indicate the number of the carbon atom to which the —OH or =O group is attached.

$$\text{H}-\underset{\underset{\text{H}}{|}}{\overset{\overset{\text{H}}{|}}{\text{C}}}-\underset{\underset{\text{H}}{|}}{\overset{\overset{\text{H}}{|}}{\text{C}}}-\underset{\underset{\text{H}}{|}}{\overset{\overset{\text{H}}{|}}{\text{C}}}-\underset{\underset{\text{H}}{|}}{\overset{\overset{\text{H}}{|}}{\text{C}}}-\text{OH}$$

1-butanol

$$\text{H}-\underset{\underset{\text{H}}{|}}{\overset{\overset{\text{H}}{|}}{\text{C}}}-\underset{\underset{\text{H}}{|}}{\overset{\overset{\text{OH}}{|}}{\text{C}}}-\underset{\underset{\text{H}}{|}}{\overset{\overset{\text{H}}{|}}{\text{C}}}-\underset{\underset{\text{H}}{|}}{\overset{\overset{\text{H}}{|}}{\text{C}}}-\text{H}$$

2-butanol

2-pentanone

3-pentanone

The location of a double or triple bond is indicated by the IUPAC name of a compound. Such a compound is named so that the lowest numbered carbon attached to the double bond is indicated. Several examples are given as follows.

1-butene

2-butene

1-pentyne

2-pentyne

The business of naming organic compounds can become quite complicated. It would be impossible to cover all the rules for naming such compounds in a book this size. Indeed, even organic chemists have a little trouble naming some of the more complicated compounds. However, systematic naming of compounds is very helpful in understanding organic chemistry.

Chapter Summary

Organic chemistry is the study of the vast variety of chemical compounds involving *carbon*. Carbon atoms bond to each other and to different kinds of atoms in a large variety of ways. This produces a huge number of chemical compounds with very different properties.

Many organic compounds contain only carbon and hydrogen. These compounds are called *hydrocarbons*. The *alkanes*, or paraffins, have only single bonds. They may be in straight chains, branched chains, or rings. Alkanes which have the same chemical formula but differences in structure due to branching are called *isomers*. Hydrocarbons with double bonds involving 4 electrons per bond are called *alkenes* or *olefins*. Those with triple bonds made up of 6 electrons are *alkynes*. Acetylene, commonly used in welding and cutting torches, is the simplest alkyne.

Aromatic compounds involving rings of six carbon atoms held together by special carbon-carbon π chemical bonds are especially stable. The simplest of these is benzene, C_6H_6. Several benzene rings may be grouped together to form *polycyclic aromatic hydrocarbons*, some of which cause cancer.

Various groups containing atoms other than hydrogen and carbon can be bonded to hydrocarbon molecules to give new types of compounds with much different properties. They are called *functional groups*. Some of these are the —OH (hydroxyl) group in alcohols, $>C{=}O$ (carbonyl) groups in aldehydes and ketones, $-CO_2H$ groups in carboxylic acids, and $-NH_2$ (amino) groups in amines.

Systems have been developed for naming organic compounds. The one now used is the IUPAC system. The IUPAC system of organic compound nomenclature, which has been very helpful in organizing organic chemistry, enables the chemist to tell the structure of a compound from its name.

Chapter Review Questions

The following questions are designed as a self-teaching tool to help you review Chapter 10. The answers to each question follow. See Chapter Review Questions for Chapter 1 for further instructions.

1. The structure of octane, a straight-chain alkane with 8 carbon atoms, is

    _____, that of isooctane is _____

    and that of cyclooctane (a ring compound) is _____.

2. Alkanes contain only _____ bonds; alkenes (olefins) have at least one _____ bond; and alkynes have at least one _____ bond.

3. The most important use for methane in industry is the production of _____ by the reaction, _____.

4. Methane is commonly known as the fuel called _____.

5. The structures of the three possible isomers of the 5-carbon alkane, pentane, are

_____, _____, and _____.

6. The two formulas

$$H-\overset{\overset{\displaystyle H}{|}}{\underset{\underset{\displaystyle Cl}{|}}{C}}-\overset{\overset{\displaystyle Cl}{|}}{\underset{\underset{\displaystyle H}{|}}{C}}-H \quad \text{and} \quad H-\overset{\overset{\displaystyle Cl}{|}}{\underset{\underset{\displaystyle H}{|}}{C}}-\overset{\overset{\displaystyle Cl}{|}}{\underset{\underset{\displaystyle H}{|}}{C}}-H$$

are actually the same. However, the formulas,

$$\overset{Cl}{\underset{H}{}}C=C\overset{Cl}{\underset{H}{}} \qquad \overset{H}{\underset{Cl}{}}C=C\overset{Cl}{\underset{H}{}}$$

are for two different compounds because a double bond cannot _____.

7. In the first of the two compounds with double bonds shown in Question 6, the chlorines are said to be _____ relative to each other, and those in the second compound are said to be _____ relative to each other.

8. The compound

$$\overset{Cl}{\underset{H}{}}C=C\overset{H}{\underset{H}{}}$$

is called _____, and it forms a polymer called _____.

9. Benzene consists of a ring of _____ carbon atoms each bonded to one _____ atom.

10. Benzene rings are often shown by the symbol, _____, which indicates that the π electrons are not confined to one specific carbon atom.

11. Several aromatic rings condensed together in a "chicken wire" type of structure make up _____, some of which are carcinogenic.

12. Specific arrangements of atoms involving at least one atom other than carbon or hydrogen and occurring in various classes of organic compounds are called _____.

13. Alcohols contain the group called the _____ group having the formula _____.

14. An "alcohol" in which the hydroxyl group is bonded to an aromatic hydrocarbon ring is called a _____ and may be extracted into water from organic matter such as coal tar because it forms a _____ by reacting with _____.

15. Ethers consist of two hydrocarbon groups linked by _____.

16. A ketone consists of the _____ group bonded to two hydrocarbon groups. If H is substituted for one of the hydrocarbon groups, the compound is called _____.

17. The removal of H_2 from 2-propanol at 400°C is used to prepare the important industrial chemical called _____.

18. Fehling's solution is used to test for the general class of compounds called _____.

19. Carboxylic acids contain the group having the formula _____.

20. An ester is a combination of _____ and _____ that have lost one molecule of water in linking together.

21. Addition of water to an ester to form the two types of compounds from which it was formed is called _____.

22. Fats and oils are _____ in which the alcohol is _____.

23. Three common types of nitrogen-containing organic compounds are _____, _____, and _____.

24. The general term applied to the naming of chemical compounds is _____.

25. A system for naming organic compounds, which helps to tell the structure from the name, is the _____ system.

26. The IUPAC name of the compound

$$\begin{array}{cccc} \text{H} & \text{H} & \text{H} & \text{H} \\ | & | & | & | \\ \text{H}-\text{C}-\text{C}-\text{C}-\text{C}-\text{H} \\ | & | & | & | \\ \text{H} & \text{Cl} & \text{H} & \text{H} \end{array}$$

is _____.

Answers to Chapter Review Questions

1.

2. single covalent, double, triple

3. hydrogen, $CH_4 + H_2O \longrightarrow CO + 3 H_2$ 4. natural gas

5.

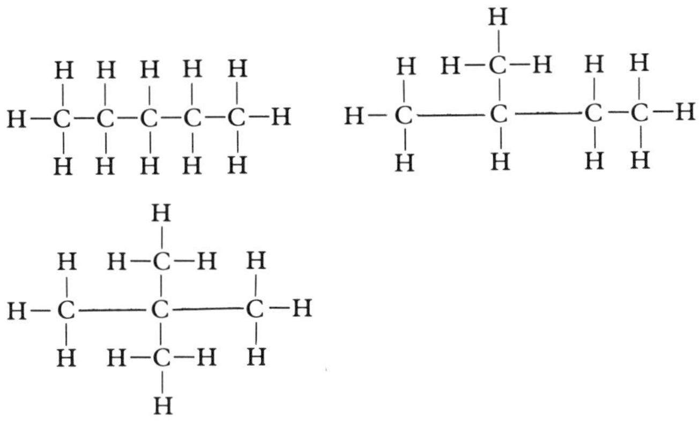

```
    H   H   H   H   H          H  H—C—H  H   H
    |   |   |   |   |          |    |    |   |
  H—C—C—C—C—C—H              H—C————C————C—C—H
    |   |   |   |   |          |    |    |   |
    H   H   H   H   H          H    H    H   H
```

```
        H
        |
    H  H—C—H  H
    |    |    |
  H—C————C————C—H
    |    |    |
    H  H—C—H  H
         |
         H
```

6. rotate

7. cis, trans

8. vinyl chloride, polyvinyl chloride

9. six, hydrogen

10.

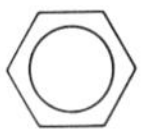

11. polycyclic aromatic hydrocarbons

12. functional groups

13. hydroxyl, —OH

14. phenol, salt, base

15. an oxygen atom

16. $\diagdown$C=O, an aldehyde

17. acetone

18. aldehydes

19.
```
    O
    ‖
  —C—OH
```

20. an organic acid, an alcohol

21. hydrolysis

22. esters of fatty acids, glycerol

23. amides, amines, nitriles

24. nomenclature

25. IUPAC

26. 2-chlorobutane

Exercises for Chapter 10

1. In the left-hand column, some structures and names of alkanes are given. In the blank spaces, show the structures and give the names of the alkenes, alcohols, aldehydes, ketones, and carboxylic acids having the same carbon skeleton. Several examples are given.

Alkane	Alkene	Alcohol	Aldehyde	Ketone	Carboxylic acid
H | H—C—H | H	None			None	O ‖ H—C—OH
methane	_____ _____				formic acid

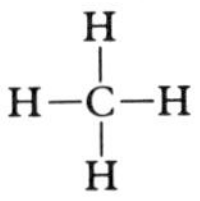

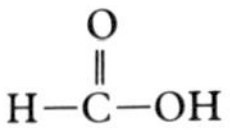

Alkane	Alkene	Alcohol	Aldehyde	Ketone	Carboxylic acid

Alkane:

$$H-\overset{\overset{\displaystyle H}{|}}{\underset{\underset{\displaystyle H}{|}}{C}}-\overset{\overset{\displaystyle H}{|}}{\underset{\underset{\displaystyle H}{|}}{C}}-H$$

ethane

Aldehyde:

$$H-\overset{\overset{\displaystyle H}{|}}{\underset{\underset{\displaystyle H}{|}}{C}}-\overset{\overset{\displaystyle O}{\|}}{C}-H$$

acetaldehyde

Ketone: None

Alkane:

$$H-\overset{\overset{\displaystyle H}{|}}{\underset{\underset{\displaystyle H}{|}}{C}}-\overset{\overset{\displaystyle H}{|}}{\underset{\underset{\displaystyle H}{|}}{C}}-\overset{\overset{\displaystyle H}{|}}{\underset{\underset{\displaystyle H}{|}}{C}}-H$$

propane

Alkene:

$$H-\overset{\overset{\displaystyle H}{|}}{\underset{\underset{\displaystyle H}{|}}{C}}-\overset{\overset{\displaystyle H}{|}}{C}=\overset{\overset{\displaystyle H}{|}}{C}-H$$

1-propene

Alcohol: _____ (2 possible)

Alkane:

$$H-\overset{\overset{\displaystyle H}{|}}{\underset{\underset{\displaystyle H}{|}}{C}}-\overset{\overset{\displaystyle H}{|}}{\underset{\underset{\displaystyle H}{|}}{C}}-\overset{\overset{\displaystyle H}{|}}{\underset{\underset{\displaystyle H}{|}}{C}}-\overset{\overset{\displaystyle H}{|}}{\underset{\underset{\displaystyle H}{|}}{C}}-H$$

butane

Alkene: _____ (2 possible)

Alcohol: _____ (2 possible)

Ketone:

$$H-\overset{\overset{\displaystyle H}{|}}{\underset{\underset{\displaystyle H}{|}}{C}}-\overset{\overset{\displaystyle H}{|}}{\underset{\underset{\displaystyle H}{|}}{C}}-\overset{\overset{\displaystyle O}{\|}}{C}-\overset{\overset{\displaystyle H}{|}}{\underset{\underset{\displaystyle H}{|}}{C}}-H$$

2-butanone

2. Where x is the number of carbon atoms in a straight-chain alkane, fill in the blank in the general chemical formula for an alkane.

$$C_x H\text{_____}$$

If x is the number of carbon atoms in a straight-chain alkene with *one* double bond, what would the general formula be? Would these numbers be different if the compound had a branched chain?

3. Propyne has 3 carbon atoms and a triple bond between two of the carbons. All of the rest of the bonds in this compound are single bonds. Show the bonds in propyne, both as pairs of dots and as dashed lines. Put the correct number of hydrogen atoms in the right places in the structure.

C C↑C   C C↑C
     └triple   └triple
      bond   bond

4. Reforming of petroleum alkanes consists of breaking up the molecules somewhat and rearranging the structure. The product is often an alkane with the same molecular weight and formula, but a different arrangement of atoms than the starting compound. Draw one of the structures that could result from reforming *n*-octane. Why do you think reforming is such a common practice?

$$H-\overset{\overset{\displaystyle H}{|}}{\underset{\underset{\displaystyle H}{|}}{C}}-\overset{\overset{\displaystyle H}{|}}{\underset{\underset{\displaystyle H}{|}}{C}}-\overset{\overset{\displaystyle H}{|}}{\underset{\underset{\displaystyle H}{|}}{C}}-\overset{\overset{\displaystyle H}{|}}{\underset{\underset{\displaystyle H}{|}}{C}}-\overset{\overset{\displaystyle H}{|}}{\underset{\underset{\displaystyle H}{|}}{C}}-\overset{\overset{\displaystyle H}{|}}{\underset{\underset{\displaystyle H}{|}}{C}}-\overset{\overset{\displaystyle H}{|}}{\underset{\underset{\displaystyle H}{|}}{C}}-\overset{\overset{\displaystyle H}{|}}{\underset{\underset{\displaystyle H}{|}}{C}}-H$$

n-octane

5. Match each compound in the left column with its isomer in the right column.

```
              H                              H  H  H  H
              |                              |  |  |  |
    H   H−C−H  H                         H−C=C−C−C−H
    |    |    |                             |  |
  H−C────C────C−H                           H  H
    |    |    |
    H    H    H                    H  H  H  H  H  H
                                   |  |  |  |  |  |
                                 H−C−C−C=C−C−C−H
              H                    |  |     |  |
              |                    H  H     H  H
    H   H−C−H  H
    |    |    |                              H
  H−C────C────C−H                            |
    |    |    |                    H  H  H−C−H  H
    H  H−C−H  H                    |  |    |    |
         |                       H−C−C────C────C−H
         H                         |  |    |    |
                                   H  H    H    H

              H
              |                              H   H
    H  H  H−C−H  H                           C───C
    |  |    |    |                          ╱       ╲
  H−C−C────C────C−H              H−C−H  H   H     H  H−C−H
    |  |    |    |                       H         H
    H  H  H−C−H  H                        C───C
              |                           |   |
              H                           H   H

                                              H
                                              |
    H  H  H  H                      H  H−C−H  H       H
    |  |  |  |                      |    |    |       |
  H−C−C=C−C−H                     H−C────C────C────C−H
    |     |                         |    |    |      |
    H     H                         H    H  H−C−H    H
                                              |
                                              H

                                    H  H  H  H
                                    |  |  |  |
                                  H−C−C−C−C−H
                                    |  |  |  |
                                    H  H  H  H
```

6. Ethyl chloride

```
        H  H
        |  |
      H−C−C−Cl
        |  |
        H  H
```

may be produced from two different hydrocarbons by two different reactions. One of these reactions consumes HCl, the other produces it. What are the two hydrocarbons that could be used as starting materials? Write the chemical reactions involved.

7. Why is it not correct to visualize benzene as an alkene having 3 double bonds and 6 carbon atoms in a ring?

8. If benzene were in fact an alkene, what would be the formula of the compound resulting from the reaction of 1 Br_2 molecule with 1 benzene molecule? What is the actual reaction?

9. What is the chemical formula, C_____H_____, of the polycyclic aromatic hydrocarbon (PAH) shown below?

10. Various chemical groups, called *functional groups,* are characteristic of particular kinds of organic compounds. In the formulas in the left column, below, R represents a hydrocarbon group in general. The functional group is indicated with color. Match each functional group with the name of the class of compound in the right column.

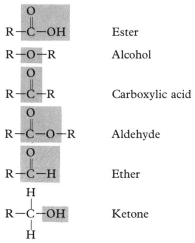

11. In the days when methanol was widely used as auto antifreeze, it was called "temporary antifreeze." More well-to-do motorists purchased ethylene glycol, called "permanent antifreeze." Examining the physical properties of these two alcohols, why do you think they were given these names?

12. Phenol is a weak acid. It is desired to remove phenol from water-insoluble crude oil and reclaim the phenol as an uncharged compound. Describe how this might best be done and show the chemical reactions involved.

13. Identify each of the following reactions as an addition reaction, a replacement reaction, or a dehydration reaction.

$$H-\underset{\underset{H}{|}}{\overset{\overset{H}{|}}{C}}-\underset{\underset{H}{|}}{\overset{\overset{H}{|}}{C}}-OH \longrightarrow \underset{H}{\overset{H}{\diagdown}}C=C\underset{\diagdown H}{\overset{\diagup H}{}} + H_2O$$

$$\underset{H}{\overset{H}{\diagdown}}C=C\underset{\diagdown H}{\overset{\diagup H}{}} + H_2O \longrightarrow H-\underset{\underset{H}{|}}{\overset{\overset{H}{|}}{C}}-\underset{\underset{H}{|}}{\overset{\overset{H}{|}}{C}}-OH$$

$$H-\underset{\underset{H}{|}}{\overset{\overset{H}{|}}{C}}-\underset{\underset{H}{|}}{\overset{\overset{H}{|}}{C}}-H + Cl_2 \longrightarrow H-\underset{\underset{H}{|}}{\overset{\overset{H}{|}}{C}}-\underset{\underset{H}{|}}{\overset{\overset{H}{|}}{C}}-Cl + HCl$$

14. What is the difference between an aldehyde and a ketone?

15. What two common types of oxygen-containing organic compounds studied in this chapter react with bases to form salts? Show two such reactions with sodium hydroxide.

16. What two carboxylic acids, or their salts, are used to preserve food?

17. What general type of oxygen-containing organic compound contains many flavor and aroma compounds among its members?

18. What are the two products of the chemical reaction which occurs when water is added to an ester?

19. What is the difference between oleic acid and stearic acid? To what general class of carboxylic acids do they belong?

20. Propane requires O_2 from an outside source to burn. Show by some chemical reactions why nitroglycerin "burns" (explodes) without outside oxygen.

21. What keeps soap micelles suspended in water?

22. Why is soap in water effective in removing grease?

23. Calcium stearate is insoluble. Look up "hardness" (a property of drinking water). Now write a chemical reaction showing why soap does not work well in hard water.

24. What is the difference between an amine and an amide? Draw the structures of chemical compounds to show these differences.

25. The groups

show up in the structures of aromatic compounds. Add carbon and hydrogen atoms to show what these groups really signify.

26. Draw the structures of four carcinogens (cancer-causing chemicals) mentioned in this chapter.

27. Match each nitrogen-containing group in the left column with the appropriate description on the right.

—NH₂	Found in synthetic fibers such as Acrilan
—NO₂	Attached to benzene by the action of HNO_3
—C≡N	Found in amines.

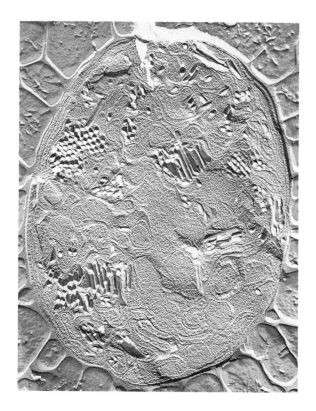

An electron micrograph of a blue-green algal cell showing photosynthetic membranes and numerous gas vesicles. (Courtesy of Dr. Daniel Branton, The Biological Laboratories, Harvard University)

11

The Chemistry of Life

11.1

The Best Chemical Factory

Most people have had the experience of looking through a microscope at a single cell. It may have been an ameba, alive and oozing about like a blob of jelly on the microscope slide. It may have been a cell of bacteria, stained with a dye to make it show up more plainly. Or, it may have been a beautiful cell of algae with its bright green chlorophyll. Even the simplest of these cells is capable of carrying out chemical reactions that would require a chemical factory costing billions of dollars, if it could be built at all. These life processes fall under the heading of **biochemistry**. There is not space in a book of this size to cover this vast, complicated subject in detail. However, it will be introduced. Those readers going on in medically related studies, agriculture, and similar fields will almost certainly take a course dealing specifically with biochemistry.

Life chemical processes are carried out in **cells**. A cell is a very small building block of a living organism. Cells are of the order of a micron in size. A micron is only one-millionth of a meter, or about 40-millionths of an inch. You can see that an individual cell is very small. Bacteria, yeasts, and some algae consist of single cells. However, most living things are made up of many cells. In a more complicated organism the cells have different functions. The liver cells, muscle cells, brain cells, and skin cells in our bodies are quite different from each other and do different things.

Even a very small human cell has many distinct parts. Observe the diagram of a mammal cell in Figure 11.1. The cell is enclosed with a **cell membrane**. This membrane protects the contents of the cell from undesirable outside influences. Its **permeability** varies for different substances. This means that the membrane controls the chemical species that can enter or leave the cell.

The cell **cytoplasm** contains proteins, nucleic acids, and other biochemical substances involved in the cell processes. The cytoplasm of an animal cell contains small spots called **ribosomes**, where proteins are synthesized. Proteins are the basic structural elements of cells. Their role in living systems will be discussed later in the chapter.

The **nucleus** acts as a sort of "control center" of the cell. It contains the genetic directions the cell needs to reproduce itself. The genetic material in the nucleus is deoxyribonucleic acid, **DNA**, which will be discussed later in the chapter. **Chromosomes** are made up of combinations of DNA and proteins. Each chromosome stores a separate quantity of genetic information. Human cells contain 46 chromosomes.

Mitochondria are bodies in the cell that function as "powerhouses." By a complex series of processes, they are capable of breaking down carbohydrates, proteins, and fats to yield carbon dioxide, water,

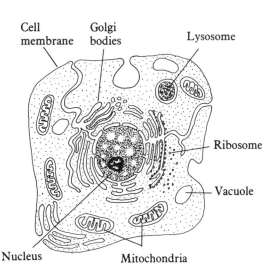

Cell membrane   Golgi bodies   Lysosome

Ribosome

Vacuole

Nucleus   Mitochondria

FIGURE 11.1
Structure of a human cell.

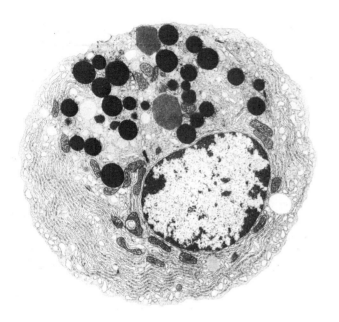

An electron micrograph of a representative animal cell showing the nucleus, mitochondria, endoplasmic reticulum with associated ribosomes and numerous secretary zymogen granules. (Courtesy of Dr. Don Fawcett, Harvard Medical School)

and energy, which is then used by the cell. The best example of this is the oxidation of the sugar glucose, $C_6H_{12}O_6$:

$$C_6H_{12}O_6 + 6\,O_2 \longrightarrow 6\,CO_2 + 6\,H_2O + \text{energy}$$

This kind of process is called **cellular respiration**.

Specific bodies in the cell, such as mitochondria, are called **organelles**. Another common type of organelle in the cell is the **lysome**. These contain potent substances capable of digesting liquid food material. Such material enters the cell through a "dent" in the cell wall, which eventually becomes surrounded by cell material. This surrounded material is called a **food vacuole**. The vacuole merges with a lysosome, and the substances in the lysosome bring about digestion of the food material. The digestion process consists largely of **hydrolysis** reactions in which large, complicated food molecules are broken down into smaller units by the addition of water. A simple hydrolysis reaction for the breakdown of methyl acetate was discussed in Section 10.11. Cells also contain flattened bodies of material called **Golgi bodies**. In some types of cells these bodies serve to hold and release substances produced by the cells.

Plant cells differ from animal cells in several important features as shown in Figure 11.2. The plant cell must have a **cell wall** that is quite strong. Cell walls are the basic structures that provide stiffness and strength. Cell walls are composed mostly of cellulose, which will be discussed later in this chapter. Inside plant cells there are usually large vacuoles. These bodies contain materials dissolved in water. Plant cells that are involved in photosynthesis (the chemical process which uses energy from sunlight to convert carbon dioxide and water to organic matter) also contain highly structured organelles called **chloroplasts**.

FIGURE 11.2

Structure of a plant cell.

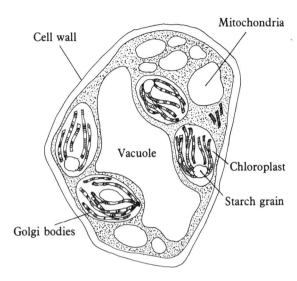

Photosynthesis occurs in these bodies. Food produced by photosynthesis is stored in the chloroplasts in the form of **starch grains**.

Plants cannot always get the energy that they need from sunlight. During the dark they must use stored food. Plant cells, like animal cells, contain mitochondria in which stored food is converted to energy by cellular respiration.

Plant cells, which use sunlight as a source of energy and CO_2 as a source of carbon, are said to be **autotrophic**. Basically they bring about the reaction

$$6\ CO_2 + 6\ H_2O + \text{sunlight} \longrightarrow \underset{\text{sugars}}{C_6H_{12}O_6} + 6\ O_2\uparrow$$

to produce sugars with a high energy content. These sugars can be converted to water-insoluble starch, cell-wall cellulose, and other materials. They serve as the basic energy source for the rest of the plant's life processes.

Animal cells must depend upon organic materials manufactured by plants for their food. These are called **heterotrophic** cells. They act as "middlemen" in the chemical reaction between oxygen and food material

$$\underset{\substack{\text{food}\\ \text{(sugar)}}}{C_6H_{12}O_6} + 6\ O_2 \longrightarrow 6\ CO_2\uparrow + 6\ H_2O + \text{energy}$$

using the energy from the reaction to carry out their life processes.

We have started this chapter on biochemistry with a discussion of complicated processes that occur in living cells. Now we may turn our attention to an even smaller level and discuss the actual types of chemicals found in living systems. With these in mind, we will discuss the special chemical processes that they undergo in living cells.

11.2

Proteins

Proteins are nitrogen-containing organic compounds which are the basic units of live systems. **Cytoplasm**, the jelly-like liquid filling the interior of cells is made up largely of protein. Enzymes, which act as catalysts of life reactions, are made of proteins. These will be discussed later in the chapter. Proteins are made up of **amino acids** joined together in huge chains. Amino acids are organic compounds which contain the carboxylic acid group, $-CO_2H$, and the amino group, $-NH_2$. They are sort of a hybrid of carboxylic acids (Section 10.10) and amines (Section 10.13).

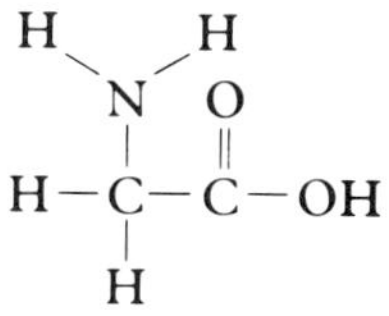

glycine,
the simplest amino acid

Natural amino acids all have the following chemical group:

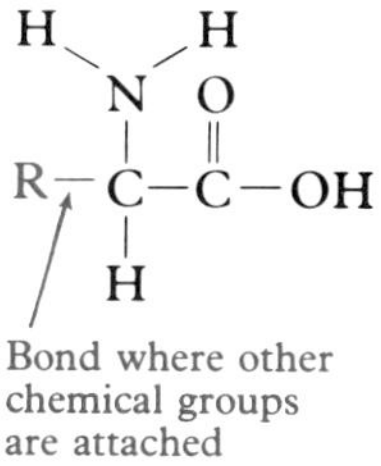

Bond where other
chemical groups
are attached

In this structure the $-NH_2$ group is always bonded to the carbon next to the $-CO_2H$ group. This is called the "alpha" location, so natural amino acids are alpha-amino acids. Other groups, designated as "R," are attached to the basic alpha-amino acid structure. The R groups may be as simple as an atom of H found in glycine. Or, they may be as complicated as the structure

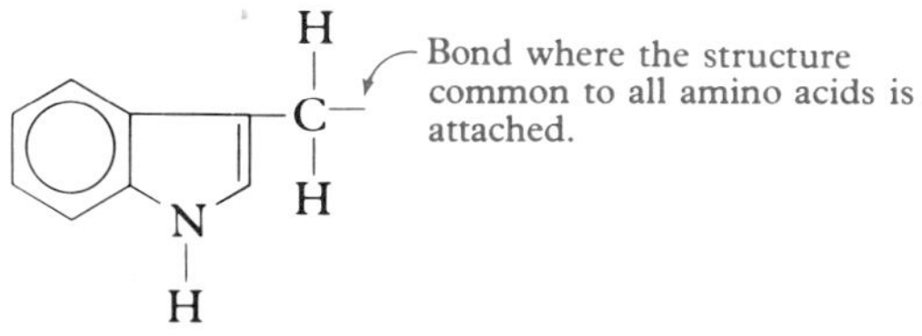

Bond where the structure
common to all amino acids is
attached.

tryptophan

found in tryptophan. As shown in Table 11.1, there are 20 common amino acids in proteins.

Amino acids are joined together in long chains to form proteins. Proteins are polymers, as are polyethylene (Section 10.3) or polyvinyl

TABLE 11.1

The amino acids commonly found in protein.

Name	Structural Formula
Glycine (gly)	$\overset{\overset{\displaystyle NH_3^+}{\mid}}{H-CH-CO_2^-}$
Alanine (ala)	$\overset{\overset{\displaystyle NH_3^+}{\mid}}{CH_3-CH-CO_2^-}$
Valine (val)	$\begin{array}{c} H_3C \\ \diagdown \\ H_3C \diagup \end{array} \overset{\overset{\displaystyle NH_3^+}{\mid}}{CH-CH-CO_2^-}$
Phenylalanine (phe)	$\bigcirc -CH_2-\overset{\overset{\displaystyle NH_3^+}{\mid}}{CH}-CO_2^-$
Serine (ser)	$HO-CH_2-\overset{\overset{\displaystyle NH_3^+}{\mid}}{CH}-CO_2^-$
Threonine (thr)	$CH_3-\overset{\overset{\displaystyle OH}{\mid}}{CH}-\overset{\overset{\displaystyle NH_3^-}{\mid}}{CH}-CO_2^-$
Asparagine (asn)	$H_2N-\overset{\overset{\displaystyle O}{\|}}{C}-CH_2-\overset{\overset{\displaystyle NH_3^+}{\mid}}{CH}-CO_2^-$
Leucine (leu)	$\begin{array}{c} H_3C \\ \diagdown \\ H_3C \diagup \end{array} CH-CH_2-\overset{\overset{\displaystyle NH_3^+}{\mid}}{CH}-CO_2^-$
Isoleucine (ile)	$\begin{array}{c} H_3C \\ \diagdown \\ CH_3-CH_2 \diagup \end{array} CH-\overset{\overset{\displaystyle NH_3^+}{\mid}}{CH}-CO_2^-$
Proline (pro)	$\begin{array}{c} H_2C-CH_2 \\ H_2CCH-CO_2^- \\ \diagdown N \diagup \\ H H \end{array}$
Methionine (met)	$CH_3-S-CH_2-CH_2-\overset{\overset{\displaystyle NH_3^+}{\mid}}{CH}-CO_2^-$
Cysteine (cys)	$HS-CH_2-\overset{\overset{\displaystyle NH_3^+}{\mid}}{CH}-CO_2^-$
Tyrosine (tyr)	$HO-\bigcirc -CH_2-\overset{\overset{\displaystyle NH_3^+}{\mid}}{CH}-CO_2^-$

TABLE 11.1 (*continued*)

Name	Structural Formula

Glutamine (gin)

$$\underset{H_2N-\overset{\displaystyle O}{\overset{\|}{C}}-CH_2-CH_2-\overset{\displaystyle NH_3^+}{\overset{|}{C}H}-CO_2}{}$$

Tryptophan (try)

$$-CH_2-\overset{\displaystyle NH_3^+}{\overset{|}{C}H}-CO_2^-$$

Aspartic acid (asp)

$$HO-\overset{\displaystyle O}{\overset{\|}{C}}-CH_2-\overset{\displaystyle NH_3^+}{\overset{|}{C}H}-CO_2$$

Histidine (his)

$$-CH_2-\overset{\displaystyle NH_3^+}{\overset{|}{C}H}-CO_2$$

Glutamic acid (glu)

$$HO-\overset{\displaystyle O}{\overset{\|}{C}}-CH_2-CH_2-\overset{\displaystyle NH_3^+}{\overset{|}{C}H}-CO_2$$

Lysine (lys)

$$H_3\overset{+}{N}-CH_2-CH_2-CH_2-CH_2-\overset{\displaystyle NH_3^+}{\overset{|}{C}H}-CO_2$$

Arginine (arg)

$$H_2N-\overset{\displaystyle NH_2^+}{\overset{\|}{C}}-NH-CH_2-CH_2-CH_2-\overset{\displaystyle NH_3^+}{\overset{|}{C}H}-CO_2$$

chloride (Section 10.6). They are, in fact, **giant molecules** or **macromolecules**. For a macromolecule to behave like a protein, it must have at least approximately 100 amino acid units. More commonly, proteins are made by linking approximately 300 amino acid molecules.

Amino acids in proteins are joined together in a specific way. These bonds are called the **peptide linkage**. The formation of peptide linkages is a condensation process involving the loss of water. The formation of esters (Section 10.11) is also such a process. Consider the condensation of alanine, leucine, and tyrosine shown in Figure 11.3. When these three amino acids join together, two water molecules are eliminated. The product is a *tri*peptide since there are three amino acids involved. When approximately 100 or more amino acids are joined together in a polymer, it is a protein.

A key characteristic of a protein is its structure. Some proteins are **fibrous** proteins. The molecules in these proteins are long and threadlike. The molecules are laid out parallel in bundles as shown in Figure 11.4. The individual molecules in the bundles are held together by hydrogen

bonds between $\diagdown$C$=$O groups on one molecule and $\diagdown$N$-$H groups

FIGURE 11.3
Condensation of alanine, leucine, and tyrosine.

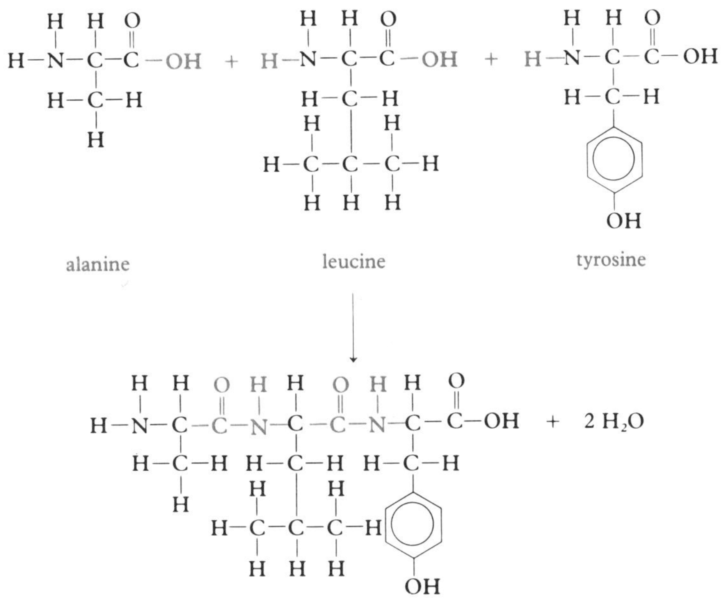

A tripeptide consisting of three amino acids joined
by peptide linkages (see type in color).

in another molecule. (Hydrogen bonds are discussed in Section 6.3.) In some cases other types of bonds are involved in linking the parallel protein molecules together. Fibrous proteins are quite tough and strong. They do not dissolve in water. They occur in skin, hair, wool, feathers, silk, and tendons.

An interesting fibrous protein is keratin, which is found in hair. The cross-linking bonds between protein molecules in keratin are —S—S— bonds formed from two HS— groups in two molecules of the amino acid, cysteine. These bonds largely hold hair in place, thus keeping it curly or straight. A "permanent" consists of breaking the bonds chemically, setting the hair as desired, then reforming the cross-links to hold the desired shape.

The other major type of protein form is the **globular** protein. These proteins are in the shape of balls or oblongs. Globular proteins are relatively soluble in water. A typical globular protein is hemoglobin, the oxygen-carrying protein in red blood cells. Enzymes, which will be discussed later in the chapter, are generally globular proteins.

Protein structure can be divided into the three levels of **primary**,

FIGURE 11.4 *Fibrous protein molecules held together in a bundle.*

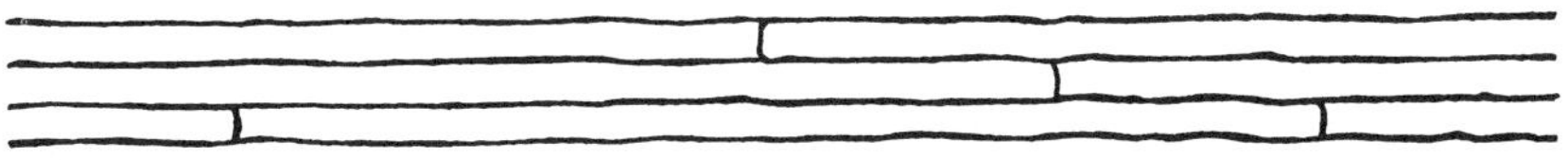

secondary, and **tertiary** structure. The order, or sequence of amino acids in the protein molecule determines the primary structure. The nature of the R groups on the amino acids

$$R-\underset{\underset{H}{|}}{\overset{\overset{H}{|}}{C}}-\underset{}{\overset{\overset{O}{\|}}{C}}-OH \qquad \underset{H}{\overset{H}{\diagdown}}N\underset{}{\diagup}$$

determines the secondary structure. Small R groups enable protein molecules to be hydrogen-bonded together in a parallel arrangement. With larger R groups the molecules tend to take a spiral form. Such a spiral is known as an **alpha-helix**. Tertiary structures are formed by the twisting around of alpha-helices into specific shapes. Tertiary structures are very important in the processes by which enzymes identify specific proteins and other molecules upon which they act. It is also involved with the action of antibodies in blood which recognize foreign proteins by their shape and react to them. This is basically what happens in the case of immunity to a disease where antibodies in blood recognize specific proteins from viruses or bacteria and reject them.

Secondary and tertiary protein structures are easily changed. These changes can be quite damaging. They are known as **denaturation**. Heating, acids, bases, and even violent physical action can cause denaturation to occur. The protein, albumin, in egg white is denatured by heating so that the white sets up as a semisolid mass. Somewhat the same thing can be accomplished by violent physical action with an egg beater in the preparation of meringue. Heavy metal poisons, such as lead and cadmium, change the tertiary structures of proteins by binding to the protein surface.

Proteins are, of course, important nutrients. It is essential for people to have an adequate supply of protein. The protein that we eat must also have the right balance of amino acids for adequate nutrition. A shortage of protein is one of the greater nutritional problems facing many "third-world" nations.

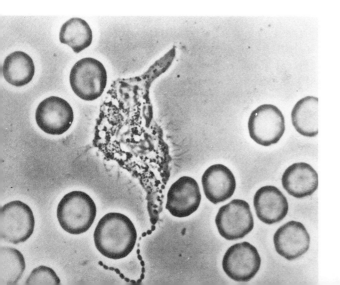

One of the ways white blood cells protect the body against invaders is by extending a temporary protrusion around the foreign substance and then ingesting it with the help of enzymes. A white blood cell is shown devouring a chain of streptococci bacteria. (Courtesy of Pfizer, Inc.)

11.3

Carbohydrates

Carbohydrates are biological compounds with an approximate simple formula of CH_2O. Their major function is to transfer and store food in living systems. When photosynthesis occurs in a plant cell (Section 11.1), the energy from sunlight is converted to chemical energy in a carbohydrate, $C_6H_{12}O_6$. This carbohydrate may be transferred to some other part of the plant for use as an energy source. It may be converted to a water-insoluble carbohydrate for storage until it is needed for energy. Or it may be converted to cell wall material and become part of the structure of the plant. If the plant is eaten by an animal, the carbohydrate is used for energy by the animal.

The simplest carbohydrates are the **monosaccharides**. These are also called **simple sugars**. Because they have 6 carbon atoms, simple sugars are sometimes called *hex*oses. Glucose

$$
\begin{array}{l}
H-C=O \\
\ \ \ \ | \\
H-C-OH \\
\ \ \ \ | \\
HO-C-H \\
\ \ \ \ | \\
H-C-OH \quad \text{glucose} \\
\ \ \ \ | \\
H-C-OH \\
\ \ \ \ | \\
H-C-H \\
\ \ \ \ | \\
\ \ \ \ OH
\end{array}
$$

is the most common simple sugar involved in cell processes. Other simple sugars with the same formula but somewhat different structures are fructose, mannose, and galactose. These must be changed to glucose before they can be used in a cell. Because of its use for energy in body processes, glucose is found in the blood. Normal levels are from 65 to 110 mg glucose per 100 ml of blood. Higher levels may indicate diabetes.

Units of two monosaccharides make up several very important sugars known as **disaccharides**. When two molecules of monosaccharides join together to form a disaccharide,

$$ C_6H_{12}O_6 + C_6H_{12}O_6 \longrightarrow C_{12}H_{22}O_{11} + H_2O $$

a molecule of water is lost. Recall that proteins are also formed from smaller amino acid molecules by condensation reactions involving the loss of water molecules. Disaccharides include sucrose (cane sugar sold in the grocery store), lactose (milk sugar), and maltose (a product of the breakdown of starch).

Polysaccharides consist of many simple sugar units hooked together. One of the most important polysaccharides is **starch**, which is produced by plants for food storage. Animals produce a related material called **glycogen**. The chemical formula of starch is $(C_6H_{10}O_5)_n$, where

n may represent a number as high as several hundreds. What this means is that the very large starch molecule consists of many units of $C_6H_{10}O_5$ joined together. For example, if n is 100, there are 6 times 100 carbon atoms, 10 times 100 hydrogen atoms, and 5 times 100 oxygen atoms in the molecule. Its chemical formula is $C_{600}H_{1000}O_{500}$. The atoms in a starch molecule are actually present as linked rings represented by the structure shown in Figure 11.5. Starch occurs in many foods, such as bread and cereals. It is readily digested by animals, including humans.

FIGURE 11.5
Part of a starch molecule showing units of $C_6H_{10}O_5$ condensed together.

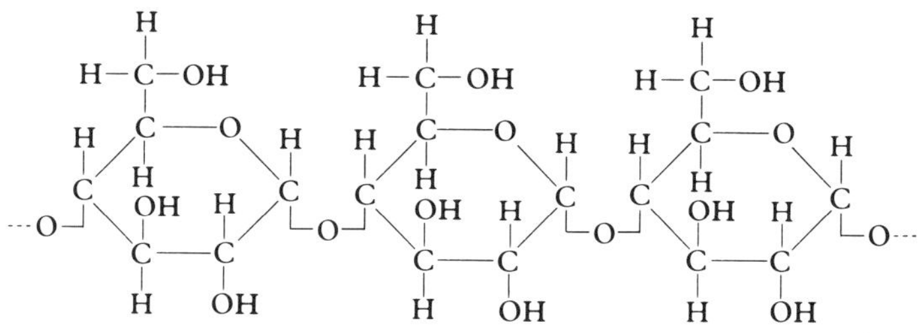

Cellulose is a polysaccharide which is also made up of $C_6H_{10}O_5$ units. Molecules of cellulose are huge, with molecular weights of around 400,000. The cellulose structure (Figure 11.6) is similar to that of starch. Cellulose is produced by plants and forms the structural material of plant cell walls. Wood is about 60 % cellulose, and cotton contains over 90 % of this material. Fibers of cellulose are extracted from wood and pressed together to make paper.

FIGURE 11.6
Part of the structure of cellulose.

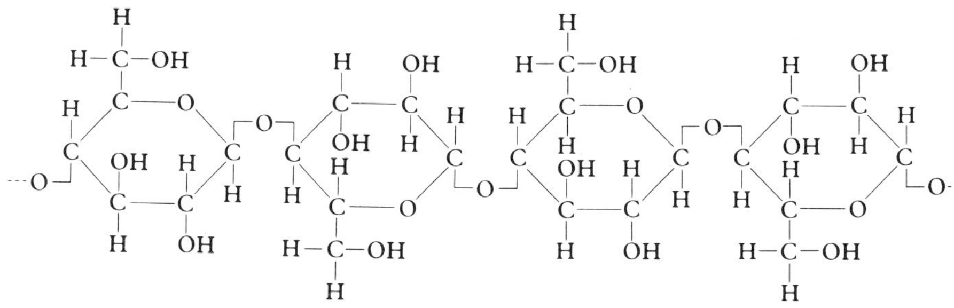

Humans and most other animals cannot digest cellulose. Ruminant animals (such as cattle and sheep) have bacteria in their stomachs that break down cellulose into products which can be used by the animal. Chemical processes are available to convert cellulose to simple sugars by the reaction

$$(C_6H_{10}O_5)_n + n\,H_2O \longrightarrow n\,C_6H_{12}O_6$$

cellulose   glucose

where n may be 2000–3000. This involves breaking the linkages between units of $C_6H_{10}O_5$ by adding a molecule at each linkage. It is a hydrolysis reaction. (Recall the hydrolysis of esters discussed in Section 10.11.) Large amounts of cellulose from wood, sugar cane, and agricultural products go to waste each year. The hydrolysis of cellulose enables these products to be converted to sugars, which can be fed to animals.

11.4

Lipids

Some substances can be extracted from biological materials by organic solvents such as benzene, chloroform, or ether (Figure 11.7). These substances are called **lipids**. The most common of these are the fats and oils discussed in Section 10.12. They also include waxes, some vitamins, sex hormones (steroids), and cholesterol. Common foods, such as butter and salad oils are lipids. The longer chain fatty acids discussed in Section 10.12 are also organic-soluble and are classified as lipids.

Recall from Chapter 10 that fats and oils are esters of the alcohol,

FIGURE 11.7
Lipids are extracted from some biological materials with a soxhelet extractor.

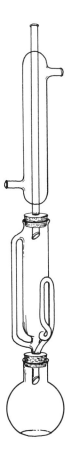

glycerol. The other component is a fatty acid.

$$
\begin{array}{c}
\text{H} \\
| \\
\text{H}-\text{C}-\text{OH} \\
| \\
\text{H}-\text{C}-\text{OH} \\
| \\
\text{H}-\text{C}-\text{OH} \\
| \\
\text{H}
\end{array}
$$

glycerol,
an alcohol

$$
\text{HO}-\overset{\displaystyle \text{O}}{\underset{}{\overset{\|}{\text{C}}}}-\overset{\text{H}}{\underset{\text{H}}{\text{C}}}-\overset{\text{H}}{\underset{\text{H}}{\text{C}}}-\overset{\text{H}}{\underset{\text{H}}{\text{C}}}-\overset{\text{H}}{\underset{\text{H}}{\text{C}}}-\overset{\text{H}}{\underset{\text{H}}{\text{C}}}-\overset{\text{H}}{\underset{\text{H}}{\text{C}}}-\overset{\text{H}}{\underset{\text{H}}{\text{C}}}-\overset{\text{H}}{\underset{\text{H}}{\text{C}}}-\overset{\text{H}}{\underset{\text{H}}{\text{C}}}-\overset{\text{H}}{\underset{\text{H}}{\text{C}}}-\overset{\text{H}}{\underset{\text{H}}{\text{C}}}-\overset{\text{H}}{\underset{\text{H}}{\text{C}}}-\overset{\text{H}}{\underset{\text{H}}{\text{C}}}-\overset{\text{H}}{\underset{\text{H}}{\text{C}}}-\overset{\text{H}}{\underset{\text{H}}{\text{C}}}-\overset{\text{H}}{\underset{\text{H}}{\text{C}}}-\text{H}
$$

stearic acid,
a typical fatty acid

The carbon chain on a fatty acid may be quite long, as in stearic acid. However, some important natural fatty acids have fairly short chains. Typical of these is butyric acid,

$$
\text{HO}-\overset{\displaystyle \text{O}}{\underset{}{\overset{\|}{\text{C}}}}-\overset{\text{H}}{\underset{\text{H}}{\text{C}}}-\overset{\text{H}}{\underset{\text{H}}{\text{C}}}-\overset{\text{H}}{\underset{\text{H}}{\text{C}}}-\text{H} \qquad \text{butyric acid}
$$

the fatty acid found in butterfat. Recall also that many of the fatty acid groups bound to glycerol contain double bonds in their chains. These produce unsaturated fats, which are often oils at room temperature.

There are many different esters of glycerol that are classified as fats and oils. The general formula of such a lipid is

$$
\begin{array}{c}
\overset{\text{H}}{\underset{|}{}} \qquad\quad \overset{\text{O}}{\underset{\|}{}} \\
\text{H}-\text{C}-\text{O}-\text{C}-\text{R} \\
| \qquad\qquad\quad\; \text{O} \\
\phantom{\text{H}-\text{C}-\text{O}-}\; \| \\
\text{H}-\text{C}-\text{O}-\text{C}-\text{R} \\
| \qquad\qquad\quad\; \text{O} \\
\phantom{\text{H}-\text{C}-\text{O}-}\; \| \\
\text{H}-\text{C}-\text{O}-\text{C}-\text{R} \\
| \\
\text{H}
\end{array}
$$

in which R represents a hydrocarbon chain. The three R groups need not all be the same.

Waxes are also esters of fatty acids. However, the alcohol in a wax is not glycerol. The alcohol in waxes is often a very long chain alcohol.

For example, one of the main compounds in beeswax is myricyl palmitate

$$(C_{30}H_{61}) - \overset{\overset{\displaystyle H}{|}}{\underset{\underset{\displaystyle H}{|}}{C}} - O - \overset{\overset{\displaystyle O}{\|}}{C} - (C_{15}H_{31})$$

$\underbrace{\qquad\qquad}$ $\underbrace{\qquad\qquad}$
alcohol portion   fatty acid portion
of ester   of ester

in which the alcohol portion of the ester has a very large hydrocarbon chain. Waxes are produced by both plants and animals, largely as protective coatings. Waxes are found in a number of common products. Lanolin is one of these. It is the "grease" in sheep's wool. When mixed with oils and water, it forms stable colloidal emulsions consisting of extremely small oil droplets suspended in water. This makes lanolin useful for skin creams and pharmaceutical ointments. Carnauba wax occurs as a coating on the leaves of some Brazilian palm trees. Spermaceti wax is composed largely of cetyl palmitate

$$(C_{15}H_{31}) - \overset{\overset{\displaystyle H}{|}}{\underset{\underset{\displaystyle H}{|}}{C}} - O - \overset{\overset{\displaystyle O}{\|}}{C} - (C_{15}H_{31}) \qquad \text{cetyl palmitate}$$

extracted from the blubber of the sperm whale. It is very useful in some cosmetics and pharmaceutical preparations.

Steroids are lipids found in living systems which all have the ring system shown in Figure 11.8 for cholesterol. Steroids occur in bile salts,

FIGURE 11.8

$$H_3C - \overset{\overset{\displaystyle H}{|}}{\underset{\underset{\displaystyle H_3C}{|}}{C}} - CH_2 - CH_2 - CH_2 - CH \overset{\displaystyle CH_3}{\underset{\displaystyle CH_3}{<}}$$

cholesterol

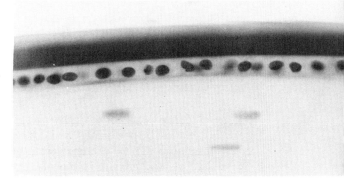

A type of protective cell making up the epidermis of the skin and linings of organs is called an "epithelial cell." Shown is a photomicrograph of the epithelium of the eye lens with a continuous layer of small cuboieal cells resting on an unusually thick basement membrane. (Courtesy of Dr. Don Fawcett, Harvard Medical School. From William Bloom and Don Fawcett, Textbook of Histology, W. B. Saunders Co., Philadelphia, Pa., 1968)

which are produced by the liver and then secreted into the intestines. Their breakdown products give feces its characteristic color. Bile salts act upon fats in the intestine. They suspend very tiny fat droplets in the form of colloidal emulsions. This enables the fats to be broken down chemically and digested.

Some steroids are **hormones**. Hormones act as "messengers" from one part of the body to another. As such, they start and stop a number of body functions. Male and female sex hormones are examples of steroid hormones. Hormones are given off by glands in the body called **endocrine glands**. The locations of the important endocrine glands are shown in Figure 11.9.

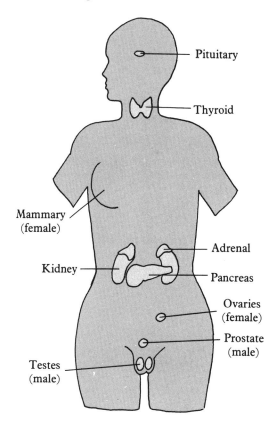

FIGURE 11.9
Locations of important endocrine glands.

Pituitary

Thyroid

Mammary
(female)

Kidney

Adrenal

Pancreas

Ovaries
(female)

Prostate
(male)

Testes
(male)

11.5

Nature's Catalysts: Enzymes

Catalysts are substances that speed up a chemical reaction without themselves being consumed in the reaction. The most sophisticated catalysts of all are those found in living systems. They bring about reactions that could not be performed at all, or only with great difficulty, outside a living organism. These catalysts are called **enzymes**.

Most enzymes are proteins. One of the main features of enzymes is their **specificity**. This means that they are very choosey about the chemical groups that they act upon. This results from the shapes of enzymes. Recall from Section 11.2 that proteins may have a very specific tertiary structure. The enzyme proteins have a structure that fits like a part of a jigsaw puzzle to the substance that it acts upon (Figure 11.10). This substance is called the **substrate**.

Enzymes are named for what they do. For example, the enzyme given off by the stomach, which splits proteins as part of the digestion process, is called *gastric proteinase*. The "gastric" part of the name refers to the enzyme's origin in the stomach. The "proteinase" tells us that it splits up protein molecules. The common name for this enzyme is

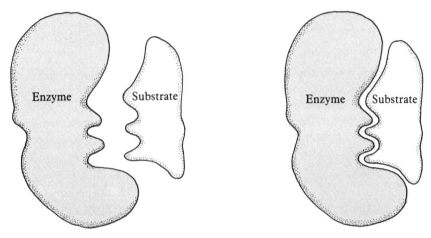

FIGURE 11.10
Enzymes are so specific in their action because they fit the structure of the substrate upon which they act.

pepsin. Similarly, the enzyme given off by the pancreas that splits fats (lipids) is called *pancreatic lipase*. Its common name is steapsin. As with organic chemistry, systematic names are very helpful in understanding biochemistry.

Enzymes perform many functions. These can be classiffed into several general categories. **Hydrolyzing enzymes** bring about the breakdown of high molecular weight biological compounds by the addition of water. This is one of the most important types of the reactions involved in digestion. The three main classes of energy-yielding foods that we eat are carbohydrates, proteins, and fats. Recall that the higher carbohydrates we eat are largely disaccharides (sucrose, or table sugar) and polysaccharides (starch). These are formed by the joining together of units of simple sugars, $C_6H_{12}O_6$, with the elimination of an H_2O molecule at the linkage where they join. Proteins are formed by the condensation of amino acids, again with the elimination of a water molecule at each linkage. Fats are esters which are produced when glycerol and fatty acids link together. A water molecule is lost for each of these linkages. The reverse process must occur to break down complicated carbohydrates, proteins, and fats to simple, soluble substances which can penetrate a cell membrane and take part in chemical processes in the cell. This reverse process is accomplished by hydrolyzing enzymes.

Biological compounds with long chains are broken down into molecules with shorter chains by the breaking of carbon-carbon bonds. This commonly occurs by the elimination of $-CO_2H$ groups from carboxylic acids. For example, *pyruvic decarboxylase* enzyme acts upon pyruvic acid

$$H-\overset{\overset{\displaystyle H}{|}}{\underset{\underset{\displaystyle H}{|}}{C}}-\overset{\overset{\displaystyle O}{\|}}{C}-\overset{\overset{\displaystyle O}{\|}}{C}-OH \quad \xrightarrow[\text{decarboxylase}]{\text{pyruvate}} \quad H-\overset{\overset{\displaystyle H}{|}}{\underset{\underset{\displaystyle H}{|}}{C}}-\overset{\overset{\displaystyle O}{\|}}{C}-H + CO_2$$

pyruvic acid   acetaldehyde

to split off CO_2 and produce a compound with one less carbon. It is by such carbon-by-carbon breakdown reactions that long chain compounds are eventually degraded to CO_2 in the body.

Oxidation and reduction are the major reactions for the exchange of energy in living systems. Cellular respiration discussed in Section 11.1 is an oxidation reaction in which a carbohydrate, $C_6H_{12}O_6$, is broken down to carbon dioxide and water with the release of energy.

$$C_6H_{12}O_6 + 6\,O_2 \longrightarrow 6\,CO_2 + 6\,H_2O + \text{energy}$$

Actually, such an overall reaction occurs in living systems by a complicated series of individual steps. Some of these steps involve oxidation. The enzymes that bring about oxidation in the presence of free O_2 are called **oxidases**.

In addition to the types of enzymes discussed above, there are many enzymes that perform miscellaneous duties in living systems. Typical of these are **isomerases**, which form isomers of particular compounds. For example, there are several simple sugars with the formula $C_6H_{12}O_6$. However, only glucose can be used directly for cell processes. The other isomers are converted to glucose by the action of isomerases.

The basic process for an enzyme reaction is

enzyme + substrate ⇌ enzyme-substrate complex ⇌ enzyme + product

Several important things should be noted about this reaction. Recall that an enzyme acts upon another molecule called a substrate. As shown in Figure 11.10, it acts on a specific substrate because of the fit between their structures. An enzyme-substrate complex is formed. As a result, something happens to the substrate molecule. For example, it might be split in two at a particular location. Then the enzyme-substrate complex comes apart, yielding the enzyme and products. The enzyme is not changed in the reaction and is now free to react again. Note that the arrows in the formula for enzyme reaction point both ways. This means that the reaction is **reversible**. An enzyme-substrate complex can simply go back to the enzyme and the substrate. The products of an enzymatic reaction can

A photomicrograph of skeletal muscles showing the cross-banded patterns of a myofibrils. (Courtesy of Dr. Don Fawcett, Harvard Medical School. From William Bloom and Don Fawcett, Textbook of Histology, W. B. Saunders Co., Philadelphia, Pa., 1968)

react with the enzyme to form the enzyme-substrate complex again. It, in turn, may again form the enzyme and the substrate. Therefore, the same enzyme may act to cause a reaction to go either way.

Enzyme action may be affected by many different things. Enzymes require a certain hydrogen ion concentration to function best. For example, gastric proteinase requires the acid environment of the stomach to work well. When it passes into the much less acidic intestines, it stops working. This prevents damage to the intestine walls, which would occur if the enzyme tried to digest them. Temperature is critical. Not surprisingly, the enzymes in the human body work best at around 98.6°F (37°C), which is the normal body temperature. Heating these enzymes to around 140°F permanently destroys them. Some bacteria that thrive in hot springs have enzymes which work best at relatively high temperatures. Other "cold-seeking" bacteria have enzymes adapted to near the freezing point of water.

One of the greatest concerns regarding the effects of surroundings upon enzymes is the influence of toxic substances. Among the toxic substances that damage enzymes are heavy metals, cyanide, and organic compounds such as formaldehyde. Some of these denature the enzymes, causing them to "unravel" and altering their shape. Heavy metals bond to the enzyme surface. In both cases, the enzyme is changed so that it no longer fits the substrate correctly and no longer functions.

Some enzymes cannot function by themselves. In order to work, they must first be attached to **coenzymes**. Coenzymes normally are not protein materials. Some of the vitamins are important coenzymes.

11.6

The Blueprints of Life

As mentioned in Section 11.1, the cell nucleus contains the genetic directions for cell reproduction. These are in the form of a special material called deoxyribonucleic acid, **DNA**. In combination with proteins, DNA makes up the cell chromosomes. The nature and function of DNA are extremely important for life processes. Its malfunction results in birth defects. The failure to control cell reproduction results in cancer.

Biochemists are doing a lot of work to understand the nature of DNA and what it does.

DNA molecules are made up of simple sugars, amines, and derivatives of phosphoric acid, H_3PO_4. The simple sugar is deoxyribose, with the structure

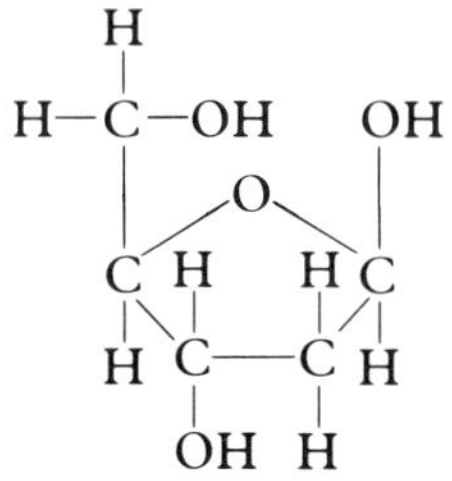

deoxyribose,
a simple sugar

The four amines involved are **cyclic amines**, which means that the amine nitrogen is present in a ring structure. These are **adenine**, **guanine**, **cytosine**, and **thymine**. A material related to DNA is

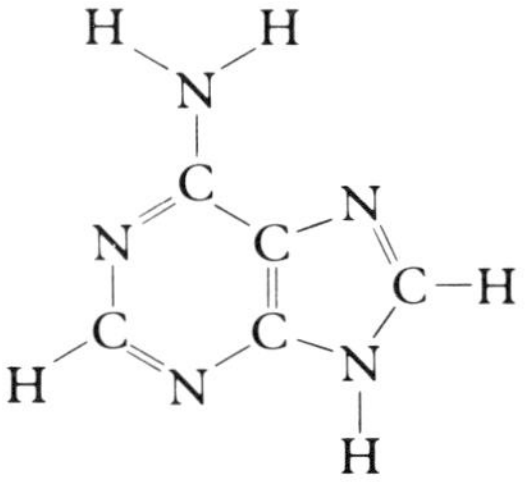

adenine 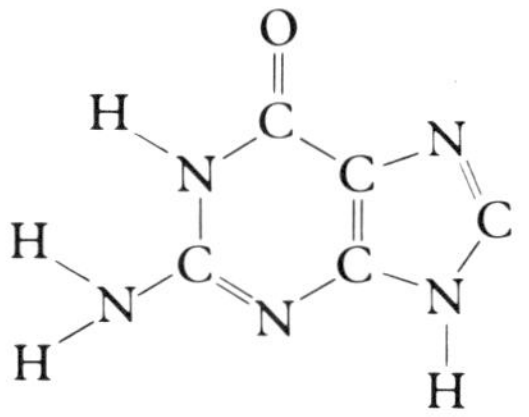   guanine 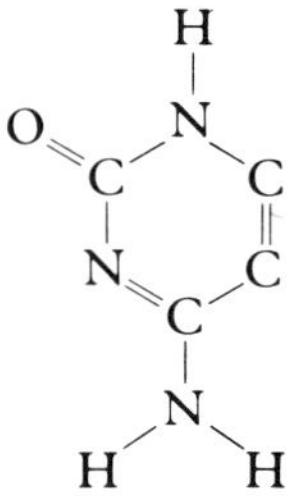   cytosine 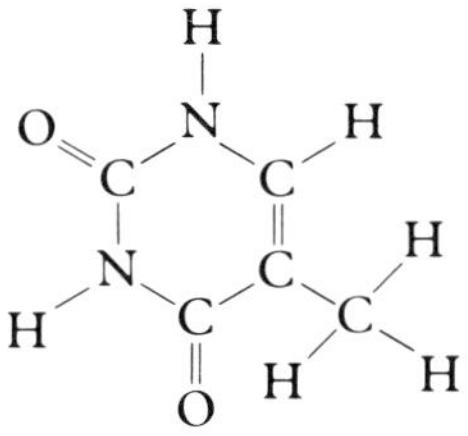   thymine

obtained if deoxyribose is replaced by the sugar, ribose,

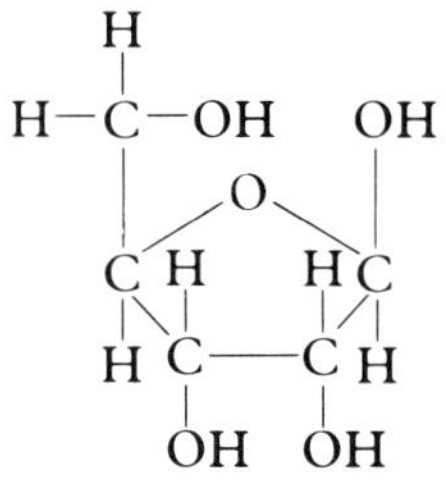

ribose, a sugar

and if thymine is replaced by the cyclic amine, uracil,

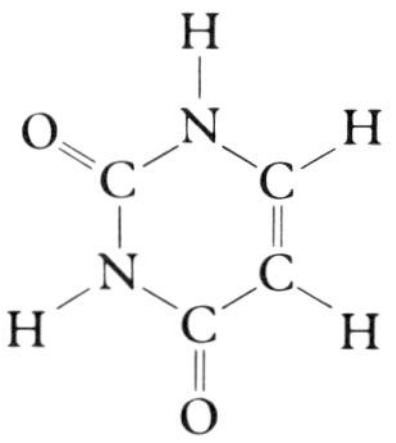

uracil, a cyclic amine

This material is ribonucleic acid, RNA.

The molecules of DNA are huge. Their molecular weights are greater than one billion. Molecules of RNA are also quite large. The structure of DNA is that of the famed "double helix." It was figured out in 1953 by an American scientist, James D. Watson, and Francis Crick, a British scientist. They received the Nobel prize for this scientific milestone in 1962. Basically, the structure of DNA is that of two spiral ribbons, as shown in Figure 11.11.

The molecule of DNA is sort of like a coded message. The "message" is written by variations in the order of the cyclic amine bases

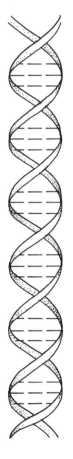

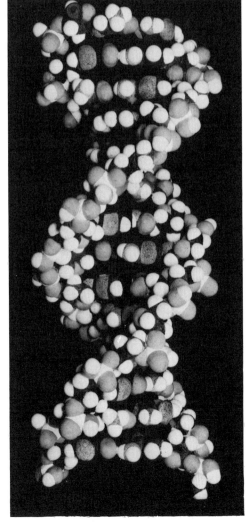

FIGURE 11.11
Representation of the DNA double helix structure.

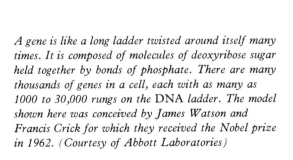

A gene is like a long ladder twisted around itself many times. It is composed of molecules of deoxyribose sugar held together by bonds of phosphate. There are many thousands of genes in a cell, each with as many as 1000 to 30,000 rungs on the DNA ladder. The model shown here was conceived by James Watson and Francis Crick for which they received the Nobel prize in 1962. (Courtesy of Abbott Laboratories)

along the molecule. It is somewhat like the message sent by telegraph, which consists only of dots, dashes, and spaces in between. The two strands of DNA are **complementary**. This means that a particular portion of one strand fits like a key in a lock with the corresponding portion of another strand. If the two strands are pulled apart, each manufactures a new complementary strand, so that two copies of the original double helix result. This occurs during cell reproduction.

Portions of the DNA double helix may unravel, and one of the strands of DNA may produce a strand of RNA. This substance then goes from the cell nucleus out into the cell and regulates the synthesis of new protein. In this way, DNA regulates the function of the cell and acts to control life processes.

As mentioned in Section 11.5, toxic substances cause changes in protein structure. This results in disruption of life processes. Alteration of DNA structure is an even more serious concern. Because of the role of DNA in controlling reproduction and life processes, such a disruption may cause serious damage to an organism. Altered DNA often keeps reproducing itself. The result is frequently a **mutation**. Not all mutations are bad, of course. They are in fact necessary for evolution to occur. However, most mutations are harmful. A number of hereditary diseases are the result of faults in directions given to the body by DNA. Among these are diabetes, sickle cell anemia, hemophilia (failure of blood to clot properly), and phenylketonuria (which causes mental retardation in affected infants).

One of the greater concerns of our time is the unknown effect of low levels of synthetic chemical substances upon DNA. Particularly since World War II, the ingenuity of research chemists combined with the tremendous productivity of industry have served to introduce a large variety of chemicals into our surroundings. Many of these are environmental pollutants, such as pesticides (Section 8.14). As discussed in Chapter 15, we consume many synthetic chemicals in the form of food additives. Some of these may have bad effects upon cell DNA and cause mutations or birth defects. Some drugs may have similar effects. The Thalidomide tragedy of the 1960's, which resulted from the effects of a tranquilizer upon unborn fetuses reminds us of this possibility. Radiation from X rays and radioactivity also disrupts DNA and causes mutation. In a sense, people alive today are guinea pigs to a vast experiment to determine the biochemical effects of chemicals upon man.

Chapter Summary

We began the discussion of biochemistry with an individual cell. Although the cells of living organisms are extremely small, they may be quite complicated. They have a "control center" nucleus, a surrounding cell membrane, and a number of individual bodies with specialized duties inside the cell. An individual cell is capable of supporting chemical

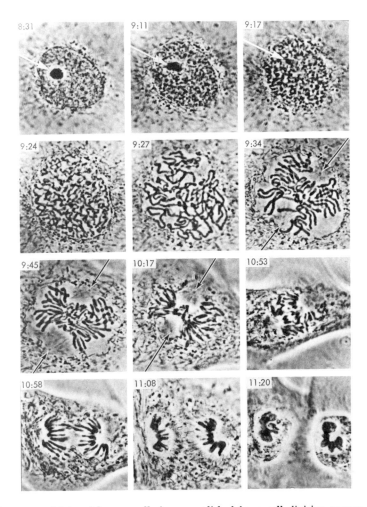

Replacement of injured human cells is accomplished by a cell division process called "mitosis." Shown is a phase-contrast photomicrograph of living cells in a tissue culture at different stages of mitosis. (Courtesy of Dr. Don Fawcett Harvard Medical School. From William Bloom and Don Fawcett, Textbook of Histology, *W. B. Saunders Co., Philadelphia, Pa., 1968)*

processes that could not be carried out in even the most huge chemical plant. Cells vary considerably, depending upon the type of organism and their function.

One of the chief functions of cells is to carry out respiration. Respiration can take several forms but most commonly is the oxidation of sugar

$$C_6H_{12}O_6 + 6\,O_2 \longrightarrow 6\,CO_2\uparrow + 6\,H_2O + \text{energy}$$

to produce carbon dioxide and energy. The cell extracts some of the energy for its own use. Plant cells also carry out the reverse process, photosynthesis.

The three major types of biological material manufactured by organisms, and used by organisms as food, are *proteins, carbohydrates,* and *lipids* (fats and oils). With the exception of simple sugars, all of these substances consist of simpler molecules which have condensed together with the elimination of water. Proteins contain nitrogen. They are made by the joining together of *amino acids,* which are organic acids containing both the $-NH_2$ group and the $-CO_2H$ group. Carbohydrates have carbon, hydrogen, and oxygen in the approximate ratio, CH_2O. They range from simple sugars such as glucose $(C_6H_{12}O_6)$ to giant molecules of cellulose having molecular weights around 400,000. Fats and oils are esters of organic acids with glycerol.

Enzymes are biological catalysts. They enable the complicated processes involved with life chemistry to occur. They are specific for the substrates upon which they act. This is because of the shapes of enzymes which fit with the shapes of substrates.

The "master plan" for cells is contained in *DNA.* This substance has a very high molecular weight. The order of arrangement of four cyclic amines in DNA makes up a "genetic code." DNA produces RNA, which in turn brings about the synthesis of proteins and enzymes in a cell.

Chapter Review Questions

The following questions are designed as a self-teaching tool to help you review Chapter 11. The answers to each question follow. See Chapter Review Questions for Chapter 1 for further instructions.

1. The study of chemical processes and products of living organisms is called _____.

2. A very small unit of a living organism in which biochemical processes occur is the _____.

3. A cell is enclosed by a _____ which has different _____ for various substances.

4. Two organelles in cells are _____ in which cellular respiration is carried out and _____ which contain potent substances capable of digesting liquid food substances.

5. Unlike animal cells, plant cells have a very strong _____ made up mostly of cellulose.

6. Naturally occurring amino acids are called alpha-amino acids because _____.

7. Amino acids in proteins are linked together by the _____ whose basic structure is _____.

8. In terms of structure, protein in hair belongs to the class of _____ proteins, and most enzymes are _____ proteins.

9. The order of amino acids in a protein determines the _____ structure; the nature of the R groups determines the _____ structure; and overall outward shape of the protein is called the _____ structure.

10. Disturbance of protein structure by heating or other means is called _____.

11. Compounds with formulas of $C_6H_{12}O_6$ or $(C_6H_{11}O_5)_n$ are examples of _____.

12. A carbohydrate with a formula of $C_6H_{12}O_6$ belongs to the general class of _____.

13. Disaccharides have the formula _____.

14. Three examples of dissacharides are _____, _____, and _____.

15. A high molecular weight carbohydrate, which is produced by plants and which can be digested by humans, is _____, and a similar material produced by animals is _____.

16. A high molecular weight carbohydrate, which cannot be used as food by most animals but which serves as food for ruminant animals, is _____.

17. Lipids are biological materials which can be _____

18. From the standpoint of nutrition the significant lipids are _____.

19. Fats and oils are _____ formed from the reaction of the alcohol, _____ with _____.

20. The thing that distinguishes oils and "unsaturated" fats from harder fats is _____.

21. The main thing distinguishing waxes from fats and oils is _____.

22. The purpose of bile salts in the intestines is _____.

23. Gastric proteinase, pancreatic lipase, and pyruvate carboxylase are all examples of _____.

24. Three major classifications of enzymes, according to what they do, are enzymes that bring about _____, _____, and _____.

25. Enzymes react with a _____ to form _____.

26. The "blueprints" of a cell are contained in the material _____, which forms molecules of _____ to direct protein synthesis.

Answers to Chapter Review Questions

1. biochemistry
2. cell
3. cell membrane, permeability
4. mitochondria, lysosomes
5. cell wall
6. the $-NH_2$ group is on the carbon next to the $-CO_2H$ group

7. peptide linkage, $\overset{\displaystyle O \quad H}{\overset{\displaystyle \|\quad |}{-C-N-}}$
8. fibrous, globular
9. primary, secondary, tertiary
10. denaturation
11. carbohydrates
12. simple sugars or hexoses
13. $C_6H_{22}O_{11}$
14. sucrose, lactose, maltose

15. starch, glycogen
16. cellulose
17. extracted into organic solvents such as benzene, chloroform, or ether
18. fats and oils
19. esters, glycerol, fatty acids
20. the presence of the $-C=C-$ group in the fatty acids in oils
21. that some alcohol other than glycerol is present in the ester of waxes
22. to suspend fats in the form of very fine emulsions so that they may be digested
23. enzymes
24. hydrolysis reactions, carbon-carbon bond splitting, oxidation-reduction
25. substrate, an enzyme-substrate complex
26. DNA, RNA

Exercises for Chapter 11

1. The formula of simple sugars is $C_6H_{12}O_6$. The simple formula of higher carbohydrates is $C_6H_{10}O_5$. Of course, many of these units are required to make a molecule of starch or cellulose. If higher carbohydrates are formed by joining together molecules of simple sugars, why is there a difference in the ratios of C, H, and O atoms in the higher carbohydrates as compared to the simple sugars?

2. Why does wood contain so much cellulose?

3. What would be the chemical formula of a *tri*saccharide made by the bonding together of three simple sugar molecules?

4. The general formula of cellulose may be represented as $(C_6H_{10}O_5)_x$. If the molecular weight of a molecule of cellulose is 400,000, what is the estimated value of x?

5. During one month a factory for the production of simple sugars, $C_6H_{12}O_6$, by the hydrolysis of cellulose processes one million pounds of cellulose. The percentage of cellulose that undergoes the hydrolysis reaction is 40%. How many pounds of water are consumed in the hydrolysis of cellulose each month?

6. What is the structure of the largest group of atoms common to all amino acid molecules?

7. Glycine and phenylalanine can join together to form two different dipeptides. What are the structures of these two dipeptides?

8. One of the ways in which two parallel protein chains are joined together, or cross-linked, is by way of an $-S-S-$ link. What amino acid do you think might be most likely to be involved in such a link? Explain your choice.

9. Fungi, which break down wood, straw, and other plant material, have what are called "exoenzymes." Fungi have no teeth and cannot break up plant material physically by force. Knowing this, what do you suppose an exoenzyme is? Explain how you think it might operate in the process by which fungi break down something as tough as wood.

10. Many fatty acids of lower molecular weight have a bad odor. Speculate as to the reasons that rancid butter has a bad odor. What chemical compound is produced that has a bad odor? What sort of chemical reaction is involved in its production?

11. The long-chain alcohol with 10 carbons is called decanol. What do you think

would be the formula of decyl stearate? To what class of compounds would it belong?

12. Write an equation for the chemical reaction between sodium hydroxide and cetyl stearate. What are the products?

13. What are two endocrine glands that are found only in females? What are two of these glands found only in males?

14. The action of bile salts is a little like that of soap. What function do bile salts perform in the intestine? Look up the action of soaps in Section 10.12, and explain how you think bile salts may function somewhat like soap.

15. If we represent the structure of an enzyme as illustrated,

how should the structure of its substrate be represented?

16. Look up the structures of ribose and deoxyribose. Explain where the "deoxy" came from in the name, deoxyribose.

17. In what respect is an enzyme and its substrate like the two opposite strands of DNA?

18. For what discovery are Watson and Crick noted?

19. Why does an enzyme no longer work if it is denatured?

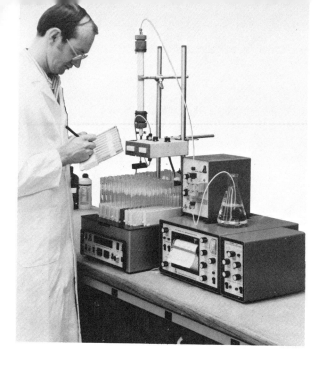

Column chromatography is used to separate components of a sample. These components are collected in many different test tubes by an automatic sample collector. (Courtesy of ISCO, Lincoln, Nebraska)

12

Instruments Used in Chemical Analysis

12.1

"Itai, Itai"

"Itai, itai" ("Ouch-ouch"—cadmium poisoning). The Japanese have coined this descriptive term to describe the painful symptoms of the malady caused by the ingestion of cadmium. The ingestion of too much of this metal with food, with water, or by inhaling air contaminated with cadmium causes severe deterioration of bones. The strain of sneezing can be enough to break a rib. One can well imagine how painful the disease must be.

One of the best known episodes of "itai, itai" occurred in Japan's Jintsu River basin where many people were afflicted. The cadmium came originally from mine waste water that was drained directly into the river. This water was used to irrigate rice which then became contaminated with cadmium. The water was also used for drinking water by persons living near the river. As a result, the victims ingested cadmium with both contaminated river water and contaminated rice.

Cadmium is a "heavy metal," and "itai, itai" is one of several dreadful diseases caused by heavy metal poisoning. Recall that heavy metals were discussed as water pollutants in Section 8.10. Many heavy metals besides cadmium are very poisonous to man and animals. Included in the list of poisonous heavy metals are lead, mercury, barium, bismuth, and antimony.

A listless, wheezing man going through the motions of his make-work job in a petroleum refinery, prematurely aged by lead poisoning reminds one of the dangers of lead. He was poisoned by cleaning a reactor which used lead salts in an ill-fated petroleum refining process years before. A mother who unknowingly ate mercury-contaminated seafood before her blind, deformed baby was born clearly shows the horrors of mercury poisoning. A diseased cow, afflicted with "blind staggers," collapses and dies from eating grass contaminated with selenium grown on soil containing too much of this element. A member of the country club set enjoys a fish dinner from a large bass caught in a golf course lake, not knowing that the mercury level in the fish exceeds recommended safe levels. Mercury pesticides have been used to control fungus on the golf course. The mercury from rainfall runoff has gotten into the lake water and accumulated in the fish over the years. Mercury poisoning is not new. Lewis Carroll's Mad Hatter in *Alice in Wonderland* characterizes this affliction, which was an occupational health hazard among hatters a century ago.

Some of the rice consumed by the victims of "itai, itai" in the Jintsu River basin contained as much as 88 ppm (part per million) of cadmium. If we consider a million pounds of rice in terms of tons, we would have 500 tons of rice such as could be hauled by 500 somewhat overloaded pickup trucks. It is a lot of rice. Should it contain 88 ppm of cadmium, we would have 88 lb of cadmium out of the whole lot. The 88 ppm amount of cadmium could be carried with relative ease by a person in good physical condition, or with a little strain by most of the rest of us. As environmental pollutants go, however, 88 ppm is a lot—an awful lot. The U.S. Public Health Service recommends that any water supply containing in excess of only 0.01 ppm of cadmium should be rejected. Similar standards are set for other heavy metals in water and food. If one million pounds of rice contained 0.01 ppm of cadmium, it would have only a fraction of an ounce of cadmium.

The detection and analysis of substances present at a level of around a part per million is very challenging. Very sensitive methods are needed to analyze for such low levels of heavy metals. There are other substances besides metals that frequently must be analyzed at very low concentrations and that may be much more difficult than metals to analyze. Included are pesticides, fertilizers, air pollutants, vitamins, and drugs. Such substances sometimes are called **trace substances** because in some cases the best we can do is find a "trace" of the material. This was particularly true 20 or so years ago before the development of modern sophisticated instruments and techniques made possible the analysis of very low levels of many substances. In this chapter we will discuss some of the methods that are used to detect the presence of trace substances.

12.2

Chemical Analysis by the Absorption of Light

You have probably observed that solutions have different colors. A solution of copper sulfate is blue. A solution of phenolphthalein, used to indicate the endpoints in acid-base titrations, is red in base. A solution of potassium chromate, K_2CrO_4, is yellow. You may have also observed that the intensity of the color of a solution depends upon the concentration. A solution with just a small amount of copper sulfate appears "light blue." If a lot of copper sulfate is dissolved in the solution, it is "dark blue."

The color and the intensity of the color of a solution may be used for its chemical analysis. The type of color tells us something about *what* is in the solution. We can conclude that a yellow solution is potassium chromate, rather than copper sulfate, by its color. The intensity of the color can tell us *how much* solute is in solution. Instruments can be used to measure both the color of light absorbed and the amount of light absorbed. These instruments are **spectrophotometers** (see the diagram in Figure 12.1). The absorption of light by a solution is called **absorption spectrophotometry**. If visible light is used, the technique is often called **colorimetry**. Some instruments can also observe the absorption of ultraviolet light, which we cannot see. Organic chemists, particularly, make use of the absorption of infrared radiation, which is a very low energy form of "light."

Basically absorption spectrophotometry consists of measuring the amount of light passing through an absorbing solution as compared to the amount going through a **blank**. The blank contains everything in the solution except for the substance being analyzed. The percentage of light getting through the sample as compared to the blank is called the **percent transmittance**. Generally a related quantity called **absorbance** is used because it is easier to handle mathematically. The symbol for absorbance

FIGURE 12.1

A spectrophotometer has several parts. Light is produced in a light source, such as an incandescent bulb. A particular color of light is isolated by a monochromator. This light goes through a solution where part of the light is absorbed. The amount getting through is measured with a detector (photocell).

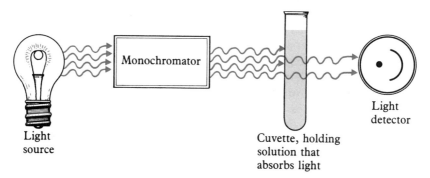

Light source

Monochromator

Cuvette, holding solution that absorbs light

Light detector

Simple colorimeters that measure the amount of light absorbed by a solution are widely used in chemical analysis. (Courtesy of Fisher Scientific Co.)

is A. It ranges in value from 0, for a solution that absorbs none of the light, to infinity, for a solution that absorbs all of the light. Values of A between 0.2 and 0.8 give the greatest accuracy in chemical analysis. In addition to A, several other things are involved. One of these is the concentration, C. Another is the length of the light path through the solution, b. A third is the **absorptivity**, a. Absorptivity is a characteristic of the particular substance that is absorbing the light.

Beer's law is

$$A = abC$$

It states that the absorbance is equal to the absorptivity multiplied times the path length multiplied times the concentration. A direct increase of A with a corresponding increase in C at constant path length indicates that Beer's law is followed. In many cases analyses may be performed even when Beer's law is not obeyed by preparing a plot of A versus C. This plot is curved if Beer's law is not followed. However, the A value of an unknown solution can still be used to obtain the corresponding value of C.

Absorption spectrophotometry is very widely used to analyze water samples, clinical specimens, fertilizers, industrial samples, and many other things. Only a few of these samples absorb light strongly enough to be analyzed directly. Therefore, a color-developing step is usually required. This consists of a chemical process by which the sought-for substance produces a strongly colored material. Often the colored substance is extracted from water into an organic solvent to provide a more intense color and a more concentrated solution. Among the common water pollutants analyzed by the absorption of light are ammonia, arsenic, boron, bromide ion, chlorine (from water chlorinated to kill bacteria), cyanide, fluoride, nitrate, nitrite, phenols, phosphate, selenium, silica, and sulfide.

Ultraviolet and visible light are absorbed by "exciting" bonding electrons in molecules to higher energies. Longer wavelength light in the infrared region is also absorbed by many compounds. This is the "light" that can be felt as heat energy when a hand is held near a red-hot piece of metal. It does not have enough energy to excite electrons, but it does have enough energy to make atoms and groups of atoms in molecules vibrate, twist, and bend on their chemical bonds. This can be visualized as a ball attached to a rubber band. The ball represents an atom and the

Infrared spectrophotometers are especially useful for determining the characteristic "fingerprints" of organic compounds. (Courtesy of Beckman Instruments, Inc.)

rubber band a chemical bond. The ball can be pulled down (analogous to the absorption of infrared energy) and released to vibrate at the end of the rubber band.

Infrared spectrophotometry is so useful because small differences in the weights of atoms, strengths of chemical bonds, and the structure of the rest of the molecule determine the exact energy and wavelength of infrared radiation absorbed. For that reason, a plot of the percent of infrared light transmitted through a sample with varying energy (wavelength) may be quite detailed. Examination of this spectrum tells a lot about the atoms, groups of atoms, types of bonds, and other features of the molecule. The infrared spectrum of a pure compound is much like a fingerprint of the compound and is very useful in identifying it (see Figure 12.2). Therefore, infrared spectrophotometry is widely used for the identification of organic compounds.

FIGURE 12.2

Infrared spectrum of chloroform, $CHCl_3$, showing absorption peaks due to stretching between C—H atoms and C—Cl atoms.

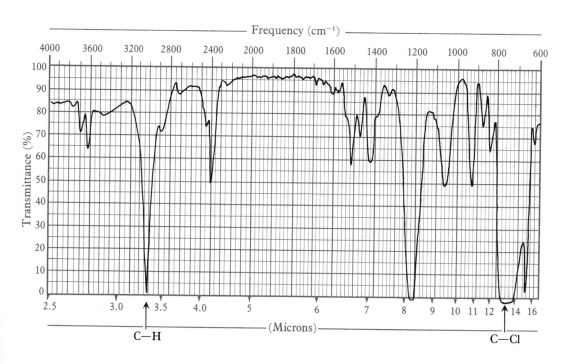

12.3

Atomic Absorption Analysis

A special type of absorption spectrophotometry is that involving the absorption of light by atoms, which are usually formed in a flame. Atomic absorption spectrophotometry, AAS, is a fairly recent development. Only a few trial instruments were available in 1965. Within three years AAS had become the analytical method of choice for most common metals. Now, AAS instruments are found in virtually all analytical laboratories of any size.

The principles of atomic absorption are very simple. They are shown in Figure 12.3. The sample in solution is drawn into a flame in a

FIGURE 12.3
Basic components of an atomic absorption instrument.

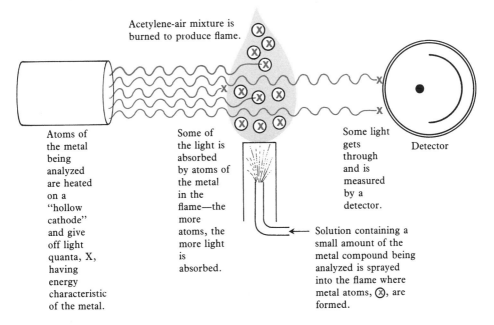

Acetylene-air mixture is burned to produce flame.

Atoms of the metal being analyzed are heated on a "hollow cathode" and give off light quanta, X, having energy characteristic of the metal.

Some of the light is absorbed by atoms of the metal in the flame—the more atoms, the more light is absorbed.

Some light gets through and is measured by a detector.

Detector

Solution containing a small amount of the metal compound being analyzed is sprayed into the flame where metal atoms, Ⓧ, are formed.

very fine spray. In the flame the metal being analyzed is changed to the form of metal atoms and produces an "atomic cloud" of these atoms. The hollow cathode light source is the key to the success of atomic absorption. A different hollow cathode lamp is normally required for each metal, and it produces light by heating atoms of the specific metal being analyzed to very high temperatures. These heated atoms give off light (in the form of packets of energy called light "quanta") having a definite wavelength and energy highly characteristic of the metal. This is sort of an atomic signature. The light absorbed is specific to the atoms of the metal in the flame and is not absorbed by other atoms that may be present in the flame even in high concentrations. The amount of light absorbed is proportional to the number of atoms in the flame and, therefore, to the concentration of metal in solution. The amount of light getting through the flame is measured by a detector.

Now we see that atomic absorption is very specific for the element being analyzed. This is one of its tremendous advantages because "interfering substances" can be very troublesome for most low level analyses. Certainly, atomic absorption is not completely free of interferences, but generally it represents an enormous improvement over previously used techniques. The instrument is quite sensitive as well. With a quality instrument, the analysis of part per million levels of many metals is relatively easy. Special techniques may be used to increase the sensitivity markedly. For example, special chemical treatment may be used to extract the metal from a large volume of solution into a small volume of a solvent. The metal is concentrated manyfold in the solvent. The solvent containing the metal is aspirated into the flame giving a much higher concentration of metal atoms in the flame than would have been the case with the original solution. Although it can be used for the analysis of some nonmetals, atomic absorption generally is used only for metals.

12.4

Chemical Analysis by the Emission of Light

Light given off by a sample can be used for chemical analysis. This may be accomplished in several ways. Several clinically important metals, such as sodium, potassium, magnesium, and calcium, are analyzed by **flame emission** spectroscopy. The sample is drawn into a flame in the same way as shown for atomic absorption spectroscopy in Figure 12.3. The heat of the flame "excites" the metal atoms in the flame so that they give off light of a wavelength which is exactly characteristic of the metal. This is easily seen by dipping a moist wire in sodium chloride (table salt) and holding the salt in a flame. The flame has an intense yellow color from light given off by hot sodium atoms. These sodium atoms are formed from sodium ions in the flame. The brightness of the light from a particular metal is a measure of the concentration of the metal. The wavelength (color) of the light tells which metal is present.

A flame is hot enough to "excite" only a few metals—those in the two left columns of the periodic table. Other metals may be excited to give off visible and ultraviolet light by heating to even higher temperatures in an electrical arc between two electrodes. The arc is similar to an electrical welding arc. The technique is called **optical emission spectroscopy**, OES. When OES is used to analyze for metals in steels and alloys, the sample itself may serve as one of the electrodes. Liquid samples are absorbed onto the end of a carbon electrode. Solids may be ground with powdered graphite (a form of carbon) and also analyzed. As discussed in Chapter 17, this technique is very useful for some

An FBI laboratory examiner uses a flame emission spectrograph to determine the chemical composition of a paint sample. (Courtesy of the FBI, U.S. Dept. of Justice)

types of samples used as evidence of a crime. These include samples of glass or paint chips.

High energy ultraviolet light ("black light") can be used to excite some things to give off lower energy light. The lower energy light is often visible. This phenomenon is called **fluorescence**. The principle is the same as that used to make "handstamps" appear when one's hand has been stamped with invisible ink for readmission to an amusement park or athletic event.

When used for chemical analysis, ultraviolet light is directed through a sample and the visible light which it produces is measured at a right angle to the beam of incoming ultraviolet light. This widely used technique is very sensitive for the analysis of a number of kinds of samples such as vitamins. It is especially useful in clinical analysis.

12.5

Neutron Activation Analysis

We mentioned in Chapter 1 that isotopes of some elements give off radiation from the atom nucleus. These atoms are called radioactive isotopes. The radiation given off by radioactive isotopes may be used for the analysis of elements. The process is known as **neutron activation analysis**. Gamma rays are particularly useful for analysis. They are similar to X rays but more energetic and penetrating. The gamma ray, beta particle, or other type of radiation coming from a *single radioactive atom* may be detected. Thus, production of radioactive isotopes is potentially an extremely sensitive method of analysis.

Basically neutron activation analysis consists simply of placing the sample in a nuclear reactor to produce radioactive isotopes, then measuring the radioactivity produced. The types and characteristics of the radiation produced tells us what kinds of elements are in the sample. The amount of a specific kind of radiation tells us how much of a specific element

FIGURE 12.4 *Neutron activation analysis of magnesium.*

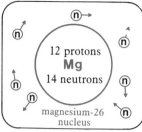

Nonradioactive magnesium is placed in the reactor core where it is bombarded with neutrons.

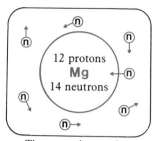

The magnesium nucleus absorbs a neutron

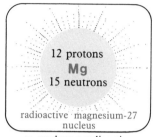

to produce a radioactive isotope with one more neutron in the nucleus.

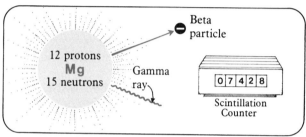

The radioactive magnesium emits a gamma ray, which is detected by a scintillation counter, and a beta particle

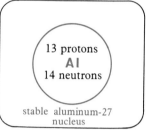

producing stable aluminum-27. (When a nucleus loses a beta particle, 1 neutron is changed to a proton.)

is in the sample. Figure 12.4 shows the basic principles of neutron activation analysis as applied to the analysis of magnesium. The sample is first placed in a nuclear reactor where it is exposed to neutrons. Sometimes only a very brief exposure is wanted. In such cases the sample is driven by air pressure in a tube that goes through the reactor making possible exposure times of as little as a few seconds. The sample is driven through the tube in a plastic container appropriately called a "rabbit."

Inside of the reactor neutrons are absorbed by the nuclei (recall from Chapter 1 that the nucleus of the atom is the central part orbitted by electrons) of the atoms in the sample. Those atoms absorbing neutrons become radioactive. These radioactive isotopes then decay to stable products by emitting beta particles (high energy electrons) and gamma rays. This radiation is "counted" by a Geiger counter or scintillation counter. The counters can distinguish the energies of the radiation emitted. These energies are often very specific for the elements that were activated. Thus, the analyst can tell which elements are in the sample.

Another distinguishing characteristic of the radioactive isotopes produced is their half-life (Figure 12.5). During a specific time period known as the half-life, exactly one-half of the radioactive nuclei of a given radioactive isotope will decay. During the next time period of equal length exactly half of the remaining nuclei will decay, and so on.

In the case of the neutron activation analysis of magnesium, the

FIGURE 12.5

Radioactive decay. At the end of each half-life, only one-half of the radioactive atoms that were present at the beginning of the half-life remain.

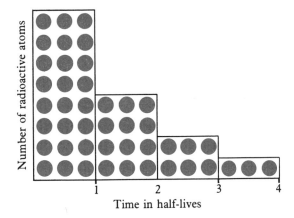

nonradioactive naturally occurring magnesium isotope with an atomic weight of 26 (which comprises 11.1 % of natural magnesium) absorbs neutrons to produce unstable radioactive magnesium-27. The magnesium-27 decays with a half-life of 9.5 min giving off gamma rays and beta particles. The gamma radiation with an energy of 1.04 MeV is measured. (The term, MeV, stands for million electron volts and is a convenient measure of the energy of gamma radiation. We need not worry about its exact definition here.) The gamma radiation is measured with a scintillation counter. This interesting device has a detector which produces a flash of light when the gamma ray goes through it. The flash of light is recorded as a "count" by a photodetector. Other types of detectors, such as the Geiger counter, operate through the production of an electrical discharge by the radiation.

Neutron activation is very useful for the analysis of very small quantities of many elements. One of its big advantages is that it is non-destructive, and a small sample can be kept for further analysis. This capability is especially useful for crime laboratories. For example, a small chip of paint found at the scene of a crime can be analyzed by neutron activation and compared to paint from a suspected source, then saved as further evidence.

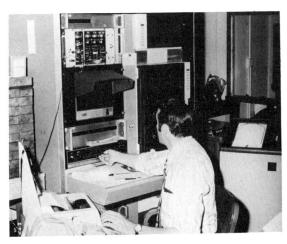

Neutron activation analysis is capable of analyzing a number of elements. It can yield an "elemental fingerprint" of samples such as paint chips or glass fragments. (Courtesy of the Bureau of Alcohol, Tobacco, and Firearms, U.S. Dept. of the Treasury)

12.6

Gas Chromatography

Atomic absorption and neutron activation analysis are used almost exclusively for the analysis of elements. With presently available technology, the analysis of most elements is reasonably easy down to very low levels. However, frequently a knowledge of the kinds and quantities of elements present in a sample does not tell us much about the sample. Often we need a knowledge of the specific compounds present. Organic compounds are of particular importance because they are produced in such a large variety and may have very marked effects upon the environment and upon living things. Compounds with very similar formulas and structures may have very different properties. Many industrial products, pesticides, food additives, drugs, paints, and so forth, are organic compounds. It is very important to have the capability of analyzing for very low levels of specific organic compounds. An instrumental technique especially useful for such analyses is **gas chromatography**.

Gas chromatography was first developed during the early 1950's and now is widely used for chemical analysis. As the name implies, it is used for the analysis of gases and for liquids which can be vaporized. The gas chromatograph has been used in a number of applications. It has analyzed a few picograms of DDT in Antarctic penguins (1 picogram is 0.000000000001 g). It has separated petroleum into hundreds of components. It has found that terpenes, naturally occurring air pollutants from trees, make the Smokey Mountains smokey; and in so doing, it has aroused the suspicions of some local residents who suspected, with some justification, that it could detect the vapors from local moonshine operations.

The major component of the gas chromatograph is a column of tubing that may consist of copper, stainless steel, or glass as shown in the cross-sectional view in Figure 12.6. The vapor to be analyzed is carried

FIGURE 12.6

Separation of a mixture of two vaporized compounds in the column of a gas chromatograph.

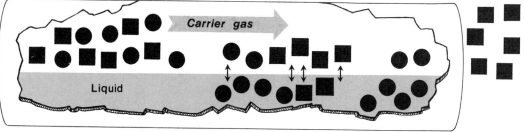

Two sample components (squares and circles) enter the column together, carried by a carrier gas. Each molecule will spend part of its time in the carrier gas and part of its time dissolved in the liquid phase.

One component (circles) likes the liquid phase better than the other component does. The circles spend more of their time dissolved in the liquid and are delayed more in going through the column.

As a result, the component represented by squares emerges from the column ahead of the other component and completely separated from it.

through the column in a stream of gas which can be helium, nitrogen, or hydrogen. The column contains some liquid, a "liquid phase" coated on small solid particles packed in the column. The vaporized components of the sample start passing through the column together. Each component spends part of its time in the moving gas stream and part of its time dissolved in the liquid phase. As a consequence those components that are more soluble in the liquid phase are held back (retained) longer and come out of the column later than those that are less soluble. A separation is thus obtained. We can use the idea of two persons walking for a mile along a sandy beach. One person likes the water, the other does not. Chances are, the one who likes the water will take frequent detours to do a little swimming. He will spend more of his time "in the liquid phase." The one who does not like the water will spend more of his time walking along the beach and will arrive at his destination first.

One of the bigger challenges in gas chromatography is detecting the gases coming out of the end of the column. Imagine having to find 0.000000000001 g of material! All kinds of detectors have been devised for this purpose. Some detectors work by sensing the very small difference in the way the gas coming from the column conducts heat as materials being separated come from the end of the column. This kind of detector is called a *thermal conductivity detector*. Other detectors burn hydrogen gas used as a carrier gas. An electrical current is passed through the flame. Organic compounds coming from the end of the column increase the ability of the flame to conduct electrical current, and the organic compounds are thus detected. This is a *flame ionization detector*. A third type of detector is called the *electron-capture detector*. This detector uses radioactive tritium as a source of electrons (beta particles). These electrons are captured by organic compounds containing N, P, F, Cl, Br, and I. The electron-capture detector is very useful for organochlorine pesticides.

The signal from the gas chromatograph detector is recorded on chart paper by a recorder. The result is a **gas chromatogram**. A gas chromatogram shows "peaks" like those shown in Figure 12.7. Each peak represents a compound separated by the column from the mixture of compounds originally injected into the column. The location of each peak indicates how rapidly that particular compound moved through the column. This location tells something about what the compound is, and often may be used to identify it. The area of the peak tells us how much of the compound is present. Thus, the gas chromatograph may be used for both qualitative and quantitative analyses.

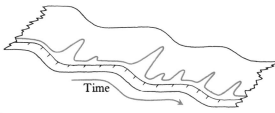

FIGURE 12.7
Gas chromatogram showing separation of compounds by a gas chromatograph.

The basic components of a gas chromatograph are illustrated in Figure 12.8. The carrier gas normally is contained in a gas cylinder and its flow is regulated by a pressure regulator. The sample is injected into the carrier gas, ordinarily by a hypodermic syringe, where the gas enters the column. After going through the column, the various components of the sample are detected by the detector. The detector response is recorded by a recorder which draws the gas chromatogram on chart paper. Frequently, recorders are equipped with "integrators," devices which calculate and record the areas of the peaks. This greatly simplifies calculations of the concentrations of materials coming out of the column.

FIGURE 12.8
Gas chromatograph.

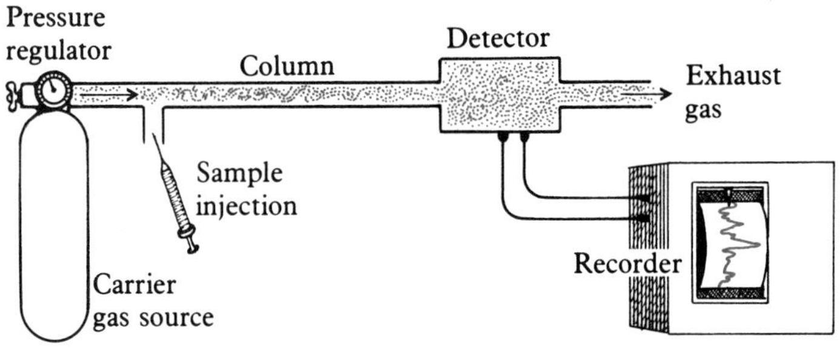

Pressure regulator · Column · Detector · Exhaust gas · Sample injection · Carrier gas source · Recorder

As mentioned previously, gas chromatography is useful for the analysis of drugs. Figure 12.9 shows a gas chromatogram giving the separation of three of the ingredients of marijuana. The structures of these compounds appear in Figure 12.10. Like most compounds of biological origin, their chemical structures are a little complicated. Note that they are very similar; indeed one has some difficulty picking out the differences. Yet the powerful tool of gas chromatography can separate these very closely related compounds.

Gas chromatography has been an exceptionally good tool in the

FIGURE 12.9
Gas chromatogram of some ingredients of marijuana.

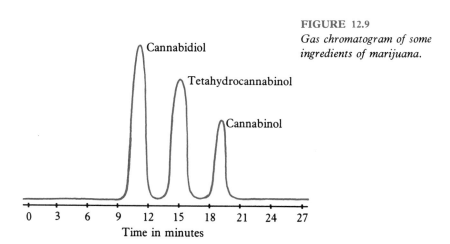

Cannabidiol

Tetahydrocannabinol

Cannabinol

0   3   6   9   12   15   18   21   24   27
Time in minutes

FIGURE 12.10

Three compounds found in marijuana, which may be separated by gas chromatography.

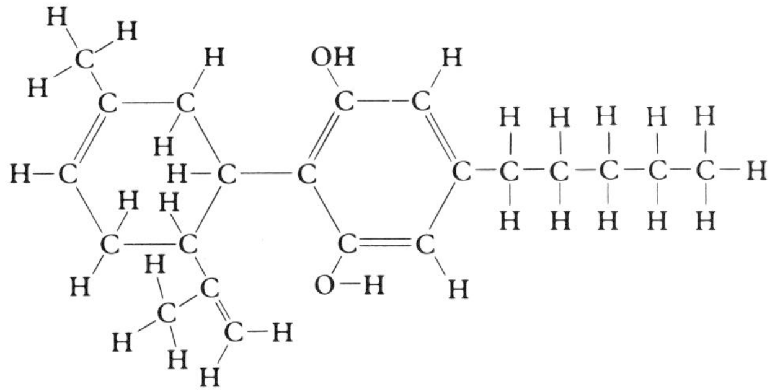

cannabidiol

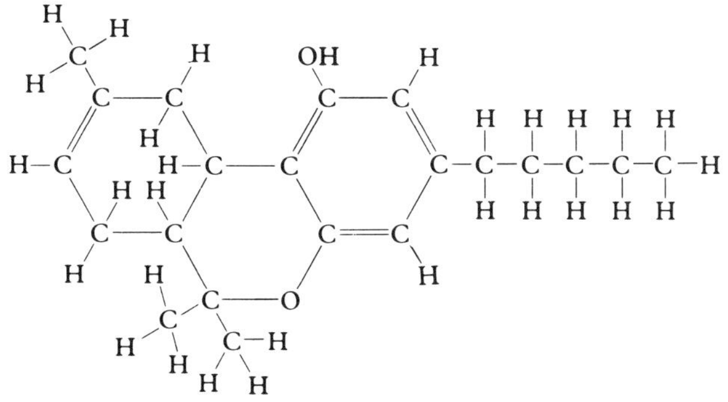

tetrahydrocannabinol

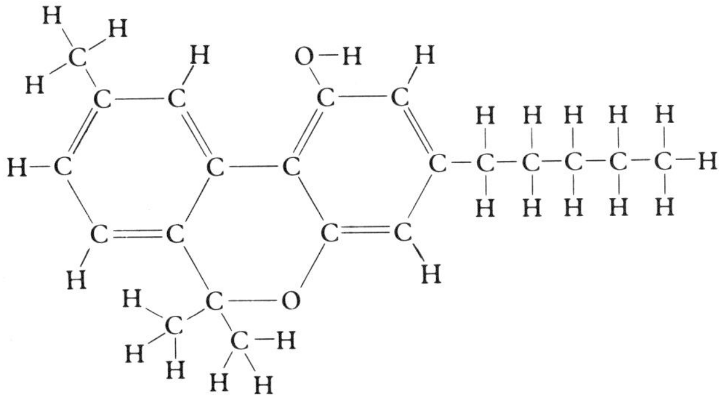

cannabinol

analysis of pesticides. Detectors have been developed which respond specifically to the chlorine in chlorinated hydrocarbons, and the analysis of chlorinated hydrocarbon pesticides in extremely small quantities can be done very successfully by gas chromatography. A gas chromatogram of a mixture of chlorinated hydrocarbon pesticides is shown in Figure 12.11. Each of the pesticides is present at a level of only one or two micrograms. A microgram is only a millionth of a gram.

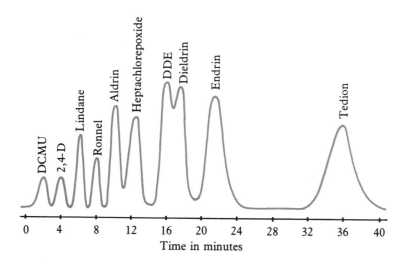

FIGURE 12.11
Gas chromatogram of a mixture of chlorinated hydrocarbon pesticides.

One of the most difficult problems in the analysis of pesticides by gas chromatography is extraction and preparation of the sample. Ordinarily the pesticides are extracted from a biological sample with an organic solvent. The solvent must be extremely pure and great care has to be used to prevent contamination.

12.7

Mass Spectrometry

Electrically charged atoms, molecules, and pieces of molecules may be separated and identified by the mass spectrometer. We call these charged particles ions. The mass spectrometer is an extremely sensitive instrument and can distinguish between particles having very similar weights. For example, benzamidine is an organic compound with the formula $C_7H_8N_2$ and a molecular weight of 120.069. Ethyl toluene is another organic compound having the formula C_9H_{12} and an exact molecular weight of 120.094. The molecular weights are almost identical, as you can see, but a high quality mass spectrometer can separate these two molecules because of the very slight difference in their molecular weights.

Mass spectrometry came into use around 1940 when commercial instruments first became available. One of its first big successes was in identifying and determining the concentrations of the many hundreds of compounds found in petroleum. During World War II, mass spectrometers were even built to separate the uranium isotope with an atomic weight of 235 (the isotope used to make atomic bombs) from the uranium isotope with an atomic weight of 238. The huge mass spectrometers required for this purpose needed a tremendous amount of

The gas chromatograph-mass spectrometer combination along with a data system is used to analyze organic materials. (Courtesy of Hewlett-Packard Corp.)

electrical wire in their construction. Copper was in short supply so silver was used instead!

Several different ways are used to separate ions. The easiest to understand is the principle of the *time of flight* mass spectrometer. This instrument measures how long it takes an ion to travel through a tube several feet long. The larger the ion, the longer it takes to go through the tube. Whatever process is used to separate ions, the path that they follow must be in an almost perfect vacuum. Otherwise the ions collide with molecules and are lost.

Ions are produced from molecules by passing through an electrical discharge. If the discharge is energetic enough, the molecules are broken up. This is useful because these fragments can tell us a lot about the "parent" molecule. Once produced, the ions are accelerated to a high speed by being attracted to negatively charged plates in the "ion gun."

The basic components of a mass spectrometer appear in Figure 12.12. A time of flight mass spectrometer is shown analyzing a mixture of

FIGURE 12.12

*A **time of flight** mass spectrometer is shown analyzing a mixture of propane and butane.*

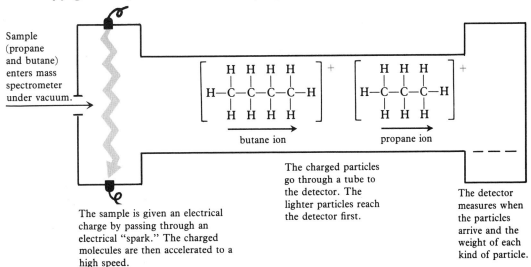

propane gas and butane gas, such as is found in liquid petroleum gas, LPG. If the molecules are exposed to a relatively high voltage electrical discharge, they are broken up. This can be very useful in determining the structures of molecules. For example, butane may break up as shown. The mass spectrometer can measure the weights and numbers of each of the types of charged particles produced by "cracking" the butane molecule (Figure 12.13). The recorder hooked to the mass spectrometer can record this information on paper, producing the resulting "mass spectrum" of butane (Figure 12.14).

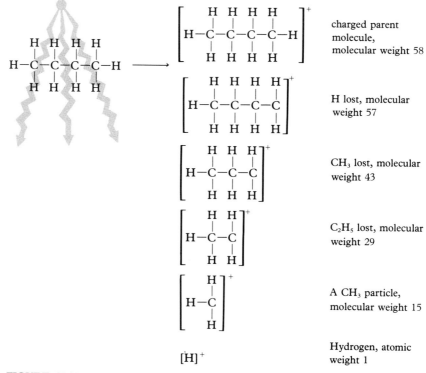

FIGURE 12.13

Fragments of butane produced by an electrical discharge in a mass spectrometer.

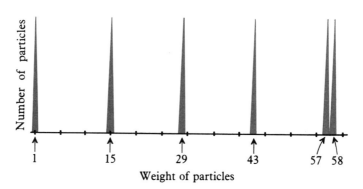

FIGURE 12.14   *The mass spectrum of particles resulting from the breakdown of butane in a mass spectrometer.*

What good is a mass spectrum such as that shown? Well, suppose that instead of butane we were looking at some organic compound isolated from a plant and known to have some useful properties as a drug. Suppose that we did not quite know how this compound was put together. If we knew its structure, we might learn why it works as a drug, or we might be able to make it in the laboratory. By breaking up the compound in the mass spectrometer and looking at the pieces produced, we often can tell what the structure of the original compound was.

Sometimes it is very difficult to isolate a pure compound to put into the mass spectrometer. If we are looking at a mixture of compounds in the mass spectrometer, it is sometimes impossible to tell much about the structure of any one of the compounds. Recently the mass spectrometer has been teamed up with the gas chromatograph to help solve that problem. The gases coming from the column of the gas chromatograph are run through the mass spectrometer. Each of the gases is analyzed by the mass spectrometer as it comes from the column. The gas chromatograph is very good at separating mixtures into pure compounds. The mass spectrometer is very good at identifying compounds and telling us about their structure. When teamed together these instruments make a powerful combination. Good gas chromatograph-mass spectrometer instruments became commercially available in the late 1960's. This should result in a lot of advances in biochemistry, medicinal chemistry, pesticide chemistry, and other areas where it is very important to have information about complicated organic molecules.

12.8

The pH Meter

Probably no instrument is more used (or is the subject of more comment when it does not work properly) than the pH meter. The idea of pH was discussed in Section 7.5, which the reader may want to review at this point. The measurement of pH is one of the most common and important laboratory measurements performed. If the pH of water in a water system gets too low, the pipes carrying the water are rapidly eaten up. If the pH of blood varies more than slightly from normal, a person becomes very ill. If the pH of soil is too high, or too low, plants will not grow well. If the pH of fruit juice is not near the right value, it will have a bad taste. If the pH of sewage is too extreme, the sewage treatment plant will not operate properly.

How do we measure pH? Normally a device called a pH meter is used. This meter is really a glorified voltmeter such as the TV technician uses to check out a television set that is operating poorly. It measures a voltage, and does so very accurately. Where does the voltage come from? It comes from a special glass electrode dipping in the solution. The glass electrode has a special glass membrane which H^+ ions will try to pass through. In trying to penetrate the glass membrane, the electrically charged hydrogen ions set up a voltage which is measured by the pH meter. In order to set up the proper kind of an electrical circuit, the solution must also contain a reference electrode against which the glass electrode voltage is measured. We won't worry much about the reference electrode here, but be sure to use one when you try to measure pH! Figure 12.15 gives a diagram of a pH meter and its electrodes.

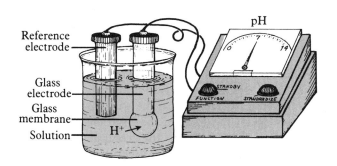

Reference electrode
Glass electrode
Glass membrane
Solution
H⁺

pH

FIGURE 12.15
A pH meter and electrodes.

To measure pH one must first calibrate the pH meter. To do so, a standard buffer solution is needed, that is, a solution whose pH is known very accurately. Standard buffer solutions may be purchased for several specific pH values. Let us say that we have a buffer solution known to have a pH of exactly 7.00. The glass and reference electrodes are dipped into this buffer solution. Then the pH meter is adjusted to read exactly 7.00. The electrodes are then rinsed and dipped into the solution whose pH we need to know. The pH value is read directly from the meter. If we need to adjust the pH of a solution to a certain value, the electrodes may be left in the solution and acid or base added until the desired pH is reached.

12.9

The Computer and Chemistry

The computer is with us to stay. It processes student enrollments, keeps track of charge accounts, predicts the dates when the world will end due to pollution and consumption of natural resources, and touches every aspect of our lives. It multiplies enormously the capacity of competent people to perform useful work and compounds the errors of the incompetent to a distressing degree. The computer handles numbers marvelously well and, since modern chemical instruments produce numbers in huge quantities, the computer has found wide application in chemistry.

Basically the computer is a very rapid calculating machine. It would take the average person several minutes to divide 4,972,318 by 3018. Some computers can do more than a thousand such calculations in one second. A computer can remember numbers, in some cases hundreds of thousands of them. These numbers are stored in a memory core, which receives information, stores it, and makes it available upon demand.

One way in which the chemist uses the computer is to make long tedious calculations involving many mathematical operations. The chemist may "punch" the numbers to be given the computer on cards. These cards, along with cards containing the instructions for the operations to be performed by the computer are "fed into" the computer; and the results of the calculations are printed out on paper or on more cards. Sometimes the computer is hooked to an instrument and processes the numbers produced by the instrument directly. For example, the combination gas chromatograph-mass spectrometer instrument, which we discussed earlier produces such huge quantities of numbers that a computer generally is hooked to the instrument to handle the data produced.

It is becoming more and more common for computers to be hooked to an instrument or to a chemical processing unit to control the unit itself. For example, a computer might be hooked to a chemical reactor in which a reaction is being carried out. The computer receives information such as the temperature, the pressure, quantities of ingredients added to the reactor, and so on. If the computer has been properly "programmed," it may calculate just how the reaction will be proceeding several minutes or several hours in the future. It may then make corrections, such as the addition of more of a specific ingredient, long before any real problem develops with the process.

Chapter Summary

We all depend upon chemical analysis and the instruments that are used for it. If one were to name a specific branch of chemistry with which the average citizen is most likely to come into contact, it would probably be *analytical chemistry*. Decisions involving huge sums of money, or even life and death, depend upon the accuracy and speed of chemical analysis. Should a factory be closed because of the pollutants that it is producing? Should a patient be subjected to a dangerous treatment which might save—or take—his life? Is an accused person really guilty of a hit and run accident? Should taxes be raised to build a new sewage treatment plant? All of these are decisions that depend upon chemical analysis. Modern chemical analysis makes much use of sophisticated instruments. The more common of these are discussed in this chapter.

Chemical species have effects upon various physical phenomena, which enable an analytical instrument to tell what is present, and how much of the specific species is present. This is the basis for instrumental analysis. The physical phenomena usually involve some form of light or electricity. The instrument used converts the particular phenomenon to an electrical signal, which is displayed by a recorder, cathode ray (television) tube, or fed into a computer.

Many chemical analyses depend upon the absorption of ultraviolet ("black"), or visible light. When the chemicals are in solution, a chemical reaction is usually performed to produce a compound that absorbs light very well. For example, neither the ferric ion (Fe^{3+}) nor the thiocyanate ion (SCN^-) absorb light very well in solution. But they combine to form a "complex" ion with the formula, $FeSCN^{2+}$. This complex ion absorbs light very well and can be used for the analysis of iron in solution.

Atomic absorption spectrometry is the method most commonly used for the analysis of many metals. This technique depends upon the absorption of light by atoms of a particular metal. The metal atoms are generated from compounds of the metal, usually in a flame. The light which is absorbed is generated from the same kind of metal in a hollow cathode lamp.

The emission of light can be used for chemical analysis. Metal atoms heated in a flame emit light whose wavelength is specific for the metal and whose intensity is a measure of the metal concentration. This is called *flame emission spectroscopy*. *Optical emission spectroscopy* depends upon light emitted by elements in an electrical arc. Fluorescence involves emission of longer wavelength light from species that have absorbed short wavelength (ultraviolet) light.

Neutron activation analysis is a sensitive way of analyzing many elements. It is based upon the production of radioactive isotopes by atoms that have absorbed neutrons.

Gas chromatography is a very useful, sensitive technique for the analysis of substances that can be put into the form of a vapor. It depends upon the fact that different compounds are retained for different periods of time while being carried through a column in a stream of gas.

Mass spectrometry is a technique in which charged particles are formed and their mass ("weight") determined. It is very sensitive.

An electrical potential developed at a glass electrode is used to measure pH. It is one of the most common measurements made.

The gas chromatograph is widely used to analyze gases and liquids that can be vaporized. (Courtesy of Varian Instrument Division)

Chapter Review Questions

The following questions are designed as a self-teaching tool to help you review Chapter 12. The answers to each question follow. See Chapter Review Questions for Chapter 1 for further instructions.

1. Regarding the absorption of light, the symbol, A, refers to _____, which may range in value from _____ to _____.

2. Beer's law is stated _____.

3. Metals are commonly analyzed by a technique that depends upon the absorption of light by _____.

4. This technique is called _____.

5. The reason that atomic absorption analysis is reasonably free of interferences is _____.

6. Sodium, potassium, magnesium, and calcium are readily analyzed by a technique called _____, which depends upon _____.

7. Very high temperatures required to get most metal atoms to emit some light are accomplished in an electrical _____ by a technique called _____.

8. Absorption of ultraviolet light may cause _____ _____, a phenomenon that is used in an analysis technique called fluorescence.

9. The smallest number of radioactive atoms that can be detected is _____.

10. When an atom nucleus absorbs a _____ produced in a nuclear reactor, a _____ may be produced.

11. This is the basis for a chemical analysis method called _____ _____.

12. If the "counts" from a particular radioactive isotope are 10,000 counts per minute at the start of the counting and 2500 counts per minute after one hour, the half-life of the isotope is _____.

13. The technique used for the analysis of gases and liquids that can be put into a vapor form is called _____.

14. Two gases may separate on a gas chromatograph column because _____ _____.

15. The three kinds of gas chromatograph detectors mentioned in the text are _____, _____, and _____.

16. The time at which a gas chromatography peak comes out of the column tells something about the _____, and the area of the peak is a measure of _____.

17. A mass spectrometer produces _____, which are then separated on the basis of their _____ (assuming they have the same charge).

18. One of the first major uses of the mass spectrometer was _____ _____.

19. One way of separating charged particles with different weights is based upon _____.

20. The path inside a mass spectrometer through which the ions travel must be occupied by _____.

21. The input of a mass spectrometer is often attached to another instrument, the _____.

22. An instrument that measures a potential developed at a glass electrode is the _____.

23. The potential of a glass electrode is developed because _____ _____.

24. The pH of a solution of 0.01 M H$^+$ is _____.

25. The pH of a solution of 0.006 M H$^+$ is between _____ and _____.

26. The glass electrode must always be used in combination with _____ _____.

27. The first step in measuring pH is to standardize with a _____ solution.

28. The computer is basically a very rapid _____.

Answers to Chapter Review Questions

1. absorbance, zero, infinity
2. $A = abC$
3. atoms
4. atomic absorption analysis
5. metal atoms absorb light of very specific wavelengths
6. flame emission spectroscopy, emission of light by atoms in a flame
7. arc, optical emission spectroscopy
8. emission of longer wavelength light
9. one
10. neutron, radioactive isotope
11. neutron activation analysis
12. one-half hour
13. gas chromatography
14. they are held up (retained) for different lengths of time
15. thermal conductivity, flame ionization, electron-capture
16. identity of the substance, quantity of the substance
17. charged particles, or ions, weights
18. determining identities and quantities of compounds in petroleum
19. the length of time they take to go the length of a tube
20. essentially nothing—a high vacuum
21. gas chromatograph
22. pH meter
23. H$^+$ ions "try to go through" the glass membrane
24. 2.0
25. 2, 3
26. a reference electrode
27. buffer
28. calculating machine

Exercises for Chapter 12

1. Why is atomic absorption generally so specific for given metals? What role does the hollow cathode lamp play in making atomic absorption so specific?

2. What do atoms react with in a nuclear reactor to make them radioactive?

3. A sample of a radioactive isotope with a half-life of 10 min has an activity of 64,000 "counts" per minute. What should the activity be 20 min later?

4. For what kinds of compounds is gas chromatography a very useful analytical technique?

5. What is the purpose of the carrier gas in a gas chromatograph?

6. Of the techniques that we have discussed, which ones would you think would be the most helpful in determining the molecular weight and structure of a complicated organic molecule?

7. A solution contains hydrogen ions at a concentration of 0.0005 mole/liter. The pH of the solution lies between:
   a. 1 and 2, **b.** 2 and 3, **c.** 3 and 4, **d.** 4 and 5, **e.** 5 and 6.

8. The pH meter measures:
   a. light, **b.** radioactivity **c.** a voltage, from the glass electrode.

9. Canned fish from a particular lot number are suspected of containing cadmium. Which instrument should be chosen to analyze for this heavy metal? Explain your choice.

10. Beer's law is $A = abC$. Put into words, this law says that the absorbance is equal to the absorptivity multiplied by the path length of light (through the absorbing solution) multiplied by the concentration of absorbing substance. The absorbance of a solution in a cell having a path length of 1 cm is 0.2. The absorbance of the same solution in a 3 cm cell is _____.

11. The absorbance, A, of a solution was 0.500. Exactly 25 ml of this solution were placed in a 50-ml volumetric flask, and the solution diluted to exactly 50 ml. The absorbance of the resulting solution was _____.

12. Exactly 1 lb of polybrominated biphenyl, a fire retardant, was accidentally added to 500,000 lb of cattle feed during the feed mixing process. What was the concentration of polybromated biphenyl in the feed, expressed as parts per million?

13. The following graph shows a calibration plot for atomic absorption analysis showing absorbance, A, for several known concentrations of lead in solution. An unknown lead solution had an absorbance of 0.350. What was the concentration of lead?

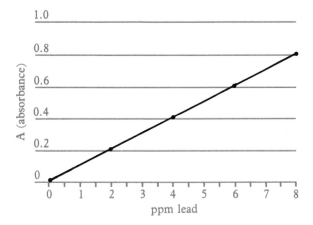

14. What is one approach to increasing the sensitivity of atomic absorption analysis?

15. Over a useful range of analysis, the amount of light given off by fluorescence increases in direct proportion to the concentration of fluorescing substance. If a meter measuring light intensity registers 50 with a 10 ppb (parts per billion) standard of a substance and 40 with an unknown sample of the substance, what is the concentration of the unknown?

16. The following gas chromatogram shows peaks of known substances identified as *A*, *B*, *C*, and *D*.

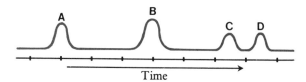

A chromatogram of an unknown taken under the same conditions is the following:

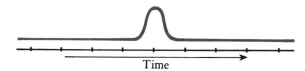

If the compound in the unknown is the same as one in the knowns, which is it?

17. The area of a gas chromatographic peak recorded on chart paper for a compound was measured as 80 mm². This resulted from injection of exactly 1 μg of the compound. How many micrograms of the substance would give an area of 120 mm²?

18. A sample of a radioactive isotope started with an activity of 8400 counts per minute. Exactly 38 min later, the activity was 4200 counts per minute. What was the half-life of the isotope?

19. A pH meter was calibrated to read 7.00 on the pH scale when the electrodes were dipped in a pH 7.00 buffer. When the electrodes were dipped into a sample of lake water, the pH meter read 6.00. What was the concentration of H^+ in the water?

The Aluminum Co. of America (ALCOA) provides high strength forgings for use as structural members for the DC-10 airbus. These forgings lock into the plane's fuselage frame, providing support for its 155-ft. wingspan. (Courtesy of Aluminum Co. of America)

13

Industrial Chemistry and Occupational Health

13.1

The Chemical Industry: An Economic Giant

In recent years chemistry as a science and chemistry as an industry have advanced together. Before the turn of the century, the chemical industry ran far ahead of chemistry as a science. Gunpowder was manufactured centuries before its chemistry was understood. Dyes were extracted, purified, and used with no knowledge of their complicated organic structure. Soap was manufactured in primitive backyard factories by people who had no idea that the water leached from ashes, which was used in soap manufacture, contained potassium carbonate. They did not know that this basic potassium carbonate broke down the fatty acid esters of glycerin (from fat) to make the organic salts known as soap.

369

As the chemical industry developed, a body of chemical knowledge developed along with it. Observations were made of chemical phenomena which occurred during various manufacturing processes. This information slowly came together to form the body of knowledge making up the nucleus of chemical science. Along with it came the contributions of others, less interested in making sudsier soap or gunpowder with a bigger bang. These were the natural philosophers. Some were eccentrics, living in the worst kind of poverty, working in fume-filled cellar laboratories. (Indeed, some modern day chemistry professors would agree that this description still applies to them.) In their pursuit of knowledge of strange chemical phenomena, they often suffered great damage to their own bodies and minds from the careless and unknowing use of toxic chemicals. Others were people born to wealth who worked with chemicals as an entertainment.

Eventually it became clear that a knowledge of chemistry could lead to the production of new and profitable chemical products. A new organic compound, prepared in the laboratory with no particular objective in mind, would reveal properties with commercial use. Those who noticed that inhaling chloroform led to drowsiness and even unconsciousness set the stage for the use of this chemical as the first anesthetic. True, it was a dangerous anesthetic, but one welcomed by the poor devil with a gangrene infected leg that had to be amputated. As more and more chemicals were made in the laboratory, commercial uses were found for them.

And so, catalyzed by the growing body of chemical knowledge and fueled by the possibilities of large profits, the chemical industry grew. Plastics were developed and used to manufacture articles never dreamed of before. Drugs cured diseases that were previously incurable. Herbicides

Hot effluent emptied into rivers by industrial plants is often lethal to marine organisms. Even a gradual change in water temperature can disrupt the life cycles of these organisms since they depend very closely upon water temperature for their migration and spawning cues. (Courtesy of EPA-Documerica; Harry Schaefer, photographer)

were synthesized, which eliminated the need for farmers to cultivate corn, or even laboriously chop out weeds with a hoe. The fixing of nitrogen from air by chemical means made possible production of huge quantities of inexpensive fertilizer. Worn out, eroded farm land with its pitiful production of scrawny plants suddenly burst forth with a bounty of crops and grain. By the 1950's the chemical industry had come of age.

Now the chemical industry is entering a new era. Along with the unquestionable benefits of chemical products and processes came disturbing evidence of some undesirable side effects. Workers exposed to vinyl chloride for years developed a rare form of liver cancer and died. Others working with pesticides developed brutal nervous disorders. Fish exposed to a few parts per trillion of some pesticides in water became grotesquely deformed. Birds failed to reproduce as a result of pesticide poisoning. The thalidomide babies were born without useable arms or legs. As a result of these and many other factors, the chemical industry is putting much more effort into determining the health and environmental effects of chemical products. It is expensive, and we shall all bear the cost. It is also time consuming, so that some desirable products will take many years to reach the market. But, it is necessary. As the chemical industry emerges from a youth characterized by amazing growth, it enters a more mature age. From this new age, we may anticipate safer products used in safer ways. Eventually everyone will benefit.

The chemical industry, alone, in the U.S. is an approximately 60 billion dollar industry. Add to that allied chemical products and it is even larger. Its annual sales are about half that of annual food sales. Chemicals, along with agricultural products, are the major positive factors in the U.S. balance of trade. From about 1950 to 1970, chemical sales approximately doubled each decade. The contribution of the chemical industry to the U.S. economy is very great indeed.

13.2

Major Types of Industrial Chemical Products

The major types of chemicals that are manufactured are synthetic fibers, industrial gases, agricultural chemicals, toilet preparations, synthetic rubber, detergents, organic chemicals, plastics, pharmaceuticals, wood-product chemicals, chlorine, paint, inorganic chemicals, printing ink, sulfuric acid, cellulose fibers, and other miscellaneous chemicals. In each category, there are many, sometimes hundreds, of individual chemicals and chemical formulations. The rates of production growth for these chemicals differ with the type of chemical. In recent years synthetic fibers (Dacron, nylon) have had very rapid increases in production. The production of wood chemicals has not grown nearly so rapidly. The more established products do not generally grow as rapidly as new products. This chapter discusses some of these chemical products and their means of production.

13.3

Inside the Chemical Plant

Producing a chemical product in a factory is much more complicated than making the same thing in the laboratory. The heat required to make a reaction go in the laboratory can be supplied by placing a flask on a hot plate. On an industrial scale, the engineer must figure out how to transfer the heat safely to thousands of pounds of material. Heat energy is expensive, and the cost of heating the reaction mixture must be figured carefully. In the laboratory the chemist can wait for hours to filter a product that tends to clog a filter. On an industrial scale this may mean that the product cannot even be prepared.

Chemical engineering is the profession that deals with industrial chemical processes. Just as the chemist may think largely in terms of chemical reactions and chemical compounds, the chemical engineer thinks in terms of *unit operations*. A unit operation is a process such as distilling or filtering in which a particular step of a chemical manufacturing operation is carried out. Various unit operations are connected together in sequence to make a particular product. Some of the important unit operations are discussed here.

Heat exchange is one of the most common unit operations. It may be used to increase the temperature of a gas or liquid. In some cases heat exchange is used to remove heat. Recovery of heat is extremely important in chemical processes. Heat is energy, and, particularly with higher fuel prices, energy is money.

The device used for heat exchange typically consists of a bundle of tubes inside a shell shown in Figure 13.1. Generally a hot gas flows through the shell and transfers much of its heat to a liquid flowing through the tubes as shown in the drawing. The flow is such that the incoming hot gas first contacts that part of the exchanger where the liquid is leaving. This results in the highest temperature in the outgoing liquid. Heat exchangers require metals that transfer heat well. The metals must also be corrosion-resistant.

Distillation is used to separate liquids with different boiling points.

FIGURE 13.1
Tube-and-shell heat exchanger with a hot gas heating a cold liquid.

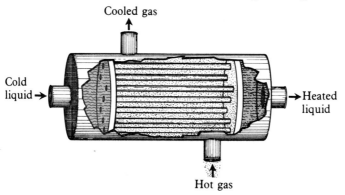

Cooled gas

Cold liquid →

→ Heated liquid

Hot gas

This procedure has already been mentioned for the separation of different fractions of crude oil. Simple distillation is used to remove a volatile (easily vaporized) liquid from a liquid that is not so volatile, or from a dissolved solid. Fractional distillation is employed to separate several liquids from each other. As with many processes, distillation can be either a *batch process* or a *continuous process*. In a batch process the volatile liquid is distilled off, the residue (bottoms) is removed, the still is refilled, and the operation is repeated. In a continuous process raw liquid is continually fed to the distillation tower. If it is a fractional distillation, the most volatile products are taken off the top of the tower, the bottoms are removed from the bottom of the tower, and products with volatility in between are removed from the middle. A distillation tower for fractional distillation is shown in Figure 10.3. In some continuous processes the bottoms are reintroduced with the feed to increase efficiency.

The separation of liquids and solids is most commonly done by *filtration*. Commonly filtration is used to remove solid impurities from drinking water. A layer of sand resting on top of a layer of gravel is usually used in purifying water for a municipal water system. The rotary vacuum filter is a more sophisticated device used for continuous filtration. It is used, for example, in removing water from sewage sludge. With this device, a filter material is held on a rotating drum. A vacuum in the drum sucks water into it. The drum rotates in the material to be filtered and collects a layer of solid. This layer is scraped off by a scraper and collected.

In some chemical processes, it is necessary to separate dust from gas. This is especially useful for the removal of solids from air before discharge to the atmosphere. This unit operation commonly uses a *cyclone separator* shown in Figure 13.2. Gas containing dust enters the separator at the top in such a manner that the gas spirals downward along the walls of the device. As a result, solid particles suspended in the gas are deposited. The gas then goes up the center of the separator, leaving the collected dust in the bottom.

FIGURE 13.2
A cyclone separator is used to separate dust from gas.

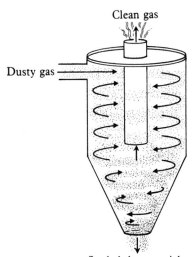

13.4

Control of Chemical Operations

The control room of a chemical processing unit contains many recorders and gauges. These enable the operator to keep a close watch on every step of the chemical process. These functions are increasingly being taken over by computers. The measurement and control of a chemical process are crucial for the production of an acceptable product. Profitability depends upon accurate control so that energy, materials, and time are not wasted. Certainly, safety depends upon accurate measurement and control where potentially explosive or otherwise hazardous processes are being carried out.

Temperature is one of the most important measurements in a chemical manufacturing plant. Temperature is commonly measured as a voltage produced at a *thermocouple*. A thermocouple consists of two wires, each made of a different metal, joined together (Figure 13.3). This combination produces an electrical voltage which varies with temperature. The voltage is measured with a voltmeter, and the temperature may be calculated from the voltage, or calibrated directly on the voltmeter dial. The electrical resistance of some materials changes with temperature. This resistance can be measured by an ohm-meter to give the temperature. Carbon, platinum, and platinum-rhodium alloys are commonly used. A more sophisticated device called a *thermistor* is widely used.

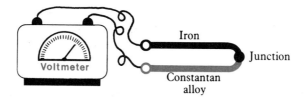

FIGURE 13.3 *A thermocouple is made from joining an iron wire and a constantan alloy wire at a junction. The voltage changes with temperature.*

Viscosity is an important measure of the characteristics of a chemical product. Motor oil is a good example. A motor oil designed for use during the midsummer months (a 40-weight oil) must be rather viscous. A 10-weight oil is much less viscous and is used during the winter in very cold climates. Viscosity is measured by the ease with which a liquid is stirred. A stirring paddle mounted on a shaft is dipped into the liquid and rotated. The shaft has a place on it that can twist against the force of a spring. The harder the liquid is to stir, the more the shaft will twist. The degree of twist is measured and related to viscosity.

Pressure is important in many chemical processes, particularly those involving gases. Pressure may determine the type of products formed and the speed of the reaction. A rapid rise in pressure may indicate that trouble is brewing in the process. Pressure is usually measured with a pressure gauge consisting of a sort of "box" with a flexible wall (see

Figure 13.4). The more the wall is pushed out, the higher the pressure
gets inside the box. The flexible wall can be connected to a gauge, or
some other device calibrated to read in pressure units.

FIGURE 13.4
Simple pressure measuring device.

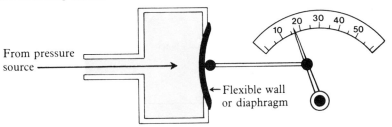

The flow rate of gases and liquids must be measured to determine
how rapidly materials are moving through a chemical reactor. A
rotameter is commonly used to measure the flow of gas or liquid. It
consists of a cone-shaped device. The gas or liquid flows upward through
this cone and holds up a little "float," as illustrated in Figure 13.5. The
higher the float is held by the flowing material, the greater the flow rate.

FIGURE 13.5
A rotameter.

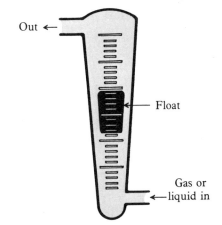

All of the devices discussed above are **transducers**. These are
devices which respond to a property such as temperature in a form that
can be seen, or an electrical signal that can be measured. These signals
are recorded. This is commonly done with a **recorder**, which draws a
line on a piece of paper (see Figures 13.6 and 13.7). The paper comes
off a roll or rotates on a disc. The location of the line provides a reading
of the temperature, flow, or whatever else is being measured.

Chemical processes must be controlled. The most primitive way
of doing this is for an operator to watch the charts and turn the appropriate
valves to keep everything at the right level. This is now done by automatic
devices. Small computers have revolutionized chemical process control

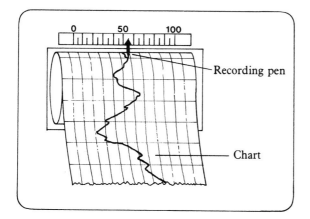

FIGURE 13.6
Strip chart recorder.

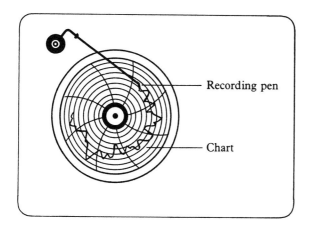

FIGURE 13.7
Round chart recorder.

by measuring every pertinent thing at the same time and making adjustments anywhere in the process, the instant they are needed.

13.5

Sulfuric Acid

Sulfuric acid, H_2SO_4, is the most widely produced synthetic chemical. About 34 million tons of this chemical are produced each year. Most of it is used to manufacture other chemicals. Aside from the fact that it is a strong acid, it has several other properties that make it very useful. It takes up water very strongly and is a good dehydrating agent. When it is hot and concentrated, it produces reactive oxygen,

$$H_2SO_4 \longrightarrow \quad O \quad + SO_2\uparrow + H_2O$$

oxygen atom
reacts with a
reducing agent

so that it is a good oxidizing agent. Finally, of all the common, inexpensive acids, it is the least volatile.

The greatest use of sulfuric acid is in the production of phosphate fertilizers. Phosphate fertilizers generally are manufactured from a mineral called fluorapatite. In the U.S. this mineral occurs largely in Florida. This is reacted with sulfuric acid,

$$2\ Ca_5(PO_4)_3F + 7\ H_2SO_4 + 3\ H_2O \longrightarrow 2\ HF\uparrow + 7\ CaSO_4 + 3\ CaH_4(PO_4)_2 \cdot H_2O$$

fluorapatite   superphosphate,
                                                                                                   a water-soluble
                                                                                                   phosphate salt

to produce *superphosphate*, which dissolves pretty well in water so that the phosphate is available to plants. Sulfuric acid is also used widely to produce ammonium sulfate, titanium dioxide, and high-octane gasoline. *Pickling* of steel is accomplished with sulfuric acid. This consists of dipping the steel into a vat of the acid, which dissolves coatings of oxides and scale, leaving a clean surface. Sulfuric acid is the *electrolyte* in lead storage batteries used in automobiles.

Most sulfuric acid is now made by the *contact process*. In this process sulfur dioxide is reacted with O_2 over a vanadium pentoxide (V_2O_5) catalyst,

$$2\ SO_2 + O_2 \longrightarrow 2\ SO_3$$

to produce sulfur trioxide. This product is then dissolved in sulfuric acid to produce fuming sulfuric acid (oleum),

$$H_2SO_4 + SO_3 \longrightarrow H_2S_2O_7$$

oleum

which is mixed with water to produce approximately 97 % sulfuric acid.

$$H_2S_2O_7 + H_2O \longrightarrow 2\ H_2SO_4$$

It should be pointed out here that mixing sulfuric acid and water liberates a lot of heat. In the laboratory sulfuric acid should always be added to water. This avoids generating so much heat that highly dangerous sulfuric acid is spattered out of the container.

13.6

Sodium Hydroxide

Sodium hydroxide, NaOH, is also a major inorganic chemical. Annual production in the U.S. is about 12 million tons. It is marketed as a solid, which is frequently called **lye**. Like sulfuric acid, sodium hydroxide is used largely to make other chemicals. Large quantities are used to break down wood to make paper. The NaOH dissolves the "natural glue" that holds the wood fibers together. Sodium hydroxide is employed to extract Al_2O_3 from aluminum ore, called bauxite.

$$Al_2O_3 \quad + 2\,NaOH \longrightarrow \quad 2\,NaAlO_2 \quad + H_2O$$

aluminum oxide
mixed with
impurities in bauxite

sodium aluminate,
a soluble compound
of aluminum

The reaction of sodium hydroxide with aluminum oxide isolates the aluminum from impurities in the ore. The manufacture of rayon, soaps, and detergents also accounts for much sodium hydroxide consumption.

Sodium hydroxide and chlorine gas, Cl_2, are manufactured together by **electrolysis** of NaCl dissolved in water. This process uses an electrical current passing through the water to break up the NaCl. It is accomplished in an **electrolysis cell** designed to keep the NaOH and Cl_2 products apart, so that they will not react with each other. The chlor-alkali process shown in Figure 13.8 is widely used. An electrical current is forced through a solution of NaCl in the left-hand compartment. The graphite anodes are positively charged and take electrons away from chloride ion

$$2\,Cl^- \longrightarrow Cl_2\uparrow + 2\,e^-$$

producing Cl_2 gas. Sodium ion is reduced at the flowing mercury cathode in the same compartment,

$$Na^+ + e^- \longrightarrow Na\ (\text{dissolved in mercury})$$

to produce a solution of sodium metal dissolved in mercury. Such a solution is called an **amalgam**. The reaction is a reduction, and the electrode at which it occurs is the **cathode**. So long as the electrical current is flowing, the sodium metal stays dissolved in the mercury.

FIGURE 13.8

The chlor-alkali process for the manufacture of chlorine and sodium hydroxide.

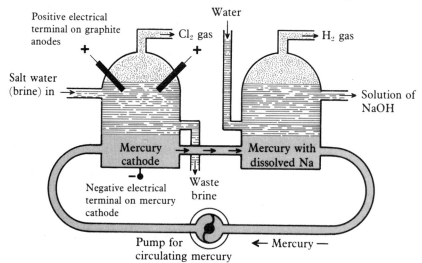

The mercury is pumped to a container where the reaction,

$$2 \, Na \text{ (dissolved in mercury)} + H_2O \longrightarrow 2 \, NaOH + H_2\uparrow$$

occurs to produce sodium hydroxide and hydrogen gas. The sodium hydroxide is sold as a 50% solution in water, or it can be removed from solution and sold as solid lye.

Some of the mercury used in the chlori-alkali process does get into waste brine. Release of this brine would cause mercury pollution in water, which is discussed in Section 8.10. The effects of sodium hydroxide are likewise dangerous. This compound is often called *caustic soda* for a very good reason. In its dry form and in concentrated solutions, it will cause severe chemical burns on the skin and any other organic tissue.

13.7

Chlorine

Approximately 11 million tons of chlorine are produced in the U.S. each year. The greatest industrial use of chlorine is in the manufacture of chlorinated hydrocarbons. Chlorine reacts with practically any hydrocarbon

$$CH_4 \; + \; Cl_2 \; \longrightarrow \; CH_3Cl \; + HCl$$

methane   chlorine   methyl chlorine,
a chlorinated hydrocarbon

to produce chlorinated hydrocarbons. Some typical chlorinated hydrocarbons and their uses are given in Table 13.1.

TABLE 13.1

Chlorinated Hydrocarbon*	Use
Benzene hexachloride: C_6Cl_6	Insecticide
Carbon tetrachloride: CCl_4	Industrial degreasing, Freon manufacture
Chlorobenzene: C_6H_5Cl	Manufacture of phenol and aniline
Tetrachloroethylene: $\underset{Cl}{\overset{Cl}{>}} C = C \underset{Cl}{\overset{Cl}{<}}$	Most widely used dry cleaning fluid
Vinyl chloride: $\underset{H}{\overset{H}{>}} C = C \underset{Cl}{\overset{H}{<}}$	Manufacture of polyvinyl chloride

* Chlorinated hydrocarbons cause liver damage and depress the central nervous system resulting in dizziness, drowsiness, and confusion. Vinyl chloride causes liver cancer. Toxicity varies with the compound. Occupational exposure should be limited.

Chlorine is also used to produce chemicals other than chlorinated hydrocarbons. The reaction of chlorine and calcium hydroxide produces calcium hypochlorite.

$$2 \text{ Ca(OH)}_2 + 2 \text{ Cl}_2 \longrightarrow \underset{\substack{\text{calcium} \\ \text{hypochlorite}}}{\text{Ca(OCl)}_2} + \text{CaCl}_2 + 2 \text{ H}_2\text{O}$$

This chemical, like chlorine, is a very good bleaching agent. It is a common ingredient of household bleaches. Most of the chlorine used for bleaching is consumed by the pulp and paper industry. When it is first extracted from wood, pulp has a dark color. The compounds which give it this color are destroyed by contact with chlorine water.

A smaller percentage of the total chlorine produced in the U.S. is used in water treatment where it serves as a very important disinfectant that kills bacteria. There is evidence to suggest that chlorine reacts with organic compounds in water to produce possibly toxic organochlorine compounds.

The manufacture of chlorine is accomplished by the same electrolytic process by which sodium hydroxide is made. This process was described above. It is not surprising that the annual production of chlorine is always about the same as that of sodium hydroxide.

Chlorine is an extremely dangerous chemical. When inhaled, it quickly ruins the lining of the lungs and causes a fatal deterioration of these organs. A large chlorine leak is particularly dangerous because the gas is two and one-half times as dense as air and spreads along the ground in a deadly green layer of gas.

13.8

Ammonia

Ammonia production in the U.S. amounts to about 17 million tons each year. This number does not take into account about 7.5 million tons of ammonium nitrate that require ammonia for manufacture. Ammonia is certainly a major inorganic chemical. Almost three-fourths of the synthetic NH_3 produced goes into the manufacture of nitrogen fertilizers. Ammonia can be applied directly to the soil, either as a gas or a solution in water. This requires special applicators to prevent the escape of toxic ammonia gas to the atmosphere. In a smaller scale operation it is more convenient to add nitrogen to the soil as ammonium nitrate, NH_4NO_3. Other major nitrogen fertilizers prepared from ammonia include ammonium sulfate, $(NH_4)_2SO_4$; ammonium phosphate, $(NH_4)_3PO_4$; and urea, $(NH_2)_2CO$. In addition to its uses as a fertilizer, ammonia is employed in the manufacture of livestock feed, fertilizer, plastics, and other chemicals.

Ammonium nitrate fertilizer is applied to the soil with a grain drill as shown. (Courtesy of International Harvester Co.)

Ammonia makes a very good gas for industrial refrigeration (Figure 13.9). It is a better heat-transferring material than even water. When many gases such as ammonia are compressed to a high pressure, they become liquids and release heat. (Anybody who has ever grabbed the screw connector of a bicycle tire pump after vigorously pumping on it knows that compressing a gas releases heat.) If the liquefied gas is allowed to evaporate in a metal coil under reduced pressure, heat is taken up from the surroundings, which become cold. The now gaseous ammonia is then compressed again and the whole cycle repeated.

Ammonia is manufactured by the *Haber process.* This consists of

FIGURE 13.9
Ammonia refrigeration plant.

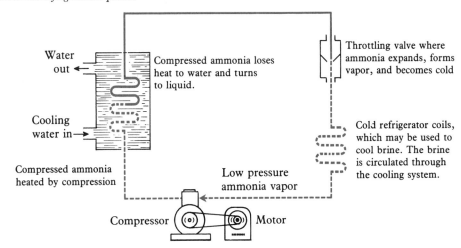

the reaction of nitrogen gas and hydrogen gas

$$3\,H_2 + N_2 \longrightarrow 2\,NH_3$$

at extremely high pressures (200–600 atm) and 450–600°C temperature. The hydrogen required for this process is normally produced from hydrocarbons. The reaction of methane and steam over a nickel catalyst at 650–1100°C

$$CH_4 + 2\,H_2O \longrightarrow CO_2 + 4\,H_2$$

produces hydrogen gas, which can be used for the manufacture of ammonia. As hydrocarbons come into shorter supply, it will be necessary to find other sources of hydrogen. One such source is from the reaction of hot coal and steam

$$C\ (coal) + H_2O \longrightarrow CO + H_2$$

to produce a *synthesis gas* consisting of a mixture of hydrogen and carbon monoxide. Further reaction of this product with steam over a catalyst

$$CO + H_2O \longrightarrow CO_2 + H_2$$

produces hydrogen gas and consumes carbon monoxide. This important reaction is called the *water-gas shift reaction*.

Ammonia vapor can be toxic. Inhaling too much of it damages the lungs. Exposure to air containing 5–10 ppm of ammonia is rapidly fatal. Some cases of ammonia poisoning have occurred in the handling of this chemical and in refrigeration system leaks.

13.9

The Other Big Inorganic Chemicals

Sulfuric acid, sodium hydroxide, chlorine, and ammonia make up the "big four" inorganic chemicals, each with a production in excess of 10 million tons per year. The tonnage of pure oxygen produced is even greater than that of sodium hydroxide or chlorine. It is not made by a chemical process but is recovered from pure air by liquefaction followed by distillation. Large quantities of pure nitrogen are made in the same way. Both of these elements are widely used in the chemical industry as liquids or gases. Liquid nitrogen is very widely used in cryogenic (very low temperature) processes.

Several other inorganic chemicals are produced in large quantities. Most of these are simple compounds whose manufacture and uses have been described previously. They are summarized in Table 13.2.

TABLE 13.2
Some major inorganic chemicals.

Chemical	Production	Approximate Annual U.S. Production, Millions of Tons	Uses and Hazards
Ammonium nitrate, NH_4NO_3	Reaction of ammonia and nitric acid, $$NH_3 + HNO_3 \longrightarrow NH_4NO_3$$	8	Mostly for fertilizer, some for explosives and industrial use. This compound can be very explosive.
Carbon dioxide, CO_2	Combustion, $C + O_2 \longrightarrow CO_2$ Byproduct from fermentation	1.8	Refrigeration (dry ice), carbonated beverages, chemical manufacture, fire extinguishers. Gas can suffocate.
Hydrochloric acid, HCl	Reaction of hydrogen and chlorine, $$H_2 + Cl_2 \longrightarrow 2\,HCl$$ Byproduct from hydrocarbon manufacture	2.5	Manufacture of chemicals, metals processing, manufacture of glucose and other foods, acid treating oil wells. Acid can be harmful to skin but is one of the safer acids.
Nitric acid, HNO_3	Made by oxidizing ammonia in several steps for which the overall reaction is $$NH_3 + 2\,O_2 \longrightarrow HNO_3 + H_2O$$	8	Three-fourths of nitric acid production used in fertilizer manufacture, most of the rest for explosives and chemicals. It is harmful to skin.
Phosphoric acid, H_3PO_4	From fluorapatite mineral by reaction with sulfuric acid, $$Ca_5F(PO_4)_3 + 5\,H_2SO_4 + 2\,H_2O \longrightarrow$$ $$3\,H_3PO_4 + 5\,CaSO_4 \cdot 2\,H_2O + HF\uparrow$$	11	About two-thirds of production used for fertilizer, about 20% in soap and detergents (detergent builders), the remainder for other applications including water treatment to precipitate calcium and iron.

TABLE 13.2 *(continued)*
Some major inorganic chemicals.

Chemical	Production	Approximate Annual U.S. Production, Millions of Tons	Uses and Hazards
Sodium carbonate, natural and synthetic, Na_2CO_3	From NaCl and $CaCO_3$ by Solvay process, also produced by mining and heating trona, a mineral with the formula $$Na_2CO_3 \cdot NaHCO_3 \cdot 2\,H_2O$$	7.6	Used as an inexpensive base for neutralizing acid, for water treatment, in detergents, and for the manufacture of other chemicals
Titanium dioxide, TiO_2	From volatile $TiCl_4$ made by the action of chlorine on rutile, a mineral containing impure TiO_2, $$TiO_2(\text{rutile}) + C + 2\,Cl_2 \longrightarrow$$ $$TiCl_4\uparrow + CO_2\uparrow$$ The $TiCl_4$ is oxidized to produce pure TiO_2, $$TiCl_4 + O_2 \longrightarrow TiO_2 + 2\,Cl_2$$	0.8	Most common modern white paint pigment, also a food additive.

13.10

Industrial Production of Organic Chemicals

There are many specific classes of organic chemicals and organic chemical formulations, including simple organic compounds, agricultural pesticides, pharmaceuticals, paints, and synthetic rubber. The greatest quantities of organic chemicals produced can be placed in three classes. The first of these is made up of simple chemicals such as acetone, most of which have been described in Chapter 10. For the most part these chemicals are consumed in making other products. The second major class of organic chemicals consists of plastics. The third class is made up of man-made fibers such as nylon or rayon.

There are about 24 major organic chemicals, which are produced in quantities of at least approximately one million pounds per year in the U.S. A few of these, such as tetrachloroethylene (dry cleaning fluid), have direct uses. However, the majority are used to make other products and, in many cases, may not even leave the plant where they are manufactured. These major organic chemicals are summarized in Table 13.3. The approximate annual production of each chemical is given. This production varies markedly with economic conditions. Declines of 20–25% in production were registered between 1974 and the deep recession year, 1975.

TABLE 13.3

Names and formulas of major organic chemicals.

Name of Chemical	Formula	Approximate Annual U.S. Production, Millions of Tons
Acetic acid	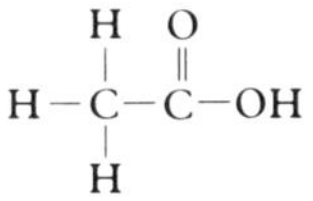 $H-\underset{\underset{H}{\mid}}{\overset{\overset{H}{\mid}}{C}}-\overset{\overset{O}{\parallel}}{C}-OH$	1.2
Acetone	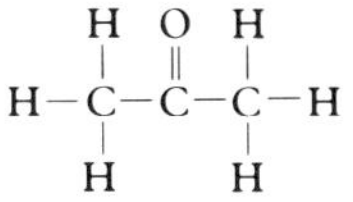 $H-\underset{\underset{H}{\mid}}{\overset{\overset{H}{\mid}}{C}}-\overset{\overset{O}{\parallel}}{C}-\underset{\underset{H}{\mid}}{\overset{\overset{H}{\mid}}{C}}-H$	1.1
Acrylonitrile	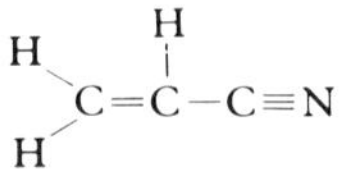 $\underset{H}{\overset{H}{>}}C=\underset{\underset{H}{\mid}}{\overset{\overset{H}{\mid}}{C}}-C\equiv N$	0.80
Benzene	 ⬡*	1600 (millions of gallons)
Butadiene	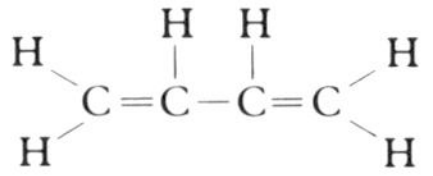 $\underset{H}{\overset{H}{>}}C=\underset{\underset{H}{\mid}}{\overset{\overset{H}{\mid}}{C}}-\underset{\underset{H}{\mid}}{\overset{\overset{H}{\mid}}{C}}=C\underset{H}{\overset{H}{<}}$	1.9
Carbon tetrachloride	CCl_4	0.5
Cumene	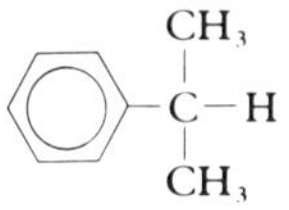 ⬡$-\underset{\underset{CH_3}{\mid}}{\overset{\overset{CH_3}{\mid}}{C}}-H$	1.6
Cyclohexane	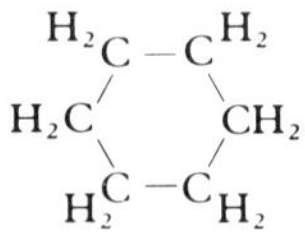 $\underset{H_2\overset{\mid}{C}}{\overset{H_2C-CH_2}{}}\underset{C-CH_2}{\overset{CH_2}{}}$	1.3
Ethylene	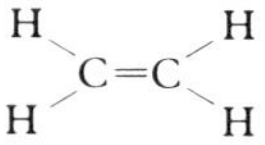 $\underset{H}{\overset{H}{>}}C=C\underset{H}{\overset{H}{<}}$	13
Ethylene oxide	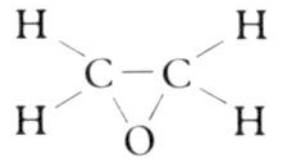 $\underset{H}{\overset{H}{>}}\underset{O}{\overset{C-C}{}}\underset{H}{\overset{H}{<}}$	2.3
Formaldehyde (37% solution)	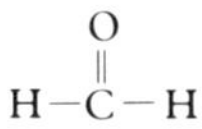 $H-\overset{\overset{O}{\parallel}}{C}-H$ (in H_2O)	3.2
Isopropyl alcohol	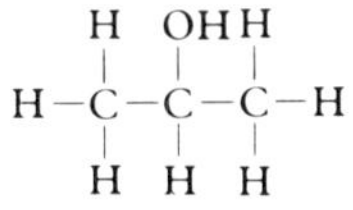 $H-\underset{\underset{H}{\mid}}{\overset{\overset{H}{\mid}}{C}}-\underset{\underset{H}{\mid}}{\overset{\overset{OH}{\mid}}{C}}-\underset{\underset{H}{\mid}}{\overset{\overset{H}{\mid}}{C}}-H$	1.1
Methanol	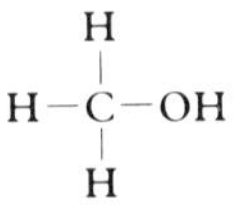 $H-\underset{\underset{H}{\mid}}{\overset{\overset{H}{\mid}}{C}}-OH$	3.3
Phenol	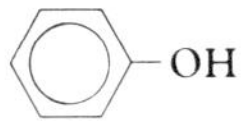 ⬡$-OH$	1.3
Phthalic anhydride	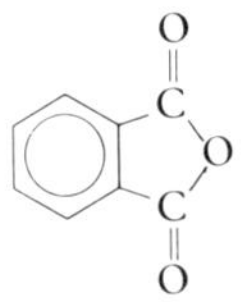 (benzene ring fused with) $\overset{\overset{O}{\parallel}}{C}-O-\overset{\overset{}{}}{C}\overset{O}{\parallel}$	0.5
Propylene	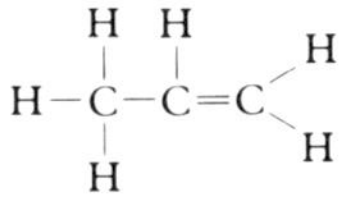 $H-\underset{\underset{H}{\mid}}{\overset{\overset{H}{\mid}}{C}}-\underset{\underset{H}{\mid}}{\overset{\overset{H}{\mid}}{C}}=C\underset{H}{\overset{H}{<}}$	5
Propylene oxide	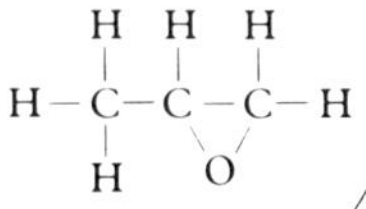 $H-\underset{\underset{H}{\mid}}{\overset{\overset{H}{\mid}}{C}}-\underset{\underset{O}{\mid}}{\overset{\overset{H}{\mid}}{C}}-\overset{\overset{H}{\mid}}{C}-H$	1.1
Styrene	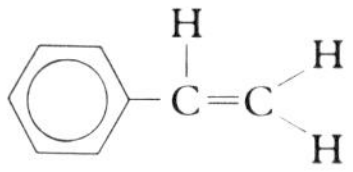 ⬡$-\overset{\overset{H}{\mid}}{C}=C\underset{H}{\overset{H}{<}}$	3.5

* Recall that the structure shown as ⬡ is a benzene ring consisting of 6 carbon atoms in a ring. Each of these is bonded to one H, unless some other group is shown. See the examples in Figure 13.10.

TABLE 13.3 *(continued)*
Names and formulas of major organic chemicals.

Name of Chemical	Formula	Approximate Annual U.S. Production, Millions of Tons
Tetrachlorethylene	$\begin{array}{c} Cl \\ \diagdown \\ Cl \end{array} C = C \begin{array}{c} Cl \\ \diagup \\ Cl \end{array}$	0.4
Toluene	⬡—CH₃	1100 (millions of gallons)
Urea	$\begin{array}{c} H \\ \diagdown \\ H \end{array} N - \overset{\overset{\displaystyle O}{\|}}{C} - N \begin{array}{c} H \\ \diagup \\ H \end{array}$	3.9
Vinyl acetate	$\begin{array}{c} H \\ \diagdown \\ H \end{array} C = C \begin{array}{c} H \\ \| \\ \end{array} - O - \overset{\overset{\displaystyle O}{\|}}{C} - \overset{\overset{\displaystyle H}{\|}}{\underset{H}{C}} - H$	0.9
o-xylene	⬡ with CH₃ CH₃	0.6
p-xylene	CH₃ ⬡ CH₃	1.6

FIGURE 13.10

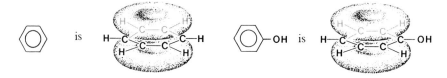

A number of classes of plastics are manufactured on a large scale. Within each class there are plastics with special characteristics. The bulk of plastic production is found among five major classes. These are summarized in Table 13.4. If you compare the production data in Table 13.4 with those in Table 13.3, you can readily see that the manufacture of plastics accounts for the very large quantities produced of some of

TABLE 13.4
Major classes of plastic production.

Types of Plastic	Approximate Annual U.S. Production, Millions of Tons
Phenolic resins made from polymers containing phenol and related compounds	0.60
Polyethylene, polymers of ethylene	4.9
Polypropylene, polymers of propylene	1.4
Polystyrene, polymers of styrene	2.0
Polyvinyl chloride, polymers of vinyl chloride	2.7

the organic chemicals. Particularly, phenol, ethylene, propylene, styrene, and vinyl chloride are used in huge quantities for plastics manufacture.

The manufacture of man-made fibers accounts for another very high proportion of the consumption of organic chemicals. The major types of man-made fibers are listed in Table 13.5. The synthetic fiber industry had its beginning in 1891 when rayon was first made from treated cellulose. Nylon was developed during the 1930's. It proved to be ideal for many applications, including stockings. Shortly after the public developed a craving for nylon stockings, they were withdrawn from the market because of wartime needs. After World War II very rapid growth occurred in synthetic fiber development and production. The synthetic fiber industry is a truly huge one now.

TABLE 13.5
Major types of synthetic fiber production.

Type of Synthetic Fiber	Approximate Annual U.S. Production, Millions of Tons
Acrylic and monacrylic	0.38
Cellulose acetate	0.24
Nylon	1.2
Olefin and vinyon	0.35
Polyester	2.0
Rayon	0.43

13.11

Plastics

A "plastic" substance is one which can be molded and shaped. According to such a definition, bread dough is a plastic material. So is the glob of street asphalt that sticks to one's shoe on a hot summer day. But, this definition does not seem to fit materials such as plastic water pipes, which are hard and rigid. The reason that plastic water pipes, stereo cabinets, and picnic eating utensils are called plastics is that at one step in their manufacture these materials were soft and pliable. While they are in that form, they can be molded to a desired shape and then caused to undergo chemical reactions, which make the plastic object hard and strong. Note that also according to the definition, synthetic textiles, rubber, and a number of other substances are plastics. However, textiles and rubber will be discussed separately.

There are many kinds of plastics with many different properties. There is not room to discuss them all here. However, the main ones will be described. *Bakelite* was one of the first major plastics to be manufactured. This plastic is formed by the bonding together (condensation) of formaldehyde and phenol molecules to form a large network of phenol molecules, which are connected together by $-CH_2-$

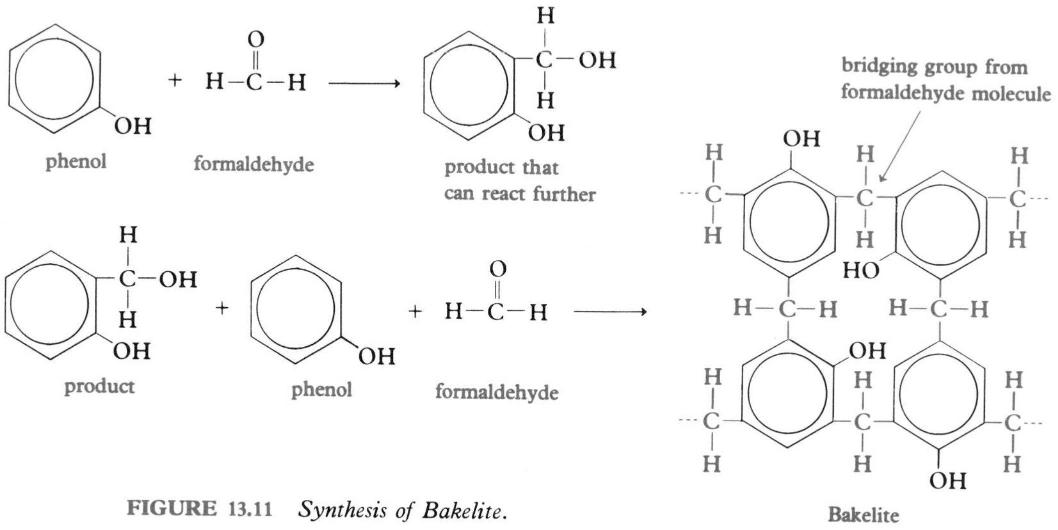

FIGURE 13.11 *Synthesis of Bakelite.*

Bakelite

bridges (see Figure 13.11). The product is a **polymer**. The molecules used to make it are **monomers**. Bakelite and related plastics containing phenol are called **phenolic resins**. Notice in the Bakelite structure that the formaldehyde molecules form the bridging $-CH_2-$ groups which hold the giant Bakelite molecules together. The number of these bridges vary. If there are not many $-CH_2-$ bridges, the plastic melts when it is heated and forms a solid again when it is cooled. Such a plastic is called **thermoplastic**. Many plastics do not soften appreciably when they are heated. These are called **thermosetting** plastics. These two terms are widely used to classify plastics.

As everyone knows, plastic objects contribute a lot to litter. To help with this problem, development is continuing on plastics that are biodegradable and do not accumulate in the environment. Recyclable plastics, which can be melted down and cast into new objects, have also been developed.

Polyethylene is the plastic produced in the largest quantities. It is made by polymerizing many ethylene molecules to form extremely long chains of $-CH_2-$ groups as shown in Section 10.3.

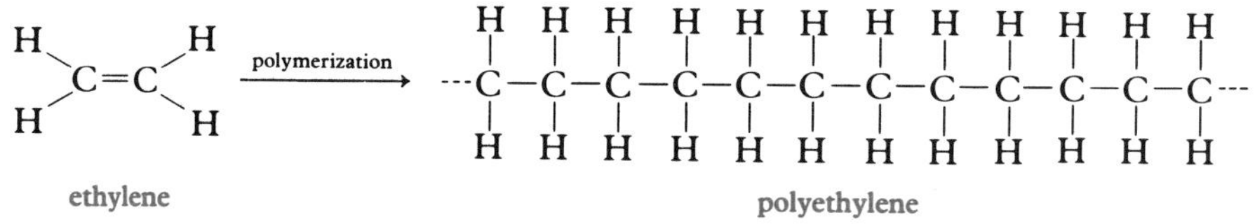

ethylene

polyethylene

Polyethylene is used to make bottles, toys, plastic sheeting, plastic bags, and many other things. Commercial production of this plastic began in 1939.

Polypropylene is a harder, tougher plastic than polyethylene. It is made by polymerizing propylene.

propylene → polymerization → polypropylene

It is used to make battery cases, bottles, pipes, and valves. It resists water and rot and is used to make indoor-outdoor carpets.

Styrene forms a polymer known as *polystyrene.*

styrene → polymerization → polystyrene

This popular plastic is used to make wrapping materials, insulting foams, and many other products.

Polyvinyl chloride, PVC, is a popular plastic used to make a variety of things ranging from sturdy plastic pipes to raincoats. It is made by the polymerization of vinyl chloride.

vinyl chloride → polymerization → polyvinyl chloride, PVC

A major occupational health hazard developed in the PVC industry when, in the early 1970's, workers who had been exposed to vinyl chloride developed a rare form of liver cancer. This has forced controls, which have resulted in greatly decreased exposure levels. A rather expensive retooling of the PVC industry has been necessary as a result.

Several other plastics are important in specialized applications, though not produced in such large quantities as those described above. A polymer of methyl methacrylate forms clear, glass-like sheets and is used in plastic windows under the names Plexiglas and Lucite.

methyl methacrylate, a monomer → polymerization → Plexiglas or Lucite plastic

Teflon is an especially interesting and useful plastic. It is made by polymerizing tetrafluoroethylene.

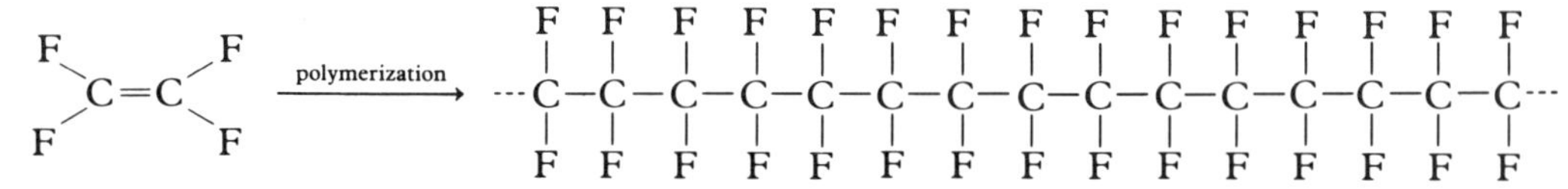

tetrafluoroethylene   teflon

The product is very resistant to heat and chemical attack. It can be shaped to make valves and other mechanical parts and is especially useful for coating surfaces exposed to chemicals and heat. The "no-stick" frying pan is the most familiar example.

13.12

Synthetic Fibers

Next to detergents and cosmetics no product of the chemical industry is advertised more widely than synthetic fibers. As the chemical nature of natural fibers became known, chemists began to think of the possibilities for making synthetics. Chemists found, for example, that cotton is a cellulose polymer and silk and wool are protein polymers. So, it was reasoned that similar substances, with perhaps improved properties, could be made synthetically.

The first synthetic fiber was rayon, made in 1891 by French chemists trying to prepare synthetic silk. This polymer is made by treating cellulose with sodium hydroxide and carbon disulfide, CS_2 (Figure 13.12). This process breaks up the cellulose polymer, which is then reformed and squeezed in liquid form through tiny holes in a

FIGURE 13.12

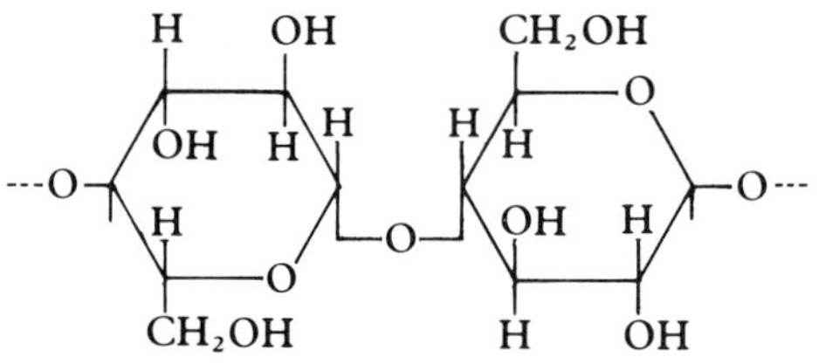

cellulose

device called a spinnaret. The tiny continuous filaments that are produced are then spun into threads or cords of the desired size. What this process accomplishes is the conversion of short cellulose fibers, useless for making thread, into long, continuous fibers, which are quite strong (see Figure 13.13).

In 1927 the du Pont, company started a massive effort to discover laboratory preparations for synthetic fibers and other useful polymers.

FIGURE 13.13 *Structures of cellulose and rayon fibers.*

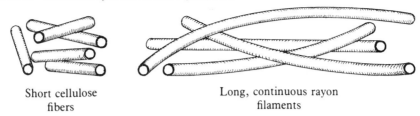

Short cellulose
fibers

Long, continuous rayon
filaments

This resulted in the preparation of nylon in 1935, probably the most successful synthetic fiber of all time. The term, "nylon," describes a class of materials with an amide group linking the parts of the polymer together.

nylon polymer

Nylon filaments are made by squeezing hot, melted nylon through holes in a spinnaret. The size of the filament can be varied all the way from the ultrafine ones used in making nylon pantyhose to large, sturdy filaments in the cord bodies of truck tires. Thus, a thin nylon filament makes up the 3-lb test line on the reel of a fisherman who likes to pretend that a scrappy sunfish is a genuine challenge. A thicker filament is used for the 20-lb test line favored by fishermen who are more interested in the certainty of a catch than in the challenge of wrestling the fish to the net by skill rather than force.

The structure of the nylon molecule is such that nylon fibers stretch. This feature is lacking in many other synthetic fibers. The basic nylon structure can be varied greatly by changes in the organic molecules linked together by the amide linkage. Specialized nylons have been developed, which are used for making solid parts, such as bearings. One interesting nylon called Nomex stands up to high temperatures. It is made into fire retardant clothing.

Success with rayon and nylon, coupled with increased knowledge of organic chemistry and polymers, has led to the development of a wide variety of synthetic fibers. These go by brand names such as Acrylan, Creslan, Orlon, Dacron, Kodel, and Dynel. Orlon and Acrylan are made by polymerizing acrylonitrile.

acrylonitrile   Orlon and Acrylan type fibers

Since nylon was first introduced commercially in 1938, it has been manufactured in a wide range of textures and physical forms, some of which resemble silks, wools, cotton flannels, and brush bristles made from animal hair. (Courtesy of E. I. du Pont de Nemours and Co.)

Polymerization of terephthalic acid and ethylene glycol produces textile fibers of the Dacron type.

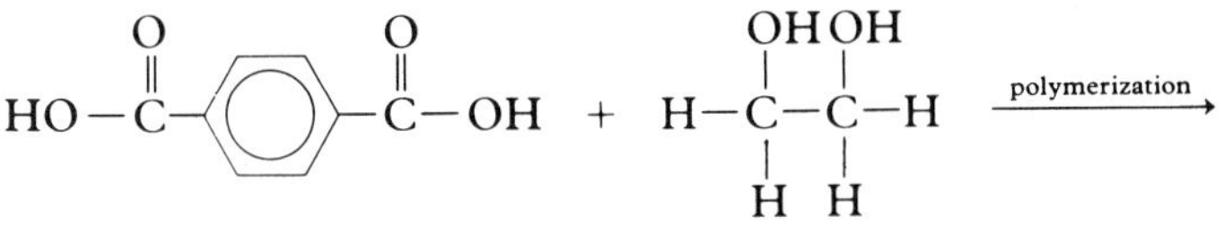

$$HO-\underset{\underset{O}{\|}}{C}-\bigcirc-\underset{\underset{O}{\|}}{C}-OH \quad + \quad H-\underset{\underset{H}{|}}{\overset{\overset{OH}{|}}{C}}-\underset{\underset{H}{|}}{\overset{\overset{OH}{|}}{C}}-H \xrightarrow{\text{polymerization}}$$

terephthalic acid   ethylene glycol

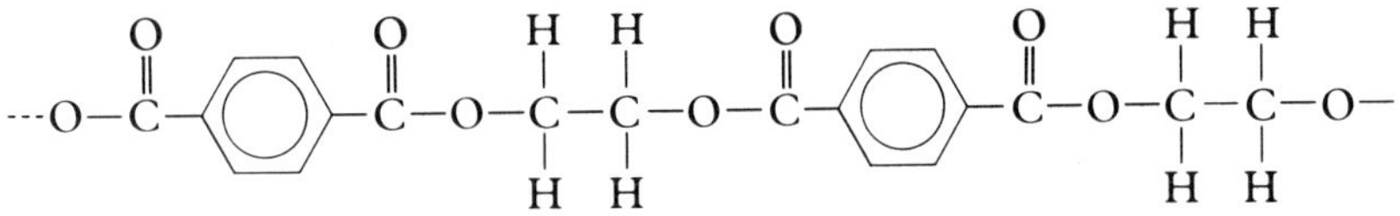

$$\cdots O-\underset{\underset{O}{\|}}{C}-\bigcirc-\underset{\underset{O}{\|}}{C}-O-\underset{\underset{H}{|}}{\overset{\overset{H}{|}}{C}}-\underset{\underset{H}{|}}{\overset{\overset{H}{|}}{C}}-O-\underset{\underset{O}{\|}}{C}-\bigcirc-\underset{\underset{O}{\|}}{C}-O-\underset{\underset{H}{|}}{\overset{\overset{H}{|}}{C}}-\underset{\underset{H}{|}}{\overset{\overset{H}{|}}{C}}-O-$$

Dacron-type textile fibers

13.13

Synthetic Rubber

The story of synthetic rubber in the U.S. is an interesting one. It may contain some lessons which can be applied to the current energy shortage. All rubber used to be manufactured from latex, a sap from rubber trees growing in the South Pacific area. Natural rubber is a polymer of isoprene

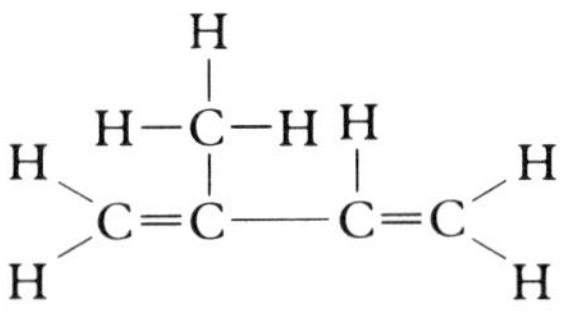

isoprene

and its basic structure is

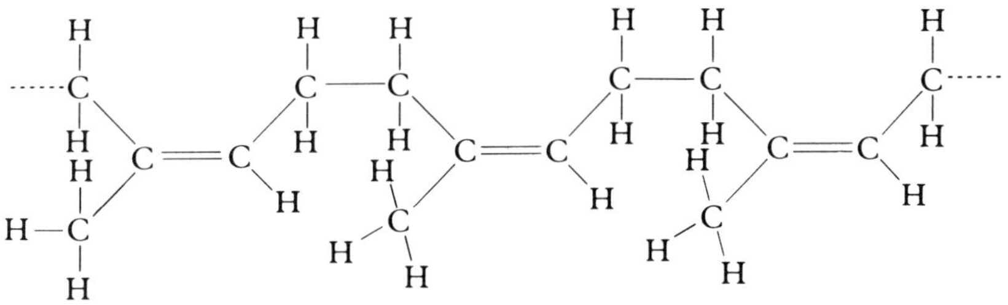

natural rubber

By 1920 most of the rubber tree plantations in the world were under the control of the empires of Great Britain and the Netherlands. In 1922 England set up a program called the Stevenson Plan designed to control the supply and price of rubber. Under the direction of Britain's Foreign Secretary, young Winston Churchill, the price of rubber on foreign markets went up fourfold in only four years. Interestingly, this drastic price increase was not sufficient to produce a synthetic rubber industry in the U.S. The British rubber cartel was joined by the Dutch in 1934, and prices were controlled to the benefit of both nations until World War II. With the fall of Malaya and Indonesia to Japan in 1942, the rubber situation in the U.S. became desperate. Synthetic rubber plants were constructed in an incredibly short time. U.S. production of synthetic rubber went from zero in 1940 to 670,000 tons in 1944.

Ironically, the synthetic rubber, which the U.S. was able to make during World War II, was developed in Germany. This styrene-butadiene rubber was first produced on a large scale by Germany's IG Farbenindustrie in 1933. It is a polymer of styrene and butadiene with about 70 parts butadiene and 30 parts styrene.

styrene   butadiene   synthetic rubber (Buna-S)

Although, with the state of the art at that time, it was not as good as natural rubber for the manufacture of tires and other applications, it did make the difference in providing rubber crucially needed by the U.S. in World War II.

Although natural rubber made a comeback after World War II, new developments in the rubber industry, combined with cheap petroleum raw material, gradually gave synthetic rubber the bulk of the rubber market. One of the major developments that helped synthetic rubber was the development of cold polymerization. This is a process that enables the rubber polymer to form at temperatures as low as 5°C. The rubber polymer has fewer branching side chains, which makes it of much higher quality. Oil extension and the addition of carbon black have made synthetic rubber an excellent material for tires by improving the properties of the rubber.

Polymers other than those made from styrene and butadiene are now used to manufacture rubber. These include polybutadiene, polyisoprene, and neoprene.

chloroprene   neoprene, a synthetic rubber,
                                         resistant to flame, chemicals, oil, heat

The major types of rubber and 1976 world production of each are given in Table 13.6. It is seen that synthetic rubbers account for

acrylonitrile   butadiene   butadiene, an
                                            acrylonitrile polymer rubber

Resistant to oils, fats, solvents; performs well at
extreme temperatures; used for making foam rubber.

approximately two-thirds of world production. This fraction is expected
to grow in coming years. This growth will depend upon the availability
and price of petroleum. Some authorities have even suggested "super"
rubber trees as a source of hydrocarbons for energy!

TABLE 13.6
World production of rubber in 1976.

Rubber Type	Production, Thousands of Tons
Natural rubber	3000
Synthetic rubber	
Styrenebutadiene	3800
Polybutadiene	810
Butyl rubber	370
Neoprene	300
Polyisoprene	280
Ethylene-propylene	210
Nitrile	180
Miscellaneous synthetics	110
Total synthetic rubber	6060

13.14

Paints

Paints are used to coat and protect surfaces and to provide a desired
color. Over 3 billion dollars are spent on paints, varnishes, and related
coatings in the U.S. each year. A paint is a liquid substance which can
be applied to a surface and form a solid or flexible film on the surface.
Most paints contain a *pigment*, which is suspended in the paint and
gives it color. The protective film of paint itself is called a *binder*,
or *nonvolatile vehicle*. A *volatile vehicle* (carrier) is included to thin the
paint and to act as a solvent.

Paint pigments are often made of metal oxides or metal salts.
These pigments absorb different colors of light and thus give the paint

its characteristic color. In addition they absorb ultraviolet light. The energy of ultraviolet light is so high that when it is absorbed by organic compounds in the paint, it breaks chemical bonds and causes the coating of paint to crack and deteriorate. When the light is absorbed by pigments, the energy is converted to harmless heat energy which does not damage the paint film.

The most widely used paint pigment is titanium dioxide, TiO_2, described earlier in this chapter. This pigment is used for white paint. It also gives the paint *hiding power,* the ability to cover and hide older paint or bare wood from view. Yellow color is provided by lead chromate, $PbCrO_4$. Various shades of red or brown are provided by mixtures of iron oxides. Chromium oxide, Cr_2O_3, is used in green pigments.

Carbon black is commonly used as a black pigment in paint. This substance is pure, finely divided carbon. It can be made in several ways. Typically, methane is burned without sufficient oxygen to complete the combustion

$$CH_4 + O_2 = C + 2 H_2O$$

and the carbon is collected. This may be done by allowing the carbon to deposit on a relatively cold steel surface, which is scraped continuously, or by recovering it in a cyclone (described as one of the unit operations in Section 13.3).

Metals are employed as pigments. Among these are powders of bronze, gold, and zinc. The most widely produced metal pigment is aluminum powder. It is made by pounding metallic aluminum into a fine powder.

Carbon black, produced commercially by the decomposition of hydrocarbons, is used by the rubber industry to reinforce elasticity, stiffness, and strength of the rubber. Some major applications of the fortified rubber are car tires, wire insulation, and recently car bumpers. About one quarter the weight of a tire amounts to carbon black. (Courtesy of Cabot Corp.)

Carbon black is used to give black pigment to paints, printers' ink, and even typewriter ribbon. (Courtesy of Cabot Corp.)

Insoluble dyes, or dyes bound chemically to an insoluble material such as aluminum oxide (lakes) are used as paint pigments. The dyes consist of a large variety of organic compounds. The manufacture of lakes for paint pigments can be a very complicated process, more of an art than a science. For example, one of the oldest organic pigments is madder lake. The dye in this lake is alizarin,

alizarin

a red dye which has been extracted from the root of the madder plant since ancient times. The recipe for making madder lake consists of boiling a mixture of an aluminum salt, a calcium salt, alizarin, and Turkey-red oil. Despite the fact that this pigment is widely used, the exact chemical nature of it is not known.

The nonvolatile vehicle in paint is a substance which, when exposed to the atmosphere or heat, reacts to form a dry coating. The natural products used for this purpose are called crying oils. Linseed oil is a typical drying oil. It contains a lot of fatty acids with double bonds which react with oxygen from the air to form complicated products of a polymer type. The fatty acids may also react with calcium salts (added as driers) to form insoluble soaps. With the development of synthetic polymers, many other kinds of nonvolatile vehicles are now possible. The names of some of these and their characteristics are listed in Table 13.7.

TABLE 13.7
Types of paint binders and nonvolatile vehicles.

Type of Binder	Characteristics
Acrylics	Durable, good color
Alkyds	General purpose, often blended with other binders
Amino resins	Used in baking finishes blended with alkyds. Contributes to good color and toughness. Known as ureas and melamines.
Cellulose nitrates and acetates	Fast drying binder used in lacquers
Epoxies	Resistant to chemicals
Phenolics	Yellow colored binders, which are resistant to chemicals
Polyurethanes	Flexible, resistant to abrasion
Polyvinyl acetates	Latex-form binders, which are low in cost and have good color retention
Silicones	Heat-resistant binders
Styrene-butadiene	Latex-form binders, which are low in cost and resistant to alkali

The volatile vehicle in paint often functions only as a thinner. In such cases it allows easy spreading of a nonvolatile vehicle, which otherwise would be too difficult to spread. Volatile hydrocarbons are used as vehicles for organic-soluble binders. Turpentine used to be widely employed for this purpose. Water is used for water-soluble binders, particularly in latex paints. The volatile vehicle, which may make up 50% of the paint volume, evaporates after the paint is applied, allowing the binder to form a smooth, hard coating.

Since World War II the nonprofessional painter has been blessed with water-based paints (see Figure 13.14). Such paints do not use organic

FIGURE 13.14
Formation of paint film.

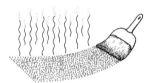

Styrene and butadiene are present as an emulsion of colloidal (very small) particles in water-based paints.

This paint is spread on a surface and the water evaporates.

A continuous rubber-like film of paint forms as the styrene and butadiene polymerize.

thinners and cleaners. Blobs of paint in unwanted locations, such as floors, sidewalks, and the painter's hands, can be washed off with water before the binder sets. These *latex paints* are a kind of synthetic rubber. One type contains about 85 parts styrene and 15 parts butadiene. This mixture forms an emulsion consisting of colloidal styrene and butadiene suspended in water.

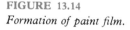

85 parts
styrene

15 parts
butadiene

$\xrightarrow[\text{polymerization}]{\text{drying}}$ coating of water-based latex paint

After the paint is spread, the water vehicle evaporates allowing the emulsion particles to bind together chemically to form a continuous film of paint. Although inexpensive, styrene-butadiene resin has some disadvantages. It does not adhere very well to surfaces, has a relatively long curing time, and often turns yellow with age. Polyvinylacetate has largely replaced it. The newer acrylic resins are even better. Though considerably more expensive, "acrylic latex" paints have become quite popular because of their high quality.

A typical water-based paint contains a number of ingredients. In addition to the polymeric nonvolatile vehicle suspended in a nonvolatile water vehicle, it contains pigment, such as titanium dioxide, to provide color and hiding power. To keep the pigment dispersed in the paint, dispersing agents are added. These are chemical compounds

The afterglow of fluorescent paints is due to certain phosphors mixed with the pigment. Flourescent paint is used industrially to coat equipment that will be used in dark, underground conditions. (Courtesy of Lawter Chemicals, Inc.)

such as tetrasodium pyrophosphate ($Na_4P_2O_7$). The large pyrophosphate anions bind to the colloidal particles of pigment, giving them an electrical charge and preventing them from clumping together. Clays, gums, and various organic compounds are added to prevent the colloidal particles of latex from sticking together. These are called protective colloids. Water-based paints tend to foam, so defoaming agents are added. One such compound is octyl alcohol, a straight-chain alcohol with 8 carbon atoms. Ethylene glycol may be added as antifreeze because freezing destroys the paint emulsion. The pH of the paint is important. Ammonia, NH_3, is sometimes added to prevent the paint from becoming too acidic. The ammonia odor often may be detected as the paint is applied.

Exposure to turpentine vapor was an occupational health hazard for painters before turpentine was replaced. Kidney damage sometimes resulted. Now the greatest hazard is from inhalation of paint droplets during spray painting.

13.15

Industrial Fermentation

Microorganisms—bacteria, fungi, and yeasts—are excellent chemical factories capable of making a number of chemicals ranging all the way from simple acetic acid to complicated antibiotics. The production of ethanol in alcoholic beverages is the oldest industrial chemical process. This process is carried out by yeasts. Fermentation processes by which microorganisms degrade organic materials and produce useful compounds have been employed to make a wide range of organic compounds for use in industry and elsewhere. The pattern has been for these processes to be replaced by chemical processes as soon as the chemists figure out how to do what the microorganisms accomplish so easily. However, microorganisms can make complicated organic compounds, which the chemists cannot synthesize in the laboratory. So fermentation is widely used to make expensive speciality chemicals.

The microorganisms employed in industrial fermentation belong to three classes (Figure 13.15). *Bacteria* are single-cell organisms which multiply by splitting in two (fission). They are quite small, about one-millionth of a meter (a micron) in size. They come in a variety of shapes, the most common of which are spherical and oblong. Different species of bacteria perform very different functions. Some are versatile and can use a variety of things for food. Others are very specialized in their functions. *Fungi* are microorganisms, largely characterized by branching structures or filaments known as hyphae. The diameters of these structures are usually little more than those of bacteria, but they can be several centimeters long. *Yeasts* are specialized forms of fungi which are used in a number of industrial processes. They do not form hyphae. Instead they occur as individual cells having spherical or oblong shapes. Yeasts are larger than bacteria, normally several microns across. Their occurrence as individual cells enables them to be suspended in liquids and to move when the medium is stirred. They multiply by forming buds. *Actinomycetes* are midway between bacteria and fungi. They are especially useful in producing antibiotics.

FIGURE 13.15
Common types of microorganisms used for industrial fermentation processes.

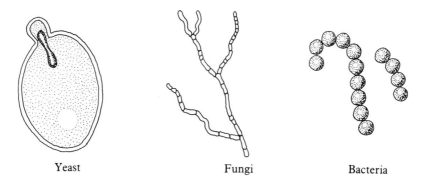

Yeast   Fungi   Bacteria

Fermentation is the process by which microorganisms use a raw material (often as a food) and convert it to a useful product. This raw material is called a *substrate*. In the chemical industry fermentation is a unit operation, just as a chemical reaction occurring in a chemical reactor is a unit process. Like chemical processes, fermentation requires a very careful control of conditions. The input of raw material must be controlled precisely. Products that are often toxic to the bacteria must be removed. Temperature must be controlled accurately. The micro-organism "catalysts" are especially important in fermentation processes. Like chemical catalysts, they are easily "poisoned." Contamination is an especially difficult problem because undesirable microorganisms can take over and ruin the process.

A mushroom is the fruitbody of a fungus. Its only function is to produce and disperse microscopic spores that can germinate under suitable conditions. Many mushroom species are toxic to man, and a few lethal. (Courtesy of Massachusetts Audubon Society; Grant Haist, photographer)

The production of ethyl alcohol from carbohydrates is the best example of a fermentation process. Normally some form of grain starch is the basic raw material used. This carbohydrate is treated with an enzyme, diastase,

$$2\,(C_6H_{10}O_5)_x \quad + x\,H_2O \xrightarrow[\text{diastase}]{\text{enzyme}} x\,C_{12}H_{22}O_{11}$$

starch,   maltose,
a large polymer carbohydrate   a dissacharide sugar

to produce a dissacharide sugar. This sugar can be utilized as an energy source by yeast. In the absence of oxygen, the yeast first breaks the dissacharide down to a simple sugar

$$C_{12}H_{22}O_{11} + H_2O \xrightarrow[\text{enzyme}]{\text{maltase}} 2\,C_6H_{12}O_6$$

maltose   glucose

with an enzyme called maltase. Another yeast enzyme, zymase, then acts on the glucose to produce ethyl alcohol.

$$C_6H_{12}O_6 \xrightarrow[\text{enzyme}]{\text{zymase}} 2\,C_2H_5OH + 2\,CO_2\uparrow + \text{energy for the yeast}$$

glucose   ethyl alcohol

After the alcohol level reaches a concentration of several percent in the solution, the yeast action stops.

Vinegar is manufactured by a fermentation process that is an extension of the one just described. Special bacteria called acetic acid bacteria are capable of converting the ethyl alcohol in hard cider, wine, and other substances to acetic acid. On an industrial scale this is accomplished by pumping the liquid over wood shavings in a large tank (Figure 13.16). The shavings develop a layer of acetic acid bacteria. The bacteria are exposed to both air and the fermenting liquid. This enables the reaction to go very rapidly. The dilute solution of ethyl

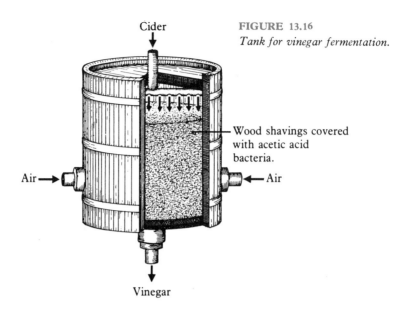

Cider

FIGURE 13.16
Tank for vinegar fermentation.

Wood shavings covered
with acetic acid
bacteria.

Air →   ← Air

Vinegar

alcohol is oxidized to form a dilute solution of acetic acid, which is vinegar.

$$C_2H_5OH + O_2 \xrightarrow[\text{bacteria}]{\text{acetic acid}} CH_3CO_2H + H_2O$$

ethyl alcohol   acetic acid
in hard cider   in cider vinegar

Fermentation is most commonly used for the production of anti-biotics including penicillin, streptomycin, chloramphenicol, dureomycin, and erythromycin. Amino acids can be produced from fermentation processes. The most important of these is lysine, synthesized by a mutant strain of the bacteria, *Escherichia coli,* which converts carbo-hydrates and ammonia to lysine. (See Chapter 11 for a discussion of amino acids, proteins, and carbohydrates.) Since lysine is the amino acid most frequently lacking in proteins which do not have a good amino acid balance, this conversion is potentially very important for improving nutrition. Citric acid, widely used as a food additive, is produced by the action of *Aspergillus niger* on molasses. The vitamin, riboflavin, is synthesized by fungi called *Eremothecium ashbyii* or *Ashbya gossypii.* Vitamin B$_{12}$ is synthesized by several types of bacteria. Fermentation processes for producing this essential vitamin have become so efficient that the price dropped from about $140 per gram in 1960 to $8.00 per gram in 1970.

Industrial fermentation remains an important industry for the production of chemicals that cannot be manufactured by man. In many cases it is the most efficient means of manufacture, even when a chemical process is available. Advances in genetics continue to make available specialized types of microorganisms, which can carry out new fermentation processes, or accomplish older ones more efficiently.

One of the exciting possibilities for fermentation processes is the manufacture of food from waste materials, or inexpensive raw materials. In principle, yeasts and bacteria could be used to produce protein from cellulose wastes and synthetic nitrogen. This could be one solution to the world protein shortage.

13.16

Wood Products and Paper

For centuries wood was the predominant organic raw material. It is still a source of a vast variety of materials in the U.S. and ranks first world-wide. The wood and wood products industry is the fifth largest industry in the U.S. (Figure 13.17). Forests cover one-third of the U.S. surface area.

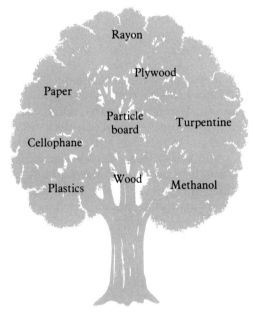

FIGURE 13.17
Many important products come from trees.

Chemically, wood is a complicated substance composed of long cells having thick walls of cellulose (see Figure 13.12) and lignin. Lignin is a complex binding material containing groups such as those shown in Figure 13.18. The lignin acts as a sort of glue to hold the wood structure together.

Wood contains a variety of resins, tars, and pitches that can be extracted with an alcohol-benzene mixture. The wood remaining from such an extraction is about three-fourths cellulose and other polysaccharides. Inorganic ash makes up several tenths of a percent of solid wood.

FIGURE 13.18

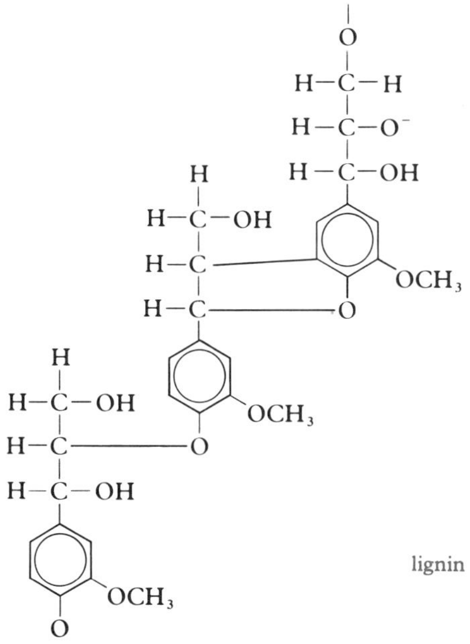

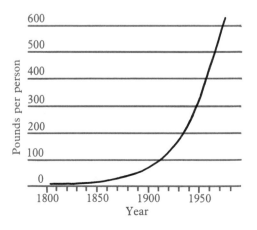

lignin

A wide variety of organic compounds can be extracted from wood by water, alcohol-benzene, ether, and steam distillation. These compounds include tannins, pigments, sugars, starch, cyclitols, gums, mucilages, pectins, galactans, terpenes, hydrocarbons, acids, esters, fats, fatty acids, aldehydes, resins, sterols, and waxes. Substantial amounts of methanol (sometimes still called wood alcohol) are extracted from wood. Wood alcohol used to be a major source of liquid fuel.

A chief use of wood is for paper manufacture. The widespread use of paper is a mark of an industrialized society. Per capita consumption of paper has increased throughout U.S. history as shown in Figure 13.19. The manufacture of paper is a highly advanced science (and an art). Paper consists essentially of cellulosic fibers tightly pressed together. The lignin fraction must be removed from wood leaving the cellulosic fraction for paper manufacture.

FIGURE 13.19
Per capita paper consumption in the U.S.

Many products besides paper are made from wood fibers and particles. These include fiberboard (such as that used for insulation, panelling, furniture, and electrical instrument panels), paper-base laminates (layers of paper held together by a resin and formed into the desired structures at high temperatures and pressures), particle board (consisting of wood particles bonded together by a phenol-formaldehyde or urea-formaldehyde resin), and nonwoven textile substitutes consisting of wood fibers held together by adhesives.

Wood is an excellent source of many chemical products. Charcoal from wood has been prized for cooking and heating since ancient times. The volatile fraction of wood (about two-thirds by weight) yields water, tar, turpentine, oils, acetic acid, methanol, acetone, pyroligneous acid, creosote oil, and pitch. Distillation of wood is no longer an industry widely practiced in the U.S. because of the development of cheaper petroleum substitutes. However, with increasing petroleum prices, there may be some revival of this industry.

Wood cellulose and hemicellulose are hydrolyzable by acid to yield the sugars glucose, arabinose, mannose, xylose, and galactose. This hydrolysis of cellulose

$$[C_6H_{10}O_5]_x + x\ H_2O = x\ C_6H_{12}O_6 \qquad x = 10,000\text{--}15,000$$

yields around 90% glucose. Sugars decompose under the conditions required to hydrolyze cellulose and hemicellulose, so that conditions must be balanced carefully to attain maximum yields. Fortunately, glucose is the most resistant to decomposition.

The two major processes employed for wood hydrolysis are the Bergius-Rheinau process and the Madison process. The Bergius-Rheinau process consists of (1) treating wood chips with 40–45% by weight hydrochloric acid at ambient temperatures, (2) removing the solution containing hydrochloric acid and approximately 25% by weight sugar, (3) removal of hydrochloric acid by distillation, and (4) recovery of sugar by spray-drying. The Madison process makes use of 0.5% sulfuric acid in digesters at pressures of approximately 150 lb/in² and at temperatures of 130°–180°C. The digesters first used in Germany were lead lined, and one can wonder if anybody ever thought to analyze the product for lead! Lime is added to remove the sulfuric acid as calcium sulfate, and sugar is left in solution.

Considering that total wood wastes in the U.S. amount to around 60 million tons each year, the potential of sugar production from wood looks very attractive, particularly when sugar prices are high. Added to this may be the enormous tonnage of cellulosic agricultural wastes produced each year. Recovery of sulfur from high-sulfur fuels promises relatively abundant and cheap sulfuric acid. Fermentation-produced ethanol shows promise as a useful gasoline supplement. All of these factors involving shortages of energy, shortages of food, over-production of solid wastes, and the necessity of removing pollutant sulfur may converge to result in thriving wood hydrolysis industries in major wood-producing countries.

Obviously wood is an extremely important resource, not only as a structural material but as a raw material for the manufacture of paper, chemicals, and even food. Although current (1977) production of wood in the U.S. exceeds demand to a slight extent, demand almost certainly will continue to rise so that severe shortages are projected for the year 2000. Trees may be grown on soil and terrain not practical for agricultural crops, and increased production of wood should be encouraged by every means possible. Because of improper care and management, hundreds of thousands of acres of U.S. land are covered with "junk trees" and brush. This is a waste that can no longer be afforded, and some of this land could be converted to well-managed, properly maintained, productive forests. New "super trees," advanced forest management, fertilization, and pest control can increase wood production substantially.

13.17

Industrial Health Hazards

As pointed out throughout this chapter, many chemicals are hazardous to worker health. Additional health hazards continue to be revealed, often only after years of worker exposure. One such example is provided by vinyl chloride, which was recognized as causing a rare form of liver cancer in the mid-1970's, approximately two decades after industrial use of this chemical became widespread. Another example is that of Kepone, a pesticide that produced dreadful health problems for exposed workers. Under the auspices of the U.S. Department of Labor Occupational Safety and Health Administration (OSHA), industrial exposure to chemicals has been increasingly regulated. Setting up reasonable regulations that protect workers without being unnecessarily cumbersome and expensive is quite a difficult problem.

Substances known to be quite toxic should be handled in a regulated area. Only employees with specific training and equipment are

WARNING!!
CANCER-SUSPECT SUBSTANCE
EXPOSED IN THIS AREA.
Impervious Suit
Including Gloves, Boots,
and Air-Supplied Hood
Required at ALL Times.

AUTHORIZED
PERSONNEL
ONLY

allowed to enter regulated areas. A daily roster of employees entering the area is kept. Activities likely to lead to ingestion of hazardous substances, either by mouth or inhalation, are prohibited in a regulated area. Such activities include eating, drinking, smoking, and sweeping. Showers and changing rooms may be required in connection with the regulated area. The area must be under negative air pressure. This means that air flows into the area, preventing vapors from getting out into unregulated areas. Signs are required warning of the specific hazard.

Cancer causing substances, carcinogens, are of most concern among the chemicals that are occupational health hazards. Fourteen of these, which have been recognized and are regulated, are listed in Table 13.8.

TABLE 13.8
*Carcinogens to which workers should not be exposed.**

Compound	Uses	Hazards
4-nitrobiphenyl	Chemical analysis	May cause bladder cancer
Alpha-naphthylamine	Anti-oxidant, dye manufacture, color film manufacture	May cause bladder cancer
4,4'-methylene bis(2-chloroaniline)	Plastic curing agent	May cause bladder cancer
Methyl-chloromethyl ether	Ion exchange resin manufacture	Usually contaminated with carcinogenic bis(chloromethyl) ether
3,3'-dichlorobenzidine	Dye manufacture	Known carcinogen
Bis(chloromethyl) ether	Ion exchange resin manufacture	Causes lung cancer
Beta-naphthylamine	Dye manufacture, reagent	Causes bladder cancer
Benzidine	Manufacture of dyes, rubber, plastics, printing ink	Causes bladder cancer
4-aminodiphenyl	No longer produced	Causes bladder cancer
Ethyleneimine	Paper and textile treating	Known carcinogen
Beta-propiolactone	Plastics manufacture	Suspected human carcinogen
2-acetylaminofluorene	No longer produced	Suspected human carcinogen
4-dimethylaminoazobenzene	No longer used, once a widely used dye	Suspected human carcinogen
N-nitrosodimethylamine	No longer used	Known carcinogen

* Most compounds listed are known to cause cancer in animals. The assumption is made that they are carcinogenic to humans, too.

Chapter Summary

The chemical industry is vast, complex, and an essential part of any industrialized society. About 9% of shipments from U.S. industrial plants consist of chemicals and allied products. In 1975, the dollar value of these products in the U.S. was $87 billion, exceeding the value of output from automobile assembly plants or steel mills. The U.S. chemical industry employs more than 1 million people.

Much of the production of the chemical industry is in big volume chemicals such as oxygen, nitrogen, ammonia, sodium hydroxide, chlorine, ethylene, benzene, and sulfuric acid. For each U.S. citizen, American industry processes 150 pounds of ammonia, 300 pounds of sulfuric acid, and 100 pounds of ethylene per year. Other products, such as drugs, specialty chemicals, and dyes, may be produced in quantities of only a few thousand pounds or less. Nevertheless, these products are quite important.

Chemicals and allied chemical products are manufactured in a series of operations called *unit operations*. These involve processes such as *heat exchange* and *distillation*. The measurement of processes in a chemical plant is crucial to the control of processes. Various things measured include *temperature, pressure,* and *flow rate.*

There are many classes of organic chemicals produced by the chemical industry. Much of this production is used in the manufacture of plastics, synthetic fibers, synthetic rubber, paints and surface coatings, and other allied chemical products.

Bacteria, yeasts, and fungi are used to produce some chemicals. The process for doing this is called *industrial fermentation*. Wood is an important natural source of many chemical products. Paper making from wood is a sophisticated chemical process.

Many chemicals are hazardous to health. Exposure to these chemicals in industry is regulated. Persons working with chemicals should be well aware of any hazards involved and follow precautions carefully.

Chapter Review Questions

The following questions are designed as a self-teaching tool to help you review Chapter 13. The answers to each question follow. See Chapter Review Questions for Chapter 1 for further instructions.

1. The types of unit operations discussed in this chapter are _____, _____, _____, and _____.

2. In terms of continuity, distillation can be either a _____ process or a _____ process.

3. Temperature in a chemical process is commonly measured with a _____ or a _____.

4. The most widely produced chemical in the U.S. is _____, manufactured mostly by the _____ process.

5. Among the many uses of sulfuric acid is production of _____ fertilizer, _____ of steel, and as an _____.

6. Two major chemicals produced together by the same process are _____ and _____.

7. These two chemicals are produced by the _____ of brine.

8. Chlorine is made at the electrode known as the _____; sodium is made at the _____.

9. Benzene hexachloride, carbon tetrachloride, and vinyl chloride are all examples of a class of compounds called _____.

10. Almost three-fourths of the synthetic ammonia produced in the U.S. each year goes for the manufacture of _____.

11. A major use for ammonia, which involves alternately liquifying it and allowing it to evaporate, is _____.

12. The five major types of plastics are _____, _____, _____, _____, and _____.

13. The two most widely produced types of synthetic fibers are _____ and _____.

14. The physical definition of a plastic is a substance which can be _____.

15. A plastic that melts when heated is called a _____ plastic.

16. Physically, polypropylene is _____ and _____ than polyethylene.

17. The plastic used to make plastic pipe is _____.

18. The first common synthetic fiber, which is made from cellulose, is _____.

19. Nylon monomers are held together with the _____ linkage.

20. Natural rubber is a polymer of _____.

21. The two monomers in the first synthetic rubber produced on a large scale in the U.S. are _____ and _____.

22. Paint receives its color from the _____.

23. The protective film in paint is called the _____, which is carried by a _____.

24. The general name of a process that makes use of bacteria, fungi, and yeasts to produce chemical products is _____.

25. The cell walls in wood are made of _____ and _____.

26. The Bergius-Rheinau process is used to _____ wood and make _____ from it.

Answers to Chapter Review Questions

1. heat exchange, distillation, filtration, separation of dust from gas

2. batch, continuous

3. thermocouple, thermistor
5. phosphate, pickling, electrolyte
7. electrolysis
9. chlorinated hydrocarbons
11. industrial refrigeration

4. sulfuric acid, contact
6. sodium hydroxide, chlorine gas
8. anode, cathode
10. nitrogen fertilizers
12. phenolic resins, polyethylene, polypropylene, polystyrene, polyvinyl chloride

13. polyester, nylon
15. thermoplastic
17. polyvinyl chloride
19. amide
21. styrene, butadiene
23. binder or nonvolatile vehicle, volatile vehicle
25. cellulose, lignin

14. molded and shaped
16. harder, tougher
18. rayon
20. isoprene
22. pigment
24. industrial fermentation

26. hydrolyze, sugar

Exercises for Chapter 13

1. A laboratory chemist finds that a particular reaction must be carried out at 100°C. This is accomplished by heating the reaction flask on a hot plate. The next reaction in making the product requires that the reaction mixture be cooled to 25°C. Describe how the chemical engineer would accomplish that step in designing a chemical plant.

2. Define what is meant by unit operation.

3. Describe an industrial chemical that is cheap, a strong acid, a good dehydrating agent, and nonvolatile.

4. The preparation of sodium hydroxide and chlorine gas are shown in the text as two half-reactions (involving electrons) and one reaction involving sodium dissolved in mercury metal. Combine these reactions to show one overall reaction for the preparation of sodium hydroxide and chlorine from sodium chloride in water.

5. Hydrogen gas is produced in the manufacture of sodium hydroxide. Explain why it might be desirable to locate an ammonia manufacturing plant next to a sodium hydroxide manufacturing facility.

6. Calcium hypochlorite slowly decomposes to give oxygen gas in water. Write a chemical reaction for this process.

7. Why do most of the organic compounds used to make plastics have $C = C$ bonds? Illustrate with a chemical reaction.

8. In earlier chapters oxidation was defined in terms of what happens to electrons. Fluorine has a very strong attraction for electrons. Try to write a chemical reaction for the reaction of teflon and O_2. Then explain why this reaction does not go.

9. Organic dyes used in paints are normally put in the form of *lakes*. Why cannot the dye ordinarily just be added to the liquid plant?

10. A paint contains the compounds H_2O, $Na_4P_2O_7$, TiO_2, octyl alcohol, and ethylene glycol. Name the purpose served by each.

11. Calculate the volume of carbon dioxide gas at standard temperature and pressure produced in the manufacture of 1000 liters of beer, which is 3.2% alcohol. Assume that a liter of beer weighs 1000 g.

12. Match the microorganism in the left column with the fermentation product in the right column.

Aspergillus niger	ethyl alcohol
Escherichia coli (special strain)	vinegar
Eremthecium ashbyii	riboflavin
yeast	lysine
acetic acid bacteria	citric acid

13. In addition to the electrolysis process described in this chapter, sodium hydroxide can be produced by the reaction of sodium carbonate and slaked lime. Write this chemical reaction.

14. What does the enzyme, diastase, have in common with hydrochloric acid or sulfuric acid?

15. A hot, liquid, organic chemical is to be cooled by cold water flowing through a tube and shell heat exchanger. Label in the following drawing each of the inlets and outlets for (a) cold water (b) warmed water, (c) cooled organic chemical and explain the reasons for your choice.

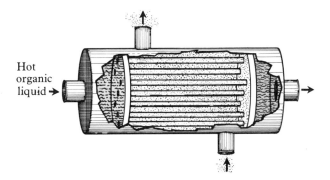

Hot
organic
liquid →

16. Sulfuric acid has a strong attraction for water. A lot of heat is released when sulfuric acid and water react. Explain the reason for the rule that sulfuric acid is always added to water, water is *never* added to sulfuric acid.

17. In purchasing fertilizer, a farmer has a choice between anhydrous ammonia, NH_3, at $150 per ton or NH_4NO_3 at $100 per ton. Calculate which is the best buy per ton of nitrogen.

Cornfield. (Courtesy of Massachusetts Audubon Society; Mary S. Shakespeare, photographer)

14

Agricultural and Soil Chemistry

14.1

Production of Food

Food is the most basic of human needs. In recent years chemistry has made an enormous impact upon food production. The relationship of chemistry to food production is discussed in this and the following chapters. The ability to produce food is the most important asset that almost any nation may have. This is true even in the U.S., a nation that produces more food than it consumes. Agricultural products are a major item of trade with which petroleum and other scarce raw materials may be obtained. In the field of international relations, a well-stocked granary has more influence than a nuclear arsenal—and is certainly a more powerful influence for good.

Any consideration of food must start with soil. Therefore, most of this chapter deals with soil. The tissue-thin layer of soil on the Earth's surface produces the food upon which most living things depend for their survival. In agricultural areas the standard of living is directly related to the quality of soil. Good soil—and a good climate to make it productive—are extremely valuable.

The importance of soil conservation has been realized by agriculturists for many decades. Long before ecology became a popular movement, soil conservation had received much emphasis. This was reinforced by the disastrous dust bowl days of the 1930's when large quantities of valuable topsoil were blown away from the land in many areas. Because of their efforts to save and enhance the quality of soil, enlightened farmers were the first of the environmentalists.

14.2

The Nature of Soil

Soil is the term used to describe many substances found on the Earth's surface that are capable of supporting plant life. Soil generally has a loose texture. It consists of solid mineral and organic matter, water, and air spaces. The mineral part of soil is formed from the parent rock by **weathering**. This is the process involving physical, chemical, and biological action that breaks rock down to smaller crumbly particles. The organic portion of the soil consists of the remains of plants in various stages of decay. There is a lot of life in soil. Generally, bacteria, fungi, and small animals, such as earthworms, are abundant.

The solid fraction of a typical productive soil is approximately 5% organic matter and 95% inorganic matter. Some soils such as "peat" soils, may contain as much as 95% organic material. Other soils have as little as 1% organic matter. Typical soils show distinctive layers with increasing depth. These layers are called **horizons**. The top layer is the *A* horizon, or **topsoil**. It is usually several inches thick. It is the layer where most of the biological activity occurs, and where most of the organic matter can be found. The next layer is the *B* horizon, or

Aerial view of farmland. (Courtesy of Aero Service Division, Western Geophysical Company of America)

subsoil. It receives material such as organic matter, salts, or clay particles leached from the topsoil. The *C* horizon is composed of weathered parent rocks from which the soil originated. These horizons and their subdivisions make up the soil profile shown in Figure 14.1.

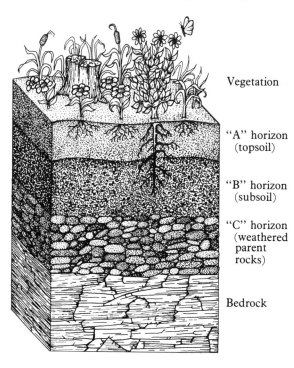

Vegetation

"A" horizon
(topsoil)

"B" horizon
(subsoil)

"C" horizon
(weathered
parent
rocks)

Bedrock

FIGURE 14.1
*Soil profile
showing soil
horizons.*

14.3

Water and Air in the Soil

A tremendous amount of water is required in the production of most plant materials. For example, several hundred pounds of water are required to produce one pound of dry hay. This water comes from the soil and passes upward through the plant structure carrying nutrients and other materials with it. It enters the atmosphere through the plant leaves in a process called transpiration (see Figure 14.2). Not all water in soil is held to the same degree. Water present in the larger spaces, or pores, in the soil structure readily drains away. Water held in smaller pores is held much more strongly. Soils high in organic matter may hold a relatively large amount of water compared to other soils but do not make the water so available to plants because of physical and chemical sorption of the water by organic matter.

A waterlogged (water-saturated) soil undergoes drastic changes in physical, chemical, and biological properties. Oxygen in such soil is rapidly used up by the respiration of microorganisms as they decompose organic matter. In waterlogged soils the bonds holding very small soil

Shoestring rills indicating soil erosion appear on a devegetated hillside. Vegetation would have protected the soil surface from the force of water that can stir up fine soil particles and wash them off the land. (Courtesy of USDA, Soil Conservation Service; Frank M. Roadman, photographer)

particles together are broken, resulting in a breakdown of soil structure. Thus, the excess water in such soil is detrimental to plant growth; and the soil does not contain the air required by most plant roots. Most useful crops, with the notable exception of rice, cannot grow on water-logged soils.

Roughly 25% of the volume of a typical soil is composed of air-filled pores. Whereas the normal dry atmosphere at sea level contains 20.95% oxygen and 0.0314% carbon dioxide, by volume, these percentages may be decidedly different in air held by soil because of the decay of organic matter (represented by the general formula [CH$_2$O]):

$$[CH_2O] + O_2 \longrightarrow CO_2 + H_2O$$

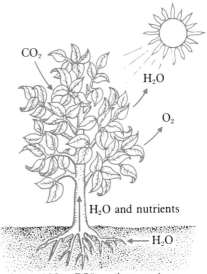

FIGURE 14.2

Plant transporting water from the soil to the atmosphere by transpiration. Nutrients are also carried from the soil to the plant extremities by this process. Plants remove CO$_2$ from the atmosphere and add O$_2$ by photosynthesis. The reverse occurs during plant respiration.

Soil air generally contains proportionately less oxygen than atmospheric air and may consist of as little as 15% oxygen. The proportion of carbon dioxide in soil air may range up to several hundred times as much as in the atmosphere. Thus, the decay of organic matter in soil may increase the equilibrium level of dissolved carbon dioxide in ground water, a phenomenon of considerable geochemical significance. Figure 14.3 illustrates the fine structure of soil showing solid matter, water, and air spaces.

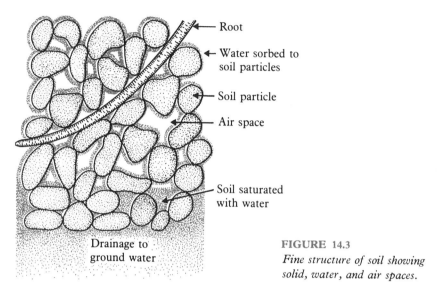

— Root

← Water sorbed to soil particles

— Soil particle

— Air space

— Soil saturated with water

Drainage to ground water

FIGURE 14.3

Fine structure of soil showing solid, water, and air spaces.

14.4

Mineral Matter in the Soil

Among the common elements in the Earth's crust are oxygen, 46.6%; silicon, 27.7%; aluminum, 8.1%; iron, 5.0%; calcium, 3.6%; sodium, 2.8%; potassium, 2.6%; and magnesium, 2.1%. Minerals composed of these elements constitute most of the mineral fraction of the soil. Since 74.3% of the Earth's crust consists of silicon and oxygen, minerals containing these two elements are especially prevalent in soil. Finely divided quartz, SiO_2, is a common soil mineral component. Among the silicates, orthoclase ($KAlSi_3O_8$), albite ($NaAlSi_3O_8$), and epidote ($4\,CaO \cdot 3\,(AlFe)_2O_3 \cdot 6\,SiO_2 \cdot H_2O$) are very common components of soil minerals. Iron oxides, particularly goethite, $FeO(OH)$, and magnetite, Fe_3O_4, make up much of the mineral fraction of many soils; some iron oxides give soils a red color. Manganese oxides and titanium oxides are encountered in abundance in some soils. Of the carbonates, calcium carbonate is a common soil constituent.

The clay minerals occur widely and are chemically significant components of soils. These minerals are basically oxides of silicon, aluminum, and iron. They contain water and serve to bind cations, such as Ca^{2+}, Mg^{2+}, K^+, Na^+, and NH_4^+. Thus, these cations are held from leaching (washing away) by water but are available as plant nutrients. In water many clays are readily suspended as colloidal particles. As such, they may be leached from the soil or carried to lower soil layers.

14.5

Organic Matter in Soil

Although a good soil may consist of less than 5% organic matter, the organic matter in soil plays a very important role in determining soil productivity. It serves as a source of food for microorganisms in soil, undergoes important chemical reactions in soil, and helps determine its physical properties. Most of the soil's organic matter is **humus**. This is a dark, water-insoluble material left over when plants decay. It resists further decay. Peat moss is a humus material.

Getting enough organic matter into an organic-poor soil is difficult. Sometimes clover, which forms large plants containing a lot of organic matter, is used for this purpose. The clover is allowed to grow tall and then is plowed under to provide organic matter.

14.6

Nutrients in Soil

Plants, like humans, require good nutrition. Plant **macronutrients** are those which are required in large amounts. They go into making up the plant material itself and the fluids in the plant. **Micronutrients** are elements that are essential, but only at very low levels. They are generally involved in the enzymes that carry out biochemical processes in the plant.

The elements generally recognized as essential macronutrients for plants are carbon, hydrogen, oxygen, nitrogen, phosphorus, potassium, calcium, magnesium, and sulfur. Of these, carbon, hydrogen, and oxygen are obtained from the atmosphere and from water. Nitrogen may be obtained directly from the atmosphere by some plants. This occurs through the action of nitrogen-fixing bacteria which exist with the plants. Most of the nitrogen and the rest of the macronutrients must be obtained from the soil. Of these, nitrogen, phosphorus, and potassium are the most likely to be lacking. They are commonly added to the soil as **fertilizers**.

Nitrogen is an essential component of proteins and other constituents of living matter. Plants and cereals grown on nitrogen-rich soils not only provide higher yields but are often substantially richer in protein and, therefore, more nutritious. Nitrogen is most generally available to plants as nitrate ion, NO_3^-. However, some plants such as rice may utilize ammonium nitrogen; other plants find this form of nitrogen toxic. When nitrogen is applied to soils in the ammonium form, nitrifying bacteria perform an essential function in converting it to available nitrate ion.

Plants may absorb excessive amounts of nitrate nitrogen from soil. This phenomenon occurs particularly in heavily fertilized soils under drought conditions. When forage crops containing excessive amounts of nitrate are fed to animals, particularly ruminant animals such as cattle, poisoning may result. Plants containing excessive levels of nitrate can endanger man when used for ensilage, an animal food consisting of finely chopped plant material such as partially matured whole corn plants fermented in a structure called a silo. Under the reducing conditions of fermentation, nitrate in ensilage may be reduced to NO_2 gas, which can accumulate to high levels in enclosed silos. It is not generally realized that NO_2 is highly toxic, and in some respects it is more dangerous than hydrogen cyanide. There have been many reported cases of persons being killed by NO_2 that had accumulated in silos. For this reason, NO_2 poisoning is commonly called "silo-fillers disease."

Nitrogen fixation is the process by which atmospheric N_2 is converted to nitrogen-containing chemical compounds, which can be used by plants. Before widespread introduction of nitrogen fertilizers, soil nitrogen was provided primarily by legumes. These are plants such as soybeans, alfalfa, and clover that contain on their root structures bacteria capable of fixing atmospheric nitrogen. Leguminous plants have a symbiotic (mutually advantageous) relationship with the bacteria that provide their nitrogen. Legumes may add very significant quantities of nitrogen to soil. This may be as much as 100 lb of nitrogen per acre each year. This is an amount comparable to that commonly applied as synthetic fertilizer. Soil nitrogen levels may be maintained by rotating legumes with plants that only consume nitrogen. This fact was recognized by agriculturists as far back as the Roman era.

As shown in Figure 14.4, nitrogen-fixing bacteria exist in legumes on **root nodules**. The rod-shaped bacteria, which fix the nitrogen in the root nodules, are members of a special genus of bacteria called *Rhizobium*. They carry out the overall reaction

$$N_2 \text{ (atmosphere)} \xrightarrow{Rhizobium} \text{chemically bound N (plant material)}$$

Curiously, legume root nodules also contain a form of hemoglobin (the oxygen-carrying substance in blood) that is involved in the nitrogen-fixing process.

The addition of nitrogen compounds to soil by man's activities has caused some problems. Groundwater and surface water is contaminated by nitrate salts in many agricultural areas. Some of this comes from nitrogen fertilizers. Livestock feedlots are also a major source of nitrate pollution. Modern feedlots are often very large and have a high population of animals. A steer produces about 18 times as much waste as a human. Therefore, water pollution from feedlots has become

FIGURE 14.4

A soybean plant showing root nodules where nitrogen is fixed. The soybean is a legume which makes much of its own nitrogen fertilizer. Producing up to 20 times as much protein per acre of land as beef, the soybean is emerging as a major source of protein for direct human consumption. Over 1.5 billion bushels of soybeans are produced in the U.S. each year. This crop and its products, such as soybean oil, are major export items.

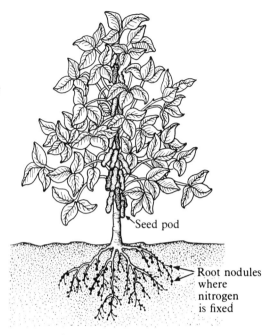

Seed pod

Root nodules
where
nitrogen
is fixed

A characteristic of certain plants called "legumes," such as the blackeyed pea plant, is that they can provide their own nitrogen by means of a Rhizobium bacteria stored in nodules on their roots. The bacteria convert atmospheric nitrogen into proteins the plant can utilize. (Courtesy of USDA, Soil Conservation Service; Morrison W. Liston, photographer)

a serious problem, even in areas with low human populations. Streams and reservoirs in such areas frequently are just as polluted as those in densely populated, highly industrialized areas. Feedlot waste treatment facilities (generally holding ponds) are now required for feedlots in some areas.

Waste treatment facilities are now required in some feedlots.

Nitrate in farm wells is an especially severe problem in some areas. This nitrate often comes from feedlots. Ruminant animals are especially susceptible to nitrate poisoning. These are animals, such as sheep and cattle, whose stomachs contain special bacteria that can break down plant cellulose, which humans and other animals cannot use for food. The stomachs of ruminant animals also contain bacteria capable of changing nitrate ion to toxic nitrite ion by the reduction reaction

$$NO_3^- + 2\,H^+ + 2\,e^- \longrightarrow NO_2^- + H_2O$$

Adult humans have a high tolerance for nitrate. However, in the stomachs of infants, nitrate is reduced to nitrite. Nitrite inactivates hemoglobin by displacing oxygen carried by the hemoglobin causing a condition known as methemoglobinemia (blue babies). A number of cases of this disease, including several deaths, have been attributed to nitrate in farm well water.

The origin of most nitrate produced from feedlot wastes is amino nitrogen ($-NH_2$) present in nitrogen-containing waste products. Approximately one-half of the nitrogen excreted by cattle is contained in the urine. Part of this nitrogen is bonded to protein as $-NH_2$, and the other part is in the form of urea, NH_2CONH_2. As a first step in the degradation process, the amino nitrogen is probably hydrolyzed to ammonia, or ammonium ion.

$$R-NH_2 + H_2O \longrightarrow R-OH + NH_3 \text{ (or } NH_4^+)$$

(R represents the rest of the organic molecule, usually protein.) This product is then oxidized through microorganism-catalyzed reactions to nitrate ion.

$$NH_3 + 2\,O_2 \longrightarrow H^+ + NO_3^- + H_2O$$

Under some conditions, an appreciable amount of the nitrogen originating from the degradation of feedlot wastes is present as ammonium ion or lost as NH_3 gas. Ammonium ion is bound rather strongly to soil. Because nitrate ion is not bound strongly to soil, it is readily carried through soil formations by water. Many factors, including soil type, moisture, and level of organic matter, affect the production of ammonia and nitrate ion originating from feedlot wastes. A marked variation is found in the levels and distributions of these materials in feedlot areas.

Although the percentage of phosphorus in plant material is relatively low, it is an essential component of plants. Phosphorus, like nitrogen, must be present in a simple inorganic form before it can be taken up by plants. In the case of phosphorus, the utilizable species is some form of phosphate ion. In the pH range predominant in most soils, $H_2PO_4^-$ and HPO_4^{2-} are the predominant phosphate species.

Phosphate is most available to plants at pH values near neutrality. In relatively acidic soils, it is believed that phosphate ions are precipitated or sorbed by species of Al(III) and Fe(III). In alkaline soils, phosphate may react with calcium carbonate to form relatively insoluble hydroxylapatite.

$$3\ HPO_4^{2-} + 5\ CaCO_3 + 2\ H_2O \longrightarrow Ca_5(PO_4)_3(OH) + 5\ HCO_3^- + OH^-$$

$$\qquad\qquad\ \text{calcite} \qquad\qquad\qquad\qquad\qquad \text{hydroxylapatite}$$

In general, because of these reactions, little phosphorus applied as fertilizer leaches from the soil. This is important from the standpoint of both water pollution and utilization of phosphate fertilizers. More research remains to be done to fully establish the nature of the chemical interactions determining the availability of phosphates in soils.

Relatively large quantities of potassium are utilized by growing plants. Potassium activates some enzymes and plays a role in the water balance in plants. It is essential for some carbohydrate transformations. Crop yields are generally greatly reduced in potassium-deficient soils. The higher the productivity of the crop, the more potassium is removed from soil. When nitrogen fertilizers are added to soils to increase productivity, removal of potassium is enhanced. Therefore, potassium may become a limiting nutrient in soils heavily fertilized with other nutrients.

Potassium is one of the most abundant elements in the Earth's crust, occurring to the extent of 2.6%; but much of this potassium is not easily available to plants. An example is some silicate minerals, such as leucite, $K_2O \cdot Al_2O_3 \cdot 4\ SiO_2$, which contain strongly bound potassium. Exchangeable potassium held by clay minerals is relatively more available to plants. Some soil fungi produce metal-binding organic compounds such as citric acid, which react with silicate minerals and release potassium and other nutrient metal ions.

Boron, chlorine, copper, iron, manganese, molybdenum (required for N-fixation in plants), sodium, vanadium, and zinc are considered essential plant micronutrients. These elements are needed by plants only at very low levels and frequently are toxic at higher levels. It is entirely possible that other elements will be added to this list as techniques for growing plants in environments free of specific elements improve. Most of these elements function as components of essential enzymes. Manganese, iron, chlorine, zinc, and vanadium may be involved in photosynthesis.

14.7

Fertilizers

The development of the fertilizer industry, more than any other factor, was responsible for the comfortable crop surpluses that the U.S. enjoyed for many years following World War II. Fertilizers increased many crop yields several fold.

The most common elements added as fertilizers are nitrogen, phosphorus, and potassium. Fertilizers are designated by numbers such as 6-12-12. This specific number means that fertilizer contains 6% nitrogen expressed as N, 12% phosphorus expressed as P_2O_5, and 12% potassium in terms of K_2O. Other nutrients including magnesium, sulfate, and micronutrients may be present in fertilizers.

Prior to the production of synthetic fertilizers, farmers were largely dependent upon manures for fertilizer. Farm manure corresponds to approximately 0.5-0.24-0.5 fertilizer and is an inefficient means of adding nutrients to soil. Manure is very useful for adding organic matter to soil, however. It should be noted that the nutrient species utilizable by plants are simple inorganic species: NO_3^- for nitrogen, $H_2PO_4^-$ for phosphorus, and K^+ for potassium. Thus, organic fertilizers must first undergo biodegradation in which the nutrient elements are converted to simple inorganic forms that plants can assimilate. Therefore, synthetic fertilizers are in a more readily available form than are organic fertilizers.

An early source of nitrogen fertilizer was sodium nitrate obtained largely from deposits in Chile. Ammonium sulfate produced as a by-product of coke (charred coal) production was also used as a nitrogen containing fertilizer. Most modern nitrogen fertilizers are made by a synthetic nitrogen fixation process (the Haber process) in which atmospheric nitrogen and hydrogen are combined at high temperatures and pressures.

$$N_2 + 3 H_2 \longrightarrow 2 NH_3$$

The anhydrous ammonia product is very rich in nitrogen, 82%, and may be used directly in soil as a fertilizer. However, very special equipment and precautions must be used because of the toxicity of ammonia gas. Water solutions of ammonia, containing up to 30% nitrogen by weight, may be used with much greater safety.

A common form of synthetic solid fertilizer is ammonium nitrate,

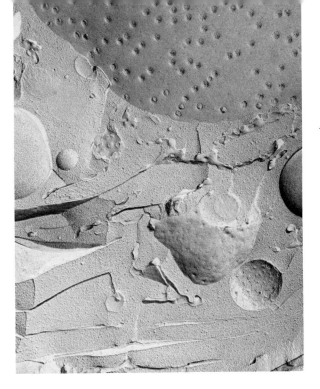

Onion root tip showing part of the nuclear membrane, vacuoles, liposome, and mitochondria. This electron micrograph is a magnification of the image 16,000 times its size. (Courtesy of Dr. Daniel Branton, The Biological Laboratories, Harvard University)

NH_4NO_3. Fixed nitrogen in the form of ammonia is oxidized by oxygen in the presence of a platinum catalyst. The nitric oxide product is converted to nitric acid, which is then permitted to react with ammonia to produce ammonium nitrate. Molten ammonium nitrate is forced through nozzles at the top of a tower called a prilling tower and solidifies while falling through the tower. The particles are coated with special materials to prevent absorption of water. Ammonium nitrate contains 33.5% nitrogen and is a convenient nitrogen-rich fertilizer. However, it is explosive and requires considerable care in manufacture and storage. Other compounds sometimes used as nitrogen fertilizers are calcium nitrate, potassium nitrate, ammonium phosphates, and urea.

Phosphate minerals are found in several states including Idaho, Montana, Utah, Wyoming, North Carolina, South Carolina, Tennessee, and Florida. The principal mineral is fluorapatite, $Ca_5(PO_4)_3F$. The phosphate from fluorapatite is relatively unavailable to plants, and it is frequently treated with sulfuric acid to produce superphosphates.

$$2\ Ca_5(PO_4)_3F + 7\ H_2SO_4 + 3\ H_2O \longrightarrow 2\ HF\uparrow + 3\ CaH_4(PO_4)_2 \cdot H_2O + 7\ CaSO_4$$

The superphosphate products are much more soluble than the parent phosphate minerals. The HF produced as a byproduct of superphosphate production can create air pollution problems. Phosphate minerals are rich in trace elements required for plant growth, such as boron, copper, manganese, molybdenum, and zinc. Ironically, these elements are lost in processing phosphate for fertilizers and are sometimes added to fertilizers later.

Potassium fertilizer components consist of potassium salts, generally KCl. Such salts are found as deposits in the ground, or may be obtained from some brines. Very large deposits are found in Saskatchewan, Canada. These salts are all quite soluble in water. One problem encountered with potassium fertilizers is the luxury uptake of potassium by some crops that absorb more potassium than is really needed for their maximum growth. In a crop where the grain is harvested leaving the rest of the plant in the field, luxury uptake does not create much of a problem because most of the potassium is returned to the soil with the dead plant. However, when hay or forage is harvested, potassium contained in the plant as a consequence of luxury uptake is lost from the soil.

14.8

Herbicides

Herbicides are chemicals that kill plants. Some herbicides kill all plants in areas where they are applied. An example of such a herbicide is arsenic trioxide, As_2O_3, which used to be applied to eliminate all the plants on soil. Incredibly large amounts ranging up to 800 lb per acre were applied for this purpose. Now herbicides have been developed that are much more selective in what they kill. Some kill only grasses, others attack broadleaved plants.

Among the most widely used herbicides are two that are similar in structure. These are 2,4-dichlorophenoxy acetic acid (2,4-D) and 2,4,5-trichlorophenoxy acetic acid (2,4,5-T).

2,4-D   2,4,5-T

These herbicides affect the growth of plants. Basically they act by speeding up the growth process so much that the plant dies. Although they have been used with relative safety since 1944, questions have now arisen regarding the widespread use of 2,4,5-T. This herbicide, widely employed for brush control, is often contaminated with dioxins, which are among the most toxic chemicals known. Dioxins are hazardous for persons applying the herbicides and plants and animals in contact with the herbicide.

Many other types of chemical compounds are used as herbicides. They are classified in several ways. Selective herbicides kill weeds without harming the desired crop. Nonselective herbicides destroy all vegetation. Another classification involves the time of application. Preplanting application is used several days or weeks before the desired crop is planted. Preemergence application of herbicides is performed before the crop or weeds come up through the soil. Postemergence application is used on established weeds and crops.

Aerial spraying of insecticides enables rapid spraying of fields where surface equipment cannot be used, but often results in a great deal of environmental contamination. (Courtesy of USDA; Charles O'Rear, photographer)

The use of herbicides has increased productivity of crops. It has resulted in energy savings from less cultivation. Herbicides have enabled mechanization of sugar beet, potato, and cotton production. There have been some bad environmental effects, however.

14.9

Insecticides and Other Pesticides

Crop production involves a constant battle between man and insect. The list of insects which attack various crops includes the corron bollworm, the Colorado potato beetle, the coddling moth (apples), the gypsy moth (trees), and the spruce budworm (trees). Many chemicals have been developed to combat insects that attack crops. The development continues as bad environmental effects of older pesticides appear and as pesticide-resistant varieties of insects develop.

Chemicals used to combat insects are called **insecticides**.

$$Cl$$
$$|$$
$$Cl-C-Cl$$
$$|$$
$$Cl-\bigcirc-C-\bigcirc-Cl \quad \text{DDT}$$
$$|$$
$$H$$

The all-time champion insecticide is DDT. Total world production of more than 2 million tons of this compound has been recorded since 1940. Approximately 1.5 million tons of this production have been used in agriculture. Although DDT has a very low toxicity to humans, it is very persistent in the environment. One of its degradation products is a compound called DDE, which accumulates in some food chains and has bad effects upon certain forms of wildlife. As a result, most uses of DDT have been banned in the U.S. since 1973.

Many insecticides are compounds in which one or more chlorine atoms are bonded to an organic molecule. DDT is such an insecticide. These are called **organochlorine** compounds. **Organophosphates** make up another class of insecticides, which are organic compounds based on phosphoric acid. Insecticides may also contain sulfur (organosulfurs) or nitrogen (carbamates) as the key parts of their structures.

Insects are not the only pests that cause trouble for crops and farm animals. Therefore, various pesticides are used against fungi (fungicides), bacteria (bactericides), "worms" (nematicides), and rodents (rodenticides).

Chapter Summary

Food is the most basic human need. Most food production depends upon soil. Therefore, this chapter has been largely devoted to soil. Soil comes in a variety of forms. It is the generally thin, loose textured material on much of the Earth's land surface. It is formed from the breaking down of rock. Soil contains a solid portion consisting of mineral matter and organic matter. It also contains water and air spaces. The fraction of mineral matter in soil ranges from very low to very high proportions but is typically around 5%. Soil normally has several layers or *horizons*. The top, most important layer is the *topsoil*. Below this layer is the *subsoil*. Below all of the horizons is *bedrock*.

The nonorganic matter in soil is made up largely of the elements most abundant in the Earth's crust. These include particularly silicon

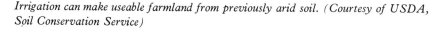

Irrigation can make useable farmland from previously arid soil. (Courtesy of USDA, Soil Conservation Service)

and oxygen, followed by aluminum, iron, and calcium. Clays are important in many soils.

Soil organic matter is called *humus*. It is a decay-resistant material left over from the decay of plant matter. It helps give the soil a good physical form with a loose texture. Like clays, soil organic matter holds and exchanges various cations needed for plant growth. These include Ca^{2+}, Mg^{2+}, K^+, Na^+, and NH_4^+.

Plants require a number of *macronutrients* in relatively large quantities in order to grow. They also require small quantities of some elements known as *micronutrients*. Macronutrients often lacking are nitrogen (nitrate ion), phosphorus (phosphate), and potassium (K^+ ion). These are added as fertilizers. Nitrogen is obtained from the air and fixed in chemical compounds by chemical processes or by plants in combination with bacteria. Phosphate minerals are mined and processed for fertilizer. Potassium salts are also mined for fertilizer.

Various chemicals are used to destroy pests that threaten crops. These chemicals include *herbicides* used against weeds and *insecticides* used to kill insects. Other pesticides include fungicides, bactericides, nematicides, and rodenticides.

Chapter Review Questions

The following questions are designed as a self-teaching tool to help you review Chapter 14. The answers to each question follow. See Chapter Review Questions for Chapter 1 for further instructions.

1. Soil is normally formed by physical, chemical, and biological action on rock. This action is called _____.

2. The three major phases of soil structure are solid, _____, and _____.

3. Soil is divided into layers called _____.

4. The layer of soil just below the top horizon is the _____.

5. Transpiration is _____ _____.

6. Water in the smaller soil pores is held very _____.

7. Soil air normally contains less _____ and more _____ than air in the atmosphere.

8. In decreasing order the five most abundant elements in the Earth's crust are _____, _____, _____, _____, and _____.

9. A type of mineral found in soil that is made largely of oxides of silicon, aluminum, and iron and that exchanges cations well is _____.

10. Most of the organic matter in soil is a dark, water-insoluble material called _____.

11. The source of most soil organic matter is _____.

12. The chemical symbols of the common plant macronutrients are _____, _____, _____, _____, _____, _____, _____, _____, and _____.

13. The plant micronutrient elements are _____, _____, _____, _____, _____, _____, _____, and _____.

14. The three chemical elements most commonly considered as "fertilizers" are _____, _____, and _____.

15. The source of nitrogen in fertilizer is _____.

16. Nitrogen (N_2) is fixed (chemically bound) as the compound, _____.

17. The function of *Rhizobium* bacteria is _____.

18. A steer produces roughly _____ times as much waste as a human.

19. The type of animals most easily poisoned by nitrate ion are _____ animals whose stomachs contain bacteria that change nitrate to toxic _____.

20. A nitrogen-containing ion that is rather strongly bound to soil is _____ ion whereas _____ ion is not at all strongly bound.

21. An important mineral containing calcium, phosphate, and fluoride ions is called _____.

22. A number such as 6-12-12 refers to the composition of _____.

23. The fertilizer element most troubled by luxury uptake by plants is _____.

24. The compound 2,4-D is a _____.

25. Regarding time of application, herbicides may be _____, _____, or _____.

26. In addition to herbicides, the major types of pesticides are _____, _____, _____, _____, and _____.

Answers to Chapter Review Questions

1. weathering
2. water, air spaces
3. horizons
4. subsoil
5. the process by which water is carried from soil, through a plant, and finally to the atmosphere through the plant leaves
6. strongly
7. oxygen, carbon dioxide
8. oxygen, silicon, aluminum, iron, calcium
9. clay
10. humus
11. partly decayed plants
12. C, H, O, N, P, K, Ca, Mg, S
13. boron, chlorine, copper, iron, manganese, molybdenum, sodium, vanadium, zinc
14. nitrogen, phosphorus, potassium
15. air
16. ammonia
17. to fix nitrogen in legume plants
18. 18
19. ruminant, nitrate
20. ammonium, nitrate
21. fluorapatite
22. fertilizer
23. potassium
24. herbicide
25. preplanting, preemergence, postemergence
26. insecticides, fungicides, bactericides, nematicides, rodenticides

Exercises for Chapter 14

1. Explain why the humidity (water vapor in air) may be higher just above a field of corn than it is above bare ground?

2. Write a chemical reaction explaining the high concentration of carbon dioxide found in soil air pockets.

3. The average composition of the Earth's crust is _____% Si, _____% O, _____% Fe, and _____% Al.

4. What are three functions of organic matter in soil?

5. Which plant macronutrient can be obtained from soil and (by some plants) from the atmosphere?

6. Give an example of a partnership between plants and bacteria.

7. Write a chemical reaction showing why the nitrate ion is dangerous to ruminant animals.

8. Completely sterile (no bacteria) soil was used to grow corn in an isolated environment from which bacteria were totally excluded. The seed was carefully treated to kill all bacteria before planting, a procedure which did not harm the seed's ability to sprout. The soil was all right except for a deficiency in potassium, phosphate, and nitrogen fertilizers. These deficiencies were made up by adding the correct amounts of KCl, superphosphate, and NH_4Cl. The right amount of light was admitted to the isolation chamber for best growth to occur. Air, carefully filtered to remove all bacteria was pumped through the chamber at all times. The corn grew very poorly. Why?

9. Typically, soil contains a large fraction of solid mineral matter. What are three other things generally found in soil?

10. A large portion of the mineral matter that is broken down to make soil is made of limestone. What is the chemical formula of limestone? This may be broken down by the indirect action of bacteria. What gas product is produced by the respiration (reaction of O_2 with food) of bacteria? What is the reaction of this gas dissolved in water with limestone?

11. How are essential plant nutrients carried from the soil to plant leaves? Why does this result in the loss of large quantities of water from the soil (transpiration)?

12. Why does a waterlogged soil rapidly become low in oxygen content?

13. If the chemical formula of organic matter is represented by the simplified formula, CH_2O, what is a chemical reaction showing the "fixing" of carbon dioxide from the air in the form of organic matter by plants? What is the source of energy for this reaction?

14. Representing blood hemoglobin as Hb, and hemoglobin bound to oxygen as HbO_2, write a chemical reaction showing why nitrite is toxic.

15. Farm manure is rated approximately "0.5-0.24-0.5" as a fertilizer. How many tons of manure would have to be applied to be equivalent to 1 ton of a 12-6-12 commercial fertilizer?

16. What is meant by prilling? Why is fertilizer "prilled"?

17. What volume of nitrogen must be fixed from the atmosphere to provide fertilization of a 100-acre field at the rate of 100 kg of nitrogen per acre. Express the volume at standard temperature and pressure.

18. Under what conditions does nitrate tend to accumulate in plants?

19. What type of chemical is a particularly dangerous contaminant of 2,4,5-T?

An abundance of food produced by modern agricultural practice is illustrated by Boston's famous open air market, Haymarket. (Courtesy of Massachusetts Dept. of Commerce and Development)

15

Chemistry of Food and Household Products

15.1

Chemical "Help" for Food

Chemistry has contributed to a remarkable change in the ways in which food is prepared, preserved, and marketed. The boring standard diet of the 1800's, prepared largely from flour, salted meats, dried beans, and similarly unexciting staples, has given way to the great collection of food available on supermarket shelves. Many of these changes have been helpful. Others are disturbing. This is especially so when one considers that many of the essential nutrients are removed in the processing of food. When a few of these are then put back in the product, it is sold as "enriched" food. The parent concerned with good nutrition can take little comfort from grocery shelves stacked with sugar-laden "cereals." The high price of many of these nutritionally questionable products is due largely to high cost advertising aimed at impressionable children. Nor can we take comfort from the fact that the average American consumes approximately *five pounds* of artificial chemical food additives each year.

Many chemicals, which were not present in the original product, are added to food. Some of the chemicals come from other foods; others are entirely synthetic. They serve a number of different purposes, such as food preservation, coloring, or flavoring. Synthetic vitamins are added to improve nutritional value. Synthetic amino acids increase the overall protein value of the food. Their addition may be very helpful because some foods are excellent protein sources except for the absence of one or two essential amino acids. Texture of food is often maintained by additives that keep the product from being too dry or moist.

Most food additives are probably harmless and improve the food appreciably. Preservation of food with additives prevents waste. Added nutritional factors (vitamins and minerals) aid nutrition. Constant attention must be given, however, to the possibility of harmful effects from food additives. Especially, the more "exotic" chemicals (such as dyes and artificial sweeteners), which bear little resemblance to natural products, should be tested exhaustively and used with great caution. During the last half century, humans have been subjected to a barrage of chemicals from pesticides, aerosol spray products, plastics, and drugs. The long term effects of these are not well known, but some are undoubtedly bad. We get enough chemicals in our bodies from exposure to outside sources without ingesting any more than necessary with food.

The many functions of food additives are discussed in the following pages. As a point of reference, the general types of additives and what they do are listed in Table 15.1. These are contained in the Food and Drug Administration's (FDA) list of about 600 chemicals "generally recognized as safe" when used in the foods, amounts, and manner specified. This list is called the GRAS list. It is undergoing constant revision with the addition of new additives, and the removal of others whose safety has become doubtful.

The "supermarket" of 1900 offered little variety. Chemistry has contributed much to the great changes in type and variety of foods available since then.

TABLE 15.1
Some major types of additives from the "generally recognized as safe" list.

Major Class of Additives	Uses	Typical Examples
pH adjusters	Improve flavor, prevent spoilage	Acids, alkalies, buffers
Colors	Provide desired color	Carotene
Flavors	Improve taste	Esters
Flavor enhancers	Substances whose presence improves flavor	Monosodium glutamate
Preservatives	Prevent bacterial and mold decay	Benzoic acid
Antioxidants	Prevent deterioration from oxidation	Ascorbic acid
Stabilizers and thickeners	Retain physical form and thickness of texture	Agar-agar, algins
Sequestrants	Chelate (bond strongly to) metal ions, which otherwise would act as catalysts in oxidizing food	EDTA
Surfactants	Detergent-like substances which allow intimate mixing of unlike substances in food (such as oil and water)	Cholic acid
Non-food sweeteners	Sweeten food without adding calories	Saccharin
Humectants	Retain water in food	Polyhydric alcohols
Softening agents	Prevent food from becoming too hard	Polyhydric alcohols
Clarifying agents	Reduce turbidity to make food more acceptable	Proteolytic enzymes
Anticaking agents	Prevent powdered or crystalline foods from caking together	Compounds which absorb water
Foaming agents	Cause foods such as whipped toppings to foam	Dextrins
Antifoaming agents	Prevent some liquids, such as fruit juice, from foaming too much	Silicones
Vitamins	Essential diet factors	Vitamins A, C, etc.
Contaminants	Undesirable materials that get into food	Pesticides, drugs, hair, insect parts
Leavening agents	Cause baking goods to "rise"	Baking soda, $NaHCO_3$

15.2

Food Preservatives

Normally foods deteriorate through the action of bacteria or fungi. This is to be expected because substances that are good food for humans should also be good food for lower organisms. The other major route leading to food deterioration is oxidation. Microorganism action on food is a form of oxidation in which the bacteria or fungi act as catalysts. Most techniques for food preservation are directed toward preventing the action of microorganisms and avoiding oxidation.

The growth of microorganisms in food can be prevented by depriving them of water, excluding oxygen, keeping the food completely sterile (canning), lowering the temperature to a point at which the organisms cannot function (freezing), or using chemicals that inhibit their growth. The last approach is quite limited because these chemicals also tend to be toxic to humans. One example, however, is the use of SO_2 in wine making and in dried fruit preservation to prevent the growth of unwanted bacteria. The odor of this gas in packaged, dried fruit can be quite strong.

Dehydration, the elimination of water from food, has been practiced for centuries. Without water the bacteria cannot grow. Beef or buffalo "jerky" was a staple in the diet of pioneers and Indians while traveling. Newly developed techniques of freeze drying in which water is removed by sublimation (direct evaporation from solid to vapor form) from frozen foods have allowed dried foods to be preserved without great loss in flavor.

Salt deprives microorganisms of water because of osmosis (see Section 6.11). If the water in food contains a lot of salt, water leaves the bacterial cells by osmosis, and the bacteria literally die of thirst. Sodium chloride can be used to preserve foods such as sauerkraut and pickles. Meats are often preserved, or "cured," with nitrate salts, such as sodium nitrate. Dissolved sugar has the same effect. That is why syrup, jellies, and sugar-cured hams can be kept without refrigeration for long periods of time although the sugar in them is a good food source for yeasts and bacteria.

Canning serves two purposes in food preservation. It sterilizes the food and keeps it sterile. It also excludes oxygen. Some bacteria, expecially those which form spores, are very resistant to heat and can survive the canning process. These spores can form bacterial cells in canned food. Some of these bacteria (anaerobic bacteria) grow very well in the absence of oxygen. If they are *Clostridium botulinum* bacteria, the extremely poisonous botulism toxin is produced. Less than one-millionth of a gram of this toxin is normally fatal. "Botulism" can be avoided by pressure cooking foods during the canning process. If water is boiled under pressure, the boiling temperature is higher. This high temperature kills even resistant bacterial spores. The toxin itself is destroyed by heat. Therefore, those foods that are not cooked heavily after opening present the greatest danger of botulism poisoning.

Microorganisms that cause food spoilage can be killed by heat treatment. A home steam-pressure technique is shown where raw food is packed into clean containers, such as glass jars, sealed, and placed in a pressure cooker to rid the food of bacteria. (Courtesy of Mirro Aluminum Co.)

Chemical preservatives are used in many foods. These are chemicals which prevent the growth of microorganisms. How they do this is not always well understood. One of the two most common chemical food preservatives is sodium benzoate

$$\text{C}_6\text{H}_5-\overset{\displaystyle O}{\overset{\|}{\text{C}}}-\text{O}^-\text{Na}^+ \qquad \text{sodium benzoate}$$

used to preserve margarines, pie fillings, jellies, pickles, flavored syrups, and fruit drinks. The other is calcium propionate

$$\text{Ca}^{2+}(^-\text{O}-\overset{\displaystyle O}{\overset{\|}{\text{C}}}-\text{C}_2\text{H}_5)_2 \qquad \text{calcium propionate}$$

used in bread, pastries, and fillings. These and other food preservatives may prevent the growth of bacteria by coating cell walls or interfering with the action of enzymes.

Unpleasant tastes can result from the chemical oxidation of foods. This is especially common with unsaturated fats in which the fatty acids contain double bonds. Oxygen reacts at these double bonds to produce peroxides, aldehydes, ketones, and shorter chain acids. Most of these substances have a bad taste and odor. Oxidized fat is said to be rancid.

Oxidation of fatty acids in food is prevented by keeping the food away from air and by keeping it cold and dry. This is frequently not possible, so chemical *antioxidants* are added to some foods. Antioxidants act by breaking up the chain reactions which cause food to be oxidized. To understand how this is done, consider what happens when an unsaturated fat reacts with oxygen. A hydrogen on the fatty acid reacts with O_2

(fatty acid)$\overset{..}{.}$H + O_2 $\longrightarrow$ (fatty acid)$\cdot$ + $HO_2\cdot$

H atom bonded to fatty acid with a
2-electron bond shown as a pair
of dots

free radicals with unpaired electrons,
represented as dots

to form two free radicals. A free radical is a chemical species which has an electron without a partner. Such unpaired electrons make the free-radical species very reactive, and the following type of chain reaction involving more oxygen can occur:

$\longrightarrow$ (fatty acid)$\cdot$ + O_2 $\longrightarrow$ (fatty acid)$O_2\cdot$

fatty acid
free radical

fatty acid free radical bound to
oxygen, also a very reactive species

(fatty acid)$O_2\cdot$ + (fatty acid)$\overset{..}{.}$H $\longrightarrow$

$\longleftarrow$ (fatty acid)$\cdot$ + (fatty acid)—OOH

fatty acid free radical,
which can react again
with O_2 to repeat the
cycle

fatty acid hydroperoxide, which can
react further to form undesirable
oxygen-containing compounds

Compounds such as butylated hydroxyanisole (BHA)

$$\begin{array}{c} CH_3 \\ | \\ H_3C-C-CH_3 \\ | \\ HO-\langle\bigcirc\rangle-OCH_3 \end{array}$$

butylated hydroxyanisole
(BHA)

and the related compounds, butylated hydroxytoluene (BHT), and propyl gallate are added to foods containing unsaturated fats to stop this chain reaction. They do so by donating a hydrogen atom to the fatty acid free radical

$$\text{(fatty acid)}\cdot + HO-\langle\bigcirc\rangle-OCH_3 = \text{(fatty acid)}:H + \cdot O-\langle\bigcirc\rangle-OCH_3$$

with $\begin{array}{c}CH_3\\|\\H_3C-C-CH_3\end{array}$ on both rings

fatty acid
free radical

BHT

original fatty
acid

BHT free radical,
relatively stable

forming the original fatty acid again and producing a BHT free radical. The BHT free radical is a comfortable home for unpaired electrons. It has a large electron cloud in the benzene ring and other parts of the molecule. The unpaired electron can move around in this system for quite some time before reacting. This breaks up the chain reaction and slows down the oxidation of the fatty acids.

15.3

When It Rains, It Pours

Many foods absorb water from the atmosphere. This can cause caking of salt, sugar, and other foods. One approach to this problem is to add a substance to food which has the ability to take up large quantities of water. Recall from Section 8.7 that such a substance is called a hygroscopic substance. Some forms of sodium aluminosilicate, $NaAlSi_3O_8$, form crystals with large cage-like pores that can take up water from the salt and prevent it from getting wet. Another approach that can be applied to table salt is to add a small quantity of sodium ferrocyanide, $Na_4Fe(CN)_6$, to the mixture when the salt crystals are being formed. The resulting crystals are kind of star-shaped. This shape does not pack together as well as ordinary salt crystals, which are shaped like cubes. Thus, caking is prevented.

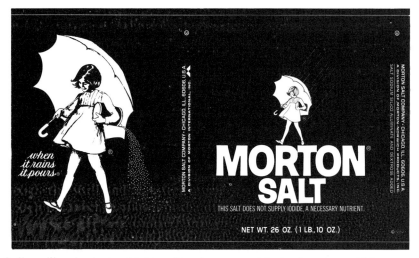

Sodium silico aluminate added to table salt acts as a dehydrating agent, which extracts water that salt absorbs from the atmosphere on a rainy day. (Courtesy of Morton Salt Co., division of Morton-Norwich Products, Inc.)

15.4

Acids, Bases, and Buffers in Food

Acids of various kinds are commonly added to food. These are called *acidulants* in the food processing industry. By far the most commonly used is citric acid, an ingredient of oranges, grapefruit, and other citrus fruits. It makes up about 60% of the acidulants added to food. Phosphoric acid, H_3PO_4, accounts for an additional 25%. The remainder are various kinds of acids. Acidulants serve many purposes as summarized in Table 15.2.

TABLE 15.2
General functions of acidulants.

General Function of Acidulant	What It Does
Preservative	Prevents germination of bacterial and fungal spores and prevents growth of these microorganisms
Flavoring	Intensify, mask, and blend tastes
Buffers	Control pH to best values
Antioxidants	Enable other antioxidants to perform better
Melting modifiers	Change melting characteristics of cheese and candy
Viscosity modifiers	Change the viscosity, or "flowing" characteristics, of dough to give baked goods best shape and texture
Meat curing agents	Used in the curing of meat to improve flavor and color and act as a preservative

Citric acid and sodium citrate serve several purposes in food.

$$
\begin{array}{cc}
\begin{array}{c}
H \\
| \\
H-C-CO_2H \\
| \\
HO-C-CO_2H \\
| \\
H-C-CO_2H \\
| \\
H
\end{array}
&
\begin{array}{c}
H \\
| \\
H-C-CO_2^-Na^+ \\
| \\
HO-C-CO_2^-Na^+ \\
| \\
H-C-CO_2^-Na^+ \\
| \\
H
\end{array}
\\
\text{citric acid} & \text{sodium citrate}
\end{array}
$$

Citric acid neutralizes base in food, and sodium citrate neutralizes acid. Mixed together, they prevent the food product from becoming either too acidic or too basic, acting as a *buffer*. Another very important effect of citrate is its ability to act as a chelating agent (in the food industry this is called a *sequestrant*). Chelating agents bind very strongly to metal ions. Citrate is especially effective in chelating iron.

$$
\begin{array}{c}
H \\
| \\
H-C-CO_2^- \\
| \\
HO-C-CO_2^- \cdots Fe^{3+} \qquad \text{citrate chelate of ferric ion} \\
| \\
H-C-CO_2^- \\
| \\
H
\end{array}
$$

Citric acid is a normal part of biochemical cycles and body metabolism. Therefore, it is by no means artificial and is a safe additive. Citric acid is added to a large variety of foods including salad dressing, mayonnaise, French dressing, sherbet, and prune juice. It is used to lower the pH of canned artichokes to 4.5 or less. It is widely employed to increase the acidity of dairy products. Increased acidity can improve the aroma and flavor of foods by changing some organic salts to the volatile acidic form.

Sodium citrate is an ingredient of some ice creams, evaporated milk, and other foods. Both citric acid and sodium citrate are added to fruit juices, carbonated beverages, and cured meats. Other citrate salts used in foods include potassium citrate, calcium citrate and stearyl and isopropyl citrate esters. These esters are made from the combination of stearyl or isopropyl alcohol with citric acid. Esters are discussed in Section 10.11.

Because of the high citrate content of many fruits, citric acid can be obtained commercially as a fruit byproduct. Lemons and pineapple wastes are good sources of citric acid. On a larger scale, citric acid is obtained by the fermentation of treated molasses diluted with water. The fermentation is carried out by the mold, *Aspergillus niger*. The overall reaction of sugar to produce citric acid is

$$2 \text{ C}_6\text{H}_{12}\text{O}_6 + 3 \text{ O}_2 \xrightarrow[\text{niger}]{\text{Aspergillus}} 2 \text{ C}_6\text{H}_8\text{O}_7 + 4 \text{ H}_2\text{O}$$

sugar   citric acid

The citric acid is precipitated from the solution with lime

$$3 \text{ Ca(OH)}_2 + 2 \text{ C}_6\text{H}_8\text{O}_7 \longrightarrow \text{Ca}_3(\text{C}_6\text{H}_5\text{O}_7)_2\downarrow + 6 \text{ H}_2\text{O}$$

calcium citrate

to produce calcium citrate. Citric acid in solution can be prepared from the calcium citrate solid by adding a dilute solution of sulfuric acid.

$$\text{Ca}_3(\text{C}_6\text{H}_5\text{O}_7)_2 + 3 \text{ H}_2\text{SO}_4 \longrightarrow 2 \text{ C}_6\text{H}_8\text{O}_7 + 3 \text{ CaSO}_4\downarrow$$

A number of other organic acids and their salts are used as food additives. These are summarized in Table 15.3.

15.5

Food Colors

The color of food is an important factor in determining its acceptability. Off colors in familiar foods can greatly reduce their marketability. Orange juice with a pale yellow color is not as acceptable as juice that has more of the typical color associated with oranges. Brown colored raw steak, perhaps even improved in flavor by aging a day in the display case, is discounted in price because it lacks the typical red meat color.

Much effort is put into marketing foods with the optimum color. In many cases this is accomplished by processing which has been developed to avoid discoloration. However, the more common practice is to enlist the help of chemicals for food colors, which are derived from natural sources for the most part. Certified food colors are synthetic substances. Both are regulated by the FDA.

Incredible as it may sound, food coloring was not regulated in the U.S. until passage of the Food and Drug Act of 1906. Until that time the usual practice was to use any available dye to color candy or other

TABLE 15.3

Organic acids and their salts used as food additives.

Organic acid	Structure	Typical uses
Acetic acid*	H O | || H—C—C—OH | H	Acid found in vinegar. Used in foods such as pickles, sauces, catsups, salad dressings, and mayonnaise for flavor, to increase acidity, and as a preservative.
Propionic acid	H H O | | || H—C—C—C—OH | | H H	Added generally as sodium, potassium, or calcium salts. Used to suppress growth of bacteria in baked goods.
Sorbic acid	H H H H H O | | | | | || H—C—C=C—C=C—C—OH | H	This acid and its potassium salt are used as *antimycotics* (substances which kill molds) in food.
Succinic acid★	O H H O || | | || HO—C—C—C—C—OH | | H H	A natural acid found in asparagus, beets, broccoli, and other foods. Now used as a food additive. It does not absorb water like some acidulants.
Adipic acid	H H O | | || H—C—C—C—OH | H | H O | || H—C—C—C—OH | | H H	Used to neutralize base and as a buffer. It gives a very low pH and prevents browning of fruits. Contributes to a smooth, tart taste in foods.
Fumaric acid*	O || H C—OH \\ / C=C HO—C H || O	Adds to flavor in fruit drinks, gelatin desserts, wines. Antioxidant in foods such as cheese, butter, and potato chips. Relatively inexpensive.
Lactic acid*	H H O | | || H—C—C—C—OH | | H OH	Occurs naturally in many foods. Prevents spoilage and adds to flavor.
Tartaric acid	O H H O || | | || HO—C—C—C—C—OH | | OH OH	Gives food a tart taste. Especially common in grape and lime beverages. Ingredient of baking powders.
Malic acid*	O H H O || | | || HO—C—C—C—C—OH | | OH H	Helps bring out tastes of foods such as fruit drinks. Stabilizes fruit drink color. Many other uses.

* These compounds appear in the normal paths of body metabolism.

foods. The same dye used to dye a ladies gown a delicate pink color could be used to concoct pink lemonade. Before the passage of the Food and Drug Act in 1906 about 80 dyes of variable purity were used to color food in the U.S. These were cut back to seven acceptable dyes. Between 1916 and 1971, eleven more dyes were added to the list.

In the early 1950's excessive use of two dyes, FD&C Orange No. 1 and FD&C Red No. 32, in candy and popcorn caused diarrhea in children in several incidents. These cases were followed up by studies on animals which showed that these food colorings were chronically toxic to animals. As a result the two food colorings were banned from further use. Soon after that FD&C Yellows 1, 3, and 4, and Yellow No. 2 were banned.

Food color additives may be used in the form of either dyes or lakes. Dyes are organic compounds that are strongly colored. Lakes (also called pigments) are dyes absorbed on aluminum hydroxide. The dyes dissolve in food. The lakes, which are insoluble, are dispersed physically in the form of extremely fine particles. Where water cannot be used to dissolve a dye in food, glycerin or propylene glycol are often employed.

The FD&C dyes are water-soluble organic compounds with relatively complicated structures. They belong to the general classes of fluorescein type, sulfonated indigo, triphenylmethanes, and azo dyes. Typical of the azo dyes is FD&C Red No. 2, which has the following structure:

$$Na^{+-}O_3S-\bigcirc-N=N-\bigcirc \quad \substack{HO \quad SO_3^-Na^+ \\ \\ SO_3^-Na^+}$$

FD&C Red No. 2

All of the FD&C dyes are water-soluble and oil-insoluble. The sulfonate groups, $-SO_3^-$, make the compounds water-soluble and prevent their solubility in oil. Although it would be desirable from the standpoint of coloring food to have oil-soluble dyes, this solubility apparently is accompanied by increased toxicity.

The FD&C lakes have increased rapidly in use since they were first allowed in foods in 1959. They are produced by precipitating aluminum hydroxide in the presence of dye

$$Al^{3+} + 3\,OH^- + dye \longrightarrow Al(OH)_3\,(dye)\downarrow$$

lake

to produce a colored lake in which the dye is bound chemically to the aluminum. The lakes are highly colored. Since the dye is bound so strongly to them, "bleeding" of color is avoided. Mixing or dispersion of the lake in the food is crucial to their success as food colorings. This is usually accomplished by physically grinding them into the food and violent agitation. The best mixing and coloring characteristics are accomplished by using very fine lake particles. Particles 1 μ (micron) across (a millionth of a meter and about the size of a cell of bacteria) are now available in "jet-milled lakes."

Some food colors have been classified among the *uncertified color additives*. These are generally natural colors. They include some interesting materials. For example, grape skin extract is used to color beverages. Dehydrated beets have a powerful red coloring effect. Ferrous gluconate

$$Fe^{2+}\left[\ ^-O-\overset{\overset{\displaystyle O}{\|}}{C}-\overset{\overset{\displaystyle OH}{|}}{\underset{\underset{\displaystyle H}{|}}{C}}-\overset{\overset{\displaystyle OH}{|}}{\underset{\underset{\displaystyle H}{|}}{C}}-\overset{\overset{\displaystyle OH}{|}}{\underset{\underset{\displaystyle H}{|}}{C}}-\overset{\overset{\displaystyle OH}{|}}{\underset{\underset{\displaystyle H}{|}}{C}}-\overset{\overset{\displaystyle OH}{|}}{\underset{\underset{\displaystyle H}{|}}{C}}-H\ \right]_2 \qquad \text{ferrous gluconate}$$

is used to help give ripe olives their characteristic dark color. Dried meal from algae (small plants that grow in water) and corn endosperm oil are added to chicken feed to give the skin of fryers a yellow color and to provide color for egg yolks. Iron oxide is used to color some pet foods. Titanium dioxide, TiO_2, can be used in quantities up to 1% to give food a white color. This compound is used as a pigment in paints and is literally used to paint tablets ("pills"). Small quantities of carbon black (finely divided pure carbon) provide a black color in food, but its use was banned in 1976 because it may contain carcinogenic polycyclic aromatic hydrocarbons.

The most important form of natural food colors are the *carotenoids*. These compounds are found in many plant and animal materials. As their name implies, they give carrots their characteristic orange color. Among the other foods in which they are found are apricots, orange juice, tomatoes, and lobsters. More than 100 forms of these compounds are known, although just a few are used in foods. The most important of these is β-carotene whose complicated chemical structure is shown as follows:

β-carotene

This substance forms vitamin A in the body and acts as a food color as well. Originally used to color oils and margarines, processes have now been worked out for adding carotenoids to ice cream, cheese, puddings, and orange drinks. They are more expensive than most food dyes. However, they have the advantage of being oil-soluble. When used in water-based foods, the carotenoids are suspended in very tiny droplets of vegetable oil and then dispersed in the food. They decompose rather easily.

When carbohydrates such as sugars and starches are heated under controlled conditions, a dark brown material called *caramel,* is produced. Various kinds of caramel with different properties can be made to be used in food coloring. The chemical composition of caramel is not known. It is a colloidal material. Caramel is widely used in baking to give a desired dark color. It is also used to color some of the "coke" type of carbonated beverages.

Debate still continues over the safety of food colors. In 1976 Red Dye No. 2 was temporarily banned on evidence that it might be a potential carcinogen and then reinstated on the approved list. Shortly after that some investigators reported that the best substitute, Red Dye No. 40, may also have carcinogenic properties. Late in 1976, Red No. 2 was banned again. Continued debate about the safety of food colorings can be anticipated.

15.6

Food Flavors

Flavorings are added to food to give it a flavor that was not present in the original product, to add to or modify the original flavor, or to cover up a bad flavor. As examples, grape flavoring is added to water containing dissolved CO_2 and sugar to produce grape soda pop; malt changes the natural grain flavor of cereals; and anise covers up bitter tastes in medicines. Food flavor is not a simple phenomenon. It is a combination of tastes, odors, textures, "feel," and other factors. Actually there are only four basic tastes. These are sweet, sour, salt, and bitter. They represent the sensations that taste buds on the tongue can distinguish. But, they cannot begin to make up all of the great variety of sensations that constitute the characteristic flavor of food. Of the sensations other than taste which may be involved, odor is probably the most important.

Essential oils are among the important flavor ingredients. These are oily materials that can be squeezed or distilled from plants or parts of plants. An essential oil has the odor characteristic of a particular plant in a very concentrated form. Some examples would be peppermint, lemon, and wintergreen. Essential oils are the largest single class of flavor ingredients.

Extracts are obtained by dissolving flavor ingredients from a source in alcohol. In effect, the flavor source is washed with alcohol, which dissolves the concentrated flavoring material. Lemon extract is a typical extract.

It is sometimes possible and desirable to separate out a particular chemical or small group of chemicals from a complex flavoring substance. Such a fraction is called an *isolate*. Citral

$$H_3C-C=C-C-C-C=C-C=O \qquad \text{citral, an isolate}$$

is the isolate which gives oil of lemon its characteristic odor. This isolate can be obtained from oils of orange, mandarin, eucalyptus, and lemon grass.

Imitation, artificial, and *synthetic* are three terms that can be readily confused when discussing flavors. A synthetic is a chemical compound not produced by natural processes through the action of some organism. It may be identical in chemical composition to the natural compound, but if the compound is produced chemically by man, it must still be called a synthetic. An imitation flavoring contains at least some imitation or non-natural materials. An artificial flavoring contains all natural materials but not in the proportions found in natural foods.

The number of compounds found in natural and artificial flavors is huge. To list even the most common ones would take many pages in this book. Figure 15.1 illustrates some typical kinds of compounds.

Just as the name implies, flavor enhancers bring out the flavors that are already there in food. The best known of these is monosodium glutamate, MSG.

$$Na^{+\ -}O-C-C-C-C-C-OH \qquad \text{monosodium glutamate}$$

The flavor-enhancing qualities of this compound were discovered in 1908 by Japanese chemists studying the seaweed *Laminaria japonica,* widely used in Japanese soups and other foods. Monosodium glutamate especially enhances the flavors of meats. It is not known how this is done, although it may affect nerve endings on the taste buds and make them more sensitive. They may also increase salivation—"make the mouth water." Some people are affected by "Chinese restaurant syndrome" after eating MSG. This is characterized by sweating, headaches, and other unpleasant symptoms. It was first reported in people who had eaten heavy meals of Chinese food containing large quantities of MSG.

Monosodium glutamate does have a flavor of its own, though it is usually not detected at the levels of MSG usually put into food. Some compounds are vastly more powerful than MSG in bringing out the flavors of foods. These are called *flavor potentiators*.

FIGURE 15.1   *Some compounds found in natural and artificial flavors.*

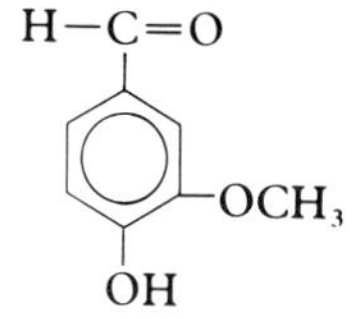

vanillin,
in vanilla flavoring

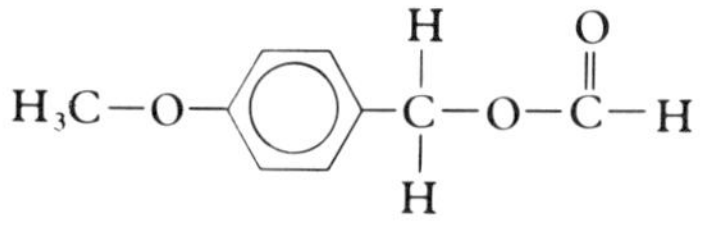

anisole formate,
strawberry

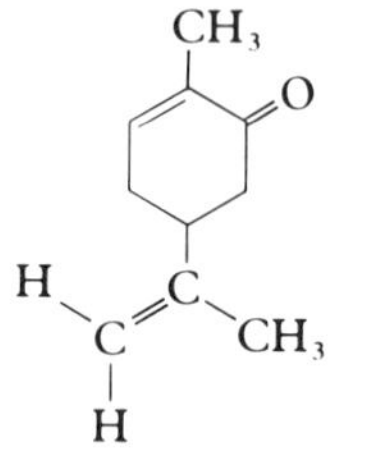

L-carvone,
spearmint

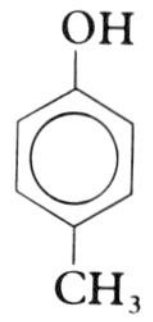

p-cresol,
burnt flavor for "body"

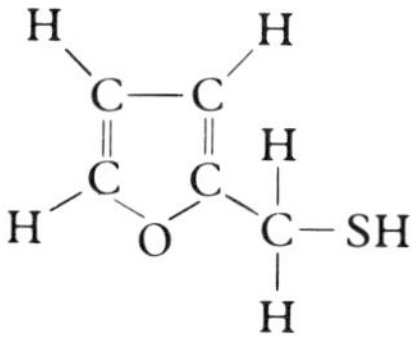

furfuryl mercaptan,
coffee, burnt

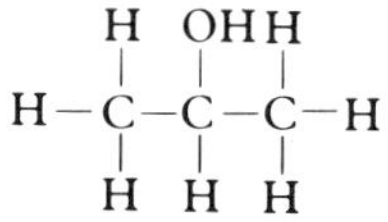

isopropyl alcohol,
sweet, apple

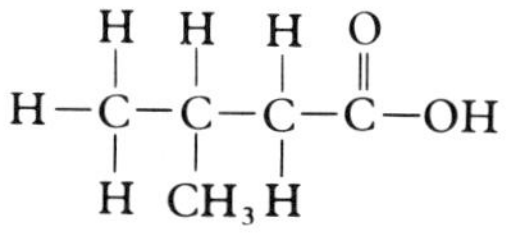

isovaleric acid,
sour, cheese-like

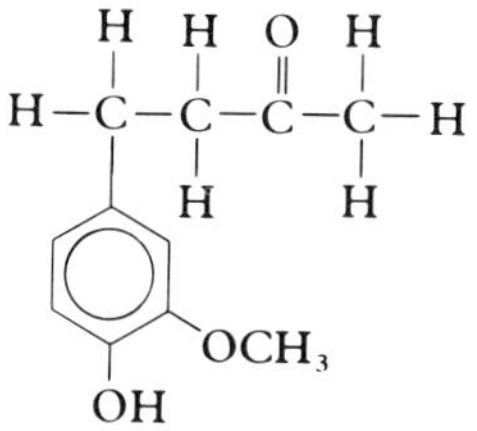

zingerone,
ginger

15.7

Sweetening Without Sugar

Nonnutritive sweeteners are compounds that have a sweet taste but do not add calories to the diet. It may take only from one three-hundredth to one-thirtieth as much of an artificial sweetener to have the sweetening power of sucrose, one of the sweetest natural sugars.

Sodium saccharin

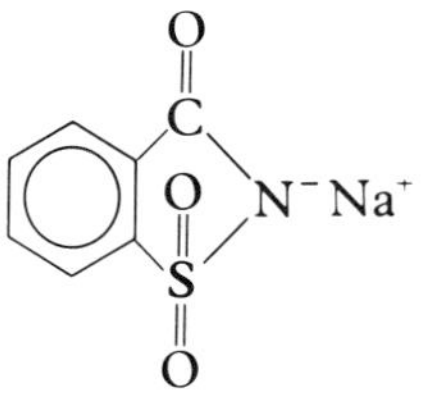

sodium saccharin

and related calcium and ammonium compounds are the most commonly used artificial sweeteners. Saccharin is available as small tablets which can be dissolved in tea or coffee. It is also available in a powdered form. It is about 300 times as effective as sucrose in stimulating "sweet" taste buds. A ban on saccharin sweeteners was announced in a controversial decision by the FDA in 1977.

Cyclohexane sulfamic acid and its sodium and calcium salts are very effective no-calorie sweeteners.

sodium cyclamate

They were commonly used in low-calorie soda beverages and diet foods until they were banned in the early 1970's. It was found that cyclamate caused cancer when fed in massive doses to rats. This illustrates the dilemma caused when trying to evaluate the safety of food additives. There is no evidence at all of harmful effects from cyclamates or saccharin when used at levels necessary to sweeten food. Yet, is there perhaps some risk? In fact, no threshold level below which there is *no* danger is known to exist for *any* carcinogen. Any risk must be balanced against the known risks of being too fat from eating sugar-rich foods.

15.8
Vitamins, Amino Acids, and Minerals in Foods

Vitamins and their importance will be discussed in Chapter 16. Vitamins are chemical substances, not actually consumed for energy, which are necessary for the body to function properly. A properly balanced diet provides enough vitamins of the right kind. In some cases vitamins are added to food to enrich it. When this is not done, nutritionists must carefully consider whether or not vitamins are being removed by the processing and cooking which food undergoes.

Some vitamins are soluble in water. Vitamin B_1, vitamin B_2, niacin, vitamin B_6, vitamin B_{12}, folic acid, pantothenic acid, biotin, and vitamin C are all water soluble. The fat soluble vitamins include vitamin A, vitamin D, vitamin E, and vitamin K.

There is considerable potential for enriching foods by adding essential amino acids to them. Vegetable proteins are usually deficient in lysine, and the addition of a small amount of lysine would greatly increase the nutritional value of these proteins. The other nutritionally limiting amino acids most commonly missing in foods are methionine, threonine, and tryptophan.

Human nutrition also requires minerals. Calcium and phosphate for "strong bones and teeth" are most commonly mentioned. However, elements at very low levels are also needed. These include trace quantities of iron, zinc, iodine, and other elements. Most of these are the same plant micronutrients mentioned in Section 14.6.

15.9

Phosphates in Food

A class of minerals deserving special attention in food and food processing are the phosphates. Humans, as well as all other living things, require some form of the phosphate ion, PO_4^{3-}. Bones and teeth are made up largely of phosphate compounds, particularly hydroxylpatite, $Ca_5OH(PO_4)_3$. Phosphates are involved in the biochemical processes that make cells function. In particular, this concerns the crucial energy transfer processes that occur in living systems.

Phosphates are used in food processing to bind to and precipitate metal ions, which would otherwise interfere with the food processing reactions. If, for example, calcium ion is to be removed from solution in food, it can be reacted with a sodium phosphate salt

$$3\,Na_2HPO_4 + 5\,Ca^{2+} + 4\,OH^- \longrightarrow Ca_5OH(PO_4)_3\downarrow + 3\,H_2O + 6\,Na^+$$

In addition to reacting with metal ions, phosphates form "complexes" with proteins and starches. The exact nature of this interaction is not understood. However, it may have some desirable properties in food processing operations of certain types.

The phosphate ions are important buffers in foods and in living protoplasm as well. At the pH values found in most foods, the phosphate ions present are mostly $H_2PO_4^-$ and HPO_4^{2-}. Typically HPO_4^{2-} reacts with hydrogen ion (acid),

$$HPO_4^{2-} + H^+ \longrightarrow H_2PO_4^-$$

and $H_2PO_4^-$ reacts with hydroxide ion (base)

$$H_2PO_4^- + OH^- \longrightarrow HPO_4^{2-} + H_2O$$

so that neither the concentration of acid or that of base becomes too high. An excess of either could cause the food to have a bad taste or could cause undesirable chemical reactions to occur in the food.

Phosphates function as *dispersants*. This means that they cause particles of proteins or other substances to spread throughout the food mass. A special case of this is the stabilization of emulsions. Emulsions are very small oil and fat particles that are suspended in water or a water-based medium. Phosphates help to make these emulsions stable. One interesting example is the ability of phosphates to stabilize the emulsions of fat in sausage.

15.10

There's Gum in My Beer!

In food terminology, *gum* refers to materials that dissolve in water and that have a thickening and gelling effect. Many chemists would call gums *hydrophilic colloids*. This means that the colloidal particles are repelled by water. There are many different kinds of gums used in foods. They are employed in an enormous number of ways. Some gums such as agar, algin, carrageenan, and furcellaran are extracted from seaweed. Others are extracted from trees or exude from trees. Gum arabic, gum ghatti, gum karaya, and gum tragacanth all come from trees. Locust bean gum and guar gum are extracted from seeds. Some very commonly used gums are made chemically from cellulose. These include sodium carboxymethylcellulose, which was first developed in Germany during World War II as a substitute for gelatin. This synthetic is now used in ice cream, baked goods, milk beverages, salad dressings, and many other foods.

The uses of gums in food make up a very long list, indeed. Agar is used as an adhesive to hold icings on baked goods. Locust bean gum in sausages acts as a binding agent to hold the sausage together. Gum arabic gives nonnutritive bulk to diet foods. Jams, sauces, gravies, and fillings are thickened with furcellaran. Carboxymethylcellulose prevents crystallization in ice cream and sugar syrups and stabilizes mayonnaise and beer. The fat in salad dressings is held in suspension (emulsified) with propylene glycol alginate. Suspended cloudy material in wine is flocculated together and settled out with sodium alginate. Carrageenan serves to suspend the flavoring in chocolate milk. Jelly candies, such as gum drops, are released from the molds in which they are formed by gum arabic. With so many uses it is little wonder that the food consumption of gums in the U.S. exceeds 10 million pounds each year.

15.11

Sequestrants in Food

Sequestering agents are chemical species that the chemist normally calls *chelating agents*. These are species that can bind to more than one place on a metal ion, thus, holding the ion very tightly. For example, glycine, an amino acid found in protein, binds strongly to copper ion. The glycine may be called a sequestrant because it isolates, or "sequesters," the Cu^{2+} ion. Tied up with glycine, the copper does not behave at all like a cupric ion. (See top of page 448.)

Metal ions play a strong role in the degradation of foods. They catalyze oxidation reactions that cause some foods to age rapidly. However, when "sequestered," traces of metal ions are not nearly so effective in catalyzing these reactions. Therefore, sequestrants play a strong role in preventing spoilage of some foods.

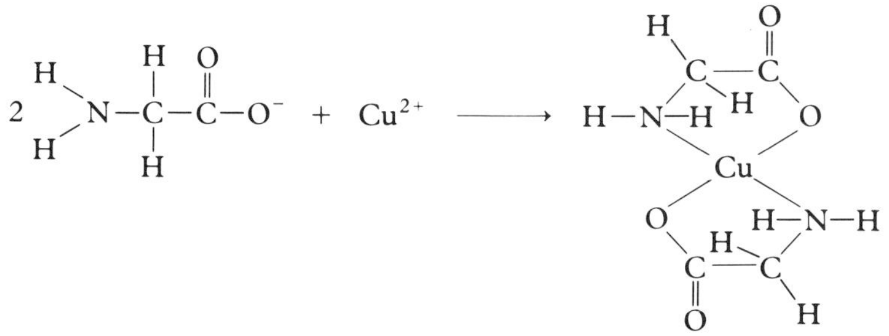

glycine anion   cupric   cupric ion,
from the amino   ion   "sequestered" by
acid, glycine   glycinate anions

The most commonly used food sequestrants are acetate salts, citrate salts, salts of ethylenediaminetetraacetate (EDTA), calcium gluconate, oxystearin, phosphate salts, calcium phytate, sorbitol, tartrate salts, and sodium thiosulfate. Some of these, such as acetate and citrate, are naturally occurring substances. The major synthetic is EDTA, a very strong sequestrant. The chemical structures of an EDTA chelate are given in Figure 15.2.

FIGURE 15.2
Structure of EDTA *chelate.*

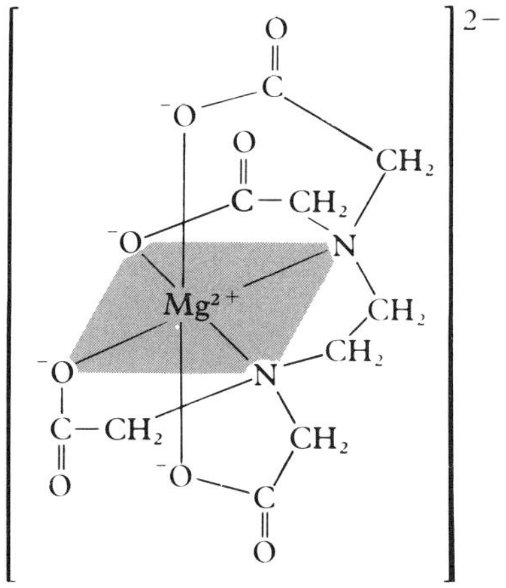

The accomplishments of sequestrants in food are impressive. Generally, they are used to prevent rancidity, bad tastes, and other undesirable characteristics resulting from air oxidation of oils and fats. Sequestrants prevent "weeping" of oleomargarine and butter. However, strong sequestrants such as EDTA are excellent heavy metal carriers that bind chemically to heavy metals and transport them through the various food processes into the body. Their uses in food should be viewed with some caution.

15.12

Chemistry and Household Products

Chemistry is an important factor in the manufacture of a wide range of household products. These include disinfectants, cleansers, deodorizers, floor waxes, furniture polish, and many other materials. Especially since World War II, the markets for these products have been advanced by massive advertising campaigns. The profits from household products sold each year are enormous. Many of these products have, indeed, greatly improved the quality and cleanliness of our domestic surroundings. In other cases too much money has been spent in the pursuit of the ultimate white wash, floors polished like fine silverware, and bathrooms without the slightest trace of odor. There have been some harmful side effects: Freon from aerosol sprays (Figure 15.3) that may damage the ozone layer in the stratosphere; drain cleaners that can kill children who accidentally swallow them; and detergent builders that pollute water. So many chemical household products are available that it is not possible to discuss them in detail here. Emphasis will be placed on soaps and detergents, which are the most widely sold household chemicals.

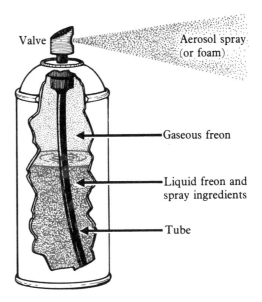

FIGURE 15.3 *Aerosol spray can.*

15.13

Chemicals that Clean

Soaps are salts of the higher fatty acids discussed in Section 10.12. For example, stearic acid, $C_{17}H_{35}COOH$, reacts with sodium hydroxide to form the salt $C_{17}H_{35}COO^-Na^+$. This salt, sodium stearate, is a soap.

The other two common components of ordinary soap are sodium palmitate, $C_{15}H_{31}COO^-Na^+$, and sodium oleate, $C_{17}H_{33}COO^-Na^+$, the latter being the salt of an unsaturated acid.

The cleaning action of soap results largely from its emulsifying power. This concept may be understood by considering the dual nature of the soap anion. An examination of its structure

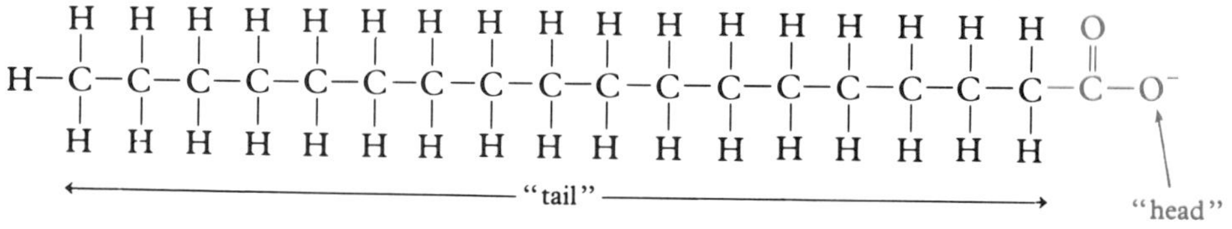

$$H-\overset{\displaystyle H}{\underset{\displaystyle H}{C}}-\overset{\displaystyle H}{\underset{\displaystyle H}{C}}-\overset{\displaystyle H}{\underset{\displaystyle H}{C}}-\overset{\displaystyle H}{\underset{\displaystyle H}{C}}-\overset{\displaystyle H}{\underset{\displaystyle H}{C}}-\overset{\displaystyle H}{\underset{\displaystyle H}{C}}-\overset{\displaystyle H}{\underset{\displaystyle H}{C}}-\overset{\displaystyle H}{\underset{\displaystyle H}{C}}-\overset{\displaystyle H}{\underset{\displaystyle H}{C}}-\overset{\displaystyle H}{\underset{\displaystyle H}{C}}-\overset{\displaystyle H}{\underset{\displaystyle H}{C}}-\overset{\displaystyle H}{\underset{\displaystyle H}{C}}-\overset{\displaystyle H}{\underset{\displaystyle H}{C}}-\overset{\displaystyle H}{\underset{\displaystyle H}{C}}-\overset{\displaystyle H}{\underset{\displaystyle H}{C}}-\overset{\displaystyle H}{\underset{\displaystyle H}{C}}-\overset{\displaystyle H}{\underset{\displaystyle H}{C}}-\overset{\displaystyle O}{\overset{\displaystyle \|}{C}}-O^-$$

The soap anion.

$\longleftarrow$ —————————— "tail" ————————————— $\longrightarrow$ "head"

shows that the stearate ion consists of an ionic carboxyl "head" and a long organic "tail." In the presence of oils, fats, and other water-insoluble organic materials, there is a tendency for the "tail" of the anion to dissolve in the organic material leaving the "head" in water. In this way the soap suspends the organic material in water in the form of very small colloidal particles (like those shown in Figure 6.9). Soap is said to **emulsify** the organic matter, and the colloidal suspension formed is an **emulsion**. Soap also lowers the **surface tension** of the water. Basically, this means that the water is made "wetter."

Soap's greatest disadvantage is its reaction with **hardness** ions (Ca^{2+} and Mg^{2+}) to form insoluble salts of fatty acids.

$$2\,C_{17}H_{35}CO_2^-Na^+ + Ca^{2+} \longrightarrow Ca(C_{17}H_{35}CO_2)_2\!\downarrow + 2\,Na^+$$

These insoluble salts do not work for cleaning. They form unsightly deposits on clothing and in washing machines. If enough soap is used, all of the hardness ions can be removed from the water by the reaction just shown. The water will then have good cleaning properties. This approach works in the bathroom sink. However, for washing clothes, water hardness must be removed before soap is used.

From an environmental viewpoint, soap is a very good product. As soon as it gets into sewage or a natural water system, soap generally precipitates as calcium and magnesium salts. This eliminates the soap from the water as a solid, which eventually biodegrades. Therefore, aside from the occasional formation of unsightly scum, soap does not cause any substantial pollution problems.

The disadvantages of soap as a cleaning agent lead to a search for other chemical compounds that are good cleaning agents but do not react with hardness ions. The result was the development of synthetic detergents. Like soap, these compounds have an ionic end and a hydrocarbon end so they emulsify grease. They also lower the surface tension of water. Unlike soap, they do not form precipitates with calcium and magnesium ions.

Until the early 1960's the most common detergent used was an alkyl benzyl sulfonate, ABS.

$$Na^+ \ ^-O-S-\bigcirc-C-C-C-C-C-C-C-C-C-CH_3$$

ABS,
an alkyl benzyl sulfonate

⟵——— alkyl chain ———⟶

ABS suffered the distinct disadvantage of being only very slowly biodegradable. The group $-C(CH_3)_3$ is highly detrimental to bacterial action. The most objectionable manifestation of the nonbiodegradable detergents, insofar as the average citizen was concerned, was the "head" of foam that began to appear in glasses of drinking water in areas where sewage was recycled through the domestic water supply. Sewage plant operators were disturbed by very spectacular beds of foam, which appeared near sewage outflows and in sewage treatment plants. Occasionally the entire aeration tank of an activated sludge plant would be smothered by a blanket of foam. Among the undesirable effects of persistent detergents upon waste treatment processes were lowered surface tension of water, dispersion of solids and grease, flotation of solids, emulsification of grease and oil, and destruction of useful bacteria. Consequently ABS was replaced by a biodegradable detergent known as LAS.

Frothy detergents resisting natural decomposition accummulate and contaminate Snow Creek in Anniston, Alabama.
(Courtesy of USDA)

LAS, α-dodecane benzene sulfonate, has the general structure

$$H-C-C-C-C-C-C-C-C-C-C-C-C-H$$

LAS,
α-dodecane benzene sulfonate

$$O=S=O$$ sulfonate group

$$O^- \ Na^+$$

where the attachment of the benzene ring may be at any point on the alkyl chain except at the ends. LAS is more biodegradable than ABS because the alkyl chain portion of LAS is not branched, which is so detrimental to biodegradability. Since LAS has replaced ABS in detergents, problems arising from the surface active agent in the detergents have greatly diminished and the levels of surface active agents found in waters have decreased markedly.

Most of the environmental problems currently attributed to detergents do not arise from the surface active agents. The "builders" added to detergents continue to cause environmental problems, however. A commercial solid detergent contains only from 10 to 30% of surfactant. In addition to the surfactant, typical detergent formulations contain from 25 to 40% polyphosphates (salts having anions made of several phosphorus and oxygen atoms in a chain), added to complex calcium and functioning as a "builder;" from 5 to 7% sodium silicates, added to prevent corrosion; from 3 to 6% amide foam stabilizers; from 0.5 to 1% soil-suspending carboxymethylcellulose; from 15 to 25% sodium sulfate, added as a dilutent; and from 6 to 15% water. Of these materials, the polyphosphates have caused the most concern as environmental pollutants. Phosphate detergents have been considered a major source of phosphate in water. Since phosphate is an essential algal nutrient that allows their rapid growth in natural waters, the removal of phosphates from detergents has become a primary goal for environmental improvement; and some local legislation has been enacted limiting detergent phosphates. But, finding satisfactory substitutes for polyphosphates has been difficult. The precipitating builders, such as sodium carbonate and sodium silicate, precipitate calcium as the carbonate and silicate. These insoluble products may deposit on clothing and make it stiff. In addition, some of the detergent formulations utilizing precipitating builders are so basic (caustic) that they constitute a toxicological hazard. Other detergent builders that are strong complexing agents (sequestrants) pose unresolved questions with regard to possible heavy-metal ion transport.

Excess nutrients from land runoff cause overgrowth of algae and other organisms that shut out sunlight to plants below the surface of this river. The amount of oxygen is reduced when the algae decays and fish begin to die. (Courtesy of Massachusetts Audubon Society; Richard Mailey, photographer)

15.14

Chemicals and Man: Where is the Balance?

After learning about the great variety of chemicals that are eaten, taken into the body unintentionally, or contacted with skin as deodorants or cosmetics, one is left with a somewhat uneasy feeling. Modern society probably could not function as it does now without many of these chemicals. The whole food processing and distribution business would be much different were it not for the chemicals that industry uses. Food would probably be much more expensive, spoil easily, and, in many cases, not have a good taste or color. Humans might suffer nutritionally if artificial nutrients were not added to food.

There must be a balance that can be attained. Consider an analogy with medicine. Tranquilizers can be remarkably helpful in getting a student through a crucial examination intact, or enabling a mother to attend to all the demands of a particularly hectic day, or assisting an overworked businessman in obtaining a badly needed full night's sleep. But one must be constantly aware of the dangers of overusing these chemical crutches that can lead to dependence.

Similarly, in food processing, the chemical "fix" is often too commonly practiced. Add a chemical here to lengthen shelf life, another to retain or change color, a third to make the flavor just right; and soon the customer may, in fact, be buying a chemical banquet. In consuming many different kinds of chemicals, there is a good probability that at least some of them are harmful to the body, especially when several are mixed. On the other hand, nature can produce some rather toxic substances, such as the potent carcinogenic aflatoxins produced by some molds in bread, peanuts, dried milk, and other foods. These carcinogens can be prevented by chemical additives.

The solutions to these problems lie in knowledge and a balanced view. We need to know everything that can reasonably be learned through research into each of the common food and consumer product chemicals. We need to realize that nothing can ever be 100% safe, and this includes food additives. We need to accept some imperfections: foods that might be slightly off color; shirts that are not dazzling white, though clean; and other things that are not worth the risk of a "chemical fix." Only through an educated public and knowledgeable decision makers—and this includes some knowledge of chemistry—can intelligent decisions be made regarding chemistry in our everyday lives.

Chapter Summary

Modern foods, expecially the more highly processed ones, enable us to have a real "chemical feast." Chemicals are added to improve taste, change color, improve texture, add nutrition, and for many other purposes. The FDA maintains a *GRAS list* of about 600 chemical additives that are "generally considered as safe."

Preservation is one of the most common uses for chemical *food additives.* Most of these additives are directed toward preventing the action of bacteria and fungi and avoiding oxidation. The two most common chemical preservatives are sodium benzoate and calcium propionate.

The acidity of food is very important for taste and preservation. The two most common acid additives, or *acidulents,* are citric acid and phosphoric acid. Many other acids and their salts are added to regulate the acid content of foods.

Food colorings have been the subject of considerable concern. Uncertainty regarding the safety of some of these continues. At the turn of the century, around 80 dyes, many certainly toxic, were used in foods. This number was cut back to seven by the Food and Drug Act of 1906. Since that time, others have been added, and some removed as questions arose regarding their safety. Colored "lakes" consisting of dyes chemically bound to aluminum hydroxide are now widely used in food. They have the advantage of not "bleeding."

Chemical food flavorings are placed in foods to add a desired flavor or cover up a bad one. These can be extracted from natural sources or synthesized chemically.

Nonnutritive sweeteners are used in foods for persons who must, or wish to, limit their sugar intake. Sodium saccharin is the most common of these. Another one which is temporarily banned is sodium cyclamate.

Vitamins and minerals are often added to food to improve nutrition. Amino acids may also be added. Other food additives discussed include phosphates, gums, and sequestrants.

Chemicals are widely used in household products. These include deodorizers, floor waxes, furniture polish, and many other products. Cleansers and detergents are especially important among these.

Chapter Review Questions

The following questions are designed as a self-teaching tool to help you review Chapter 15. The answers to each question follow. See Chapter Review Questions for Chapter 1 for further instructions.

1. The Food and Drug Administration maintains a list of approximately _____ chemicals "generally regarded as safe" called the _____ list.

2. An additive that bonds strongly to metal ions in food is called a _____.

3. An additive that helps food retain moisture is called a _____.

4. Detergent-like substances that allow intimate mixing of unlike materials in food are called _____.

5. Two ways of preserving food by depriving bacteria of water are _____ and _____.

6. The two most common chemical food preservatives are _____ and _____.

7. The two additives, BHA and BHT, are used as _____ in food.

8. Sodium aluminosilicate may be used in table salt to _____
_____.

9. The two most commonly used acidulents are _____ and
_____.

10. When it interacts with ferric ion, citrate ion acts as a _____
_____.

11. On a large scale citric acid is obtained by _____,
carried out by the mold, _____.

12. A notation, such as FD&C Red No. 2, is used to identify the class of
additives known as _____.

13. A "lake" used for food coloring is in the form of _____
_____, and the coloring matter in it is not _____
_____.

14. The most important general form of natural food colors are the _____.

15. An additive used in some carbonated beverages and other foods to give a
dark color is _____.

16. Oily flavor and odor compounds from plants are called _____
_____, and if they are washed from the plant with ethanol, the
product is called _____.

17. Three terms used to distinguish among food flavors on the basis of whether
or not they are from natural or man-made sources are _____,
_____, and _____.

18. The chemical compound thought to be responsible for "Chinese restaurant
syndrome" is _____.

19. The two most common artificial sweeteners are _____ and
_____.

20. On the basis of solubility, vitamins are divided between _____
and _____.

21. In addition to calcium, a mineral needed for bones is _____.

22. Food additives that dissolve in water and have thickening and gelling effects
are called _____, which chemically are _____ colloids.

23. Glycinate anions will _____ copper ion and other metal ions.

24. The cleaning action of soap results from its _____ power and
ability to lower _____ of water.

25. In a detergent formulation, LAS functions as a _____ and
polyphosphate as the _____.

Answers to Chapter Review Questions

1. 600, GRAS
2. sequestrant
3. humectant
4. surfactants
5. dehydration, addition of salt or sugar
6. sodium benzoate, calcium propionate
7. antioxidants
8. take up moisture and prevent caking
9. citric acid, phosphoric acid
10. sequestrant or chelating agent

11. fermentation of molasses, *Aspergillus niger*
12. food dyes
13. very fine particles, soluble in water
14. carotenoids
15. caramel
16. essential oils, an extract
17. imitation, artificial, synthetic
18. monosodium glutamate
19. saccharin, cyclamates
20. water soluble, fat soluble
21. phosphate
22. gums, hydrophilic
23. "sequester"
24. emulsifying, surface tension
25. surfactant, builder

Exercises for Chapter 15

1. Name one use of the mole, *Aspergillus niger*.

2. Fumaric acid is a common food additive. Look up its structure. Do you think it has an isomer which could have different properties? If so, draw the structure of the isomer.

3. Distinguish between a dye and a lake.

4. From the structure of β-carotene, do you feel that it might oxidize readily in air? Why?

5. What is the definition of an essential oil?

6. What is an extract in food chemistry?

7. What is an isolate?

8. Regarding flavors, distinguish among imitation, artificial, and synthetic.

9. What is the difference between a flavor enhancer and a flavor potentiator?

10. The chemical formula of sodium saccharin is given in the text. Calcium saccharin is also used for sweetening. What is the chemical formula of calcium saccharin?

11. Into what two general classes are vitamins distinguished on the basis of their solubility? Which vitamins belong in each class?

12. What type of simple inorganic substance can function as a buffer or as a dispersant?

13. What type of substance used in food is hydrophilic and has thickening and gelling effects?

14. Why is it sometimes desirable to "sequester" metal ions in food?

15. Explain how both soap and LAS detergents have "split personalities" in the way they react with grease and water.

16. What does a builder do in detergents?

17. Distinguish between a sequestrant and a surfactant. Explain how a sequestrant could help a surfactant.

18. Name five things that can be done to prevent molds and bacteria from growing on food.

19. For what purpose are sodium benzoate and calcium propionate used in food?

20. What very common natural product is used as both an acidulent and a sequestrant in food?

21. Because of a feature of their chemical structure, carotenoids decompose rather easily. Explain why this is so.

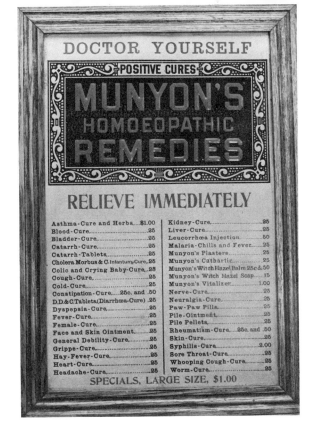

Medicine cabinet, circa 1900. Since that time drastic changes have occurred in the types of medicines available. (From the collection of Gary Jacobson; Michael E. Katin, photographer)

16
Chemistry and Medicine

16.1
The Good Old Days

Those who long for the "good old days" often forget, or are too young to know about, some of the horrible conditions of times past. New drugs and vaccines, largely the result of chemistry applied to medicine, have greatly improved our quality of life. Polio vaccines have made this disease a rare thing. Mind-altering drugs have enabled keeping the mentally ill under relatively controlled conditions. Many people who formerly would have been in institutions are now able to lead essentially normal lives. Bacterial pneumonia can now usually be cured although the appearance of a penicillin-resistant variety in South Africa in 1977 was a most disturbing development. Unwanted pregnancies can be avoided.

This chapter discusses some of the ways in which chemistry is applied to medicine. Chemistry has had a major role in improving health in this century. Many "wonder drugs" have been produced. Of course, there are some undesirable side effects. The penicillin which cures pneumonia can in rare cases kill almost instantly when a severe, "anaphilactic" reaction results. Evidence continues to accumulate that birth-control pills have some undesirable side effects in women who are over 40 years old. Mind-altering drugs have contributed to a huge "drug-traffic problem" throughout the world. But, on the whole, advances in medicinal chemistry have performed wonders in keeping people healthy, prolonging life, and improving its quality.

16.2

Types of Drugs

Drugs can be classified in several **therapeutic groups**. Something that is "therapeutic" is used in the treatment of a disease, ailment, or discomfort. The major therapeutic groups of drugs are summarized in Table 16.1 and their uses in the human body are shown in Figure 16.1. The types of drugs available change over the years. New and improved

The types of drugs available has changed drastically over the years.

drugs are introduced, and obsolete drugs are removed from the market. Some drugs are found to have such bad side effects that they are banned. Very profitable, highly advertised over-the-counter drugs are found to be ineffective and are banned. Or, dangers may become apparent which cause these drugs to require prescriptions. A fine balance is sought between preventing dangerous drugs from reaching the market, while not holding back life-saving drugs too long. To be effective, any drug has to cause some changes in the body. As a result, the potential for damage is always present. So, the physician and the patient must accept a trade-off between the potential for cure and the potential for harm.

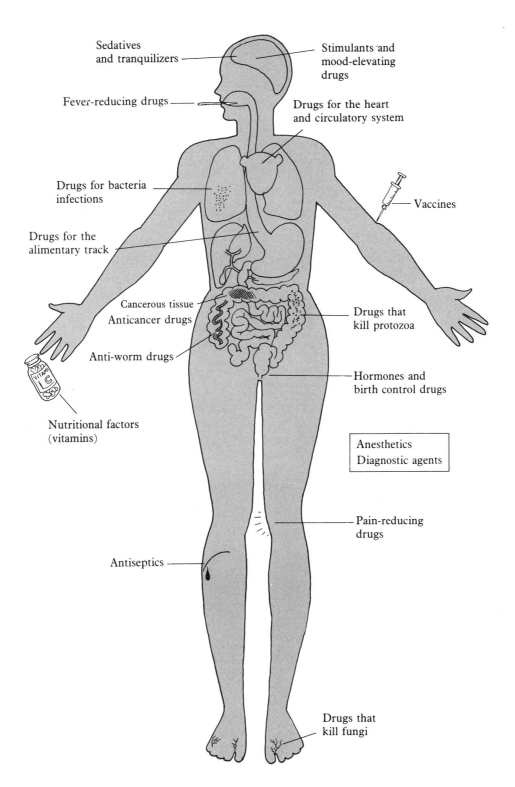

FIGURE 16.1
Drugs of various kinds are used for ailments throughout the human body.

TABLE 16.1
Major therapeutic groups of drugs.

Major Drug Group in Terms of its Use	Typical Drug or Type of Drug
Fever-reducing drugs (antipyretics)	Aspirin, Tempra, Tylenol
Pain-reducing drugs (analgesics)	Aspirin, codeine, Darvon
Drugs for the alimentary tract	Toothpaste, antacids, laxatives, antidiarrhea drugs, drugs to neutralize acid
Drugs that kill bacteria	Sulfa drugs, penicillin, other antibiotics
Drugs that kill fungi	Iodine, Amphotericin B, Desenex
Drugs that combat protozoa (single-celled animals)	Quinine (for malaria), emetine (for amebic dysentery)
Drugs used against worms in the body	Hexylresorcinol, tartar emetic
Antiseptics	Phenol, hexachlorophene, hydrogen peroxide, used to kill bacteria on skin surfaces
Sedatives and tranquilizers	Barbituates (such as Seconal), chloral (to aid sleep), Valium (tranquilizer)
Stimulants used to increase awareness and improve mood	Caffeine, amphetamines, Tofranil (antidepressant)
Anesthetics (substances that make one unconscious or prevent pain in a local area)	Ether, spinal anesthetics (procaine injected into spine), cocaine, novocaine
Drugs for the heart, blood, and circulatory disorders	Digitalis for heart failure, nitroglycerin to relieve "angina," quinidine to prevent fibrillation, rauwolfia to relieve high blood pressure, drugs for anemia, coagulants, anticoagulants
Anticancer drugs (cancer chemotherapy)	Nitrogen mustards, azathioprine to treat leukemia, radioactive iodine
Antidotes	Various compounds to counteract action of poisons, EDTA for lead poisoning
Hormones	Thyroid stimulants, growth stimulants, cortisone, birth-control pills
Vaccines	Antigens against diseases such as polio
Nutritional factors	Vitamin supplements
Diagnostic agents	Barium sulfate for X rays

16.3

Drugs for the Alimentary Tract

The *alimentary tract* refers to the long passageway through which food travels in going from the mouth to the anus. At one time or another various parts of this canal give one some grief. Ailments may range all the way from decayed teeth due to the action of bacteria in the mouth to the agony of hemmorhoids. In between lie miserable stomach upsets from virus infections, or the particularly agonizing experience of a bout of amebic dysentery (caused by small one-celled animals in the intestine). Many drugs are available to help combat these ailments.

Drugs used in the mouth include mouthwashes (which are of little real use) and dentifrices, including toothpastes. Typically toothpastes contain a detergent for cleaning action, some flavoring compounds, nonsugar sweetener, and a "vehicle" such as glycerin or propylene glycol to carry the other ingredients along. Abrasives, such as aluminum silicate, may be added (frequent brushing with these can wear teeth down). Stannous fluoride, SnF_2, is added to some toothpastes to prevent tooth decay.

Antacids are the most commonly used drugs for the stomach. The walls of the stomach secrete 0.1 *M* HCl into the stomach. This prevents the growth of bacteria and creates an environment in which enzymes can break down proteins. If there is too much acid in the stomach, discomfort can result. Many over-the-counter antacids are available to relieve excess stomach acid. A typical one of these is a mixture of aluminum hydroxide and magnesium hydroxide. Maalox is such a mixture. These hydroxides react with stomach acid, removing it from the stomach contents.

$$Al(OH)_3 + \ + 3\,H^+Cl^- \longrightarrow AlCl_3 + 3\,H_2O$$

aluminum hydrochloric acid
hydroxide (stomach acid)

$$Mg(OH)_2 + \ 2\,H^+Cl^- \longrightarrow MgCl_2 + 2\,H_2O$$

magnesium hydrochloric acid
hydroxide (stomach acid)

Too much antacid can cause an "acid rebound" whereby the stomach produces too large an excess of acid to make up for the acid removed.

Emetics are drugs that irritate the stomach and cause vomiting. They are used to make a patient vomit in case of poisoning. Common table salt is often used. Mustard water also works as an emetic. *Antiemetics* are used to prevent vomiting. Most of these are tranquilizers. A typical antiemetic is pipamazine (Mornidine), which is frequently used to treat morning sickness in pregnant women. (The structure of pipamazine is given at the top of page 462.)

Chloretics are used to increase output of bile from the gall bladder to the intestines. Bile disperses fats into very small droplets so that the fat can be digested and absorbed. If bile production is not sufficient, fatty

pipamazine

foods cannot be digested. Compounds taken from cattle bile and several synthetic compounds are used as chloretics.

Laxatives occur as a tremendous variety of materials. They are no longer widely recommended as part of normal medical practice, although they may be prescribed for special conditions. Laxatives may consist of lubricants (mineral oil), feces softeners, bulky substances (vegetable gums which swell when wet), salts ($MgSO_4$, epsom salts), and organic compounds, which are bowel irritants.

A number of compounds are used to control diarrhea. These materials work by absorbing toxic materials from the intestine contents (kaolin clay or charcoal), by preventing muscle action in the intestine (paregoric), or by forming protective coatings on intestine walls. Bloating and problems with alimentary tract gas are helped by defoaming agents such as simethicone,

several of these
groups in a chain

which helps pockets of gas to come together so that they may be eliminated by belching.

Drugs that kill or inhibit bacteria, protozoa (one-celled animals), or worms are also often used to treat infections in the alimentary tract. These drugs will be discussed separately.

16.4

Drugs that Help Get Rid of Unwanted Guests in the Body

The human body is a marvelous home for a very large assortment of other living things (Figure 16.2). A few of these are helpful. Human digestive systems would not work well without bacteria in the intestines. However, many of these "guests" are harmful. They range in size from

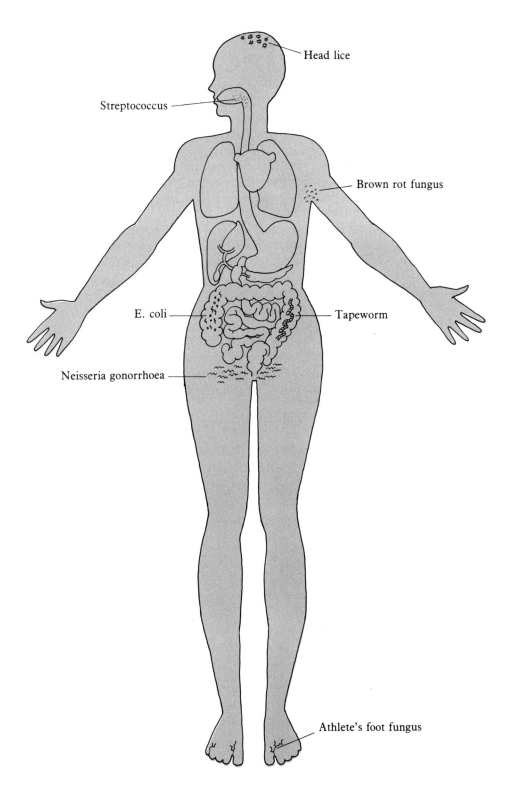

FIGURE 16.2
The body is an excellent home for many guests, not all of them welcome.

the very small viruses, which cause the aches and fever of influenza, through one-celled bacteria, which cause venereal disease, all the way up to various kinds of worms that can be seen with the naked eye. Normally the body fights these off pretty well, but sometimes help is needed. This area of medicine has made more progress than any other. Most diseases caused by bacteria can now be prevented by vaccines or cured with drugs. The same is true of fungi, protozoa, and worms. Viruses remain more troublesome, but vaccines have been developed for virus diseases such as polio, measles, mumps, and some types of influenza.

Drugs used against bacteria belong to two large classes: the sulfa drugs and the antibiotics. Both types are so important that they will be discussed in separate sections.

Fungi are organisms that do not move like animals and do not perform photosynthesis like plants. They often have structures called *mycelia,* which spread out as the fungus grows. Anyone who has had a really severe case of athlete's foot knows how hard it can be to get rid of a fungus infection. Fungi cause maladies with dreadful sounding names such as brown rot, North and South American blastomycosis, vaginal moniliasis (a yeast infection of the vagina), and intestinal moniliasis.

Drugs used to treat fungus infections may be either fungistatic or fungicidal. The fungistatic drugs stop the growth of fungi whereas the fungicidals kill them. In recent years some good antifungal drugs have been developed. Some of these have the following chemical structures:

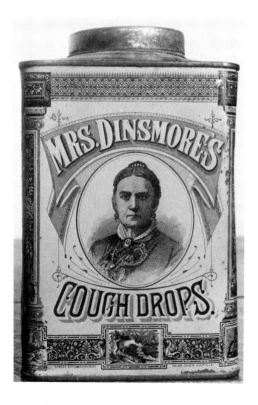

Codeine, a derivative of morphine, was thought to be effective in relieving the sufferings from a common cold. It is still used in some cough remedies today. (From the collection of Gary Jacobson; Michael E. Katin, photographer)

Griseofulvin (Fulvicin)

Taken by mouth to treat ringworm and other fungus infections.

Chlordantoin (Sporostacin)

Applied directly to tissue for treatment of vulvovaginal moniliasis and skin fungi

Zinc Omadine

Used as a fungicide and bactericide in shampoo.

Protozoa are single-celled organisms that normally can move around by their own means. One of the world's most widespread diseases, malaria, is caused by such an organism. Quinine is the drug used to combat malaria. Amebas cause another dreadful disease known as amebic dysentery. They form cysts in the intestine and can penetrate intestinal walls. Liver abscesses resulting in hepatitis can also form.

One of the greatest drugs of all time, Salvarsan,

Salvarsan

is effective against protozoa, although its greatest use was in the treatment of syphillis. It was synthesized by Dr. Paul Ehrlich in 1907. This discovery introduced modern *chemotherapy,* the treatment of disease with chemicals. Although this drug and related drugs containing arsenic are no longer used because they are toxic, many new drugs have been developed for the treatment of diseases caused by protozoa. It should be kept in mind that drugs used against any living thing are biological poisons and will be somewhat toxic to humans.

It is estimated that about one-fourth of the population of the U.S. is afflicted with roundworms and flatworms. The proportion is much higher in some of the more primitive countries. Flatworms (tapeworms) can be treated with quinacrine hydrochloride, a drug whose structure is a little too complicated to show here. Taking this medication is not a pleasant experience. The patient is denied supper the night before and is often given an enema. The typical dose of the drug is 0.8 g, which may have to be given in several portions to avoid nausea. Two hours later a strong laxative ("saline purge") is given. If the head of the tapeworm has not emerged within two hours, this may be followed with an enema.

The treatment of choice for hookworms is a little simpler. Tetrachloroethylene,

$$Cl_2C=CCl_2 \quad \text{tetrachloroethylene}$$

is taken by mouth while the patient fasts. Several doses may be required.

16.5

Bacteria Killers: The Sulfa Drugs

The success of Salvarsan in chemotherapy led to greatly increased efforts to find drugs that attacked bacteria without harming normal tissues. Some of the early efforts along these lines were concentrated upon dyes because some dyes are known to selectively stain bacteria which absorb the dyes. In 1935 scientists with I. G. Farbenindustrie Laboratories in Germany found that such a dye, prontosil, did kill bacteria. It was soon shown, though, that the effective agent is sulfanilamide, which is formed from prontosil in the body. Within a few years sulfanilamide and related compounds were in wide use to combat bacterial infections.

Sulfa drugs kill bacteria by fooling their biochemical processes. These drugs have a structure similar to that of *p*-aminobenzoic acid.

sulfanilamide   *p*-aminobenzoic acid

This compound is an intermediate in the biochemical synthesis of folic acid, which is a vitamin essential for the survival of bacteria. In the process by which bacteria make folic acid, the sulfa drugs substitute for *p*-benzoic acid. This fouls up the synthesis and prevents the folic acid vitamin from being made in bacteria cells. Humans must obtain folic acid through their diets, so the sulfa drugs do not deprive them of this vitamin.

Over 5000 sulfa drugs have been synthesized and tested. They have the general structure

where R_1 and R_2 may be one of many organic chemical groups or hydrogen. Sulfanilamide is no longer used because of side effects. However, related compounds have been made for a large number of special applications. These include treatment of wounds, burns, urinary tract infection, bacillary dysentery, and meningococcal meningitis. Sulfa drugs are also used in preparation for surgery to reduce numbers of bacteria in the body.

16.6

The First of the Miracle Drugs: Antibiotics

It is hard to imagine, but as recently as the early 1940's an abscessed tooth, a puncture wound from a dirty nail, or even a simple cut from a razor had the potential of causing a bacterial infection from which recovery might not be possible. Now even a bacterial infection that has advanced rather far usually can be stopped by one of a number of antibiotics. The first of these substances used to kill bacteria was penicillin. It remains the most widely used.

Penicillin is produced by a mold called *Penicillium notatum*. This fungus, like many other organisms in nature, wages a form of biological warfare against bacteria by producing a chemical that kills off the competition for its ecological niche. The action of penicillin was first noticed by Sir Alexander Fleming, a University of London bacteriologist, in 1928. This occurred during a study of *staphylococcus aureus*, round bacteria of the type that causes boils. One of his culture plates (a dish containing gelled bacterial nutrient) became contaminated with a colony of *Penicillium notatum*. In such a culture plate, the bacteria grow as individual colonies, each made up of so many bacteria cells clustered together that the colony is visible to the naked eye. It was observed that the bacteria in the colonies near the mold were undergoing *lysis*, or "dissolving" (see Figure 16.3). This activity could only be caused by a chemical substance coming from the mold.

It was not until 1941 that penicillin was shown to be effective in killing bacteria in humans. A crash program was undertaken to produce large quantities of penicillin for the wounded and ill in World War II. As a result many lives were saved and many amputations were avoided. Penicillin, the victor in the battle against bacteria, rightfully received the title of "miracle drug." However, troublesome penicillin-resistant micro-organisms, such as those causing some forms of venereal disease, have since emerged.

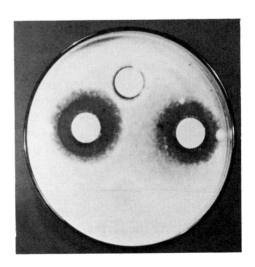

FIGURE 16.3

The absence of bacterial growth adjacent to filter discs soaked with fluid taken from growths of mold shows antibiotic (bacteria-killing) action by the mold. (Courtesy of Pfizer, Inc.)

Penicillin is a name given to a number of antibiotics that are active against bacteria infections. A green mold variety, Penicillium chrysogenum, *produces almost all of the world's commercial penicillin. (Courtesy of Pfizer, Inc.)*

The chemical structure of penicillin has been worked out. There are actually several natural and synthetic forms exhibiting slight differences in chemical structure. The most commonly used is penicillin G.

penicillin G

Penicillin is most effective against gram-positive bacteria (a type that is stained by a special coloring procedure called the gram stain). It prevents the formation of protein, which is responsible for the bacterial cell walls. Without walls to hold them together, the bacteria burst and die.

A number of other antibiotics that prevent bacteria from multiplying have been developed. Although penicillin is still the best of the antibiotics, some of the others work against bacteria that are not affected much by penicillin. They are also used for people who have built up violent and sometimes fatal allergic reactions to penicillin.

Erythromycin is commonly substituted for penicillin in cases where the patient is sensitive to penicillin or the infection has become resistant to it. Erythromycin and related compounds are isolated from *Streptomyces*, a form of bacteria. The tetracyclines are another type of antibiotic useful against both gram-positive and gram-negative bacteria. They also destroy "subbacteria," such as rickettsias, which can only be grown inside living cells. (Among the significant diseases caused by rickettsias is Rocky Mountain spotted fever.) Because of their wide range of antibacterial action the tetracyclines are called broad-spectrum or polyvalent antibiotics. The streptomycin group of antibiotics, also isolated from *Streptomyces*, is especially effective against tuberculosis. These antibiotics prevent the synthesis of essential protein in the bacteria cells.

In addition to antibiotics that are produced from fungi or bacteria, there are synthetics that are closely related to these substances. Some other antibacterial chemicals have been synthesized chemically but have little relationship to natural antibiotics. Some typical compounds are shown in the following chemical structures:

nitrofurazone (Furacin)
One of a series of antibacterial
nitrofurans

Nalidixic acid
Used for typhoid, dysentery, and
other illnesses

16.7

Antiseptics and Disinfectants

Antiseptics are germ-killing (biocidal) substances that are applied to living tissue, normally the skin surface. This is done most often in preparation for surgery or as first aid for cuts. Germ-killing substances used on floors, dishes, surgical instruments, and similar inanimate things are called *disinfectants* or *germicides*.

Antiseptics are no longer used much inside the body as part of surgery. They have been replaced by antibiotics and sulfa drugs to prevent infection by bacteria. However, it was the use of carbolic acid (phenol) antiseptic by Lister in 1867 that really began the conversion of hospitals from death houses to institutions from which the patient had a reasonable chance of recovery. Even with modern advances in the types of antiseptics available, many hospitals today are still plagued with persistent "staph" (*Staphylococcus* bacteria) infections, which have built up resistance to disinfectants and antibacterial drugs.

A huge number of compounds have been found to have germ-killing properties. These include phenols, metal compounds such as silver nitrate, halogen compounds such as iodoform (CHI_3), oxidizing agents such as H_2O_2, alcohols, dyes, quinolines, soaps, and detergents. Of these, one of the best antiseptic treatments for a simple cut remains washing it thoroughly with soap and water.

Phenol is one of the oldest disinfectants. Commonly called "carbolic acid," it was once applied to wounds as a germicide. It is no longer used directly on skin or tissue because it is too caustic and causes blistering of the skin. It is still used for disinfecting tables, floors, and other surfaces in hospitals. Chemically related compounds, the cresols, are widely used as hospital disinfectants. Solutions of these compounds are called **Lysol**.

Hexylresorcinol, a compound related to phenol, is often used as an antiseptic in mouthwashes. Hexachlorophene, another related compound, is the antiseptic of choice for use in surgical "scrubbing" to clean the hands of operating room personnel. Until around 1970, it was recommended by pediatricians for mothers to use in place of soap in washing babies, but it was shown to cause brain damage if not handled properly. This antiseptic is now available only by prescription.

phenol   cresol   hexylresorcinol   hexachlorophene

The germ killing qualities of antiseptics are often expressed as a *phenol coefficient*. For example, hexylresorcinol has a phenol coefficient of 50. This means that it is 50 times as effective as phenol in killing bacteria. Put another way, a 1% solution of a germicide with a phenol coefficient of 4 is as effective as a 4% solution of phenol.

16.8

For the Relief of Minor Pain and Fever

The American public spends something more than a quarter of a *billion* dollars each year for over-the-counter pain reducers. These belong to the general class of *analgesics,* which help relieve pain without affecting the individual's consciousness. Aspirin is by far the best example of a simple analgesic. This non-habit-forming drug gives relief from headache and muscle ache. Morphine, on the other hand, is a habit-forming drug. It raises the pain threshold, which means that the pain has to get worse before the individual feels it.

The history of aspirin goes back to 1763 when it was observed that chewing willow bark relieved the symptoms of malaria. The active ingredient was later shown to be salicylic acid,

salicylic acid

formed from naturally occurring salicin, which is present in willow bark. Unfortunately, salicyclic acid is too distasteful to take by mouth. However, in 1893 the Bayer Company in Germany had produced an acetate ester of salicylic acid,

salicylic acid	acetic anhydride	acetylsalicylic acid
A carboxylic acid and aromatic alcohol	Two acetic acid molecules joined together with the loss of 1 H$_2$O molecule	(aspirin)

in which the acetate group from acetic anhydride is bonded to the hydroxyl group on salicylic acid. This decreases both the bad taste and acidity so that aspirin can be taken by mouth.

Although aspirin is one of the most remarkable, useful, and widely taken drugs of all time, it does have some bad effects. Anyone who has fallen asleep with an aspirin tablet resting against the gum to relieve the pain of an aching tooth will wake up with a nasty "aspirin burn" to add to the misery of the toothache. The same thing happens if particles of an aspirin tablet rest against the stomach wall. Aspirin always does some damage to the stomach wall, and it is estimated that each dose of aspirin results in the loss of a half teaspoonful or so of blood in the stomach. Salicylic acid is caustic enough to be used to "burn off" warts chemically.

Many other nonaddictive pain relievers have been developed that substitute for aspirin. One of the most common of these is acetaminophen

acetaminophen (Tempra or Tylenol)

sold as Tempra or Tylenol. This compound is not so harmful to the stomach as aspirin. However, it does not relieve inflammation of joints and muscles as does aspirin.

Both aspirin and acetaminophen are *antipyretics,* drugs that reduce fever. Most parents have had the experience of taking the temperature of a feverish child every three hours or so throughout the night and giving alternate doses of aspirin and Tylenol to keep fever at a reasonable level. These two drugs are alternated so that the child will not receive an overdose of either. It should be noted that aspirin poisoning is the leading cause of poison deaths among young children. Bottles of aspirin should always be kept out of reach of children and should have "kid-proof" caps.

Opium is dried poppy juice, a milky fluid that is stored inside the pod. (Courtesy of the Drug Enforcement Administration, U.S. Dept. of Justice)

Some analgesics are classified as *narcotic analgesics*. Narcotics are habit-forming drugs. They cause biochemical changes in the body, which makes the body become dependent upon them. Among these is the oldest drug on record, opium. The Ebers papyrus of about 1500 B.C. describes prescriptions in which opium is an ingredient. Opium contains several specific addictive chemicals including morphine and codeine. Heroin, a derivative of morphine, is an excellent pain reliever but is so addictive that it is no longer manufactured in the U.S. It is the worst of the drugs involved in illegal drug traffic. This is unfortunate, because heroin is about the only drug that provides really satisfactory relief from the horrible suffering of terminal cancer patients.

One of the most common prescription pain relievers is propoxyphene hydrochloride (Darvon),

propoxyphene hydrochloride
(Darvon)

which does not usually cause addiction. On a weight basis it is about 10 times as potent as aspirin. A chemically similar compound, methadone, acts much like morphine and is addictive. However, withdrawal from methadone is easier than from heroin or morphine, and methadone is often used to treat addiction to these dangerous drugs.

16.9

Relax!

Nervous tension, along with the lack of sleep and fatigue accompanying it, is one of the most common causes of feeling poorly. The chemistry student fighting for that extra point on the final examination, which he is sure will make the grade that means admission to medical school, knows the feeling.

He may secretly long for the peaceful life of the Kansas wheat farmer living three miles from his nearest neighbor and breathing some of the world's purest air. Unfortunately, the Kansas wheat farmer is all too familiar with exactly the same feeling as he contemplates a gathering line of thunderstorms, which might contain hail that could wipe out a $20,000 wheat crop—no guaranteed annual salary for him.

Fortunately, in recent years *tranquilizers* have been developed that are useful chemical crutches for those whose nerves are made of something less stout than steel. Ideally, tranquilizers should induce calm without reducing alertness and general mental activity. In fact, they are not quite that ideal. All too often tranquilizers are prescribed when an underlying cause of the tension, often a serious physical ailment, should be diagnosed. Despite this, these drugs have done wonders for the peace, comfort, and productivity of millions of people.

Although a huge number of compounds have been used as tranquilizers, the two classical types are chlorpromazine and reserpine (Figure 16.4) Chlorpromazine and related compounds cause the patient to become more quiet and apathetic. Muscle activity is reduced and mild drowsiness may set in. The reserpine group of tranquilizers induces calm, lowers aggression, and aids sleep.

Three other commonly prescribed tranquilizers should be mentioned. Meprobamate (Miltown, Equanil) induces sleep and calm. Chlordiazepoxide hydrochloride (Librium) and diazepam (Valium) are

FIGURE 16.4

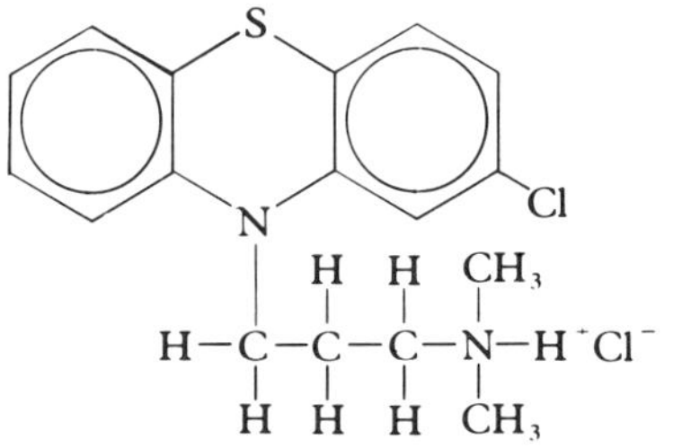

chlorpromazine hydrochloride
(Thorazine)

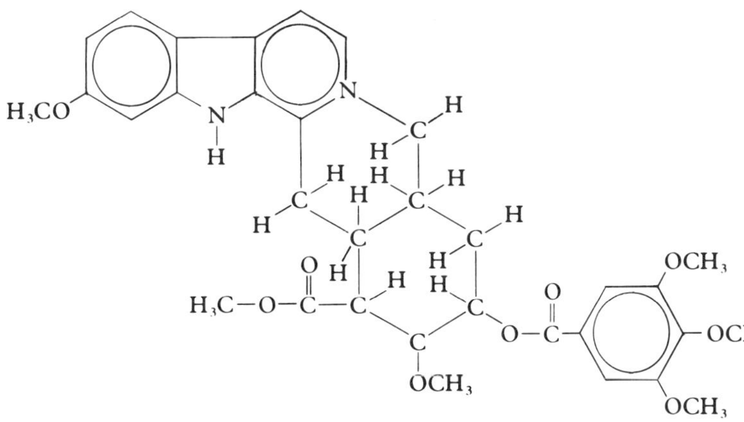

reserpine
(Serpasil)

effective in relieving anxiety and tension. They are also effective muscle relaxants, which often induces an indirect tranquilizing effect.

Sedatives are different from the true tranquilizers in that they have a direct sleep-inducing effect. They also have a calming effect. Most of the modern sedatives are rather complicated organic compounds whose structures will not be shown here. Among the more common ones are flureazepam (Dalmane, used to aid sleep and relax muscles), secobarbital (Seconal), and phenobarbital. A chemically simple compound, chloral hydrate

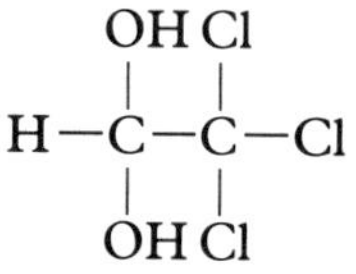

$$H-\underset{\underset{OH}{|}}{\overset{\overset{OH}{|}}{C}}-\underset{\underset{Cl}{|}}{\overset{\overset{Cl}{|}}{C}}-Cl$$

acts quickly as a sedative; and its effects are relatively shortlived.

16.10

Cheer Up!

Cerebral or psychic stimulants have come into wide use in recent years to relieve the symptoms of mental depression. This condition, to a greater or lesser extent, has afflicted millions. Drugs for the treatment of severe, acute depression or chronic depression have been a tremendous blessing to the sufferers. This malady has done great damage to society and has robbed mankind of the talents and productivity of a high percentage of the population.

Typically, the administration of antidepressants results in the patient becoming more cheerful, hopeful, and animated. They are used in the treatment of endogenous depression, which arises from internal causes. (Depression of relatively short duration caused by, for example, the death of a close family member is normal.) They are also used for the treatment of the depressive phase of persons who are manic depressives. The chemical structures of two popular antidepressants, Elavil and Tofranil, are as follows:

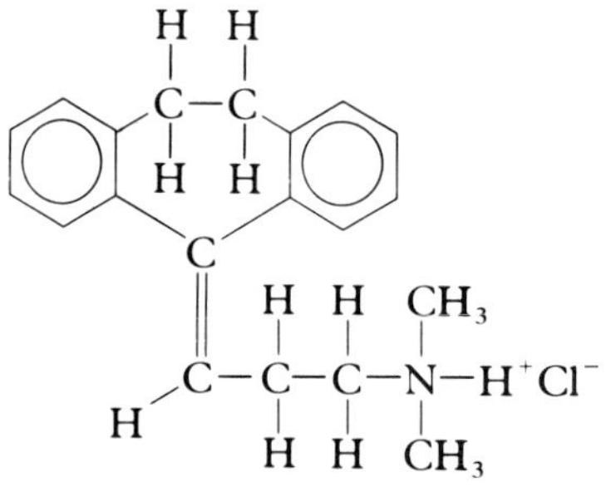

amitriptyline hydrochloride
(Elavil)

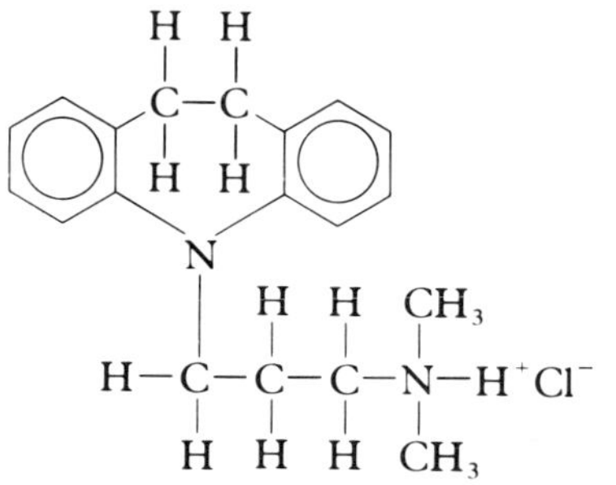

imipramine hydrochloride
(Tofranil)

16.11

Drugs for the Heart and Circulatory System

Diseases of the heart and circulatory system are the leading cause of death and illness in the U.S. The fight against heart disease and related ailments is at about the same stage that the war on bacterial diseases was at the turn of this century. We can hope that a continued high level of research and particularly the efforts of energetic and imaginative minds will someday score a major breakthrough against the dreaded killer heart disease. The progress that has been made in combatting heart and circulatory ailments and some of the medicines used are discussed in this section.

Heart fibrillation is an uncontrolled, rapid "fluttering" of the heart muscle. While in that state, the heart no longer functions as a pump for the blood, so heart fibrillation is a major cause of death during and after "heart attacks." Fibrillation, along with congestive heart failure, may often be controlled by **cardiac glycosides**. These chemicals are extracted from various sources in nature. The classic example is *digitalis* extracted from the leaves of the *Digitalis purpurea* plant. Some pure chemical compounds have been extracted from this source. Others with a similar action have been made synthetically. One such compound is digitoxin. These complicated compounds combine a sugar group, a steroid group (both described in Chapter 10), and a lactone group.

lactone group

A class of drugs known as *cardiac depressants* are used to slow down destructive, excessively rapid heartbeat. These include quinidine and procainamide hydrochloride (Pronestyl). Drugs with the opposite effect are used to increase heart rate when the heart has stopped or almost stopped. The most effective of these is isoproterenol hydrochloride (Isuprel).

isoproterenol hydrochloride
(Isuprel)

The most common cause of artery deterioration leading to heart attacks is the deposition of cholesterol compounds on artery walls. This is followed by deposits of calcium, which can clog up an artery like an old water pipe used for many years with excessively hard water.

Cholesterol, itself, is a steroid found in various fats. It is normally present in blood, but a level that is too high can indicate trouble. One obvious approach is to limit the intake of cholesterol-containing foods. Unfortunately, the body often compensates by making more of its own cholesterol. Some authorities believe that unsaturated fats (those in which the fatty acids have double bonds) lower the level of cholesterol in blood. Several chemical substances, such as the B vitamin, nicotinic acid (niacin), have been found to lower blood cholesterol levels. However, there is no actual proof that they prevent hardening of the arteries.

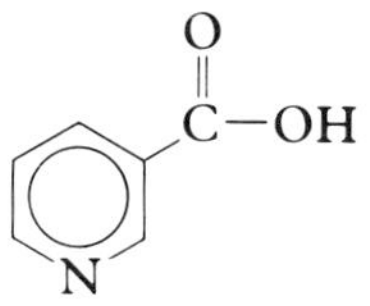

nicotinic acid
(niacin)

Excessively high blood pressure is known to contribute to heart disease and strokes. Since about 1950 tremendous progress has been made in treating hypertension with drugs. Many different kinds of drugs are available. Some of these are *rauwolfia alkaloids*, originally derived from the same plants used to make poison tips for arrows. One of this group, reserpine, was described in the section on tranquilizers. Other, more potent, synthetic drugs are available to treat hypertension.

Several kinds of drugs are used to change the properties of blood. Anemia, the lack of hemoglobin (red cells) in blood, is a common blood malady, which often used to be fatal (see Figure 16.5). *Iron deficiency anemia* is a common form of this ailment in which the body needs iron.

As far back as 1831, ferrous carbonate, $FeCO_3$, was used to treat iron deficiency anemia. Since then other forms of iron bound to organic groups have been used. Iron therapy has some bad side effects and an overdose can cause fatal deterioration of the mucous layers in the alimentary tracts of children. Excess iron may be stored in tissues and cause harm. For that reason in the absence of anemia and assuming

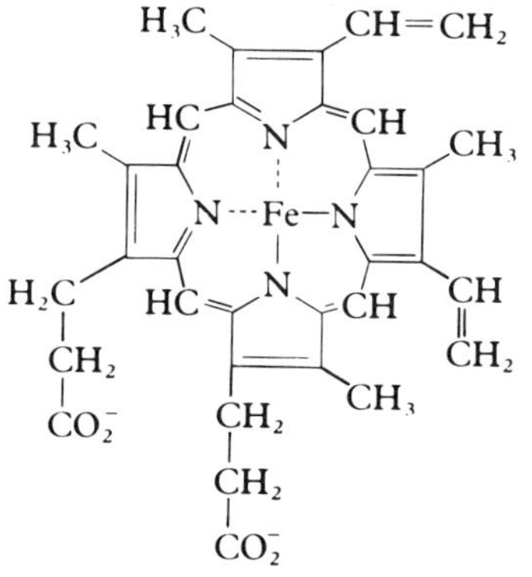

FIGURE 16.5
The heme complex is found in hemoglobin and related compounds.

a reasonable diet, patent medicines containing iron should not be taken as a regular practice.

Other forms of anemia may occur that do not result from simple iron deficiency. These are called *pernicious anemia* and *megaloblastic anemia*. They arise from conditions such as pregnancy or nutritional deficiency. Pernicious anemia is especially dangerous. It is caused by a deficiency of vitamin B_{12}, or impaired intake of this vitamin. Vitamin B_{12} is a complicated organic compound containing one ion of cobalt bound to it. It is contained in liver tissue. In former times, many young victims of pernicious anemia, who were weak, ghostly white, and well on the way to an early grave, have been saved from death by the forced feeding of large quantities of raw liver. For those of us who eat only strongly seasoned, exhaustively cooked liver once each year out of a sense of duty, the blessings of modern drugs for the treatment of anemia are obvious! Now pernicious anemia is treated by the direct injection of vitamin B_{12}. It can also be taken by mouth along with an **intrinsic factor**, which enables the body to absorb the vitamin.

The clotting of blood is an extremely important function of this vital fluid. Under normal circumstances when tissue is damaged, as by a small cut, the damaged tissue releases thromboplastin, a substance which starts a series of changes that end in the clotting of blood. These steps involve enzymes both blood and tissue, as well as calcium ions. The final product is fibrin, a fibrous substance, which covers over the wound and prevents further loss of blood. This covering protects the wound as the healing process begins. If this clotting does not occur properly, the individual will continue to lose blood and can require blood transfusions as the result of even a small cut. The victims of this blood malfunction are called *hemophiliacs* and the condition is *hemophilia*.

Blood clots that form in the circulatory system can cause much damage and even death, especially if transported to the heart, lungs, or brain. Under some circumstances, therefore, it is desirable to prevent blood from clotting, or to dissolve a clot once it is formed.

Some drugs are useful as systemic coagulants. (A systemic drug is one which is taken internally and works throughout the body.) These are primarily in the two major classes of vitamin K and related compounds and agents taken from blood, itself. Local coagulants are used at the location of a wound to form artificial clots or to enmesh oozing blood and provide strength for the fibrin which it forms. Cellulose partly oxidized with NO_2 (Oxycel, Hemopak) is used to form an artificial blood clot.

Available anticoagulants may be either systemic or local. The most well-known systemic anticoagulant is *heparin*, which is the body's natural anticoagulant. Clotted blood can be dissolved locally by the application of a local anticoagulant such as *plasmin* (fibrinolysin). This is an enzyme produced in the body to dissolve fibrin, once its job is done and healing is underway.

16.12

The Elusive Cure for Cancer

No disease is so dreaded by more people than cancer. A massive effort has been underway to find a cure for this disease, but no single cure-all is in sight. If it is never found, it will not be for lack of money and efforts of tens of thousands of researchers. Cancer is uncontrolled reproduction of cells (see Figure 16.6). Cancer cells have an abnormal shape and appearance compared to cells of the parent tissue. They do not perform the essential functions of normal cells. If not cured, cancerous tissue spreads and crowds out normal tissue. Eventually, the ability of some vital organ to do its job is stopped, and the victim dies. All kinds of tissue including bones, muscles, blood cells, and skin can become cancerous.

"Cancer" is probably a collection of a number of diseases, all characterized by uncontrolled cell growth. There is still no universal, satisfactory explanation for the cause and development of cancer. It is probably rooted in the substances that direct cell reproduction. These are nucleic acids, primarily DNA discussed in Section 11.6. Cancer results when the directions to the substances controlling cell reproduction become garbled, and the cells begin replicating uncontrollably. Viruses (small crystals of nucleic acids) have been demonstrated to cause some

FIGURE 16.6

Cancer is a disease of the cell whereby an abnormal change in a cell multiplies uncontrollably, either forming a solid mass in one part of the body or tumors in many portions of the body simultaneously. Compare in these micrographs of a urine smear the normal cell (left) with the malignant cells (right). (Courtesy of the American Cancer Society)

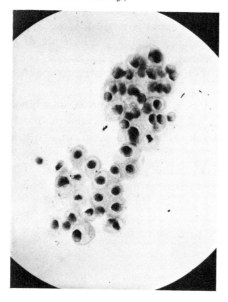 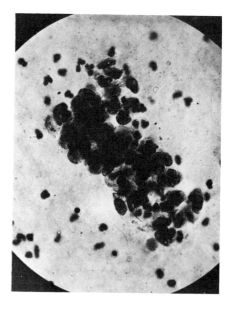

cancers in animals, and the "viral theory of cancer" has been put forward strongly in recent years. It is also known that some chemical substances known as carcinogens cause cancer by altering DNA. As far back as the late 1700's, cancer of the scrotum was recognized as an occupational hazard of chimney sweeps in London. These wretched humans started their dead-end occupation as small boys when they were small enough to fit into chimneys. Practically starved to keep them thin enough for their trade, they eventually died from cancer caused by the products of burning soft coal.

Some chemicals have been shown to slow the growth of cancerous tissue, and new chemicals are constantly tested for anticancer activity. Cancer is rapidly growing tissue, so chemicals which are toxic to such tissue are useful for cancer chemotherapy. One such common group of chemicals consists of several related to nitrogen mustard,

nitrogen mustard

a substance that can be used as a poison gas in warfare. To be effective, these chemicals must be given in doses which are somewhat harmful to normal body tissue. Diarrhea, nausea, convulsions, and bone marrow damage are common side effects.

The greatest success with cancer chemotherapy has been achieved in the treatment of leukemia in children. This cancer of the white blood cells can often by controlled for many years, greatly prolonging the lives of the victims. This is called **remission**. The compound, 6-mercaptopurine,

6-mercaptopurine

and related compounds are used in the treatment of leukemia.

As more and more chemical compounds are synthesized and tested for anticancer activity, it is possible that some very effective new anti-cancer agents will be found. It is more likely, however, that a true understanding of the biochemistry of cancer will someday be worked out. After that, a cure, or cures, can be developed with this basic knowledge.

16.13

Hormones and Oral Contraceptives

Chemical drugs are available to prevent pregnancy. These are hormones contained in **oral contraceptives**, "the pill." This is only one of many medical applications of hormones. The role of hormones in the body and in medicine is discussed in this section.

Whereas nerves in the body can be compared to telephone lines with almost instant communication links, hormones are more like first class mail. Hormones originate in one part of the body and are transported through body fluids to other parts where they tell cells what to do. Like first class mail, they sometimes are delayed or go undelivered. The results can be bad. Whereas enzymes perform very specific operations in the body, hormones oversee a whole process. One hormone may control a number of enzymes.

Hormones are produced in **endocrine glands** in the body. Several of the most important endocrine glands were shown in Figure 11.9. A portion of the **pituitary gland** in the center of the brain gives off many hormones. This gland acts as a sort of "master control" gland. An especially important pituitary hormone is the **human growth hormone**, HGH. The **thyroid gland** produces **thyroxin**, which speeds up the rate of body metabolism. The **parathyroid glands** release hormones that regulate crucial calcium and phosphorus metabolism. The **adrenal gland** produces hormones that regulate sodium and potassium metabolism, help bring about the biochemical conversion of proteins to carbohydrates, and promote development of male sex characteristics. The **pancreas** is the source of the **insulin** hormone, which regulates blood sugar levels. Failure of the body to produce insulin results in **diabetes**. **Ovaries** produced the female sex hormone, **estradiol**. The **testes** produce the corresponding male sex hormone, **testosterone**.

Many health problems come about from too low an output of an essential hormone. For example, low production of thyroxin, the thyroid hormone, can have a bad effect upon the body, resulting in low metabolism and sluggish behavior. This can be treated by administering dry, powdered thyroid gland, or one of several synthetic substances. A typical synthetic used for this purpose is liothyronine sodium.

$$HO \overset{I}{-\!\!\langle\bigcirc\rangle\!-}O \overset{I}{-\!\!\langle\bigcirc\rangle\!-}\overset{\overset{H}{|}}{\underset{\underset{H}{|}}{C}}-\overset{\overset{H}{|}}{\underset{\underset{NH_2}{|}}{C}}-\overset{\overset{O}{||}}{C}-O^- Na^+$$

liothyronine sodium

As with thyroxin, the synthetic substitutes contain iodine. Enlarged thyroid (goiter) is often caused by insufficient iodine in the diet.

A large number of hormones are steroids. Steroids are characterized by a four-ring structure in which the rings are labelled *A* through *D*.

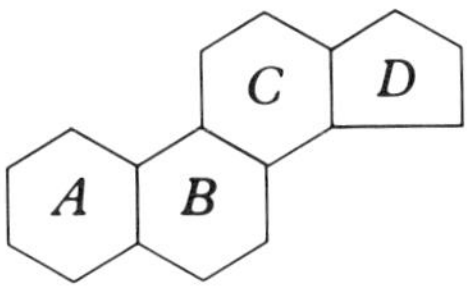

tetracyclic steroid structure

Ring *D* is a five-membered ring. The corners and intersections of the rings are occupied by carbon atoms. These atoms may have hydrogens or other groups attached. There may be double bonds in the rings, or a whole ring may be aromatic. Minor changes in the substituted groups and the locations of bonds cause large differences in the actions of the steroids.

The two major sex hormones are *progesterone* (female sex hormone) and *testosterone* (male sex hormone). As can be seen in Figure 16.7, the structures of these two hormones are remarkably similar. Estradiol and estrone are two other female sex hormones belonging to the class of *estrogens*. Each of these contains an aromatic ring.

Hormones are used in oral contraceptives, commonly known as "the pill." These birth-control drugs came into wide use during the

FIGURE 16.7 *Structures of sex hormones.*

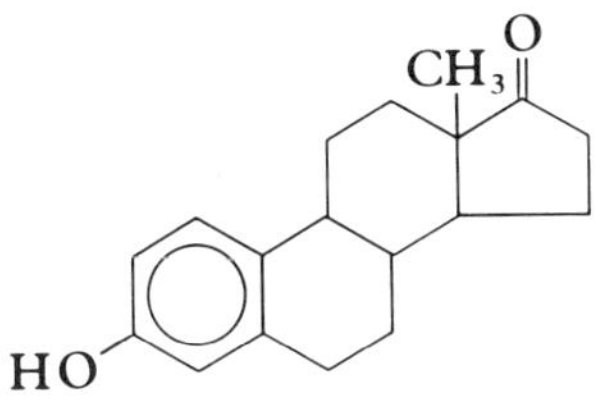

estrone

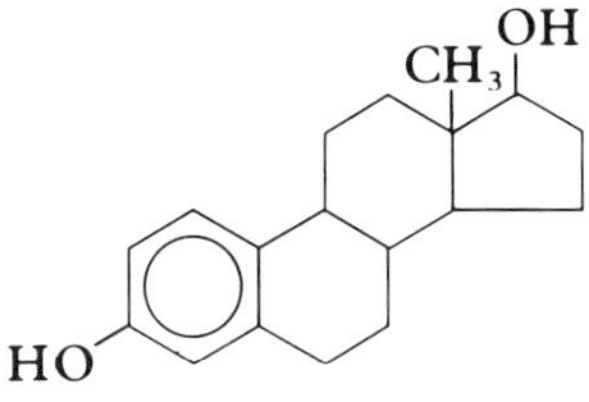

estradiol

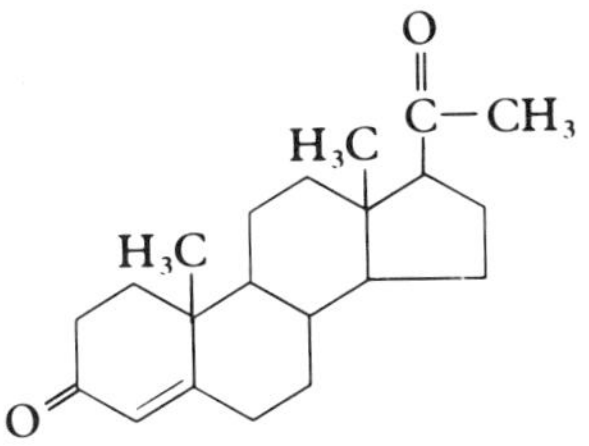

progesterone
(female sex hormone)

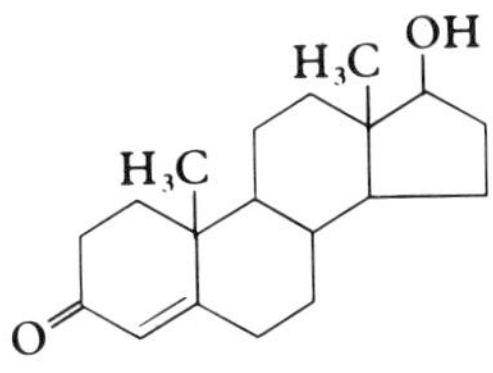

testosterone
(male sex hormone)

Oral contraceptive pills are the most reliable form of birth control available. In the making of these pills, the machine operator wears a protective mask to avoid inhaling steroids. (Courtesy of Syntax Laboratories, Inc.)

1960's. They work by preventing ovulation. This is done by fooling the body into thinking it is pregnant. Ovulation does not occur during pregnancy. A typical oral contraceptive, Enovid, consists of norethindrone and a small amount of mestranol.

norethindrone

mestranol

These steroids are very similar in structure to the male and female sex hormones.

There are some health hazards associated with taking oral contraceptives. The greatest hazard appears to be increased blood clotting, which can cause fatalities. Apparently the risks increase measureably for women over age 40. Current medical practice generally does not recommend oral contraceptives for women older than 40. Considering the overall risks associated with pregnancy, however, the net effect of oral contraceptive use is the saving of many lives. World-wide, the population problem is so great that the search for better, safer contraceptives should have a very high priority.

16.14

Vitamins

Vitamins are compounds required for normal metabolism to occur. They, themselves, do not provide energy, but they must be present. Generally vitamins act by taking part in enzyme reactions. Deficiencies of vitamins show up as various illnesses. Scurvy, a disease characterized by skin and mucous membrane hemorrhaging, spongy gums, and a generally unhealthy condition, was one of the first vitamin deficiencies to be recognized and treated. This occurred during the mid-1700's, although the disease was not recognized as a vitamin deficiency. Sailors in the British navy were given limes to eat to provide the vitamin C, the deficiency of which causes scurvy. This is how sailors in Britain came to be referred to as "limeys."

The chemical structures of many vitamins are rather complicated and need not be given here. A few of the more important vitamins will be discussed briefly.

A deficiency of vitamin A causes difficulties with vision and skin disorders. The skin may become rough and horny, a condition known as hyperkeratosis. Vitamin A takes part in the vision process through a series of rather complicated interactions. A deficiency of this vitamin frequently causes decreased vision in poor light (night blindness). Vitamin A is found in butter, cheese, eggs, fish, and liver. Carotenes, the yellow coloring matter in plants and other vegetables, are converted to vitamin A in the body.

Vitamin B_1 (thiamin) is found in cereals, nuts, and milk. Lack of this vitamin causes beriberi, a dreadful ailment characterized by inflammation of the nerves and a generally debilitated condition.

Vitamin B_2 (riboflavin) is found in a large number of foods including green vegetables, wheat germ, yeast, eggs, milk, cheese, liver, and meat from muscle tissue. Persons deficient in this vitamin suffer from skin disorders.

A deficiency of niacin

niacin

causes pellagra. This general condition includes skin lesions, nervous disorders, and gastrointestinal disturbances. Red meat and liver are good sources of niacin.

Vitamin B_{12} has already been discussed along with drugs for the heart and circulatory system. Pernicious anemia is the deficiency disease for this vitamin.

Vitamin C (ascorbic acid) mentioned above has been the subject of some recent spirited debate as a cure for the common cold. The Nobel prize winning chemist, Dr. Linus Pauling, suggested in 1970 that rather large dosages of vitamin C could prevent common colds or lessen their symptoms. This has been greeted by skepticism, ridicule, and some enthusiastic support. The debate is still continuing.

Persons eating a reasonably balanced diet normally have no difficulty with vitamin deficiencies. Large overdosages of some vitamins (A, D, E, and K) can be quite harmful, producing a variety of undesirable symptoms. These fat-soluble vitamins cannot be eliminated well through urine. Normally moderation in vitamin intake, as with other aspects of diet, is the best approach.

16.15

Antidotes

Particularly in certain occupations, the human body may be subjected to various chemical insults. Drugs that are improperly used or taken as an overdose may be very harmful to the body. Other poisons, such as the venom from snake bites or bee stings, may harm the body. In many cases it is possible to administer an *antidote* to counteract the effects of a poison in the body. The antidotes for drugs are often very specific compounds, dependent upon their structural relationships to the drug or a related enzyme. However, several other antidotes will be discussed here as examples of this kind of therapy.

One of the most common antidotes against heavy metals is dimercaprol. It was developed in Britain during World War II to counteract the effects of Lewisite, an arsenic-containing poison gas. Thus, it was called British anti-Lewisite, or BAL. It bonds strongly to heavy metals such as arsenic, antimony, copper, mercury, and tellurium and removes them from the body. It is less effective in removing cadmium, lead, and iron.

$$
\begin{array}{c}
\text{H} \\
| \\
\text{H—C—SH} \\
| \\
\text{H—C—SH} \quad + \quad \text{Hg}^{2+} \quad = \\
| \\
\text{H—C—OH} \\
| \\
\text{H}
\end{array}
\qquad
\begin{array}{c}
\text{H} \\
| \\
\text{H—C—S} \\
\quad \quad \quad \searrow \\
\text{H—C—S} \quad \text{Hg} \quad + \quad 2\,\text{H}^+ \\
| \\
\text{H—C—OH} \\
| \\
\text{H}
\end{array}
$$

BAL   mercury(II) ion   stable BAL-mercury complex

The most common antidote used for lead poisoning is EDTA, ethylenediaminetetraacetic acid. The structure of this compound with its four ionizable hydrogens removed is given as shown on page 485. (Each location on the structure that can bond to a metal ion is marked by an asterisk.) The structure of EDTA is such that it can bind all six of these locations at the same time to the *same* metal ion. Through this ability to act as a chemical contortionist, EDTA forms very stable

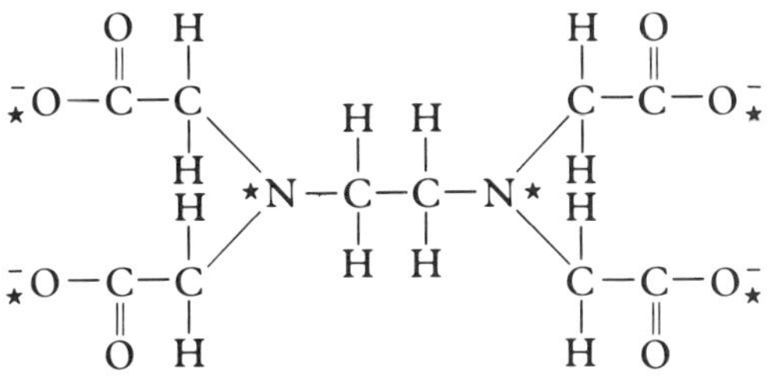

EDTA

compounds, known as *chelates,* with heavy metals. In the body it binds strongly to lead. The lead-EDTA chelate is water-soluble and is excreted from the body through the kidneys.

16.16

Clinical Chemistry

Chemical techniques are widely used to analyze various specimens from the body to determine a person's state of health. A wide range of chemical reactions and instruments are employed. There is not room here to go into detail in this important area of chemistry. However, Table 16.2, does list some common clinical tests, their importance, and the method of determination.

TABLE 16.2

Common clinical chemistry determinations, significance, and methods.

Test	Importance	Method
Acid phosphatase	Enzyme from liver, muscle, and other tissue involved in food metabolism	Breaks up a phosphate ester of *p*-nitrophenol to produce *p*-nitrophenol, which absorbs light.
Serum albumin	Important blood plasma protein	Binds chemically to bromcresol green dye, and light absorption of colored product is measured.
ALA (urinary deltaaminolevulinic acid	Indicator of lead poisoning	Reacts with acetylacetone then Ehrlich's reagent to form a red solution.
Ammonia in blood	High levels indicate liver failure	Forms an amber colored colloidal suspension with Ehrlich's reagent.
Amylase in serum and urine	Enzyme from saliva and pancreas which breaks down starch	Starch forms a blue complex with iodine. Disappearance of this complex measures amylase.
Barbituates and sedatives in blood or urine	Overdose or illegal drug use	Gas chromatography

TABLE 16.2 *(continued)*

Test	Importance	Method
Bilirubin in blood	Indicates destruction of red blood cells	Spectrophotometric
Calcium in blood	Indicates excess activity of thyroid gland	Atomic absorption analysis
Carbon dioxide in blood	Poor lung function	Carbon dioxide, absorbed in solution containing phenolphthalein indicator, causes color loss.
Lipids, total in blood	Abnormal lipid (fat) levels (either high or low) indicate various ailments	Extract with chloroform, evaporate solvent, and weigh
Uric acid in blood	Indicates kidney failure	Disappearance of ultraviolet light absorption of uric acid through action of urease enzyme.

16.17

Some Perspectives on Drugs and Medicine

This chapter has discussed the major types of drugs. They have been classified by what they do, or the area of the body in which they work. The average citizen, if lucky, will probably never need to take most of these drugs. However, it is good to know about them. People working in medically related fields, especially, need a general knowledge of drugs and how they work.

It is important to keep the matter of drugs in perspective. Several things have combined to give them a bad name. Drug abuse with illegal, mind-altering drugs has become a world-wide problem. It is not new, however, because the smoking of opium has been a vice since ancient times; and narcotics were a common ingredient of patent medicines in the U.S. during the last century. Incidents such as the thalidomide tragedy have pointed up the dangerous side effects that drugs may have. Though tested for safe dosage, thalidomide was not tested adequately for its potential to cause birth defects.

Despite some of their disadvantages, drugs have performed wonders in maintaining human health and saving lives. People with high blood pressure have returned to healthy, active lives as effective drugs were developed to treat this disabling condition. The lives of young leukemia victims, once so tragically short, have been extended for years by chemotherapy. Some may now live to see the day when a complete cure is available. Persons suffering from mental disorders have been freed from the restraints of close confinement in "insane asylums," and some have been enabled to lead productive, normal lives.

There is no doubt that drugs have been abused and overused in the past. Even the common cold was once treated by a barrage of sulfa drugs and penicillin. These did no good because the cold is a virus disease, and these drugs are effective against bacteria. In some cases violent, even fatal allergies resulted.

Now, however, perhaps we are too cautious. No drug can be completely safe. Extremely long, expensive testing procedures may be preventing some good drugs from becoming available for use. Good judgement and hard decisions regarding risk and benefit are required. We can hope for drugs which do in fact cure cancer. Drugs that are truly effective in preventing heart disease are badly needed. And, of course, the need for effective, completely safe, chemical contraceptives remains a high priority if recent, encouraging trends in the slowdown of the population explosion are to continue.

Chapter Summary

With regard to health and life expectancy, "the good old days" were not so good. Many diseases afflicted people. Even a small cut could become infected and result in death. Great progress has been made in overcoming these health problems. Chemistry has played a major role in these medical developments.

Drugs are divided among various therapeutic groups. These divisions are based on what the drug does. They include fever-reducing drugs, drugs that kill bacteria, anticancer drugs, hormones, and many others.

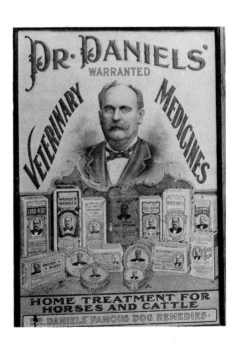

Veterinary medicine cabinet, circa 1900.
(From the collection of Gary Jacobson;
Michael E. Katin, photographer)

Many drugs, particularly over-the-counter drugs, are used for *disorders of the alimentary tract*. These range from mouthwashes, through stomach antacids, to suppositories to relieve the discomfort of hemorrhoids.

The body is an inviting source of food, shelter, and warmth for a variety of unwelcome guests. These include worms, protozoa, bacteria, and viruses. Perhaps the greatest achievement in medical history was the development of *drugs effective against bacteria*. Drugs to combat viruses are still largely lacking, although vaccines have been developed for viral diseases such as polio and measles. One of the earlier and most effective developments of purely chemical drugs (drugs which did not originally have a biological origin) was the development of *sulfa drugs*. Sulfa drugs have saved many lives by combatting bacteria. *Antibiotics* have been truly miracle drugs. Starting with penicillin, these drugs have provided cures for virtually all bacterial diseases and infections.

Mind-altering drugs have revolutionized the treatment of mental disorders. Unfortunately, they have been abused and are the subject of a huge, illegal traffic.

At the present time, much of the action in drug development involves drugs effective against the modern-day killers—heart disease and cancer. Research upon cancer chemotherapy is progressing. Drugs that prolong the lives and ease the suffering of those with heart disease also continue to develop.

Life-saving drugs have also contributed to excess population growth. "The pill" has helped counteract over-population. However, research continues upon the development of even safer birth control drugs.

Chapter Review Questions

The following questions are designed as a self-teaching tool to help you review Chapter 16. The answers to each question follow. See Chapter Review Questions for Chapter 1 for further instructions.

1. Drugs are classified in several _____.

2. The pathway taken by food from the time it enters the body until waste residues leave is called the _____.

3. Drugs used to prevent vomiting are called _____, and bile output is increased by _____.

4. The _____ drugs stop the growth of fungi whereas the _____ kill them.

5. Malaria is an example of a disease caused by single-celled organisms that normally can move around by their own means. This kind of organism belongs to the class of organisms called _____.

6. Modern chemotherapy was introduced in the year _____ when the drug, _____, was first produced.

7. A drug which is formed by the action of the body upon prontosil is _____, which belongs to the class of _____ drugs.

8. Essentially the first and most widely known antibiotic is _____.

9. The action of penicillin was first seen from the observation that bacterial colonies around a growth of mold were undergoing _____.

10. Penicillin was first shown to be effective against bacteria in the body in the year _____.

11. The antibiotic most commonly substituted for penicillin in case of an allergy to penicillin is _____.

12. The streptomycin group of antibiotics is very effective against the lung disease, _____.

13. Even with modern advances in the types of antiseptics available, many hospitals today are still troubled with persistent _____ infections from antiseptic-resistant strains of bacteria.

14. A molecule of the antiseptic of choice for use in surgical scrubbing to clean the hands of operating room personnel contains _____ benzene rings and _____ chlorine atoms.

15. By far the most commonly used simple analgesic is _____.

16. The chemical name of a common aspirin substitute which does not harm the stomach so much as aspirin is _____.

17. Habit-forming analgesics are classified as _____.

18. Propoxyphene hydrochloride is commonly known as _____.

19. Chlorpromazine and reserpine are both examples of _____.

20. Chloral hydrate is used as a _____.

21. Cerebral or psychic stimulants have come into wide use in recent years to relieve the symptoms of _____.

22. Cardiac glycosides from natural sources are useful in treating _____ _____.

23. Rauwolfia alkaloids are used to treat _____.

24. A deficiency of vitamin B_{12} causes _____.

25. Cellulose partly oxidized with NO_2 is used to form _____.

26. Chemical compounds related to nitrogen mustard are used to treat _____.

27. A drug containing norethindrone and mestranol is used in _____ _____.

Answers to Chapter Review Questions

1. therapeutic groups
2. alimentary tract
3. antiemetics, chloretics
4. fungistatic, fungicidals
5. protozoa
6. 1907, salvarsan
7. sulfanilamide, sulfa
8. penicillin
9. lysis
10. 1941
11. erythromycin
12. tuberculosis
13. "staph"
14. 2, 6
15. aspirin
16. acetaminophen
17. narcotic analgesics
18. Darvon
19. tranquilizers
20. sedative

21. mental depression

22. congestive heart failure and heart fibrillation

23. hypertension, or high blood pressure

24. pernicious anemia

25. artificial blood clots

26. cancer

27. a typical oral contraceptive, Enovid

Exercises for Chapter 16

1. Sodium fluoride is often added to drinking water to prevent tooth decay in children. Assume that the average family uses 6000 liters (about 1500 gal) of water per month. To a good enough approximation a liter of water weighs one kilogram. How many kilograms of sodium fluoride would have to be used each month for a city with 5000 families to provide 1 ppm (part per million) of F in water?

2. Assume that a stomach contains 1 liter of fluid and that it is 0.120 M in HCl. How many grams of an antacid consisting of half $Al(OH)_3$ and half $Mg(OH)_2$ would have to be taken to bring the acid level down to 0.100 M?

3. Match the chemical on the left with its corresponding drug use on the right.

$MgSO_4$ Treatment of hookworms

SnF_2 Relief of headache and fever

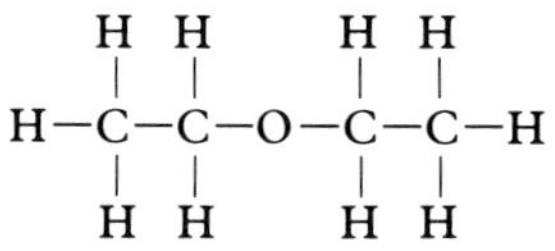

          A simple vitamin

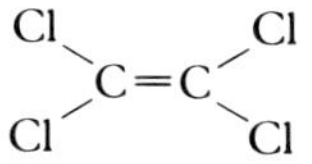

          Prevention of tooth decay

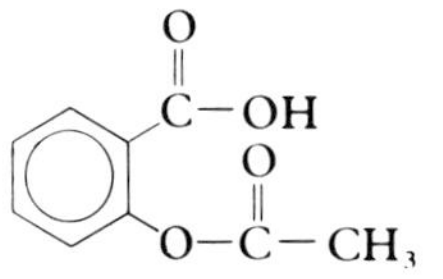

          Anesthetic

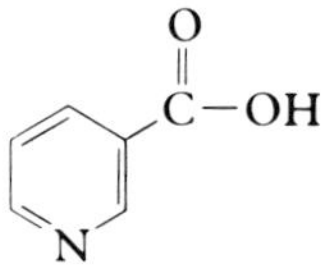

          Laxative

4. How is the term, chemotherapy, defined? Which drug is considered to be the one that really established modern chemotherapy?

5. What is the meaning of the term, lysis?

6. Of what general class of biologically significant compounds and drugs is the following structure characteristic?

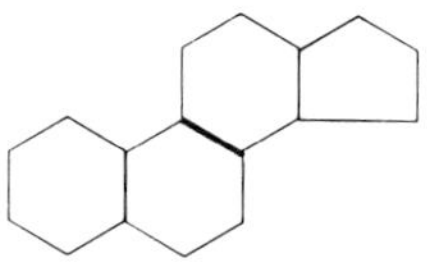

7. Phenol, cresol, hexyl resorcinol, and hexachlorophene are all antiseptics. What are one or two things that their chemical structures have in common?

8. A 1% solution of phenol killed 50% of test bacteria in a standard test. A 0.3% solution of an experimental antiseptic killed 40% of the test bacteria and a 0.4% solution killed 60% under identical conditions. Estimate the phenol coefficient of the experimental antiseptic. Explain how this estimate was obtained.

9. Aspirin can be given as sodium acetylsalicylate, a salt form. What is the formula for this salt? From what you know about the contents of the stomach, write the chemical reaction that occurs as soon as sodium acetylsalicylate enters the stomach.

10. What is the difference between a narcotic analgesic and a simple analgesic?

11. What compound that is essential for humans contains cobalt bound to a large organic molecule?

12. What is a systemic drug? Is aspirin a systemic drug? Is Hemopak?

13. Of what material does plasmin cause lysis?

14. Describe two occupational health problems that were recognized as far back as the 1700's.

15. Distinguish among the functions of hormones, enzymes, and nerves.

16. What are the differences in functional groups between the male sex hormone and the female sex hormone?

17. What is the major undesirable side effect from taking oral contraceptives?

18. Which common hormone contains iodine?

19. What do scurvy, beriberi, and pellagra have in common?

20. What is an antidote?

21. What do BAL and EDTA have in common?

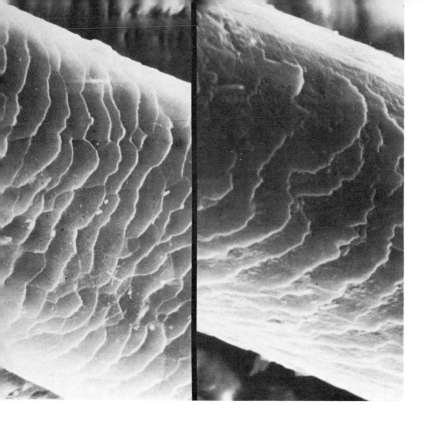

Scanning electron micrograph comparison of hair samples. (Courtesy of the Bureau of Alcohol, Tobacco, and Firearms, U.S. Dept. of the Treasury)

17

Chemistry and Crime

17.1

The Role of Chemistry in Crime and Crime Detection

Chemistry has played a role in many crimes. Chemical explosives are employed by the terrorist in cowardly bombings that destroy property and kill at random. Sometimes the terrorist falls victim to his own explosive device. Soup flavored with arsenic, or meat "tenderized" with strychnine have been the chemical agents of murder. Flammable organic chemicals have been used to commit arson. And drugs, either synthetic or extracted from natural sources by chemical means, are the object of a vast illegal traffic and the root cause of many other crimes.

It is not the purpose of this chapter to discuss in detail chemistry

INTERNATIONAL OFFICE

as a villain in crime. Chemistry is in fact overwhelmingly used to discover the criminal. An important principle considered in the use of chemistry in the war against crime is one that was developed in the 1920's by Professor Locard of the Institute of Criminalistics at the University of Lyon in France. This principle states that whenever two surfaces meet, there is an exchange of material between them. Although the amount of material may be extremely small, it is there and waits only for some person skillful enough, or some instrument sensitive enough to detect it. The most obvious example of this in crime is the telltale fingerprint left on a drinking glass, a gunstock, or a window sill. But there are other indicators of crime making up a vast assortment of chemical substances. These include things that come from the human body—bloodstains, hairs, semen, and saliva. They include organic materials such as synthetic fibers, plastic fragments, cosmetics, and motor oil. Residues from explosives may be found in traces at the scene of a bombing or on the hand of the person who has discharged a firearm. Bits of paint are usually left at the scene of a hit-and-run automobile accident. Chips of glass, crumbs of soil, cement dust, brick dust, and metal turnings are all examples of solids that may be left behind at the scene of a crime. Often the human eye is helpless to identify these bits of evidence (although the usefulness of the microscope in this task should be emphasized). As discussed in Chapter 12, modern chemical analysis instruments and techniques excel in determining the chemical identity of extremely small quantities of materials. Therefore, chemistry is employed as a kind of scientific Sherlock Holmes to provide evidence at the scene of a crime.

This branch of chemistry is called **forensic chemistry**. It is being used increasingly in **criminalistics**, the science of crime. Forensic chemistry is contributing a great deal to the capture and conviction of criminals. Often, by necessity, evidence must be taken and simple forensic chemical tests performed by officers who are relatively untrained in chemistry. A knowledge of chemistry is very helpful, which is why some

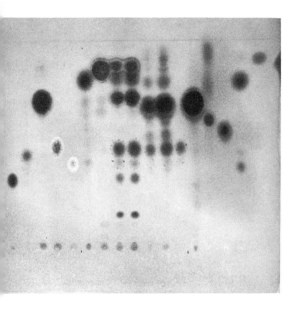

Thin layer chromatographic separation of drugs often encountered by a forensic toxicologist. The silica plate was developed in the Davidow system of ethyl acetate :methanol :ammonia (85 :10 :5) and made visible with treatment of ninhydrin, sulfuric acid, and iodoplatinate. The spots also have characteristic colors. From left to right the samples are : (1–8) standards of morphine, codeine, quinine, demerol, methamphetamine, d-amphetamine, thorazine, and methadone ; (9–10) mixtures of the first eight ; (11–12) mixtures of the last seven, (13–19) standards of quinine, nicotine, librium, pheniramine, mellaril, propoxyphene, and lidocaine. (Courtesy of Jesse H. Bidanset, Chief Toxicologist, Nassau County Medical Examiners Office, N.Y.)

of you may be reading this book. Other tests may require very expensive instruments and sophisticated techniques available only in a few specialized laboratories. When these techniques are used, however, it is crucial for the evidence, or sample, to be taken in the proper way. Therefore, the investigating officer needs to have some knowledge of forensic chemistry even if he does not actually do any of the chemical analyses. This chapter outlines some of the kinds of evidence that the forensic chemist examines. It also describes briefly some of the tools used in forensic chemistry.

17.2

Physical Marks at the Scene of a Crime

Although chemistry and chemical tests are very helpful in solving crimes, physical evidence still remains one of the most important factors. In many cases, chemistry is even used to preserve or develop physical evidence.

Fingerprints are the classic bit of evidence left at the scene of a crime. The patterns of ridges on the fingers, toes, and palms of hands and feet are unique for every individual. If a large enough print is obtained, identification is possible.

In most cases fingerprints are not readily seen. These are called **latent prints**. They are made visible by a process called development. Powders are often used for this purpose. These powders need to show a strong color contrast with the background, and they must stick to the surface well. Black powders with a base of carbon black made of very finely divided carbon are commonly used.

There are several chemical means for making latent fingerprints visible. Exposure to fumes of iodine results in the iodine being more strongly retained by oils from the skin so that the ridge pattern becomes visible. Salt left behind from perspiration may be made visible by treating the print with a solution of silver nitrate. The silver nitrate reacts with the sodium chloride to form a residue of insoluble silver chloride, AgCl.

$$Ag^+NO_3^- + Na^+Cl^- \longrightarrow AgCl \text{ (water-insoluble residue)} + Na^+NO_3^-$$

The excess silver nitrate is washed off, and the AgCl breaks up to form black, colloidal silver nitrate when exposed to light. This kind of phenomenon is explained further in Section 17.3. The formation of the black silver metal causes the prints to stand out. Exposure of the print to vapors of volatile osmium tetroxide, OsO_4, also results in the print standing out in black. This compound is very toxic and must be used with care. It is especially hazardous to the eyes because it causes blindness by coating the eyes with a dark film. Prints on paper are developed with an organic compound called ninhydrin. This substance develops a color when it reacts with protein.

Prints from shoes and tires can be useful evidence. If these marks are left in soil or sand, they can be preserved by making a cast in plaster or plastic. Plaster of Paris is used for making prints when fine detail is not required. This is a white powder of calcium sulfate containing an average of one-half water molecule for every molecule of $CaSO_4$. When it is mixed with water, it forms the hydrate with 2 H_2O's for

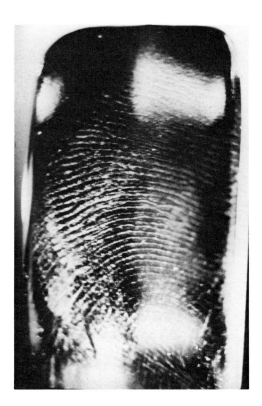

Fingerprint developed from tape placed over the object on which the print was left. The tape is then lifted off to remove an image of the print. (Courtesy of the Bureau of Alcohol, Tobacco, and Firearms, U.S. Dept. of the Treasury)

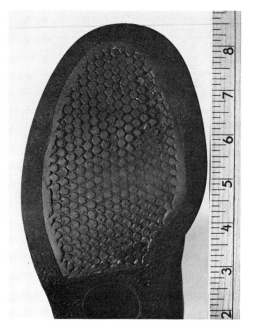 

On the left is a scaled photograph of the sole of a suspect boot. On the right is a scaled photograph of a sulfur cast of a footwear impression found at the crime scene. This impression was in snow, and the cast was made at a temperature of − 20°F. Comparison of the two reveals sufficient individual characteristics to warrant a positive identification. (Courtesy of Wisconsin State Crime Laboratory)

every $CaSO_4$. (Hydrates were discussed in Sections 7.11 and 8.7)

$$2\ CaSO_4 \cdot \tfrac{1}{2}\ H_2O + 3\ H_2O \longrightarrow 2\ CaSO_4 \cdot 2\ H_2O + heat$$

The reaction of calcium sulfate with water produces a lot of heat, which drives off some of the excess water and leaves a solid product. The fresh mixture of water and plaster of Paris is poured over the print and allowed to form a solid. This cast is then "lifted" to be preserved as evidence. For fine detail a substance called moulage is used. It is softened by heating before being applied to the print. This is the same material used for making dental casts. It is especially effective in making detailed castings of tool marks. Silicone plastics and waxes are also used for making castings. Thermoplastics, which soften when heated, are used to make extremely detailed imprints. A sheet of Vinylite or Lucite plastic is placed over the object and covered with a glass plate. Heat from an infrared light is used to soften the plastic, which picks up the outline of the object upon which it is resting. The detail is often fine enough to allow examination by a microscope.

The production of prints, casts, and other visible evidence is a crucial part of crime investigation. Chemistry contributes in this area with substances that make prints visible and with materials especially suited to making casts.

17.3

Photography in Crime Investigation

Photography is extremely useful in crime investigation. A good camera and officers skilled in its use must be a part of every good crime investigation team. Photography is a chemical process, and chemistry continues to contribute to the development of this valuable tool.

It is beyond the scope of this book to go into details of photography. Basically, it makes use of silver halide compounds, particularly AgBr. Small, colloidal **grains** of the silver compound are held suspended in an emulsion in a thin film of gelatin mounted on a plastic support film as shown in Figure 17.1. When the silver bromide is exposed to light by opening the camera shutter, silver metal and bromine are produced.

$$\text{AgBr} + \text{light} \longrightarrow \text{Ag} + \text{Br (quickly reacts with other material in the film)}$$

The silver forms dark colloidal silver particles. This produces an image that is developed by additional chemical processing. The process of making color photographs is a complicated one involving dyes in the film.

FIGURE 17.1 *Photographic film.*

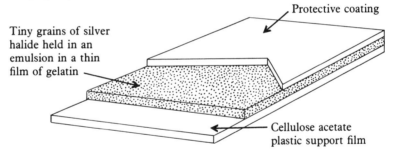

Tiny grains of silver halide held in an emulsion in a thin film of gelatin

Protective coating

Cellulose acetate plastic support film

A serial number, which had been ground off the weapon, is restored and then photographed in the FBI laboratory. (Courtesy of the FBI, U.S. Dept. of Justice)

Many aspects of photography are involved in crime investigation. Black and white photography is generally superior for showing detail, but color is extremely useful in many cases. Polaroid film, which can be developed on the spot, can be very helpful because it shows the photographer whether the picture is adequate before leaving the scene of the crime. A good lens is essential to good photography. Use is made of special lenses in forensic science. Telephoto lenses are employed for detailed photographs of distant scenes. Wide-angle lenses enable a picture to be taken with a very wide field of view, which allows the observer to see a more complete picture of the crime scene and its surroundings. Specialized lenses are used for close-up shots of very small objects. In addition, photographs may be taken through a microscope.

17.4

Clothing and Fibers

Clothing is especially useful evidence. Witnesses often remember clothing better than they do the physical features of a person. In cases of violent contact, fragments of clothing are frequently left at the scene of a crime. Considering the enormous variety of fabrics, both natural and synthetic, and colors, clothing can be a very distinctive piece of evidence.

Various chemical tests can be used to identify fibers from clothing and other sources. The action of solvents such as acetone can be used to characterize types of fibers. The reaction of fiber to heat is characteristic of the chemistry of the fiber. Fibers from ropes and cords can be valuable evidence. In general, such fibers are characterized by physical appearance.

Paper is a remarkably varied material that makes it good evidence in a criminal case. The color and manner of color application varies with the paper. Thickness and type of surface are characteristics of

Scanning electron micrograph of cotton fibers. This technique is useful for identification of fibers present as evidence of a crime. (Courtesy of the Bureau of Alcohol, Tobacco, and Firearms, U.S. Dept. of the Treasury)

various paper samples. Distinctive specks and spots may be present. On a more microscopic scale, the nature of the paper pulp (wood, cloth, recycled) may be determined by expert examination. Sizing of paper consists of treating it with glue-like materials to prevent penetration of water and other liquids. The chemical nature of various sizings differ appreciably. Various specialized chemical tests may be used to identify the sizing and help characterize the paper. In addition, printing or writing on paper provides good evidence. Paper readily absorbs many types of stains that are also helpful in forensic science.

17.5

Glass

Bits of glass are often left at the scene of a crime. Like paint, glass can be analyzed chemically. The exact composition of glass is very useful in identifying its source.

The main elements in most glass are sodium, calcium, silicon, and oxygen. Others are added to give it color or special properties. Still others are present because the minerals from which glass is made contain trace element impurities that are not easily removed. Some of the elements that can be detected by very sensitive neutron activation analysis in ordinary window glass are arsenic, aluminum, barium, calcium, cobalt, chromium, cesium, europium, iron, hafnium, lanthanum, lutecium, magnesium, manganese, sodium, rubidium, antimony, scandium, samarium, strontium, tantalum, thorium, ytterbium, and zirconium. Not all of these are found in all window glass samples. Their compositions vary considerably. For example, arsenic cannot be detected in a common type of British window glass but is present at more than a part per thousand by weight in a typical Belgian glass. The trace element compositions of two window glasses are given in Table 17.1.

As in the case of paint evidence, the first examination of a glass sample is a physical examination. Color is observed. The density can be measured. The degree to which the glass bends a beam of light is measured. This property is called the refractive index.

After physical examination, the glass can be analyzed for the elements that it contains. Neutron activation analysis is very effective for this purpose. This sensitive technique was discussed in Section 12.5. It has the advantage of leaving the glass sample intact. One problem with the neutron activation analysis of glass is that the sodium in the glass becomes so radioactive that its activity may "swamp out" the activity of many of the trace elements.

X-ray fluorescence can also be used to analyze glass without destroying the sample. X-ray fluorescence consists of bombarding the sample with a beam of X rays. X rays of lower energy are given off from the elements in the sample. The lower energy X-rays are **fluorescent**

TABLE 17.1

Trace element content of two types of window glass.

	Concentration, ppm*	
Element	Glass Brand A	Glass Brand B
Arsenic	1	1300
Aluminum	0.68%	0.48%
Barium	125	60
Calcium	6.2%	5.7%
Cobalt	0.6	0.4
Iron	850	740
Lanthanum	3.8	3.7
Magnesium	2.6%	1.9%
Manganese	98	55
Sodium	10.2%	12.5%
Rubidium	19	4
Antimony	0.7	3.9
Titanium	80	148

* Except where specified as percent (1% = 10,000 ppm).

X-rays. Their wavelengths (analogous to the color of visible light) are characteristic of the elements being analyzed. This provides a **qualitative analysis**. The intensity of the X-ray at a wavelength characteristic of a particular element is proportional to the concentration of the element in the sample. This gives a **quantitative analysis**.

It is extremely difficult to dissolve glass for chemical analysis. This can be accomplished, however, by reaction with hydrofluoric acid. Fusing the glass at high temperature with a strong base can also produce a soluble form.

17.6

Metal Fragments

Bits of metal are frequently found as evidence of a crime. These can include metal shavings from a lathe, or metal dust from a saw. The murderer responsible for the death of a taxicab driver in England was convicted upon the basis of evidence gathered from metal dust found in the teeth of a hacksaw in the murderer's basement. The metal composition matched that of the barrel of a sawed-off shotgun known to be the murder weapon. The composition of alloys used in various steels and other metals varies considerably and is quite characteristic of metal used in a particular application. In addition, metals are easy to dissolve, usually in acid. They are about the easiest materials to analyze, especially by atomic absorption. Therefore, metal fragments make very good evidence for the forensic chemist.

17.7

Paint

The composition of paint was shown in Chapter 13 to vary widely. Different binders, pigments, and miscellaneous additives are used by companies that produce paint; therefore, a great variety of compositions may be observed. Consider, in the case of automobile paint, one type of binder may be used only for the original paint whereas another type would be used only for "touch-up" paint. The differences are especially apparent in the pigments, in which there are often an appreciable variety of miscellaneous elements at low levels. The physical appearance of a paint chip also reveals much about it, including different layers, degree of weathering, and so forth.

Because of its variable composition and physical appearance, paint is the forensic scientist's ideal sample. The telltale chip of paint found at the scene of an accident has convicted many hit-and-run drivers. Practically every object contacted by the criminal is painted. These include such things as window sills, doors, and tools. Indeed, "anti-climb" paints are often used for security purposes. These paints do not dry completely and stick to a criminal's clothing or tools. They are made with special individual formulations so that they can be used as "tracers" to identify the criminal.

The first step in the analysis of a paint chip or smear always involves use of an optical microscope. By simply observing the color, texture, and layers of a chip of paint, the well-trained forensic scientist can often get a good idea of its source. Layered structure of paint is especially important. It can often show, for example, whether or not

Optical microscopic comparison of paint. First sample is from a suspect vehicle. Second sample is from the scene of a crime. The chips of paint used were approximately 1/4 in. long. This microscopic examination shows that the car had been repainted more than once and that no primer has been used. (Courtesy of Wisconsin State Crime Laboratory)

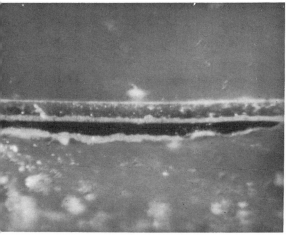

the object was repainted at some time. The more layers there are, the more evidence can be deduced from the sample. Sometimes the layered structure is best observed by casting the paint chip into a solid block of some substance such as clear plastic. This can then be ground off to expose the edge of the paint chip and make the observation of the layers much easier.

There are some simple chemical tests which can be performed on paint that reveal information about it. For example, acetone dissolves nitrocellulose-based paints but not most other types. Hydrogen sulfide blackens paints containing lead pigments because of the formation of black lead sulfide (PbS) but does not affect paints with many other types of pigments.

The absorption of ultraviolet or infrared light by paint can be useful in identifying it. These are *spectroscopic* techniques that were described in Chapter 12. Light is absorbed at different wavelengths by various chemical compounds. This helps to identify the compound. The light reflected off the paint sample can be measured to see at which wavelengths it is absorbed. For infrared analysis, the paint can be very finely ground and pressed into a disc of potassium bromide salt. The light is then passed through this disc and the absorption at different wavelengths is measured. The absorption of light by *pyrolysis products of the paint can also be measured*. These are volatile organic compounds given off when paint is heated and decomposes.

The identities and quantities of various elements, particularly metals, is a very useful method for identifying paint. Methods of analysis are available for doing this on the intact paint chip (where sample preservation is important) or on a solution formed by dissolving the paint in strong acid or some other solvent. The proportions of lead, titanium, chromium, and other elements in the paint help to identify it. Elements in an intact paint sample may be analyzed by neutron activation analysis or X-ray fluorescence. Recall from Section 17.5 that these techniques are also used for the nondestructive analysis of glass samples. If it is not necessary to preserve the paint sample intact, it may be dissolved in strong acid or some other solvent and analyzed for elements in the sample. Metals in such a sample are generally analyzed by atomic absorption spectroscopy. Recall from Chapter 12 that atomic absorption involves forming atoms from the metals in the sample, either by passing a solution of the sample through a flame or putting it in a carbon tube heated to a white hot temperature. A light beam is passed through the cloud of atoms produced. Light of a very specific wavelength is absorbed by specific metals, and the amount of light absorbed reveals how much of each metal is present.

The light emitted from atoms in a paint sample can also be used for the analysis of elements in the sample. This is called optical emission spectroscopy, which was discussed in Section 12.4. The sample is heated to a very high temperature in an electrical arc between two carbon electrodes. The light that is given off is separated according to wavelength. Various elements are measured by looking for the wavelength of light characteristic of each.

17.8

Firearms

The source of a bullet, or the identity of a person who has discharged a firearm, are often important knowledge in the investigation of a crime. Chemistry may help identify both kinds of evidence.

Microscopic examination of a bullet for characteristic grooves and marks is the method most often employed to establish whether a bullet was fired from a specific weapon. Chemical analysis can help establish

Optical comparison microscope of two bullets; one has been test-fired; the second has been recovered from the victim's body. (Courtesy of Wisconsin State Crime Laboratory)

whether or not a bullet came from a particular manufacturer, or from a specific lot of ammunition. Bullet lead contains a number of trace elements whose concentrations vary with the source of the bullet. Some of these which can be analyzed are given in Table 17.2.

TABLE 17.2
Trace elements and typical range in bullet lead.

Metal	Concentration Range, ppm
Aluminum	1–7
Copper	600–800
Tin	50–200
Cadmium	4–8
Manganese	0.5–20
Cobalt	10–70

Bullet primer mixtures generally contain barium and antimony. The presence of these rather uncommon elements upon the hand of an individual is evidence of having recently fired a gun (Figure 17.2). A sample is collected from the hand by pouring on it melted paraffin, which is peeled off after solidifying, or taken off with a swab soaked in dilute nitric acid. The elements are determined best by neutron activation analysis. It is particularly sensitive for antimony. An obvious disadvantage is lack of access to a nuclear reactor by most crime laboratories.

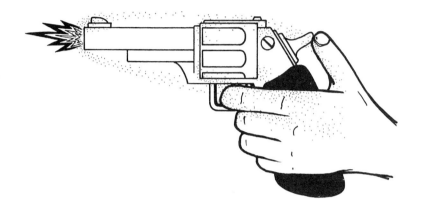

FIGURE 17.2
When a gun is fired, invisible (represented here in color) traces of antimony and barium are left on the hand from the cartridge primer. These can be detected by neutron activation analysis.

17.9

Greases, Oils, and Other Organic Liquids

Various organic compounds including greases and oils are frequently encountered as evidence of a crime. The clothing of the victim of an automobile accident may be smeared with oil from the automobile. The shoes of a thief in a factory may pick up a smear of grease. Gasoline or some other flammable liquid may be left at the scene of a fire set by an arsonist.

Organic liquids can be analyzed reasonably well by chemical means. Tests involving chemical reactions can be used. For example, a fat or vegetable oil will form glycerin and soap when treated with strong sodium hydroxide. This saponification reaction was discussed in Chapter 10. Other chemical reactions, some of which develop characteristic colors, can be used.

Several excellent instrumental analysis techniques are used to determine the identities and quantities of organic compounds. Infrared spectrometry and gas chromatography, both described in Chapter 12, are used for both qualitative and quantitative analysis of organic liquids or their decomposition products. The infrared instrument gives a characteristic infrared spectrum of percentage of infrared radiation going through a sample at different wavelengths. Gas chromatography separates

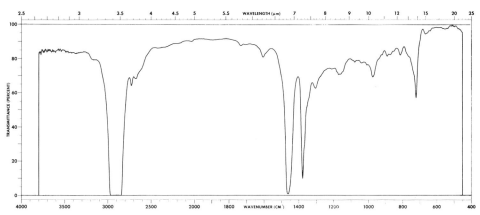

Infrared spectrum of 10W-30 motor oil. (Courtesy of Exxon Research and Engineering Co.)

out the individual chemical compounds in an organic sample, and these compounds are recorded as peaks as they come from a column.

The gas chromatograph-mass spectrometer combination described in Chapter 12 is the most useful analysis technique for organic materials. The gas chromatograph separates out the individual chemical compounds in the material. The mass spectrometer breaks these up into mass spectra, which differ characteristically for each compound. Reference mass spectra are stored in large data banks. The mass spectra from the sample can be matched with the reference mass spectra by computer giving a positive identification of the organic compound.

17.10

Blood as Evidence

Blood is a very common and useful type of crime evidence. Victims of the infamous "Saturday night specials" lose great quantities of blood. This may not be so useful if the body is left in place but can be very helpful in tracing the path of a body that is moved. In a surprising number of cases, the criminal leaves bloodstains. He may be scratched by a rape victim or cut by broken glass while breaking into a building. Sensitive biochemical tests may be employed to identify blood. If enough properties are tested, blood is almost as characteristic of an individual as a fingerprint; and it is very useful for establishing identity.

The presence of blood is not always apparent. It can be revealed by tests which detect **heme**, the protein material attached to oxygen-carrying hemoglobin in the blood. The most common test for heme takes advantage of the fact that heme acts as a catalyst that enables hydrogen peroxide (H_2O_2) to oxidize compounds to readily visible colored compounds. One of the more sensitive tests involves the oxidation of gray benzidine to a blue product.

$$H_2N-\langle\text{benzidine}\rangle-NH_2 + H_2O_2 \xrightarrow[\text{(catalyst)}]{\text{heme}} HN=\langle\text{benzidine blue}\rangle=NH + 2 H_2O$$

It should be pointed out that benzidine is one of the known human carcinogens listed in Table 13.8. It causes bladder cancer in humans. The danger is increased because of the ease with which benzidine is absorbed through the skin. Other substances using the same general principle to test for the presence of blood are phenolphthalein, leuco-malachite green, and luminol.

Blood can be characterized to the extent of almost certain identification of a specific person through the use of laboratory tests that identify **individualizing factors** in blood. These are various characteristics of blood. If enough of them are measured, they reveal a pattern that identifies the blood.

The most commonly known individualizing factors are based upon **blood groups**. It has been known for many years that the blood plasma of one person contains special proteins called **antibodies**, which cause the blood corpuscles of another person to agglutinate (clump together). For that reason, blood groups must be carefully matched for transfusions to prevent a fatal reaction in the person receiving the transfusion. About a dozen blood grouping systems have been developed. The most well known of these is the ABO system discovered around 1900. This divides blood into types A, B, AB, and O. In addition to providing evidence of the origin of a blood sample, the ABO system is useful in establishing possible parents of children. For example, a father with A blood and a mother with O blood may produce a child with either O or A blood, but not with AB or B blood. Many other such combinations have been worked out.

Next to the ABO system, the Rhesus blood type system is most commonly employed. It is especially useful because it permits 15 different classifications. These are based upon the familiar Rh-positive and Rh-negative classification, which is often involved in sometimes fatal reactions of infants to their mother's blood. It is difficult to classify old blood on this basis, but fresh blood can be tested successfully for Rh factors.

The MN system is used in combination with the ABO system. The MN system depends upon factors found in blood cells rather than the fluid part of blood. It divides blood into the categories of M (about 30% of people), N (22%), and MN (48%). Modern technology has enabled the use of this system on dried bloodstains. In addition to its applications in forensic science, it is very helpful in establishing paternity.

The three systems described above are based upon **serological examination**. These depend upon antibody-antigen reactions in blood proteins.

In addition to serological classification, there are several other characteristics that can be used to identify blood. Some of these are rather difficult to determine and their use in criminal investigations is in the development stage. However, they do offer a great deal for the identification of specific blood samples.

Serum proteins in blood serum are to a large extent controlled by genetics and are rather specific for an individual. They are difficult to determine, particularly in dried blood. Serum proteins are characterized by "factors" such as the Gm factor, Gc factor, and Inv factor.

Blood contains enzymes. These are chemical catalysts discussed in Section 11.5. Although the function of an individual enzyme is the same for each person, many of these complicated proteins are different in structure, depending upon the individual.

Hemoglobin, the oxygen-carrying substance in red blood cells, varies somewhat in structure. Now, more than 100 variations of human hemoglobin are known. These have not been widely used in criminalistics as yet. Hemoglobin can be used, however, to determine whether or not blood came from a newborn infant or fetus as compared to an older person. The blood in a fetus (unborn child) has a form of hemoglobin designated as HbF. At birth, the new hemoglobin which is synthesized is normal adult hemoglobin, HbA. These two forms may be distinguished by testing procedures. Such evidence has been used in cases of illegal abortions, for example.

The best tool for distinguishing blood proteins, including enzymes, is **electrophoresis** (see Figure 17.3). This is a separation process by

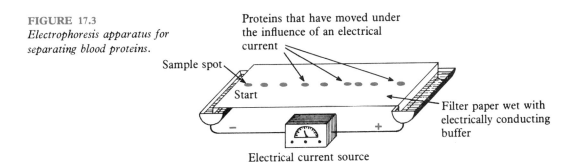

FIGURE 17.3
Electrophoresis apparatus for separating blood proteins.

Proteins that have moved under the influence of an electrical current

Sample spot

Start

Filter paper wet with electrically conducting buffer

Electrical current source

which a sample is placed as a spot upon a strip of moist filter paper or some other medium and an electrical current is passed lengthwise through the strip. Proteins are electrically charged. The charge depends upon pH, which is regulated with a buffer (Section 7.4). Usually a pH is used at which the proteins have a negative electrical charge. They migrate at different rates toward the positive electrode, separating out into different "spots." These spots are made visible by a color-developing chemical such as ninhydrin. The protein can be identified by its location on the strip. In some cases more specific tests can be used to identify a particular protein.

17.11

Body Secretions Other than Blood

Body secretions other than blood can be used in forensic analysis. These include saliva, perspiration, semen, vaginal secretions, and urine. Stains from these sources are much more difficult to observe than are prominent blood stains. The state of the art in characterizing these fluids is much less advanced than is the characterization of blood.

In sex crimes semen and even secretions from the vagina may help identify the individuals involved. Recently, antisemen antisera have been employed for the identification and characterization of semen. The type of the enzyme acid phosphatase found in semen and sperm differs from that found in other parts of the body. Methods are being developed to use this enzyme to establish the presence of semen.

Although not body secretions, hair and finger, and toenails are useful for identification. Chemistry does not play much of a role in this area of forensic science. The microscope is used to observe color, texture, and other characteristics of these samples. They do vary in trace element content, and in some cases a complete trace element analysis is useful. However, these analyses vary greatly with the handling and external surroundings of the hair. In general they would not allow for positive identification. It is interesting to note that some heavy metals and arsenic become concentrated in hair and nails. Recent neutron activation analysis of arsenic in hair from Napoleon's body indicated that he died from arsenic poisoning.

Cosmetics such as rouge, makeup, lipstick, nail polish, and mascara may make useful evidence. These materials are frequently transferred by contact during a crime. Their chemical makeup varies greatly, thus, making specific identification easier.

17.12

Drugs

Drug analysis comprises a large part of the work load of the forensic chemist. This is because drugs are involved in a large number of crimes. In addition, they are relatively easy to analyze chemically whereas other bits of evidence (such as paint chips and textile fibers) are often best analyzed by nonchemical means.

Ultraviolet absorption spectrophotometry is frequently used to analyze for drugs. Generally, the drugs are put into water solution. This is easily done because most drugs are soluble in water. Ultraviolet light of different wavelengths is passed through the sample, and the amount of light absorbed is recorded for each wavelength. This gives an absorption spectrum that is more or less characteristic of a particular drug. To verify the identity of the drug, it can be subjected to chemical treatment known to give a specific product with the suspected drug. The ultraviolet spectrum of the product can be taken, and if it corresponds with that of the supposed product, the drug can be identified. The amount of ultraviolet light absorbed measures the quantity of the drug present. One example of this kind of treatment is the analysis of heroin. Heroin is the methyl ester of morphine. When heroin is treated with sodium hydroxide, sodium morphinate is formed. When these two compounds are analyzed by ultraviolet spectrophotometry, the sodium morphinate has its maximum absorbance at a wavelength longer than that of heroin. Therefore, the measurement of two ultraviolet spectra, one before and one after a chemical reaction can be used to identify heroin. The analysis of drugs from samples in the body can be rather complicated. This is especially true in a sample from a deceased person where putrefaction has occurred. Caffeine, which is found in coffee and as an additive in a number of drug formulations, can interfere with drug analysis because it absorbs ultraviolet light very strongly.

Conversion of heroin from an ester to a salt by the action of sodium hydroxide. The morphine organic skeleton is somewhat complicated and is not shown.

Fluorescence analysis is a very sensitive method for measuring drugs. This technique was explained in Section 12.4. It makes use of a beam of ultraviolet light that shines through the sample. Some of the light is absorbed by the drug sample. The sample then re-emits light with a longer wavelength. The incoming beam of ultraviolet light is not visible to the human eye. The fluorescent light given off by the sample is often visible and can be seen as a colored glow. (This is the same effect observed when "black light" falls on fluorescent minerals causing them to "light up" with brilliant colors.) The intensity of the fluorescent light is a measure of how much of the drug is present in the solution. LSD is analyzed by this method. Sometimes drugs and other substances that fluoresce can be observed "in place," such as in a stain on a suspect's clothing. "Black light" from a portable ultraviolet lamp can be directed on a stain, causing the stain to glow if a fluorescent substance is present.

Chromatography is also used for drug analysis. Gas chromatography can be used for very sensitive analysis of drugs that can be put into a vapor form. The gas chromatographic separation of three of the ingredients of marijuana was shown in Figure 12.9. **High-speed liquid chromatography** is being used increasingly for the analysis of drugs. It is similar to gas chromatography except that a solvent under high pressure is used instead of a gas to carry the sample through the column. Its greatest advantage is that it is not necessary for the material being analyzed to be a vapor.

Thin-layer chromatography is a very simple analysis method widely used for drugs. A separation is performed on a rectangular piece of glass (essentially a microscope slide) coated with a thin layer of a powdery substance such as SiO_2 or Al_2O_3. A spot of the sample is placed near one end of the slide. This end is dipped into a solvent, which rises up the slide as it soaks the layer of powder. Different materials in the spot of sample are carried at different rates and separated as several spots. These are then treated with substances that make them show up as individual spots. The separation of several drugs by thin-layer chromatography on a plate coated with SiO_2 (silica gel) is shown in Figure 17.4. In this case a solvent consisting of ethyl acetate ester (see Section 10.11) mixed with a few percent each of methanol and a water solution of NH_3 was used. The colors of the spots were developed with a special "iodoplatinate" reagent. Each spot contains 5 μg (micrograms) of the drug.

FIGURE 17.4 *Thin layer chromatographic separation of a mixture of narcotic drugs.*

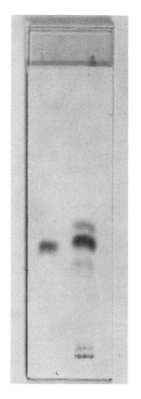

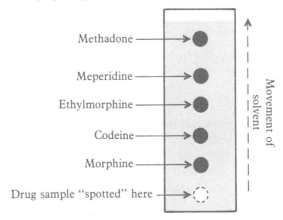

Thin layer chromatogram of extract of "green vegetable material" on right and standard THC (tetrahydrocannabinol), a principal ingredient of marijuana, on the left. Results of this chromatogram indicate that the green vegetable material contains materials consistent with standard THC. (Courtesy of Dr. Michael J. Camp, Northeastern University)

17.13

Immunological Methods of Forensic Chemical Analysis

As noted often in this chapter, the forensic chemist is frequently faced with the task of measuring a very small quantity of material. In such cases, the techniques used need to have a very high **sensitivity**. Many of the methods used, such as gas chromatography and atomic absorption analysis of some metals are remarkably sensitive. In addition, there is generally a need to analyze for a particular substance, often in complicated mixtures with other materials which tend to interfere. This means that a high degree of **specificity** is needed.

Specificity can be a severe problem. For example, many substances absorb ultraviolet light. This absorption can be measured at different wavelengths. Unfortunately, the resulting *absorption spectrum of one substance is often much the same as that of another substance*. Materials that are present with the desired substance may absorb ultraviolet light and mask out the substance being analyzed, or cause the analysis to have the wrong value. The ideal chemical reagent for analysis, therefore, is one which produces a reaction with only a sought for substance.

Although the chemist has difficulty making completely specific reagents for particular substances, the biological systems of humans and animals can do this very well. Once subjected to swine flu virus, for example, the body's system makes specific substances which effectively fight off further invasions of this malady. This occurs as part of the body's natural defense mechanisms by which it resists foreign intruders. The intruders against which the body reacts are large molecules. These are usually protein molecules. Such foreign molecules in the body are called **antigens**. When an antigen is introduced into the body of a mammal such as a horse, rat, rabbit, or human, the body produces materials called **antibodies**. Antibodies are produced especially strongly when the antigen is introduced into the bloodstream. The chemical structure of an antibody is such that it just "fits" the intruding molecule. Because of this "lock-and-key" sort of interaction, the antibody reacts specifically and binds with the antigen to remove it from the body. This same reaction can be observed outside a living system as a means of measuring a particular antigen or antibody.

Antibodies can be generated which are very specific for a particular substance that the forensic chemist might wish to analyze. For example, it is possible to do a very specific analysis for LSD or heroin using antibodies specific for these substances. Actually, living systems do not usually form antibodies against molecules as small as the ones of these drugs. However, these small molecules can be bound chemically to a carrier, usually protein albumen. In such a combination the small, non-protein molecule is called a **hapten**. The combination of the large protein molecule and the hapten is introduced into the bloodstream as shown in Figure 17.5, where antibodies specific for the hapten are produced. The antibodies are then extracted from the blood and used as reagents to analyze for the desired substance.

A relatively new technique called **radioimmunoassay** is becoming extremely useful in forensic chemistry. A standard of the substance to be analyzed is labelled with a radioactive isotope, such as carbon-14. The product is a radioactive hapten. It is reacted with an antibody specific for that particular hapten to form a combination called a **complex**. The sample to be analyzed contains the same hapten in a nonradioactive form and in an unknown concentration that is to be measured. This sample is added to the complex, and the hapten in the sample displaces the radioactive hapten in the complex to a certain extent. The amount of the radioactive hapten displaced is a measure of the amount of hapten in the sample. The complex is precipitated from the solution, and the amount of radioactive hapten displaced from it is determined by "counting" the radioactivity of the displaced hapten in the solution.

FIGURE 17.5

A hapten reacts with

a carrier, such as protein albumen,

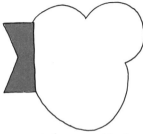

to form a combination,

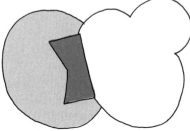

which induces the formation
of antibodies in the bloodstream.

These antibodies are specific
reagents for the hapten.

Chapter Summary

Chemistry is playing an increasing role in the fight against crime. This is largely through the use of chemical analysis to detect and characterize samples associated with a crime. These samples are produced as a result of Locard's criminalistics theory, which states that *whenever two surfaces meet, there is an exchange of material between them.*

Fingerprints are one of the most important types of evidence for establishing the presence of an individual at the scene of a crime.

Chemical treatment is used to make latent (not readily visible) fingerprints visible. Iodine, silver nitrate, and osmium tetroxide are among the chemicals used for this purpose.

Impressions of tire tracks, shoe prints, and tool marks may be preserved with various plastic materials. These include plaster of Paris, silicones, and thermosetting plastics.

Photography is an important tool in crime investigation. General photography is used for routine records of a crime scene. Special photographic techniques are used for pictures of distant objects, closeup shots, and photographs through a microscope.

The *analysis of elements* is very useful in determining the identities of samples of glass and metals. Bits of glass and metal shavings are common samples used in the investigation of criminal cases.

Paint is often available as a sample for forensic investigations. Physical examination reveals a great deal about such a sample. Chemical tests may also be employed. Greases, oils, and other organic liquids are readily examined by chemical means, especially infrared spectroscopy.

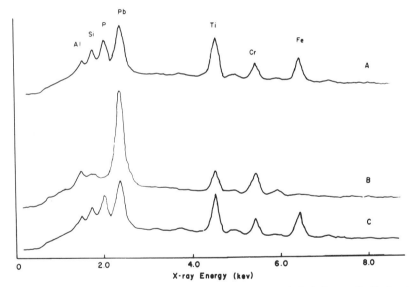

X-ray fluorescence analysis of paints: A. Red paint from victim's home; B. Red paint from suspect's home; C. Red paint from pry bar found in suspect's possession. The analysis shows a similar elemental content between A and C, and eliminated B as a possible source of C. (Courtesy of Dr. Michael J. Camp, Northeastern University)

The *characterization of biological samples* is quite useful in criminal investigations. Blood is the most common such sample. Other materials include saliva, urine, perspiration, and semen.

Drugs figure strongly in crime. Therefore, the *analysis of drugs* is an important part of forensic chemistry. Sophisticated techniques have been developed for most drug analyses.

Chapter Review Questions

The following questions are designed as a self-teaching tool to help you review Chapter 17. The answers to each question follow. See Chapter Review Questions for Chapter 1 for further instructions.

1. The branch of chemistry dealing with crime is called _____.

2. The piece of visible evidence, which most certainly establishes contact of an individual with a particular object, is the _____.

3. Three chemicals used to make latent fingerprints appear are _____, _____, and _____.

4. Some materials used to make casts or impressions of evidence such as footprints are _____, _____, _____, and _____.

5. Exposure to light causes formation of _____ in grains of _____ imbedded in a gelatin layer in photographic film.

6. Some of the things that vary in paper, making it good evidence in a criminal case, are _____, _____, _____, _____, _____, and _____.

7. Chemical analysis can be used to distinguish types of glass because of variations in _____ composition.

8. A type of sample that is easy to dissolve and analyze by atomic absorption analysis consists of _____.

9. Two things revealed from the physical appearance of a paint chip are _____ and _____.

10. "Miscellaneous elements" are especially likely to be found in paint _____.

11. Exposure to hydrogen sulfide blackens paint containing _____.

12. Volatile organic materials given off when paint is heated are called _____.

13. Some readily analyzed trace elements whose levels vary in different bullets are _____, _____, _____, _____, _____, and _____.

14. Two elements whose presence on the hand may indicate that a firearm was recently discharged by the suspect are _____ and _____.

15. A test for fats or vegetable oil involves the formation of _____ and _____ upon treatment with strong sodium hydroxide.

16. The type of spectrometry most useful in identifying specific organic compounds is _____.

17. An instrument, which is really a combination of two instruments, quite useful for the analysis of specific organic compounds in forensic chemistry, is the _____.

18. A carcinogenic compound used to test for the presence of blood stains is _____.

19. The most common way of characterizing blood is by division into _____.

20. The three most common groups determined by serological examination are _____, _____, and _____.

21. Blood proteins are most readily separated by _____.

22. Arsenic and some heavy metals tend to accumulate in _____ and _____.

23. Three instrumental methods commonly used for drug analysis are _____, _____, and _____.

24. "Black light" comes from an _____ lamp and is used to make _____ substances visible.

25. A specific example of drug analysis by fluorescence is the analysis of _____.

26. Although chemists may not be able to make a reagent which is completely specific for a particular substance, _____ can do so, a fact which is utilized in _____ methods of analysis.

Answers to Chapter Review Questions

1. forensic chemistry
2. fingerprint
3. iodine, silver nitrate, osmium tetroxide
4. plaster of Paris, silicone plastics, moulage, thermosetting plastics
5. silver metal, silver halide
6. thickness, surface type, color, type of paper pulp, sizing, printing
7. trace element
8. metal fragments
9. different layers, degree of weathering
10. pigments
11. lead pigments
12. pyrolysis products
13. aluminum, copper, tin, cadmium, manganese, cobalt
14. barium, antimony
15. glycerin, soap
16. infrared spectrometry
17. gas chromatograph-mass spectrometer
18. benzidine
19. blood groups
20. ABO, Rhesus, MN
21. electrophoresis
22. hair, nails
23. ultraviolet absorption spectrophotometry, fluorescence, chromatography
24. ultraviolet, fluorescent
25. LSD
26. biological systems of humans and animals, immunological

Exercises for Chapter 17

1. What is the best way of separating enzymes from a blood sample? Upon which property of the enzymes does this separation depend?

2. What is an "anti-climb" paint?

3. What is the major advantage of putting a gas chromatograph "upstream" from a mass spectrometer in the analysis of an organic forensic sample? What problems might be encountered if the whole organic sample were analyzed by the mass spectrometer without first separating the sample into its parts?

4. What kinds of spectra are routinely stored in large data banks for identification of organic compounds? How are they matched with unknown spectra?

5. Chemically, how does the preparation of sodium morphinate from heroin resemble a saponification reaction?

6. What is the difference between an antigen and a hapten?

7. What role does protein albumen play in the immunological analysis of a relatively simple compound such as LSD?

8. Write a general chemical reaction that describes what occurs in radioimmunoassay when a sample to be analyzed reacts with the radioactive complex.

9. Describe how the formation of a clear solid plastic from liquid chemicals can be useful for the visible examination of a paint chip.

10. What are three serological systems of blood classification?

11. Write a chemical reaction for the production of an insoluble deposit that shows perspiration from fingerprints. Write another reaction and explain how this deposit turns a dark, easily visible color.

12. What is the chemical formula of one substance commonly used to make casts of footprints?

13. Which two metals are among the four elements most abundant in common glass?

14. Give the chemical formula of a black substance which may be produced by a chemical reaction with a certain type of paint pigment.

15. In what general way does an antibody resemble an enzyme?

16. Some salt crystals were found in the trunk of an automobile belonging to a person suspected of stealing some laboratory chemicals. Among the stolen chemicals were several bottles of ammonium chloride, the chemical thought to be spilled in the suspect's car. Suggest two simple chemical tests, one involving the formation of a volatile odorous compound and the other related to a test described in this chapter, that could establish whether or not the chemical was in fact ammonium chloride.

17. A motorist sues an auto manufacturer alleging that his new car crashed into a roadside tree because of failure of the wiring system resulting in a sudden loss of lights at night. One of the headlight lenses was broken in the crash, although the headlight assembly remained reasonably intact. How might an investigator determine whether the headlight was not lit at the moment of impact? (What sort of chemical reaction might occur at the moment of impact?)

18. How should a thin layer chromatographic separation be run in order to obtain a good idea of the identity of a particular spot without doing complicated chemical tests on the spot?

19. Benzene rings absorb light well in the ultraviolet region. Does this suggest a way of telling whether or not an explosive contains nitroglycerin or TNT (trinitrotoluene)?

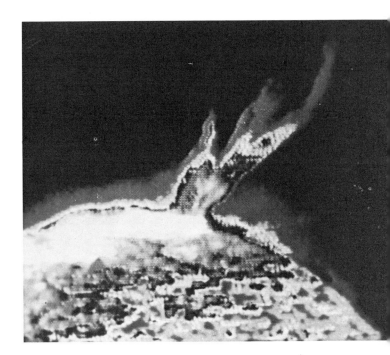

Energy from the sun gives warmth and sustains life on Earth. Solar energy has also been stored for millions of years in fossil fuels that were once plants engaged in photosynthesis. This photograph shows a solar eruption seen from Skylab. (Courtesy of NASA)

18

Chemistry and Energy

18.1

When the Lights Go Out

The shortage of domestic supplies of energy will probably have more effect upon the economic status of today's students than any other factor. The American economic system during recent decades grew rapidly, and in many respects unwisely, upon the assumption that energy would always be cheap and abundant. For years natural gas was almost a nuisance and was "flared" as waste in many oil fields. Petroleum was exported and prices were low. Of course, it was realized that supplies of natural gas and oil must some day give out. But, why worry? Nuclear power was the answer. The same scientists, engineers, research laboratories and industries that gave us the hydrogen bomb or the nuclear powered submarine would provide energy unlimited in supply and inexpensive as well. Few stopped to consider that nuclear energy was poorly adapted for use in an automobile or jet plane, or that nobody really knew what to do with the radioactive wastes produced, or that just one really bad nuclear power plant accident could be a catastrophe almost too grim to contemplate. As for coal, who wanted it? It was a filthy black rock, environmentally destructive and dangerous to mine, difficult to transport, and a nasty polluter to burn. Few considered that it was really the only energy resource which could with certainty meet U.S. needs for centuries, if necessary.

Because of our inaction in the energy area, U.S. citizens are now paying a price. Our systems of transportation, our energy-devouring homes, and our glassed-in office buildings, which require too much fuel for heating in the winter and too much electricity for cooling in the summer, have made energy conservation difficult. In fact, our energy-wasteful architecture has not changed appreciably since the 1973 energy crisis. Nuclear energy is running into severe difficulties. Facilities for alternate energy sources, such as synthetic petroleum from coal, are not in place and will require years to build. We can only hope that the seriousness of the problem is realized and acted upon by those with the influence to start the slow, painful steps necessary to assure adequate supplies of energy. Eventually, zero growth in energy consumption must be achieved. The welfare of all citizens depends upon adequate supplies of energy along with the eventual achievement of zero energy growth. As explained in this chapter, chemistry is one of the keys to solving the energy problem.

18.2

World Energy Resources

At the present time, most of the energy consumed by man consists of fossil fuels. These are hydrocarbons and forms of carbon which came from carbon dioxide in the atmosphere millions of years ago. The energy for putting the carbon in this form came from the sun and was "fixed" by photosynthesis of land and water plants. In a sense, fossil fuels are stored solar energy.

Estimates of the amounts of fossil fuels available for use differ with the source of the estimate. In the U.S. additional deposits of coal continue to be discovered. Because of undiscovered deposits of petroleum and natural gas, there may be more of these fossil fuels than is generally realized—or additional exploration may be very disappointing in its results. Whatever the estimate, however, it is certain that deposits of fossil fuels are limited. Alternative energy sources such as solar energy, nuclear energy, geothermal energy, and tidal power will have to be utilized.

Figure 18.1 shows quantities of recoverable fossil fuels that are now estimated to have been present in the world in the year 1800. The abbreviation, kW-hr, in Figure 18.1 stands for kilowatt-hour. That is the amount of energy required to light a 1000-watt light bulb (or ten

FIGURE 18.1

Initial amounts (before 1800) of the world's recoverable fossil fuels shown in thermal kilowatt hours of energy. Data taken from " The Energy Resources of the Earth," in M. King Hubbert, Energy and Power, *W. H. Freeman and Co., San Francisco, Calif., 1971.*

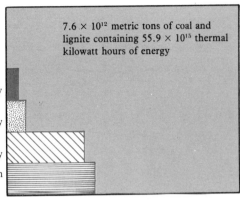

7.6 × 10^{12} metric tons of coal and lignite containing 55.9 × 10^{15} thermal kilowatt hours of energy

0.19 × 10^{12} barrels of shale oil containing 0.32 × 10^{15} kw-hr energy

0.30 × 10^{12} barrels of tar-sand oil containing 0.51 × 10^{15} kw-hr energy

1.0 × 10^{16} ft^3 of natural gas containing 2.94 × 10^{15} kw-hr energy

2.00 × 10^{12} barrels of liquid petroleum containing 3.25 × 10^{15} kw-hr energy

100-watt light bulbs) for 1 hour. The amount of energy in coal given in this figure means that there is enough coal for 55.9 million billion kilowatt-hours.

By far the greatest recoverable fossil-fuel energy resource is in the form of coal and lignite, which is a similar fuel. Only a very small percentage of the originally available coal has been consumed. However, approximately 15% of recoverable petroleum and natural gas have been consumed already.

One might question why all the concern, if only about 15% of the available petroleum and natural gas have been used already. For the U.S. citizen, the concern comes first from the fact that few of the remaining resources of these fuels are in this country, which has such a tremendous appetite for them. Furthermore, what appears to be a fairly small growth rate in use can lead rapidly to the exhaustion of even the abundant resources in some other countries. To understand why this is so, consider what would happen if you had an automobile that required only 4% more gasoline for every 20 mi travelled. Assume that it started out with 20 gallons of gasoline in the tank and was getting 20 miles to the gallon. How far could it travel? A quick answer would be 400 mi—20 gal of gasoline at 20 mi to the gallon. Now consider that it requires 4% more gasoline for every 20 mi travelled. That requires multiplying by 1.04 each time a new 20-mi marker goes by. This exercise is shown in Table 18.1. It is an interesting one to do on an electronic calculator. The calculations in Table 18.1 show that a driver who tries to travel 400 mi on 20 gal of gasoline and an automobile that starts out getting 20 mi/gal but requires 4% more gasoline for every 20 mi travelled will stop a little short of the 300-mi mark (Figure 18.2). This illustrates what an apparently small growth in the rate of consumption will do. It also shows why the growth rate must eventually reach zero.

Some of the statistics regarding energy resources and their estimated rates of use are interesting, and sobering. For oil and natural gas in "the lower 48" U.S., it is likely that peak production has been reached. The bulk of total production will occur during the years of

TABLE 18.1

Total Miles Travelled	Gallons of Gasoline for Last 20 Miles	Total Gallons of Gasoline Used	Total Gallons of Gasoline Remaining
20	1.00	1.00	19
40	1.04	2.04	17.96
60	1.08	3.12	16.88
80	1.12	4.24	15.76
100	1.17	5.41	14.59
120	1.22	6.63	13.37
140	1.27	7.90	12.10
160	1.32	9.22	10.78
180	1.37	10.59	9.41
200	1.42	12.01	7.99
220	1.48	13.49	6.51
240	1.54	15.03	4.97
260	1.60	16.63	3.37
280	1.67	18.30	1.70
300	1.73	20.03	Out of gas

approximately 1935–2000, and the rate of production will continue to decrease from now on. Alaskan oil may supply up to 10 years of U.S. petroleum demands. This is a relatively small contribution to the total needs. This 10-year period does, however, provide precious time which— *if used wisely*—will allow for the development of nonpetroleum energy. World-wide petroleum resources are approximately 10 times those of the U.S. Peak world production will be reached around the year 2000.

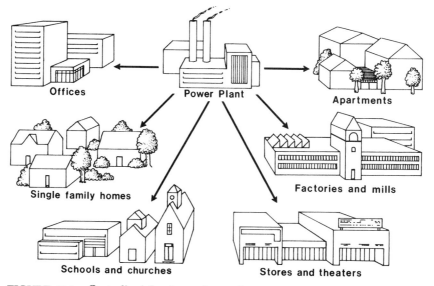

FIGURE 18.2 *Centralized heating units serving many residences and commercial buildings are an attractive option for future energy development.*

Appreciable amounts of oil remain in tar sand deposits (about 300 billion barrels in Northern Alberta, Canada). Even more oil (about 3000 billion barrels world-wide, of which at least 6% could be recovered economically with existing technology) is to be found in oil shale. Environmental and other problems involved with the development of these resources are quite great, however.

Particularly in the U.S., the coal resources picture is considerably more favorable. It is estimated that there are about 7.6×10^{12} metric tons of recoverable coal world-wide. Peak production should be reached shortly after the year 2100. If this occurs, the middle 80% of production will occur over a three-century period beginning around the year 2000 and ending around 2300. It is difficult to project coal use in the U.S. because the fraction of U.S. energy needs that will be supplied by coal in the future is not known. However, around 20% of the world's available coal is found in the U.S. In terms of the availability of at least this fossil fuel, therefore, the U.S. need not have an energy crisis for many decades.

Several nonfossil fuel energy sources show varying degrees of promise in meeting energy needs. Nuclear fission (splitting of uranium atoms to yield energy) is in fact being used to produce electricity. Geothermal energy from hot water underground is producing electricity in some areas where this source is available. Solar energy is being developed for heating buildings and water. Controlled thermonuclear fusion (sort of a harnessed hydrogen bomb) is being investigated, though it has tremendous technical problems. Relatively small contributions may be expected from giant windmills, tidal energy, and small hydro-electric installations at existing dams. These sources will be discussed in more detail later in the chapter.

The U.S. energy picture is both hopeful and grim. Liquid petroleum and natural gas are on the way out as major producers of energy. If necessary, utilization of shale oil deposits will give some relief. Nuclear power may provide an increasing share of electrical energy production although difficult technical, safety, and economic problems have severely slowed down its rate of development. Miscellaneous sources such as wind, water, tidal, and geothermal power will make some limited contributions to total energy production. In looking at the energy situation from now until the year 2000, one can predict that coal, an abundant and versatile fossil fuel, will certainly fill the energy gap until some more exotic sources can be developed. By the turn of the century, technology should be available for the utilization of nuclear fusion and solar power, each of which promises to be an abundant, relatively nonpolluting stationary source of energy.

It should be noted that most of the more promising sources of energy produce electricity and heat. This leaves unsolved the need for mobile energy sources. Liquid fuels are about the only satisfactory energy source for airplanes, trucks, and the automobile as we know it today. These modes of transportation will have to be replaced by electric railway transportation of most freight and of people over distances of less than 200–300 mi. The small electric car may well become the best individual mode of transportation for short distance trips. The larger

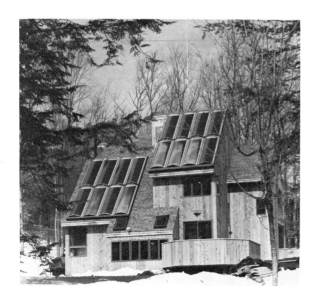

In a solar heating system, the energy collected in the solar collectors on the roof is used to heat air or water in a circulating system. No fuel costs are involved although there are occasional maintenance expenses for the glass and pipes. However, the initial cost is quite high. (Courtesy of Grumman Corp.)

automobile—for those who can afford it—will become a luxury item used primarily for pleasure trips as the availability of fuel, and the money to buy it, permit.

These changes in our basic modes of transportation will be accomplished only with considerable anguish. Despite its lethal nature, expense, and environmental pollution, the automobile is dear to the heart of most Americans. Teenagers count the days until they will be of driving age. The loss of the driver's license from the infirmities of age is often the crowning blow to a senior citizen's ego. Powerful economic and union interests will fight to retain the long distance truck for freight transport, regardless of costs to the consumer. Rotting ties, crooked tracks, and aging equipment attest to the railroads' lack of preparedness to take over the role of providing high-speed transportation of goods and people. Therefore, the problem of limited world petroleum resources is causing great social and economic difficulties as well as technological problems.

18.3

Energy Conservation

From about 1960 until 1973, the rate at which energy production increased in the U.S. was slightly over 4% per year. With such a growth rate, energy use doubles every 16 years. These numbers can be used to "prove" many things. They can show that within a few decades facilities for the production of energy must be increased by several times to meet energy demand. They can show that devastating environmental damage will occur from the exploitation of energy resources. A computer can quickly calculate the date when the whole nation will glow in the dark from increasing waste heat radiated out into space. The thing that is wrong with such projections is that they need not, should not, and indeed cannot come true.

Any consideration of energy needs and production must take energy conservation into consideration. This does not have to mean frigid classrooms with the thermostat turned down to 60°F in the dead of winter, or to sweltering hot homes with no air conditioning, or to reliance on the bicycle for transportation (although these things would in fact occur if a long, effective embargo of foreign oil occurred right now). With wise management of energy resources—and luck—these measures will not be necessary. But the fact remains that the U.S., along with other industrialized nations, has wasted energy at a deplorable rate. Is it really necessary for so many people to live 30 or 40 miles from their jobs and to commute to work with only one person in a large gas-guzzling automobile? Is the airplane, which is not a very efficient user of energy, really necessary for trips of less than 200 mi that could be served by bus and train transportation? Is there not something wrong when energy-inefficient trucks glide along magnificent interstate highways while a potentially efficient railroad is allowed to deteriorate alongside? Must a building designed for teaching chemistry be designed with so much ventilating capacity that it resembles a giant wind tunnel requiring huge turbines and large electric motors to drive them? Must the same building be designed without windows which open to provide natural ventilation? The answer to these questions is *no*. And in this answer lies a great deal of potential for energy conservation that will ease the energy problem.

As pointed out above, a great deal of energy is wasted. Much of this waste is necessary, as a result of physical laws governing the conversion of energy from one form to another. With presently existing technology, it is almost impossible to convert more than about 40% of the heat energy in coal to electrical energy in a power plant. Even here, however, there is some potential for energy conservation. Most of the energy that is lost is dissipated as waste heat to bodies of natural water or to the atmosphere. Some of this low-grade heat could be used to heat buildings. This is in fact done in many places, such as large college campuses, which combine an electrical power plant with centralized heating.

Household and commercial consumption of energy, which accounts for a little over one third of total energy use in the U.S., is the most efficient and wastes only 30% of its energy. Industry accounts for somewhat less than one-third of energy use and wastes about 40%. Transportation is by far the least efficient, wasting 85% of its energy consumption. This is a major area of potential savings because transportation takes one-third of the energy consumed in the United States. Electricity is also quite inefficient overall, with almost two-thirds of electricity wasted in transmission and conversion to other forms of energy. This does not account for the fact that the conversion of fossil fuel energy to electricity is only about 35–40% efficient in the first place. Despite this, there have been some marked improvements in the efficiency of energy utilization. For example, a modern, coal-fired electrical plant generates electricity with an overall efficiency of up to 40%, whereas in 1900 the figure was around 5%. The steam locomotive, which was the predominant source of rail power in 1940, converted heat to energy of mechanical motion with a maximum efficiency of only about 10%, compared to approximately 35% for today's diesel locomotives. Estimates are that overall efficiency of energy utilization has increased by about 4 times since 1900.

There is a high potential for energy conservation in industry. Notably, it has been reported that from 1964 to 1974 du Pont increased product output by 100% with only a 50% increase in energy consumption. In 1972 Dow *reduced* energy consumption by about 10% while increasing production of chemicals. Fundamental changes in the production of goods and services could result in tremendous energy savings without harming the overall economy. Recycling of containers would decrease energy consumption. The manufacture of appliances, automobiles, and other consumer items with emphasis on long life, durability, and ease of repair would be helpful. Policies, which encouraged employment of people in low-energy use industries (health care, education, and labor-intensive

Heat loss from the windows is evident in a comparison of the thermograph of this building with the photograph. The heat loss is measured on a scale ranging from black for the coolest, to white for the hottest areas. (Courtesy of Vogel Enterprises, Ltd.)

agriculture) rather than high-energy use industries, would ease the economic impact of a lowered output of disposable material goods.

Transportation is another area where vastly increased efficiencies can be realized. The private auto and airplane are only about one-third as efficient as buses or trains for transportation. Transportation of freight by truck is terribly inefficient compared to rail transport. Truck transport requires about 3800 Btu/ton-mile compared to only 670 Btu/ton-mile by train. Major shifts in our current modes of transportation will not come without anguish, but energy conservation dictates that they must be made.

Household and commercial uses of energy are relatively more efficient than energy consumption for transportation. Here, again, appreciable savings can be made. Considering the percentage of electricity wasted in generating and transporting electricity, the all-electric home uses much more energy than homes heated with fossil fuels. Electrical resistance heating consumes more electricity to heat a home than does an electrically driven heat pump. The sprawling ranch-style house uses more energy per person than does an apartment unit or row house. Improved insulation, storm windows, and similar measures can conserve a great deal of energy in the home.

One of the most attractive options for residential and commercial heating and cooling is the centrally located power plant that generates electricity and distributes waste heat for heating and cooling (Figure 18.2). Most large university campuses have such a facility. The city of Västra Frölunda near Gothenburg, Sweden has a heating facility providing heat for 1600 apartments. Such a unit provides some versatility in fuel type. It may double as an incinerator for trash. Pollution control is relatively simple and straightforward in a large, centralized power generating unit.

18.4

Energy Conversion Processes

As shown in Figure 18.3, energy occurs in several forms and must be converted to other forms. The efficiencies of conversion vary over a wide range. Conversion of electrical energy to radiant energy by incandescent light bulbs is very inefficient. Less than 5% is converted to visible light whereas the remainder of the energy is wasted as heat. At the other end of the scale, a large electric generator is around 80% efficient in converting mechanical energy to electrical energy. The much-publicized Wankel engine converts chemical to mechanical energy with an efficiency of about 18% compared to 25% for a gasoline-powered piston engine and about 37% for a diesel engine. A modern coal-fired steam power plant converts chemical energy to electrical energy with an overall efficiency of about 40%.

One of the most significant energy conversion processes is the conversion of thermal energy to mechanical energy in a heat engine such

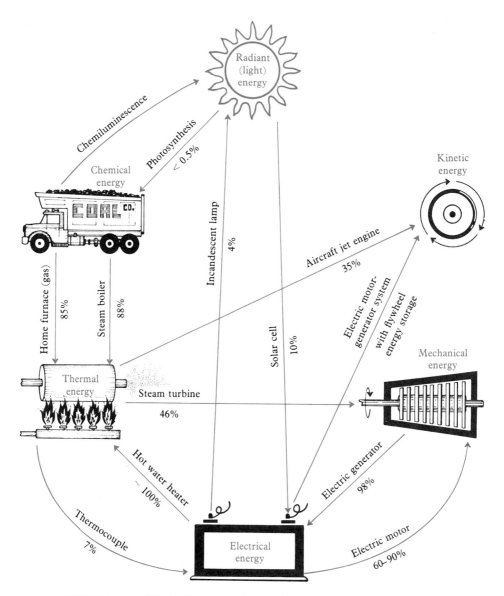

FIGURE 18.3 *Kinds of energy and examples of conversion between them, including percentage conversion efficiencies.*

as a steam turbine. The Carnot equation

$$\text{percent efficiency} = \frac{T_1 - T_2}{T_1} \times 100 \qquad \text{(excluding friction)}$$

states that the percent efficiency is given by a fraction involving the inlet temperature (for example, of steam), T_1, and the outlet temperature, T_2. These temperatures are expressed in degrees Kelvin (Centigrade temperature plus 273). Typically a steam turbine engine operates between approximately 810°K inlet temperature and 330°K outlet temperature.

These temperatures substituted into the Carnot equation give a maximum theoretical efficiency of 59%. The impossibility of introducing steam into the turbine at the maximum temperature uniformly, and mechanical energy losses, reduce the overall efficiency of conversion of thermal energy to mechanical energy in a modern steam power plant to approximately 47%. Taking into account losses from conversion of chemical to thermal energy in the boiler cuts down the total efficiency to about 40%.

Some of the greatest advances in increasing the efficiency of conversion of chemical to mechanical or electrical energy have been through increasing the peak inlet temperature in heat engines. In the early 1900's, T_1 in a steam power plant typically was 550°K; the use of superheated steam has raised that figure to around 830°K in modern power plants. Improved materials and engineering design, therefore, have resulted in large energy savings.

The efficiency of nuclear power plants is limited by the maximum temperatures attainable. Reactor cores would be damaged by the high temperatures used in fossil-fuel fired boilers and have a maximum temperature of approximately 620°K. Because of this limitation, the overall efficiency of conversion of nuclear energy to electricity is about 30%.

What is the fate of the 60% of energy from fossil-fuel fired power plants or 70% of energy from nuclear plants that is not converted to electricity? It is dissipated as heat, either to the atmosphere or to bodies of water and streams. The latter is thermal pollution, which may either harm aquatic life or in some cases actually increase bioactivity in the water to the benefit of some species. This "waste" heat potentially is very useful in applications like home heating and aquaculture (growth of food in water). Although it may not be a problem at the present time, increased production of waste heat by man could eventually result in marked changes in climate.

Some common devices for the conversion of energy are shown in Figures 18.4–18.9. One of the simplest of these is a turbine or similar device, which converts the kinetic or potential energy of a fluid such as air or water into mechanical or electrical energy. The hydroturbine generator or windmill are typical of such devices. When an energy-containing fluid is not available in the form of wind or falling water, it may be obtained by heating a gas or vaporizing a liquid with thermal energy derived from chemical reactions (burning fossil fuel), nuclear reactions (fission), or solar energy. The reciprocating internal combustion engine is a common device for the conversion of chemical energy to mechanical energy. The diesel engine is a variation of this type in which the air-fuel mixture is fired by heat produced from very high compression. Because of its higher peak temperature, it is much more efficient. The gas turbine engine is a very simple machine that provides either mechanical energy to drive a generator or aircraft propeller or kinetic energy to propel an airplane. Fuel cells are devices in which fuels such as hydrogen, hydrocarbons, or alcohol are oxidized, converting chemical energy directly to electrical energy. The rocket motor is basically a very simple device

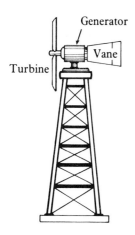

FIGURE 18.4
Turbine for conversion of kinetic or potential energy of a fluid to mechanical and electrical energy.

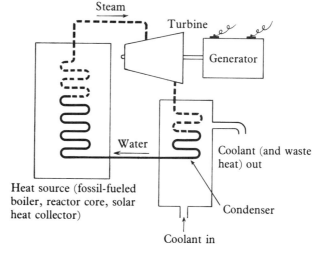

FIGURE 18.5
Steam power plant in which high energy fluid is produced by vaporizing water.

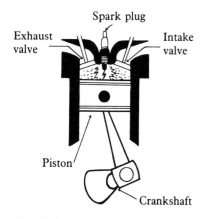

FIGURE 18.6
Reciprocating internal combustion engine.

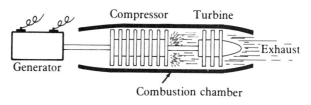

FIGURE 18.7
Gas turbine engine. Kinetic energy of hot exhaust gases may propel aircraft.

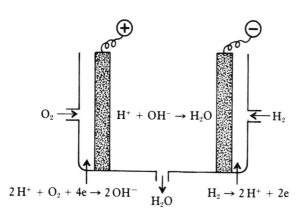

$$O_2 \rightarrow \quad H^+ + OH^- \rightarrow H_2O \quad \leftarrow H_2$$

$$2\,H^+ + O_2 + 4e \rightarrow 2\,OH^- \qquad H_2O \qquad H_2 \rightarrow 2\,H^+ + 2e$$

FIGURE 18.8
Fuel cell for the direct conversion of chemical energy to electrical energy.

FIGURE 18.9
Rocket motor.

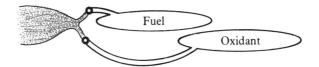

in which fuel and oxidant react to provide kinetic energy needed to propel a rocket.

Substantial advances have been made in energy conversion technology over many decades and great advances can be projected for the future. The approximately tenfold increase in efficiency of electrical power generation since 1900 was discussed in Section 18.3. An approximately fourfold increase in the efficiency of rail transport occurred during the 1950's with the replacement of steam locomotives with diesel locomotives. During the coming decades increased efficiency can be anticipated in areas such as combined power cycles in which hot exhaust gas from a turbine engine is used to generate steam for a steam turbine. The magnetohydrodynamic electrical generator (see Section 18.6) probably will be developed as a very efficient energy source used in combination with conventional steam generation. Entirely new devices such as thermonuclear reactors for the direct conversion of nuclear fusion energy to electricity very likely will be developed.

18.5

Petroleum and Natural Gas

The U.S. petroleum industry began in 1859 with the first commercial oil well in Pennsylvania. Since that time a total of 100 billion barrels of oil have been produced domestically, most of it in recent years. Proved reserves of U.S. oil are only about 38 billion barrels. This is only about a 7-year supply at the current rate of consumption. Estimates of the amount of recoverable petroleum yet to be discovered in the U.S. range from a low of 62 billion barrels to a high of 430 billion barrels. These estimates include Alaskan and offshore oil. Despite the wide variation in estimated oil reserves, it is generally believed that peak annual production of petroleum in the U.S. has been reached.

Liquid petroleum is found in rock formations ranging in porosity from 10 to 30%. Up to half of the pore space is occupied by water. The oil in these formations must flow over long distances to an approximately 6-inch diameter hole from which it is pumped. The rate of flow depends on the permeability of the rock formation, the viscosity of the oil, the driving pressure behind the oil, and other factors. In many cases oil-bearing formations do not yield oil because of limitations in these factors. Generally only a small fraction, an average of 30%, of the oil is extracted from an oil-bearing formation (Figure 18.10). The efficiency with which oil is displaced from formations by gas or water is a major limitation.

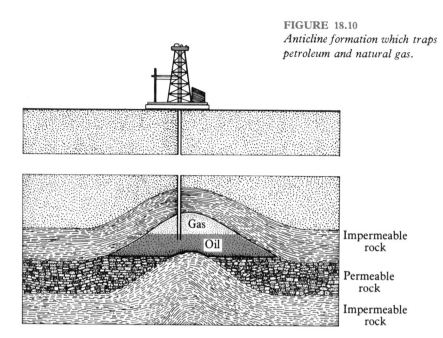

FIGURE 18.10
Anticline formation which traps petroleum and natural gas.

Solvents, underground combustion (burning), detergents, and foams have all been employed to increase the efficiency of displacement. Because of geometrical considerations oil may be bypassed in draining an oil reservoir. Fracturing of the oil-bearing formation, the use of proper displacement fluids, and proper well location can help to solve this problem.

A recovery of 60% of petroleum through secondary or tertiary recovery techniques would double the amount of petroleum available. Much of this petroleum could come from fields that have already been abandoned or essentially exhausted using primary recovery techniques. Advanced recovery techniques have not yet been widely used because of the high cost, but the sharp increases in petroleum price that occurred in 1973–74 have made advanced recovery processes much more attractive.

As is the case with liquid petroleum, huge reserves of natural gas are locked into formations that are too impermeable to release it. Recovery of gas from tight formations frequently is accomplished by hydraulic fracturing. This process consists of pumping a fluid into the well under pressure high enough to cause formation of vertical cracks extending up to 150 ft from the well. In some formations such as those found in the Piceance basin of western Colorado even hydraulic fracturing will not release the gas. Underground nuclear explosions have been attempted to release some of the estimated 100 trillion cubic feet of natural gas locked in this formation. This approach has not been very successful.

Shale oil is a possible substitute for petroleum. Approximately 1.8 trillion barrels of this hydrocarbon are entrained in deposits of shale in Colorado, Wyoming, and Utah. A quantity exceeding 100 billion barrels is located in the prime deposits found in the Piceance Creek basin region of Colorado. The availability of water, potential for saline pollution from spent shale, and other environmental constraints currently are limiting commercial production of shale oil. In late 1974 the Colony Development Corporation canceled plans to build the first commercial shale oil processing plant in the U.S., a 50,000 barrel per day unit scheduled for operation in 1977. Sharply rising costs were cited as the main reason for cancellation.

Recently (1977) partial *in situ* retorting processes have shown considerable promise for shale oil extraction. This approach calls for removal of a small quantity of the shale from underground, breaking the shale formations with explosives, and igniting the shale underground. The organic matter in the shale is kept burning with air pumped into the underground cavity. The heat generated literally "cooks" the shale and converts the organic matter (kerogen) in the shale to a petroleum-like material that is pumped from the ground.

18.6

Coal

From approximately Civil War times until World War II, coal was the dominant energy source behind U.S. industrial expansion. Smokestacks belching coal smoke became the symbols of prosperous industrial cities. Coal-fired locomotives pulled trains loaded with goods manufactured in industrial plants fueled with coal. The predawn journey to the basement to stoke up the coal-burning furnace was a wintertime ritual for the homeowner.

However, the greater convenience of low-cost petroleum resulted in a decrease in coal use in the U.S. after World War II. Even before being replaced by more efficient diesel locomotives, coal locomotives were converted largely to oil. Coal-burning home furnaces were converted to oil or natural gas. After World War II, coal production fell by about one-third, reaching a low of approximately 400 million tons in 1958. By 1973 production was back up to approximately the 600 million ton per year peak reached earlier, although the proportion of coal used for U.S. energy requirements did not change from 1958. Reviled by environmentalists as a dirty fuel, coal acquired a bad name. However, with diminishing petroleum supplies, increasing uncertainty about the overall safety of nuclear power, and the unavailability of more exotic sources of energy, coal is taking on much more importance in the total energy picture. With proper management U.S. coal resources can provide fuel and raw material for several centuries.

"Coal" describes a large range of solid fossil fuels derived from partial degradation of plants. Table 18.2 shows the characteristics of the major classes of coal differentiated largely by percentage of fixed carbon,

TABLE 18.2
Major types of coal found in the U.S.

Type of Coal	Proximate Analysis, Percent*				Range of Heating Value (Btu/lb)
	Fixed Carbon	Volatile Matter	Moisture	Ash	
Anthracite	82	5	4	9	13,000–16,000
Bituminous					
Low-volatile	66	20	2	12	11,000–15,000
Medium-volatile	64	23	3	10	11,000–15,000
High-volatile	46	44	6	4	11,000–15,000
Subbituminous	40	32	19	9	8000–12,000
Lignite	30	28	37	5	5500–8000

* Approximate values to be expected. These values may vary considerably with the source of coal.

percentage of volatile matter, and heating value. Figure 18.11 points out where the major coal reserves are located in the U.S. Chemically, coal is a very complex material and is by no means pure carbon. For example, a chemical formula for Illinois No. 6 coal would be something like $C_{100}H_{85}S_{2.1}N_{1.5}O_{9.5}$.

Anthracite, a hard, clean-burning, low sulfur coal, is the most desirable of all coals. Approximately half of the anthracite originally present in the U.S. has been mined. Bituminous coal found in the Appalachian and North Central coal fields is the most widely used. It is an excellent fuel with a high heating value. Unfortunately, most

FIGURE 18.11   *Areas with major coal reserves in the U.S.*

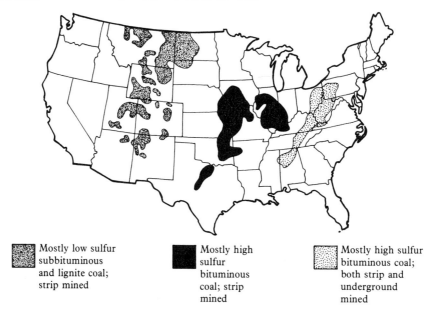

Mostly low sulfur subbituminous and lignite coal; strip mined

Mostly high sulfur bituminous coal; strip mined

Mostly high sulfur bituminous coal; both strip and underground mined bituminous coals have a high percentage of sulfur (an average of 2–3%); and the use of this fuel presents environmental problems. Huge reserves of virtually untouched subbituminous and lignite coals are found in the Rocky Mountain states and in the Northern plains of the Dakotas, Montana, and Wyoming. They have a relatively high oxygen content, so their heating value is less. These fuels have the advantage of being low in sulfur content and are finding increasing use in power plants to meet lower sulfur dioxide emission standards. The low heating value and high moisture and ash contents of these coals are disadvantages. In addition they are generally found great distances from areas having the greatest need for fossil fuels. Lignite in particular tends to lose water of hydration and crumble, as discussed in Section 8.7. Despite these disadvantages, the low sulfur content and ease of mining these low grade fuels is resulting in a rapid increase in their use.

Increased use of coal depends upon the solution of several problems. These are (1) environmental damage from coal mining, (2) removal of ash and sulfur compounds before burning, (3) removing ash and sulfur dioxide from stack gas after burning, and (4) conversion of coal to clean liquid and gas fuels (see Section 18.7).

Much progress has been made in reducing the environmental damage from mining. This damage arises largely from the production of acid mine water and disturbance of land by strip mining. Acid mine water is due to sulfuric acid produced by the reaction of oxygen with pyrite, which has the chemical formula FeS_2.

$$2 FeS_2 + 2 H_2O + 7 O_2 \longrightarrow 2 H_2SO_4 + 2 FeSO_4$$

This reaction is actually carried out by bacteria that use part of the energy produced for their own growth. As more is learned about the process of acid mine water production, more effective means can be taken to eliminate the problem. One of the most important measures is to cover exposed "hot spots" consisting of FeS_2 deposits.

Particularly in flatter areas, strip-mined land can be reclaimed reasonably well. In many cases the land can be given a more desirable contour. In other cases the original topsoil is so poor that placing more productive subsoil on the surface actually improves the productivity of the land. Those measures that work toward good land reclamation also tend to decrease production of acid mine water.

Washing and chemical processes can be used to remove ash and sulfur from coal before it is burned. The sulfur that can be removed is in the form of pyrite, FeS_2. This makes up about one-half of the sulfur in most coal. The remainder of the sulfur is chemically bound to the complicated organic structure of coal. It cannot be removed except by converting the coal to a liquid or gas fuel.

Meeting air pollution emission standards will require the removal of sulfur dioxide from stack gas, as more high sulfur coal is used as fuel. Most of the more available U.S. coal that is near industrial areas, which have the greatest demand for coal, is high sulfur coal. Therefore, stack-gas desulfurization is being practiced more widely.

Many processes have been developed for the removal of sulfur dioxide from stack gas. The most successful of these are wet scrubber systems in which the gas from the stack is washed with water containing materials that react with the sulfur dioxide. Some of these systems reclaim sulfur or some other product of commercial value. Others are "throwaway" systems in which a waste product with no present commercial value is produced. Some of the more promising systems for stack-gas scrubbing are given in Table 18.3.

TABLE 18.3
Major stack-gas scrubbing systems.

Process	Chemical Reactions	Major Advantages or Disadvantages
Wet limestone scrubbing	$CaCO_3$ + heat = CaO + CO_2 CaO + SO_2 + 2 H_2O = $CaSO_3 \cdot 2 H_2O$	Up to 350 lb of limestone are needed per ton of coal, producing huge quantities of waste product.
Magnesium oxide scrubbing	$Mg(OH)_2$ (slurry) + SO_2 = $MgSO_3$ + H_2O $MgSO_3$ + heat = MgO + SO_2 (regeneration)	The sorbent can be regenerated, and this need not be done on site.
Sodium-base scrubbing	Na_2SO_3 + H_2O + SO_2 = 2 $NaHSO_3$ 2 $NaHSO_3$ + heat = Na_2SO_3 + H_2O + SO_2 (regeneration)	There are no major technological limitations. Annual costs are relatively high.
Sodium citrate scrubbing	SO_2 + OH^- (sodium citrate buffer solution) = HSO_3^- SO_2 + 2 H_2S = 3 S + 2 H_2O (sulfur recovery)	Compact, marketable, elemental sulfur is recovered. Efficiency of sulfur dioxide removal is high. Sodium citrate is expensive.

The wet limestone process is the most commonly used scrubber system. With this process, limestone dust is injected into the boilers along with coal. The product is washed from the stack gas. It contains sulfur salts formed from the reaction of lime and sulfur dioxide. When operating properly, this system removes at least 90% of the sulfur dioxide and has the additional advantage of removing particles (fly ash). Several chemical reactions occur as part of the wet limestone scrubbing process. The first of these is the formation of calcium oxide when the limestone is heated to a very high temperature in the furnace.

$$CaCO_3 + heat \longrightarrow CaO + CO_2\uparrow$$

limestone,   lime,
calcium carbonate   calcium oxide

Coal was used for centuries as a heating fuel. In these photos, coal is being transported from the mine to shuttle cars and then from the cars to the conveyor belt, which will take the coal to the preparation plant. (Courtesy of Bethlehem Steel Corp.)

The lime that is produced reacts partially with sulfur dioxide and sulfur trioxide before reaching the scrubber.

$$2\,CaO + 2\,SO_2 + O_2 \longrightarrow 2\,CaSO_4$$

$$CaO + SO_3 \longrightarrow CaSO_4$$

Additional reactions occur after the stack gas containing CaO, $CaSO_4$, SO_2, and fly ash contact water in the scrubber.

$$CaO + H_2O \longrightarrow Ca(OH)_2$$

$$Ca(OH)_2 + SO_2 \longrightarrow CaSO_3 + H_2O$$

$$2\,Ca(OH)_2 + 2\,SO_2 + O_2 + 2\,H_2O \longrightarrow 2\,CaSO_4 \cdot 2\,H_2O$$

$$\underset{\substack{\text{dry calcium sulfate} \\ \text{from furnace}}}{CaSO_4} + 2\,H_2O \longrightarrow \underset{\text{hydrated calcium sulfate}}{CaSO_4 \cdot 2\,H_2O}$$

Recall from Section 8.7 that $CaSO_4 \cdot 2\,H_2O$ is the product obtained from adding water to plaster of Paris. The production of this plaster causes considerable scaling and other problems in the complicated scrubber mechanism. In addition, huge amounts of lime waste are produced as the scrubber operates. About 1 ton of limestone is required for each 5 tons of coal burned. A large 10,000 ton of coal per day power plant requires 2000 tons per day of limestone. The lime wastes in the form of a watery sludge are presently stored in holding ponds, which grow at an alarming rate. Although it works, the wet limestone process does not appear to be the long-term answer for removal of sulfur dioxide from stack gas.

Stack-gas scrubber systems in which elemental sulfur, sulfuric acid, or some other useful product is recovered from the scrubber are basically much more desirable than throwaway systems. Many such recovery systems have been investigated. These include systems that involve scrubbing with magnesium oxide slurry, sodium sulfite solution, ammonia solution, or sodium citrate solution.

A combination of magnetohydrodynamic power (MHD) with a conventional steam boiler promises efficiencies of electricity generation from coal reaching as high as 60%, compared to the present 40%. The MHD generator makes use of a very high temperature coal flame "seeded" with potassium or cesium salts passing through a very strong magnetic field (Figure 18.12). The potassium and cesium form a gas with many electrically charged ions. This gas is called a plasma. The rapidly moving ions in the magnetic field generate electricity, which is withdrawn at electrodes. After leaving the MHD generator, the hot gas goes to a boiler to generate steam for a steam turbine-generator. The gas is then scrubbed to remove the sulfur dioxide and recycle the seed salts.

FIGURE 18.12
Magnetohydrodynamic power generator.

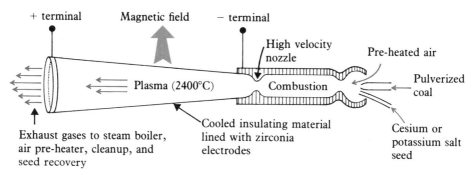

18.7

Gasification and Liquefaction of Coal

The economies of most modern industrialized nations are geared largely to the use of liquid and gaseous hydrocarbon fuels and raw material feedstocks. The conversion of coal to methane and liquid hydrocarbons is a good way of utilizing abundant coal resources with minimum economic disruption and environmental damage. Furthermore, these processes enable utilization of higher sulfur coal that otherwise could not be burned without intolerable atmospheric pollution.

Coal gasification and liquefaction processes are by no means new. The coal-fired gas plant used to be a common, and not altogether attractive, feature of the urban scene. Along with a considerable amount of pollution it produced a toxic mixture of hydrogen and carbon monoxide for use in home lighting and cooking. During World War II, German wartime petroleum demands were largely met by liquid fuels generated by Bergius and Fischer-Tropsch processes. The Bergius process is essentially a hydrogenation reaction in which coal is reacted with hydrogen at approximately 475°C and 200 atm,

$$n\,C + (n + 1)\,H_2 \longrightarrow C_nH_{2n+2}$$

to produce a mixture of liquid hydrocarbons. (The n stands for a whole number. If n is 1, C_nH_{2n+2} is CH_4, or methane. If n is 7, the product is heptane, C_7H_{16}.) These are distilled to yield gasoline, kerosene, and higher boiling hydrocarbons. The coal, used as a feedstock for the Fischer-Tropsch process, is first converted to carbon monoxide, which is reacted with hydrogen to produce both saturated

$$n\,CO + (2n + 1)\,H_2 \longrightarrow C_nH_{2n+2} + n\,H_2O$$

and unsaturated

$$n\,CO + 2n\,H_2 \longrightarrow C_nH_{2n} + n\,H_2O$$

hydrocarbons (olefins).

Several approaches look promising for the conversion of coal to fluid fuels. In the past, development of these processes has been limited by competition from low-cost crude oil. Sharply increased prices for petroleum have favored the economics of coal conversion although rapidly escalating prices for conversion facilities have in turn diminished the economic attractiveness of coal gasification and liquefaction.

The primary coal-derived fuels that are planned for commercial production in the U.S. are the following:

1. Solvent refined coal (SRC), a solid high-Btu product with low-sulfur, ash, and water content.

2. Low-sulfur boiler fuels that are liquid at elevated temperatures.

3. Liquid hydrocarbon fuels, including gasoline, diesel fuel, and naphtha.

4. Substitute natural gas (SNG), which is essentially pure methane.

5. Low-sulfur, low-Btu gas for industrial use.

Of these processes, the production of gaseous fuels is probably closest to widespread commercial development. The key unit operation that occurs in the production of such fuels involves the conversion of coal to some kind of combustible gas. This occurs in a **gasifier** (see Figure 18.13). If oxygen and steam (H_2O) react with the carbon in hot coal, the following two reactions occur:

$$C + O_2 \longrightarrow CO_2 \quad \text{(Produces heat to keep coal hot.)}$$

$$C + H_2O \longrightarrow CO + H_2 \quad \text{(Produces two gases which burn, } H_2 \text{ and CO.)}$$

The carbon monoxide and hydrogen that are produced can be used as a fuel on site. However, the mixture of these two gases does not have

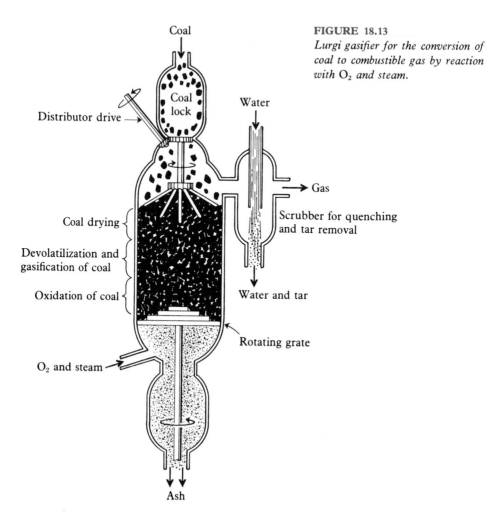

Coal

FIGURE 18.13
Lurgi gasifier for the conversion of coal to combustible gas by reaction with O_2 and steam.

Distributor drive

Coal lock

Water

Gas

Coal drying

Scrubber for quenching and tar removal

Devolatilization and gasification of coal

Oxidation of coal

Water and tar

Rotating grate

O_2 and steam

Ash

a high enough heating value to make it economical for transport over long distances by pipeline. In addition, the carbon monoxide is very toxic and hydrogen is very explosive, so that this mixture is not very good for home use. It can be converted to valuable methane gas, however, by a high-pressure, relatively high-temperature reaction over a **methanation catalyst.**

$$3\,H_2 + CO \longrightarrow CH_4 + H_2O$$

18.8

Nuclear Fission Energy

The awesome power of the atom revealed at the end of World War II held out the promise for the production of abundant, cheap electricity. For that reason, much effort and expense have gone into the development of power reactors that depend upon the splitting of uranium atom nuclei for the generation of electricity. It is actually the nucleus of the atom that is "split." As explained in Section 1.11, this process occurs when a neutron enters the nucleus of a certain kind of atom. The process is called **nuclear fission**. Each time the nucleus of an atom undergoes nuclear fission, a lot of energy is released. This is collected as heat, which is used to make steam to run turbines that drive electrical generators.

Nuclear power reactors currently in use depend upon the fission of the isotope of uranium weighing 235 amu (atomic mass units). This isotope is called uranium-235. When the uranium atom splits, it forms two lighter atoms. These fission products are radioactive. On the average, every two fissions give off 5 neutrons. These neutrons are moving very rapidly when they are first produced. However, in a nuclear reactor they are slowed down in the water that surrounds the fuel rods containing the uranium fuel. For a reactor operating at a steady power level, all but exactly one of these neutrons is absorbed by neutron-absorbing materials in the reactor and its control rods. This 1 neutron is used to cause another fission reaction to occur. The energy from these nuclear reactions is used to heat water in the reactor core and to produce steam that drives a turbine generator (Figure 18.14).

Because of limitations of structures and materials, nuclear reactors only operate at a maximum temperature of around 625°K compared to approximately 800°K in a fossil fuel power plant. The thermal efficiency of nuclear power generation as limited by the Carnot relationship is therefore inherently low, and the overall efficiency for production of electricity does not exceed 30%. That leaves 70% of nuclear fission energy to be disposed of in the environment.

FIGURE 18.14
Nuclear reactor for power generation.

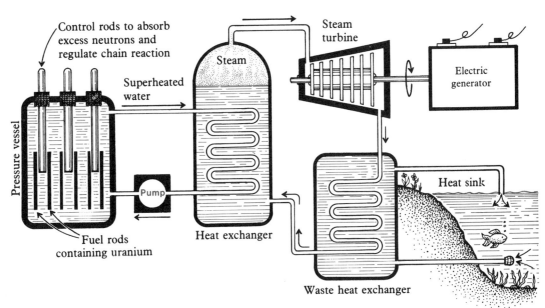

Only 0.71% of natural uranium is fissionable uranium-235, which severely limits the amount of nuclear fuel available. Hope for maximum utilization of nuclear power rests on the development of breeder reactors that convert uranium-238 (natural abundance 99.28%) to fissionable plutonium-239. However, development of the U.S. fast breeder reactor was postponed by the Carter administration in 1977. Dangers from plutonium, particularly in the manufacture of atomic weapons, were largely responsible.

The dangers of radioactive materials from nuclear reactors are of concern to many persons. There are two general aspects of this problem. The first is accidental release of radioactivity from the reactor system itself. The second is radioactivity from spent and reprocessed nuclear fuel. Minute quantities of radioactive wastes from nuclear reactors are undeniably extremely hazardous. These wastes last for thousands, even millions, of years. They must be contained and disposed of safely.

So many safety factors are built into a nuclear reactor that it is generally agreed (though with some strong dissent) that there is little danger of release of dangerous amounts of radioactivity from the reactor itself. The reactor core is designed to be self-stabilizing. Thus, increased heat from a "runaway" reactor tends to slow down the fission process. The metal cladding that holds the uranium in the fuel elements provides a barrier to the release of radioactive waste products. The primary coolant water system would absorb radioactive materials penetrating the cladding, providing a second barrier. The enormously strong reactor housing (designed to shrug off even a direct hit from a jumbo jet airliner) is a third barrier to the release of radioactive materials. The ultimate reactor disaster, which is never supposed to happen, is the sudden loss of all coolant water. Conceivably, this could result in the core melting down to a blob of highly radioactive metal. Such an occurrence would be a very serious incident, indeed.

Nuclear reactors produce both **low-level wastes and high-level wastes**. Low-level wastes come from miscellaneous sources around the reactor. A typical example is a spent ion exchanger used to remove small quantities of radioactive ions from reactor coolant water. Solid,

Tanks holding up to a million gallons are used to store radioactive liquid waste from a nuclear power plant. Sophisticated heat control and leak detection equipment are incorporated into the tanks which will be covered with earth. (Courtesy of ERDA)

low-level wastes are normally sealed in metal containers. The liquid wastes may be converted into a solid form by mixing with cement and casting into solid blocks. Low-level wastes are buried in appropriate burial sites.

High-level wastes come from radioactive isotopes generated by the fuel itself. The actual weight of these isotopes generated in a nuclear reactor is not very high. A 1000 megawatt nuclear fission power plant "burns up" only about 2 kg of uranium-235 per day, a high percentage of which ends up as high-level waste. The radioactive isotopes must be removed periodically by fuel reprocessing, partly because they absorb neutrons and stop the fission process. The separated isotopes generate a lot of heat and waste solutions of them must be cooled. The high-level wastes remain lethal for thousands of years. They must either be stored safely or disposed of permanently away from all possible human contact. Unfortunately, no foolproof disposal method has been demonstrated yet. Long-term storage does not appear to be a viable solution in view of man's inherent fallibility. At worst, stored nuclear wastes are vulnerable to sabotage. At best, past experience has shown that human error and negligence will occur in any enterprise. The result could be catastrophic release of radioactive wastes.

18.9

Nuclear Fusion Power

The two main reactions by which energy can be produced by **fusion** of two light nuclei into a heavier nucleus are the deuterium-deuterium reaction

$$^2_1 H + ^2_1 H \longrightarrow ^3_2 He + ^1_0 n + \text{energy}$$

and the deuterium-tritium reaction:

$$^2_1 H + ^3_1 H \longrightarrow ^4_2 He + ^1_0 n + \text{energy}$$

The numbers in front of the symbols are:

Weight of nucleus (or neutron) $\longrightarrow$ $^3_2 He$
Charge of nucleus (or neutron) $\longrightarrow$

The latter reaction is the most feasible from the standpoint of energy required to fuse two nuclei. The total energy from this type of fusion is limited by the availability of tritium that is made from nuclear reactions of lithium-6 (natural abundance 7.4%). Deuterium, however, is vastly more plentiful in supply; one out of each 6700 atoms of hydrogen consists of the deuterium isotope.

The power of nuclear fusion has not yet been harnessed in a sustained controlled reaction of appreciable duration. Most approaches have emphasized "squeezing" a plasma (ionized gas) of fusionable nuclei in a strong magnetic field. Recently the use of high-power lasers has been investigated for applying the enormous temperatures needed to bring about fusion in a mass of fusionable material.

Controlled nuclear fusion processes would produce almost no radioactive waste products. However, tritium is very difficult to contain, and some release of this isotope would occur. The deuterium-deuterium reaction promises an unlimited source of energy. Therefore, despite the possibly insurmountable technical problems involved in harnessing fusion energy, the promise of this abundant, relatively nonpolluting energy source makes its pursuit well worth a massive effort.

18.10

Geothermal Energy

Underground heat in the form of steam, hot water, or hot rock used to produce steam already is being used as an energy resource. This source of energy was first harnessed for the generation of electricity at Larderello, Italy, in 1904 and has since been developed around the world in places such as Japan, Russia, New Zealand, and at the Geysers in northern California.

Dry steam from beneath the ground is relatively rare but is the most desirable from the standpoint of power generation. More commonly energy reaches the surface as superheated water or a mixture of water and steam. In some cases the water is quite pure and can be used for irrigation and livestock, whereas in other cases the water is loaded with corrosive scale forming salts. Utilization of these waters generally demands their reinjection into the hot formation to prevent contamination of surface water.

The utilization of hot rocks for energy requires fracturing of the hot formation followed by injection of water and withdrawal of steam. This technology is still in the experimental stage but promises approximately 10 times as much energy production as steam and hot water sources. Land subsidence and seismic effects are environmental factors that may hinder the development of geothermal power. However, this energy source holds considerable promise and its development continues.

18.11

The Sun: A Limitless, Ideal Energy Source

The recipe for an ideal energy source calls for one that is unlimited in supply, inexpensive, does not add to the Earth's total heat burden, and does not produce chemical air and water pollutants. Solar energy fulfills all of these criteria. It is so abundant that with a collection efficiency of only 10%, less than 5% of the U.S. surface area could provide the country's energy needs projected for the year 2000. It can be used directly for heating and air conditioning. It can be used to generate electricity or to synthesize energy-containing chemical fuels.

Solar power cells for the direct conversion of sunlight to electricity have been developed and are widely used for energy in space vehicles. With present technology, however, they remain far too expensive for large scale generation of electricity. Therefore, most schemes for the utilization of solar power depend upon the collection of thermal energy followed by conversion to electrical energy. The simplest such approach involves focusing sunlight on a steam generating boiler. Parabolic reflectors can be used to focus sunlight on pipes containing heat-transporting fluids. Selective coatings on these pipes can be used so that only a small percentage of the incident energy is reradiated from the pipes.

A major disadvantage of solar energy is, of course, its intermittent nature; and development of this resource requires vast energy storage systems. Energy collected during the day can be stored as heat in melted mixtures of salts. Pumped water storage, already in use to enable operation of fossil-fueled and nuclear power plants at a constant rate, may also be used to store energy generated by a solar-electrical plant during hours of sunlight. This would involve pumping water uphill to a storage reservoir with an electric motor-water turbine combination during periods of high electricity output during daylight. At night the flow would be reversed through the turbine and the motor used as a generator to produce electricity (see Figure 18.15).

Another proposed means of solar energy storage involves production of hydrogen, an ideal chemical fuel. Hydrogen is so promising for energy storage and transport that many experts foresee a "hydrogen economy." In addition to conventional combustion,

$$2 H_2 + O_2 \longrightarrow 2 H_2O + \text{heat}$$

hydrogen can be used directly in fuel cells. These enable the oxidation of hydrogen to occur at low temperatures in a sort of battery-like device that generates electricity as shown in Figure 18.16.

FIGURE 18.15

Pumped water storage of energy has
promising applications for solar power.

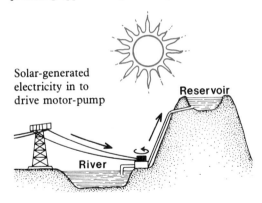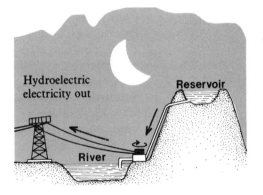

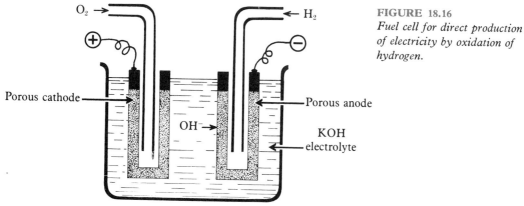

H_2 going through anode reacts to give off electrons: $2\,H_2\;+\;4\,OH^-\rightarrow 4\,H_2O\;+\;4\,e^-$

O_2 going through cathode reacts to take up electrons: $O_2\;+\;2\,H_2O\;+\;4\,e^-\rightarrow 4\,OH^-$

Overall reaction: $\overline{2\,H_2\;+\;\;\;O_2\;\;\;\rightarrow 2\,H_2O}$

No really insurmountable barriers exist to the development of solar energy, such as might be the case with fusion power. It is likely, therefore, that by the year 2000 solar energy will be providing an appreciable percentage of energy needs in areas receiving abundant sunlight.

18.12

Energy from Photosynthesis

All fossil fuels originally came from photosynthetic processes. Photosynthesis does hold some promise of producing combustible chemicals to be used for energy production and could certainly produce all needed organic raw materials. It suffers from the disadvantage of being a very inefficient means of solar energy collection (several hundredths of a percent for most common plants). However, the overall energy conversion efficiency of several plants, such as sugarcane, is around 0.6%. Furthermore, some plants—notably the heavy rubber plant grown in Malaysia and Indonesia—produce hydrocarbons directly. Conversion of agricultural plant residues to energy could be employed to provide some of the energy required for agricultural production. Indeed, until about 60 years ago virtually all of the energy required in agriculture originated from plant materials produced on the land (hay and oats for horses, home-grown food for laborers, and wood for home heating).

The idea of "energy plantations" to grow plant materials for energy needs probably is not viable due to the much greater need for land to grow food, fiber, and wood. However, nutrient-rich sewage, unsuited for food production because of the presence of heavy metals and other contaminants, could possibly be used to produce energy-rich biomass for fuel. Furthermore, photosynthetically produced materials can largely take the place of petroleum as a raw material base in producing plastics, rubber, and other organic-based products.

Chapter Summary

The availability and price of energy are major considerations of all citizens. Rapidly diminishing domestic supplies of petroleum and natural gas require that other energy sources be developed. This will involve the application of a lot of chemistry in all aspects of energy development.

The world is largely dependent upon *fossil fuels* for energy. Of these, by far the greatest resources are in the form of coal and other solid fuels. A large fraction of world coal resources are found in the U.S.

Much of the energy problem has resulted from the growth rate in energy use. Even the 4% annual growth in energy use that prevailed in the U.S. from about the end of World War II until 1973 can result in vastly increased energy use if continued over several decades. Therefore, energy conservation can be a major part of the solution to the energy problem. Eventually, a state of *zero energy growth* must be reached.

Energy occurs in a number of forms. It is converted to different forms for various uses. The efficiencies of this conversion vary widely from less than half a percent for photosynthesis to almost 100% for the conversion of electrical energy to heat in a water heater. The efficiency of conversion of heat to mechanical energy is limited by the *Carnot equation*.

Petroleum and natural gas are taken from porous rock formations underground. Only about 30% of the petroleum is recovered by conventional means. Advanced recovery techniques can extend available petroleum resources somewhat.

Coal is the most certain U.S. energy resource. Its use is accompanied by severe environmental problems. Coal can be converted to substitute natural gas and petroleum. The costs of doing this are high.

Other sources of energy that are in various stages of development include nuclear fission, nuclear fusion, hydroelectric, solar, geothermal, tidal, and wind energy. Photosynthesis offers some possibilities. It is of interest to note that only in 1974 did nuclear energy overtake photosynthetically produced wood as an energy source in the U.S.

Chapter Review Questions

The following questions are designed as a self-teaching tool to help you review Chapter 18. The answers to each question follow. See Chapter Review Questions for Chapter 1 for further instructions.

1. In terms of kilowatt hours of energy, the initial amount of petroleum resources available in the world was approximately _____% of total energy resources.

2. If one set out on a trip with an automobile that required 1 gal of gasoline to travel 10 mi and 4% more gasoline for every 10 mi interval after that, the total amount of gasoline used after going 90 mi would be _____ gal.

3. Peak petroleum production in the U.S. should be reached in the year _____.

4. The peak of world coal production will probably be reached around the year _____.

5. The approximate percentage of total energy wasted in the U.S. is ____%.

6. The diesel locomotive is about ____% efficient whereas the steam locomotive was about ____% efficient.

7. Per ton-mile, truck transportation requires about ____ times as much energy as train transportation.

8. The percent conversion efficiency of each of the following is home furnace ____%, electric generator ____%, incandescent lamp bulb ____%, and photosynthesis less than ____.

9. Where T_1 is the inlet temperature and T_2 is the outlet temperature, percent efficiency =

   _____.

10. Normally the fate of the 60–70% of "waste energy" from an electrical generating plant is _____

    _____.

11. The porosity ("percentage of holes") in rock formations containing petroleum normally ranges from ____ to ____%.

12. Among the chemicals and other measures that have been used to increase the displacement of oil from oil-bearing formations are _____,

    _____, _____, and _____.

13. Much of the 100 trillion cubic feet of natural gas in the Piceance Creek basin in western Colorado cannot be used because _____.

14. The four major types of coal are _____, _____,

    _____, and _____.

15. The major environmental problem with the combustion of most bituminous coal is _____.

16. Pyrite undergoing a chemical reaction catalyzed by bacteria is responsible for a major environmental problem, which is _____.

17. The most commonly used stack-gas scrubbing process for electrical generating plants is _____.

18. A major environmental problem with wet limestone scrubbing is ————

    _____.

19. A device that generates electricity directly from a "seeded" coal flame is the _____ generator, which requires a very strong _____.

20. The general reaction for the production of saturated hydrocarbons by the Fischer-Tropsch process is

    _____.

21. SNG is essentially pure _____.

22. The fission of a uranium-235 nucleus produces two _____, an average of 2.5 _____ plus _____.

23. Nuclear fusion may involve a _____ reaction or a _____ reaction.

24. The natural abundance of fissionable uranium-235 is _____%.

25. Geothermal energy is most commonly available as _____ or a mixture of _____.

26. Assume that a cheap, efficient solar energy cell could be developed to convert sunlight directly to electricity. One major disadvantage of solar energy that would remain is _____.

Answers to Chapter Review Questions

1. 5.2
2. 10.59
3. probably has been reached already
4. 2100
5. 59.2
6. 35, 10
7. 5.7
8. 85, 98, 4, less than 0.5
9. $\dfrac{T_1 - T_2}{T_1} \times 100$
10. to be dissipated as waste heat, either to the atmosphere or to bodies of water and streams
11. 10, 30
12. solvents, underground combustion, detergents, foams
13. the gas-bearing formation is too tight
14. anthracite, bituminous, subbituminous, lignite
15. high-sulfur content
16. production of acid mine water
17. wet limestone scrubbing
18. accumulation of large quantities of waste lime
19. magnetohydrodynamic, magnetic field
20. $n\, CO + (2n + 1)\, H_2$
    $$\longrightarrow\ C_nH_{2n + 2} + n\, H_2O$$
21. methane
22. lighter atoms, neutrons, energy
23. deuterium-deuterium, deuterium-tritium
24. 0.71
25. superheated water, water and steam
26. the fact that it is not continuous

Exercises for Chapter 18

1. Estimate the overall percentage increase in fuel consumption for automobile transport if reciprocating gasoline engines were replaced by Wankel engines. What would be the percentage saving if diesel engines were used instead?

2. What would be the increase in thermal efficiency of a modern steam turbine engine if the average inlet temperature could be increased by 50°C?

3. An increase of 1% in recovery of oil from total U.S. petroleum sources, including both depleted fuels and reserves, would amount to how many barrels of oil? What percentage of current annual consumption?

4. Calculate the percentage composition by weight of Illinois No. 6 coal with the "chemical formula" $C_{100}H_{85}S_{2.1}N_{1.5}O_{9.5}$.

5. How does lignite differ chemically from bituminous coal?

6. Annual sulfuric acid production in the U.S. is around 60 billion pounds. If sulfur were reclaimed from coal containing an average of 3% sulfur, how many tons of coal per year would fulfill this sulfuric acid demand?

7. How many tons per day of coal with a heat value of 13,000 Btu/lb are required to fuel a 1000 megawatt power plant operating with an overall efficiency of 38%?

8. What are the major steps in the production of high-Btu gas from coal?

9. What is the purpose of the "shift" reaction in coal gasification?

10. What happens to nuclei of atoms during nuclear fusion? How is the electrical charge of these nuclei involved? Why is nuclear fusion so hard to accomplish in a controlled reactor although it is relatively easy in a hydrogen bomb?

11. Standards for home furnaces fueled with gas or oil specify that the energy input produced by burning the fuel should be only about 80% of the energy output in terms of available heat. Why do you think this is done? What problems might be encountered if you tried to reclaim all the heat from the exhaust flue?

12. One economical way of transporting coal is by way of a slurry pipeline in which powdered coal is mixed with an approximately equal quantity of water and pumped through a pipeline. Wet coal will burn pretty well. Consider what happens to water when it is heated to a high temperature (Chapter 8). In terms of most efficient energy use, explain why it is desirable to remove as much water as possible from this mixture before burning it.

13. Detergents are sometimes used to increase recovery from oil wells. Recall the properties of detergents discussed in Chapter 13. How might addition of detergent increase oil recovery in formations where oil and water occur together? What problems might be encountered with such oil after it is recovered?

14. Examine Table 18.2, which describes coal on the basis of rank. From the standpoint of sulfur dioxide pollution which would be the best fuel, lignite containing 1.0% sulfur or bituminous coal containing 1.5% sulfur? Explain your answer.

15. Match the fuel in the left column with the description on the right.

SRC	Synthetic gasoline
Fischer-Tropsch product	Solid, high heat content fuel
Product of Lurgi gasifier operated with air	Used in home furnaces
SNG	Useful only "on-site" because of transportation costs

16. In the preparation of gas from coal, the "acid gases" must be scrubbed out. What are the formulas of these? What chemicals do you think might be used for removing them? Write several chemical reactions to show their removal.

17. Coal is converted to SNG which is burned to produce steam that powers a turbine-generator. This electricity is then used in an incandescent light bulb. Estimate the overall percentage of conversion of the energy in the coal to light energy.

18. Assuming water has a density of 1 g/cm^3, calculate the weight of deuterium in a cubic kilometer of water (just a "drop" in the ocean "bucket").

19. From an environmental viewpoint, why is "dry steam" much more desirable than superheated water as a source of geothermal energy?

20. At an annual increase of 4% in energy consumption per year, how much greater will U.S. energy consumption be in the year 2000 than it is now?

Answers to Selected Exercises

1. 16 amu

4. That it is very low

6. It is the science of very low temperatures.

7. H_2, H_2O

11. to detect leaks

13. No, an atom is mostly empty space.

14. No, protons have the same electrical charge and push each other away. A nucleus with more than 1 proton in it must have some neutrons that act as sort of a "glue" to keep the protons together in the same nucleus.

16. Two electrons, like all helium atoms. It weighs 3 amu compared to 4 amu for most helium atoms.

17. It exists as hydrogen molecules, H_2.

19. It is absolute zero. No lower temperature is possible.

23. 11,200 years

24. 6250 atoms

31. 2 g/cm³

33. 100 cal

1. 1.5

3. 10

5. atomic weight

8. factories and *Rhizobium* bacteria

11. :F̈:F̈:

14. an ore containing aluminum

17. phosphate detergents and fertilizers

19. potassium-40

1. :N ⋮⋮ N:, CO

3. H:N̈:H⁺ with H above and H below

5. nitrogen and phosphorus

6. 16 amu

10. 170 lb per acre

11. 190.6 kg per hectare

13. CO_2 and H_2O

15. CO_2

1. CO_2 and H_2O, or carbon dioxide and water

2. $2 C_6H_6 + 15 O_2 \longrightarrow 12 CO_2 + 6 H_2O$

3. It was obtained by changing the chemical formulas of phosphoric acid and calcium phosphate, *something that is never done to balance an equation.*

4. $2 Mg + CO_2 \longrightarrow 2 MgO + C$

5. $4 NH_3 + 8 O_2 \longrightarrow 2 N_2O_5 + 6 H_2O$
$N_2O_5 + H_2O \longrightarrow 2 HNO_3$

6. A precipitate of insoluble CaF_2 formed. The chemical equation is

$$Ca(OH)_2 + 2 HF \longrightarrow CaF_2\downarrow + 2 H_2O$$

7. It reacts with HCl in the stomach. The products are NaCl, CO_2, and water. The balanced chemical equation is $NaHCO_3 + HCl \rightarrow NaCl + CO_2\uparrow + H_2O$

8. $2 NaHCO_3 + heat \longrightarrow Na_2CO_3 + H_2O\uparrow + CO_2\uparrow$
CO_2 and H_2O smother the flame.

9.
$$\begin{array}{cccc} \text{H} & \text{H} & \text{H} & \text{H} \\ \text{H}:\overset{..}{\text{C}}:\overset{..}{\text{C}}:\overset{..}{\text{C}}:\overset{..}{\text{C}}:\text{H} \\ \text{H} & \text{H} & \text{H} & \text{H} \end{array}$$

10. $2 C_4H_{10} + 13 O_2 \longrightarrow 8 CO_2 + 10 H_2O$

11. Mg^{2+} and PO_4^{3-} form $Mg_3(PO_4)_2$

15. NO_3^- 17. H_2SO_3

20. **a.** H^+ from H_2SO_4 is reduced to produce H_2.
    b. $Al_2(SO_4)_3$
    c. $2 Al + 3 H_2SO_4 \longrightarrow Al_2(SO_4)_3 + 3 H_2$

Chapter 5, page 139

1. $2 KClO_3 \longrightarrow 2 KCl + 3 O_2$ 3. 245.2
4. 31.8 g   6. 6.2 g of HCl
8. 4.35 mg of H_2 9. 173.9 mg NaOH
11. 363.6 g of oxygen   16. H^+ ions and Cl^- ions
18. $P_2O_5 + 3 H_2O \longrightarrow 2 H_3PO_4$

Chapter 6, page 169

5. number of moles of substance per liter of solution   6. 34 g
7. 51 g   9. 1.2 liters
10. 50 ml   17. 1.50 mole/liter
18. $HCl + NaOH \longrightarrow NaCl + H_2O$

0.75 moles of HCl remain. The molar concentration of HCl was 0.375 mole/liter.
19. 0.0890 mole/liter

Chapter 7, page 203

1. $CaSO_4 \cdot 2 H_2O$ 3. 0.15 M

4. Ammonia: NH_3 7. $\begin{array}{c} \text{H}:\overset{..}{\underset{..}{\text{O}}}:\text{H}^+ \\ \text{H} \end{array}$
   Ammonium: NH_4^+

9. cathode: $Cu^{2+} + 2 e^- \longrightarrow Cu$; anode: $2 Cl^- \longrightarrow Cl_2\uparrow + 2 e^-$

10.
CaO	calcium oxide
SiO_2	silicon dioxide
K_2S	potassium sulfide
$AlCl_3$	aluminum chloride
NO_2	nitrogen dioxide
N_2O_5	dinitrogen pentoxide
NaI	sodium iodide
KBr	potassium bromide
MgF_2	magnesium fluoride
CaF_2	calcium fluoride

11.
Na_2CO_3	sodium carbonate
$CaSO_3$	calcium sulfite
$Al(OH)_3$	aluminum hydroxide
$CaSO_4$	calcium sulfate
$NaNO_2$	sodium nitrite
$Ca_3(PO_4)_2$	calcium phosphate
$NaNO_3$	sodium nitrate
$Ca(ClO)_2$	calcium hypochlorite
$KClO_4$	potassium perchlorate
$Ca_2(PO_3)_2$	calcium phosphite

12.
K_2HPO_4	dipotassium hydrogen phosphate
$KHCO_3$	potassium hydrogen carbonate
$NaHSO_4$	sodium hydrogen sulfate

KH$_2$PO$_4$ potassium dihydrogen phosphate
NaHC$_8$H$_4$O$_4$ sodium hydrogen phthalate
NaHC$_2$O$_4$ sodium hydrogen oxalate

13. *4 tetra-*   1 mono-   8 octa-   10 deca-   2 di-
     5 penta-   7 hepta-   3 tri-   9 nona-   6 sexa-

14. N$_2$O$_5$ *dinitrogen pentoxide*   N$_2$O$_4$ dinitrogen tetroxide

     NO$_2$ nitrogen dioxide   N$_2$O$_3$ dinitrogen trioxide

     NO nitric oxide   N$_2$O nitrous oxide

15. FeCl$_2$ *ferrous chloride*   or   *iron(II) chloride*

     FeCl$_3$ ferric chloride   or   iron(III) chloride

     CuCl cuprous chloride   or   copper(I) chloride

     CuCl$_2$ cupric chloride   or   copper(II) chloride

     SnCl$_2$ stannous chloride   or   tin(II) chloride

     SnCl$_4$ stannic chloride   or   tin(IV) chloride

16. $2\,N_2 + 3\,O_2 = $ 2 N$_2$O$_3$ (dinitrogen trioxide)

     $KOH + SO_2 = $ KHSO$_3$ (potassium hydrogen sulfite)

     $KOH + H_3PO_4 = $ KH$_2$PO$_4$ + H$_2$O   (potassium dihydrogen phosphate)

Chapter 8, page 233

2.   **a.** heating 1°C
    b. boiling
    c. melting ice
5.   **c.** 125 g
12.   2,600,000,000,000
21. $CaCO_3 + CO_2 + H_2O \;\rightleftharpoons\; Ca^{2+} + 2\,HCO_3^-$

4.   It should condense to form liquid water because that process gives off a lot of heat.
6.   0°C
17.   **a.** $HCl + HCO_3^- \longrightarrow H_2O + CO_2\uparrow + Cl^-$
     b. 0.00225

Chapter 9, page 264

2. 2.16×10^{14} tons
6.   380 mm
10.   48
13.   3400

3. $NO_2 + light \longrightarrow NO + O$
9.   2.49 liters
11.   1.24 liters
15.   24 g

Chapter 10, page 313

2. C_xH_{2x+2} C_xH_x no

3.   H:C̈:C ∷ C:H

         triple bond
         (electron dots)

     H−C−C≡C−H

         triple bond
         (pairs of electrons as dashes)

4.

```
              H              H
      H H─C─H    H─C─H H H
      │ │          │   │ │
  H─C───C─────────C───C─C─H
      │ │          │   │ │
      H H─C─H      H   H H
          │
          H
```

5.

```
              H
      H H─C─H H                    H H H H
      │ │    │                     │ │ │ │
  H─C───C────C─H                H─C─C─C─C─H
      │ │    │                     │ │ │ │
      H H    H                     H H H H
```

```
          H
      H H─C─H H                        H
      │ │    │                  H HH─C─H H
  H─C───C────C─H            H─C─C────C───C─H
      │ │    │                 │ │    │   │
      H H─C─H H                 H H    H   H
          │
          H
```

```
          H
      H HH─C─H H                       H
      │ │    │ │                HH─C─H H    H
  H─C─C────C───C─H           H─C───C────C───C─H
      │ │    │ │                │   │ H─C─H H
      H HH─C─H H                H   H  │
          │                            H
          H
```

```
      H H H H                      H H H H
      │ │ │ │                      │ │ │ │
  H─C─C=C─C─H                  H─C=C─C─C─H
      │     │                          │ │
      H     H                          H H
```

7. Because there are not 3 distinct double bonds, all C—C bonds in the molecule are the same

9. $C_{20}H_{12}$

15. Carboxylic acids: $NaOH + CH_3CO_2H \longrightarrow CH_3CO_2Na + H_2O$
Phenols: $C_6H_5OH + NaOH \longrightarrow C_6H_5ONa + H_2O$

17. esters

21. Attraction of negative carboxylate groups for water.

23. $2\,Na^{+}{}^{-}O_2CC_{17}H_{35} + Ca^{2+} \longrightarrow Ca(O_2CC_{17}H_{35})\downarrow + 2\,Na^{+}$

Chapter 11, page 342

3. $C_{18}H_{32}O_{16}$ **4.** 2469

5. 44,442

7.
```
    NH₂ O H  H O
    │   ‖ │  │ ‖
H─C─C─N─C─C─OH,    or
    │      │
    H─C─H
       │
       ⬡
```

```
     H NH₂ O H  H O
     │ │   ‖ │  │ ‖
⬡────C─C───C─N──C─C─OH
     │ │      │
     H H      H
```

12. Products are $(C_{15}H_{31})-\overset{\overset{\displaystyle H}{|}}{\underset{\underset{\displaystyle H}{|}}{C}}-OH$ and $Na^{+\,-}O-\overset{\overset{\displaystyle O}{\|}}{C}-(C_{17}H_{35})$.

17. They are both complementary.
19. Its structure is altered, and it no longer fits the substrate.

Chapter 12, page 366

3. 16,000 counts per minute
7. c
10. 0.6
12. 2 ppm
17. 1.5 μg

6. mass spectrometry
8. c
11. 0.250
15. 8 ppb

Chapter 13, page 410

4. $2\,NaCl + 2\,H_2O \longrightarrow 2\,NaOH + Cl_2 + H_2\uparrow$
6. $Ca(ClO)_2 \longrightarrow CaCl_2 + O_2\uparrow$
11. 15,600 liters
13. $Na_2CO_3 + Ca(OH)_2 \longrightarrow CaCO_3\downarrow + 2\,NaOH$
14. Both hydrolyze carbohydrates, such as starch, to carbohydrates of lower molecular weight.
17. 1 ton of NH_4NO_3 contains 0.35 tons of N, which costs \$100. 1 ton of NH_3 contains 0.82 tons of N, which costs \$150. The N in NH_3 costs much less per ton.

Chapter 14, page 429

2. bacterial degradation of organic matter: $O_2 + [CH_2O] \longrightarrow CO_2\uparrow + H_2O$
3. 27.7% Si
   46.6% O
   5.0% Fe
   8.1% Al
5. N
7. $NO_3^- + 2\,H^+ + 2e^-$
   $\longrightarrow H_2O + NO_2^-$ (poisonous)
10. $CaCO_3,\ CO_2,\ CaCO_3 + H_2O + CO_2 \longrightarrow Ca^{2+} + 2\,HCO_3^-$
13. $H_2O + CO_2 \longrightarrow CH_2O + O_2\uparrow$, sunlight
14. $HbO_2 + NO_2^- \longrightarrow HbNO_2^- + O_2$
15. 24 tons
17. 80,000,000

Chapter 15, page 456

3. A dye is a soluble colored substance whereas a lake is a dye chemically bound to very small, solid particles.
6. flavor washed from a source into alcohol

10.

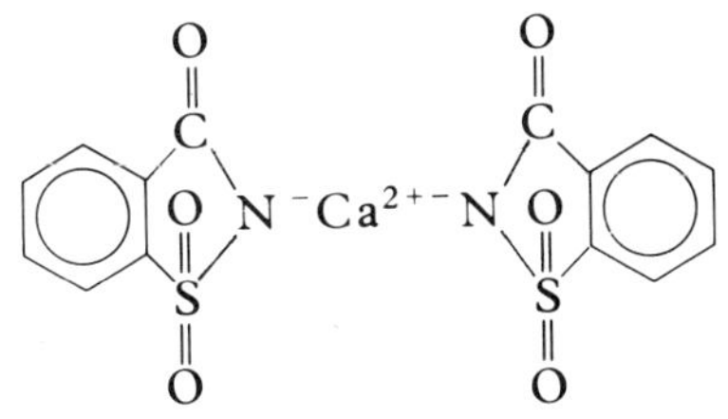

12. phosphates

19. as preservatives

16. complexes calcium and provides bulk

20. citric acid

Chapter 16, page 490

1. 66.3 kg NaF

2. 0.544 g

5. dissolving, breakdown

9.

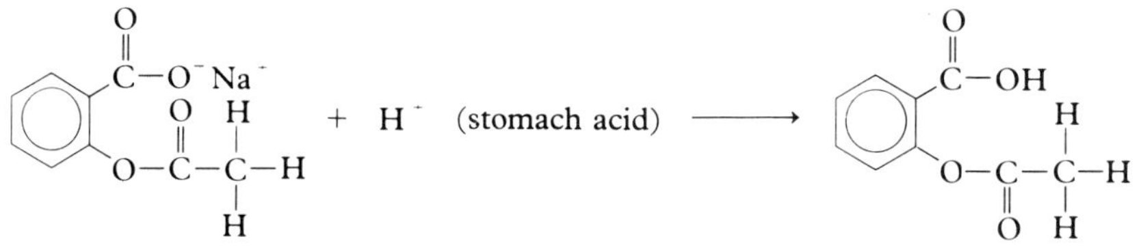

sodium
acetylsalicylate

11. vitamin B-12

18. thyroxin

Chapter 17, page 515

8. (radioactive hapten)−(antibody) + hapten

$\longrightarrow$ (hapten)−(antibody) + radioactive hapten.

11. $Ag^+ + Cl^-$ (from perspiration) $\longrightarrow$ AgCl↓

$2\,AgCl + light \longrightarrow 2\,Ag$ (dark deposit) $+ Cl_2$

12. $CaSO_4 \cdot 2\,H_2O$

13. sodium and calcium

14. PbS

16. $NaOH + NH_4Cl + heat \longrightarrow NaCl + NH_3\uparrow$ (odor) $+ H_2O$

$AgNO_3$ (soluble) $+ NH_4Cl \longrightarrow AgCl\downarrow$ (white) $+ NH_4NO_3$

18. Place a spot of a standard of the suspected substance alongside the spot of unknown, and see if it ends up in a location next to one of the spots from the separated unknown.

Chapter 18, page 547

4. 78.79% C, 5.5% H, 4.4% S, 1.4% N, 10.0% O

6. 1 billion tons

7. 8162 tons of coal per day

16. H_2S and CO_2, removed by bases: $NaOH + H_2S \longrightarrow NaHS + H_2O$,

$NaOH + CO_2 \longrightarrow NaHCO_3 + H_2O$

17. only about 2%

Index

THE METRIC SYSTEM

Length
10 millimeters (mm) = 1 centimeter (0.3937 in.)
10 centimeters (cm) = 1 decimeter
10 decimeters (dm) = 1 meter
10 meters (m) = 1 dekameter (dkm)
10 dekameters = 1 hectometer (hm)
10 hectometers = 1 kilometer (km) (0.62 mile)

Mass
10 milligrams (mg) = 1 centigram
10 centigrams (cg) = 1 decigram
10 decigrams (dg) = 1 gram
10 grams (g) = 1 dekagram (dkg)
10 dekagrams = 1 hectogram (hg)
10 hectograms = 1 kilogram (kg) (2.2 lb)

Capacity
10 milliliters (ml) = 1 centiliter
10 centiliters (cl) = 1 deciliter
10 deciliters (dl) = 1 liter
10 liters (l) = 1 dekaliter (dkl)
10 dekaliters = 1 hectoliter (hl)
10 hectoliters = 1 kiloliter (kl)
1 milliliter (ml) = 1 cubic centimeter (cc)

USEFUL CONVERSIONS

Length
1 Angstrom unit (Å) = 10^{-8} cm
1 micron (μ) = 10^{-4} cm = 1000 millimicrons (mμ) = 1×10^4 Å
1 inch (in.) = 2.54 cm
1 foot (ft) = 30.48 cm
1 meter = 39.37 in.
1 rod = 16.5 ft
1 kilometer = 0.62 mile (mi). 1 mile = 1.61 km
1 light year = 5.88×10^{12} mi (speed of light = 186,000 mi/sec = 3×10^{10} cm/sec)

Volume
1 teaspoon (tsp) = 5 ml (approx)
1 tablespoon (tbs) = 15 ml (approx)
1 cubic inch (cu in.) = 16.4 ml
1 fluid ounce (fl oz) = 29.6 ml
1 cup = 8 oz = 237 ml
1 quart (U.S. liq qt) = 0.946 liter
1 liter = 1.06 qt = 61.03 cu in.
1 gallon (gal) = 3.785 liters
1 cubic foot = 7.48 gal = 28.32 liters
1 bushel (U.S. bu) = 35.24 liters

Weight
1 carat = 0.2 g
1 ounce (avoir.) = 28.35 g
1 pound = 453.6 g
1 kilogram = 2.2046 lb
1 ton (short) = 2000 lb = 907.2 kg
1 ton (metric) = 1000 kg = 2204.6 lb
1 ton (long) = 2240 lb

Miscellaneous
1 acre U.S. = 43,560 sq ft = 0.405 hectares (ha) (sq hectometers)
1 atmosphere (atm) = 760 mm Hg = 30 in. Hg = 14.7 lb per sq in. (psi)
1 degree Fahrenheit (°F) = 5/9 degree centigrade (°C)
1 British thermal unit (Btu) = 252 calories (cal). 1 cal per g = 1.8 Btu per lb
1 kilocalorie (kcal) = 1000 cal
1 horsepower (hp) = 746 watts (W) = 550 ft-lb per sec
1 kilowatt (kW) = 1000 watts